Arthur J. Norton
Seattle

HIGH POLYMERS

Volume I: *Collected Papers of W. H. Carothers on High Polymeric Substances*
Edited by H. Mark and G. S. Whitby

Volume II: *Physical Chemistry of High Polymeric Systems*
By H. Mark

Volume III: *High Polymeric Reactions*
By H. Mark and R. Raff

Volume IV: *Natural and Synthetic High Polymers*
By K. H. Meyer

Volume V: *Cellulose and Cellulose Derivatives*
Edited by Emil Ott

Volume VI: *Mechanical Behavior of High Polymers*
By Turner Alfrey, Jr.

Volume VII: *Phenoplasts: Their Structure, Properties, and Chemical Technology*
By T. S. Carswell

In preparation

Volume VIII: *The Testing of Organic Plastics*
By H. K. Nason

Volume IX: *The High Polymer Molecule, Its Weight and Weight Distribution*
By Paul M. Doty and H. Mark

Other volumes to follow

HIGH POLYMERS

A SERIES OF MONOGRAPHS ON THE CHEMISTRY, PHYSICS, AND TECHNOLOGY OF HIGH POLYMERIC SUBSTANCES

Volume VI

Mechanical Behavior of High Polymers

By TURNER ALFREY, Jr.

INTERSCIENCE PUBLISHERS, INC., NEW YORK
INTERSCIENCE PUBLISHERS LTD., LONDON

MECHANICAL BEHAVIOR OF HIGH POLYMERS

TURNER ALFREY, Jr.
Assistant Professor of Polymer Chemistry
Polytechnic Institute of Brooklyn

1948
INTERSCIENCE PUBLISHERS, INC., NEW YORK
INTERSCIENCE PUBLISHERS LTD., LONDON

INTERSCIENCE PUBLISHERS, INC.
215 Fourth Avenue, New York 3, N. Y.

PRINTED IN THE UNITED STATES OF AMERICA
LANCASTER PRESS, LANCASTER, PA.

PREFACE

In recent years there has been a spectacular expansion in the production of synthetic organic polymers. As much as to any other factor, this expansion can be attributed to the remarkable range of mechanical properties exhibited by high polymers, permitting them to be used as "rubbers," plastics, textile fibers, films, etc. Throughout the history of the human race, important roles have been played by naturally occurring organic materials of polymeric structure—wood, cotton, wool, silk, leather, and many others. In many cases, particularly in "functional" applications, the usefulness of the material is almost *entirely* attributable to its mechanical properties, secondary factors such as chemical properties being important only as they insure permanence of the desirable mechanical characteristics. This is certainly the case with rubber and "synthetic rubbers," textile fibers, and some plastics. Even in those cases in which the usefulness of a high polymer derives principally from non-mechanical qualities, the usually necessary fabrication operations depend upon mechanical characteristics.

This book makes no attempt to catalogue the mechanical properties of the whole myriad of known high polymers; in most cases no sufficiently fundamental studies have been carried out to make such a cataloguing worth while. The attempt has been made, however, to uncover the fundamental principles underlying the mechanical behavior (or behaviors!) of high polymers, and to show how such behavior is correlated with the molecular structures involved. As a result, attention is concentrated almost entirely on the minority of polymers whose mechanical properties have been carefully studied from a fundamental point of view. (This guiding philosophy is relaxed somewhat in the chapter on ultimate strength and failure phenomena, Chapter F, since the complexity of these particular properties necessitates the use of a frankly empirical approach whether one likes it or not.)

Polymeric structures have been classified as follows: amorphous linear polymers, cross-linked polymers, crystalline polymers, and polymers admixed with components of low molecular weight. A chapter is devoted to each type of structure. In ambiguous cases, an attempt has been made to place the discussion at a point at which all significant principles would have been made available. In wool, for example, both crystallization and covalent cross linking are important structural features; wool is discussed in Chapter D. Water also plays an important role in the behavior of wool, but it was not believed that the discussion of Chapter E was a necessary prerequisite to the understanding of this factor.

The analysis of the mechanical behavior of each type of polymer has been made on two levels—a phenomenological description and a molecular interpretation. In the introductory chapter, the phenomenological framework of the theory of elasticity, viscous and plastic flow, and simple viscoelastic behavior is followed by a discussion of molecular mechanisms involved in simple elastic and viscous deformations. In Chapters B, C, D, and E, the order is altered. In each case, the discussion starts with an analysis of the molecular structure, and the phenomenological and mechanistic analyses of mechanical behavior are developed side by side. In Chapter B are found several sections that are completely phenomenological in character, and that can be applied to later chapters as well.

After the production of this book had reached a stage which did not permit substantial additions or revisions, a number of significant developments were reported in the literature or directly communicated to the author. Tobolsky and co-workers, for example, have applied the stress-relaxation method to a wide variety of polymers. Particularly in the case of Thiokol rubbers, they have been spectacularly successful in explaining viscoelastic behavior in terms of polymer structure and chemical reactions. O'Shaughnessy has carried out an extensive and informative study of creep in textile fibers, and Eley has made an exhaustive study of the mechanical properties of cordite. These two contributions will add materially to our understanding of the properties of crystalline polymers. Flory has reported an interesting study of the effects of network structure on the ultimate strengths of rubbery polymers. On the theoretical side, Rivlin has made important advances in the treatment of large strains, and Kirkwood has advanced a molecular theory of nonequilibrium viscoelastic behavior in network polymers.

In the author's laboratory, Hewitt and Lazor have carried out experimental studies of the relationships between structure and viscoelastic behavior in linear and cross-linked amorphous polymers. Many of the theoretical conjectures of Chapters B and C have been confirmed in this work. Experiments by Wiederhorn (based upon previous experiments and a suggestion made by Tobolsky) have succeeded in establishing the mechanism of viscoelastic behavior in plasticized polyvinyl chloride in a far more definite fashion than that of Chapter E.

Besides thanking the many investigators whose work has been referred to and liberally quoted throughout, the author would like to express his especial appreciation to the following persons, with whom he has had the opportunity of many stimulating conversations on the subject of this book: Arthur Tobolsky; Walter Stockmayer; R. F. Tuckett; L. R. G. Treloar; and in particular H. Mark, whose ideas are reflected in nearly every page of this book, whose help and encouragement were invaluable, and who generously contributed Section IV.3 of Chapter F.

In a number of sections the policy has been adopted of quoting rather more liberally from original sources than is customary in monographs of this kind. It seemed advisable to describe the step-by-step historical developments of the important concepts and theoretical formulations of the field. This could be best achieved—not by paraphrasing—but by quoting literally from the original publications in order to reflect properly the flavor and the emphasis of the original statements.

The quotations (with the exception of Appendices II and III) always appear in small type. It should be especially noted by the reader that the figures, tables, and equation numbers cited in the various quotations are those of the author of this book, not of the original publication. This practice was adopted in order to maintain the continuity of the numbering system throughout the book. The author wishes to take this opportunity to thank his colleagues, who have generously permitted quotation at length from their papers, and to call attention to the courtesy of the following firms and institutions for their kind permission to reproduce copyrighted material: American Chemical Society, American Institute of Physics, Inc., American Society for Testing Materials, McGraw-Hill Book

Company, Inc., New York Academy of Sciences, Oxford University Press, The Faraday Society, The Textile Foundation, and Williams & Wilkins Company.

Thanks also are extended to Dr. Richard Stein for reading the galley proofs, and most especially to Dr. M. T. O'Shaughnessy for indexing and for checking page proof critically. The Publishers have been unusually patient and cooperative during the several years' preparation of this book. The assistance of Miss Miriam T. Malakoff has been particularly helpful.

TURNER ALFREY, JR.

Brooklyn, N. Y.
December 15, 1947

CONTENTS

A. INTRODUCTION

I. PHENOMENOLOGICAL DISCUSSION

1. The Geometry of Stress

An unbalanced set of forces acting on an object causes the object to accelerate in the direction of the net, or resultant, force. In the same fashion, an unbalanced set of torques produces an angular acceleration. As far as the motion of the object as a whole is concerned, only these *resultant* forces and torques have any effect. A completely *balanced* set of forces is, in this respect, equivalent to no external force at all. A balanced set of forces does, however, affect the object internally, tending to change its shape or size, or both. An object subject to such balanced forces is said to be "stressed," and when a change of shape or size results from the stress, the object is said to be "strained." Since the concepts of stress and strain are fundamental to any discussion of the mechanical behavior of materials, we must first define both these quantities and discuss the relationships between them in the simplest examples.

The balanced external forces acting on the surface of an object are transmitted throughout the interior, each volume element of the object exerting forces on its neighbors. Consider an element of area dA located with its center at the point under consideration. The materials on both sides of this element exert forces on each other. In general, these forces are partly normal to the element and partly tangential. The stress at the point is a measure of these forces. When the stress is completely specified, the magnitude and direction of the force on the surface dA must be known *for every orientation of the tiny surface.* It will be shown that a complete specification requires the use of six "components of stress."

When the surface element dA is oriented normal to the x direction, the resultant force on the element may be resolved into three components parallel to the x, y, and z directions. Let us designate these three forces (per unit area) by the symbols s_{xx}, s_{xy}, s_{xz} (see Fig. 1): s_{xx} is *normal* to dA and is called a *tensile* component; s_{xy} and s_{xz} are *tangential* and are called *shearing* components. When surface element dA is oriented normal to the y direction, the force acting upon it can be resolved into three

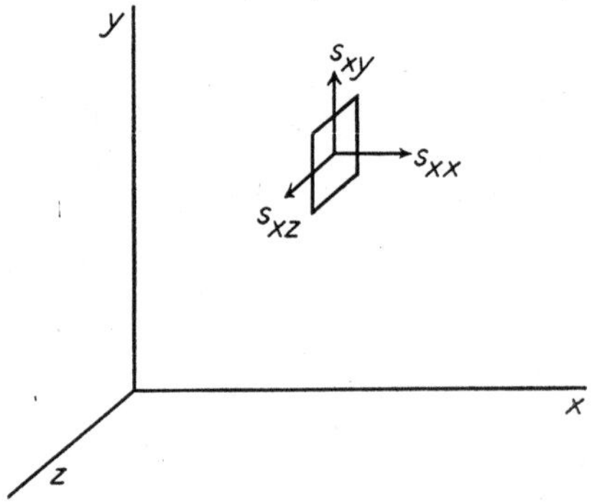

Fig. 1. Components of force acting on surface element dA oriented normal to x direction.

components which, expressed as force per unit area, are represented by the symbols s_{yx}, s_{yy}, s_{yz}. Similarly, three more quantities can be defined: s_{zx}, s_{zy}, s_{zz}. Thus, the force per unit area in the y direction, s_{zy}, acts on an infinitesimal surface element oriented normal to the z axis, etc. The force acting on an infinitesimal surface element oriented in any *oblique* direction is fixed by the values of these nine forces. Furthermore, $s_{xy} = s_{yx}$, $s_{xz} = s_{zx}$, and $s_{yz} = s_{zy}$. Hence, the values of the *six* quantities, s_{xx}, s_{yy}, s_{zz}, s_{yz}, s_{xz}, and s_{xy}, completely define the state of stress at a given point. Sometimes the symbols, s_1, s_2, s_3, s_4, s_5, and s_6 will be used instead of the above. See also Appendix I.

The physical meaning of these stress components can perhaps be more easily seen if we look at the forces acting on an infinitesimal cubical volume element.

Such a volume element must be large compared with molecular dimensions, so that the material within it can be considered as a continuum. On the other hand, if the stress varies throughout the object, the volume element considered must be small compared with any region in which there is any appreciable difference in stress. If this condition is fulfilled, the volume element can be treated mathematically as infinitesimal in extension.

Consider the volume element to be oriented with its edges parallel to the x, y, and z axes. When the sample is stressed, the element will in general have forces acting on all six faces. These forces can be either normal or tangential, or both (see Fig. 2). A complete analysis of the forces acting upon the volume element, *dx dy dz*, in this fashion would involve 18 force components, since the force on each of the six faces would have to be resolved into three Cartesian components. However, in any nonaccelerating system there are certain necessary relations between these 18 force components. The *total* force on the volume element in each direction must be zero, and the total torque around each axis must be zero. It follows that the various forces can exist only in certain "balanced" combinations, such as are shown in figure 3. These six force combinations are equivalent to the six *components of stress*, previously defined. Any stress can be expressed in terms of these six stress components. The first three components are tensile stresses, the others are components of *shear*.

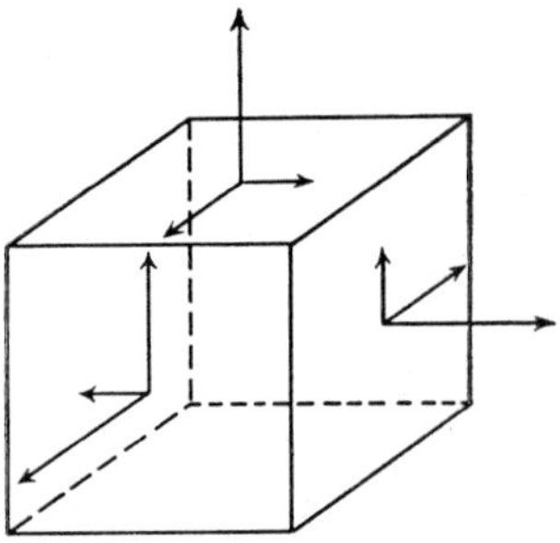

Fig. 2. Volume element showing force components acting on three faces.

In the case of a nonhomogeneous stress distribution, the surface forces acting on a volume element cannot be precisely resolved in the fashion just described. Thus, if the tensile stress in the x direction changes as

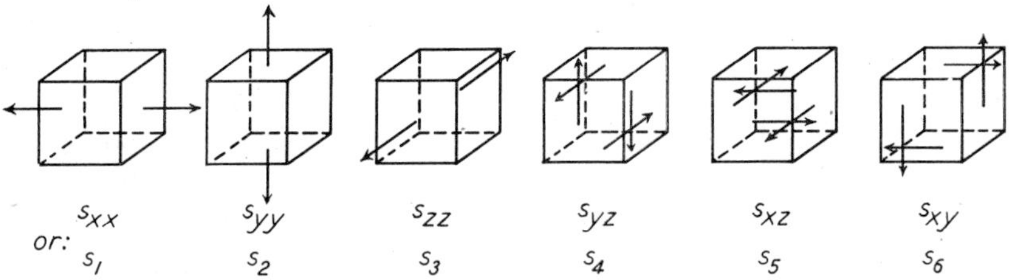

Fig. 3. Volume element showing "balanced" combinations of force components, *i.e.*, the stress components.

one moves in the x direction, then obviously the normal forces on the two opposite yz faces of the volume element cannot be exactly equal. However, if the volume element is made small enough, the difference between these normal forces becomes a differential of a higher order than the normal forces themselves. Thus, in a static problem, it is quite possible to visualize the surface forces on a volume element as being made up of a set of balanced forces—the "stress components" pictured in figure 3—even when the values of these components vary from point to point in the specimen. In a problem involving elastic waves, rather than elastic equilibrium, this is not true. It is exactly the unbalanced portion of the surface forces which cause acceleration of the volume element. As the volume element is made smaller and smaller, the unbalanced forces become smaller, but the mass of the volume element also decreases. The ratio between the magnitude of the unbalanced force in the x direction to the mass of the volume element approaches a constant limiting value as the volume element is made vanishingly small. Therefore, for problems involving elastic waves, the stress at a point must be specified in terms of the forces acting on a single infinitesimal surface element centered at the point and oriented in various ways, rather than in terms of balanced sets of surface forces acting on an infinitesimal volume element. In this work, we are primarily concerned with problems in which inertial effects can be ignored.

Transformation of Coordinates

The *stress* at any point in an object is a definite quantity. However, the *components* into which the stress is resolved depend upon the *orientation of the reference volume element used.* This is a feature common to all vector resolutions. A force, for example, is a perfectly definite quantity, but the components into which a definite force is resolved depends upon the orientation of the coordinate system used. Figure 4 shows

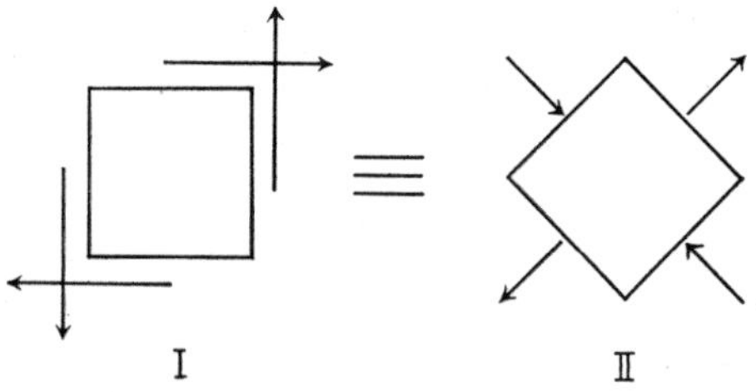

Fig. 4. Effect of rotation of coordinates on specification of a shear stress.

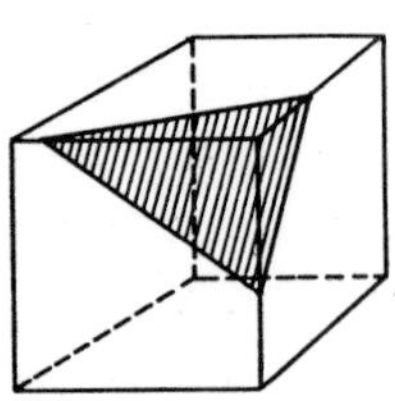

Fig. 5. Forces on an oblique plane.

this effect on a two-dimensional diagram (no forces in the third direction); in systems I and II the *same stress* is represented. In system I the forces appear as pure shear stresses, that is, a volume element oriented in this way would be subjected to a *shear*. At the same geometrical point, a volume element oriented at 45° to the first will be under pure tension in one direction and under pure compression in the other. At any intermediate orientation, the element will be subjected to both tensile and shearing components. If the stress is specified in terms of one orientation of the infinitesimal volume element, it is easy to compute the surface forces acting on a volume element with some other orientation. Consider the tetrahedron which is formed by an oblique plane cutting off one corner of the cubical volume element (Fig. 5). This tetrahedron must be in static equilibrium, hence the unknown force on the oblique triangular surface must just balance the known forces on the three mutually perpendicular right triangular surfaces. The area of the yz right triangle is a_x times the area of the oblique triangle, where a_x is a direction cosine of the normal to the oblique plane. In the same way, the area of the xy right triangle is a_z times that of the oblique triangle. Thus the surface force per unit area acting on an oblique plane, the direction cosines of whose normal are a_x, a_y, and a_z, is given by the following equations:

$$F_x = s_{xx}a_x + s_{xy}a_y + s_{zx}a_z \tag{1a}$$

$$F_y = s_{yy}a_y + s_{yz}a_z + s_{xy}a_x \tag{1b}$$

$$F_z = s_{zz}a_z + s_{zx}a_x + s_{yz}a_y \tag{1c}$$

The *normal component* of the force on the oblique surface is (per unit area):

$$F_n = F_xa_x + F_ya_y + F_za_z \tag{2}$$

In terms of the original set of stress components, this gives:

$$F_n = s_{xx}a_x^2 + s_{yy}a_y^2 + s_{zz}a_z^2 + 2\ s_{xy}a_xa_y + 2\ s_{yz}a_ya_z + 2\ s_{zx}a_za_x \tag{3}$$

In the same way, the *tangential* forces on the oblique surface can be computed. If this is done for three mutually perpendicular surfaces, all oblique to the original set of axes, the process of transforming the stress from the first set of components to the second set is completed.

It is always possible in a static system to orient the reference volume element in such a way that the stress has no shear components. This has already been indicated for the two-dimensional case in figure 4. When the reference volume element is oriented in such a fashion as to make the shear components disappear, the three perpendicular directions defined by the cube edges are called the *directions of principal stress*, and the three stress components are the *principal stresses*. For convenience we will designate the principal stresses at a point by the symbols S_1, S_2, S_3, and the directions of principal stress by x_1, x_2, x_3.

If the differential volume element used to resolve the stress into components is rotated from the above x_1, x_2, x_3 orientation, about the x_2 axis, the forces on the x_1x_3 faces (the faces normal to the x_2 axis) are unchanged. These forces remain parallel to the x_2 axis (and hence normal to these two faces). The four cube faces which are changed to oblique orientations will in general be subjected to tangential as well as normal forces. In other words, there will be a nonvanishing component of shear in the x_1x_3 plane. The other two shear components will be zero. The maximum shear component in the x_1x_3 plane is obtained when the reference volume element is turned 45° about the x_2 axis. This maximum shear stress has the value $(S_1 - S_3)/2$, and is called a *principal* shear stress. If the volume element is rotated about the x_1 direction as an axis, from the $x_1x_2x_3$ orientation, then a shearing component appears in the x_2x_3 plane. This component is a maximum for a 45° rotation about the x_1 axis, and is equal to $(S_3 - S_2)/2$. This is another principal shearing stress. The third principal shear stress is numerically equal to $(S_2 - S_1)/2$, and appears in the x_1x_2 plane when the volume element is rotated 45° about x_3. Thus the principal shearing stresses are related to the *differences* between the principal tensile stresses.

If the volume element has all six faces oblique to the x_1, x_2, x_3 orientation, then tangential forces appear on all faces, and three nonvanishing shear components are to be expected. In the special case where all three principal tensile stresses are equal, no shear stresses appear for any orientation of the volume element.

In any case, the complete description of the stress at a point requires the specification of six numerical values, but there is a certain amount of choice in the nature of the six reference quantities. The following modes of reference are, among others, possible:

(1) Orient the reference volume element without regard to the stress, *e.g.*, parallel to some externally defined system of coordinates. The stress at any point will in general have three tensile components and three shear components.

(2) Orient the reference volume element at each point in such a way as to make all shear components vanish. Only three tensile components (the principal stresses) need be specified. However, the orientation of the reference volume *changes from point to point in the stressed object.* Therefore, in order to completely specify the stress at a point, three angles must also be given—to fix this orientation.

(3) Orient the reference volume element in such a fashion as to emphasize the *shear* stresses at the point. In general this does not make

the tensile components disappear. If a principal shear is to appear as one component, three angles must be specified to define the orientation of the volume element, as well as the *magnitudes* of this shear stress, the additional isotropic tension in the plane of the shear, and the tensile stress normal to this plane. [The shear stresses are best emphasized by the use of the "deviatoric stress." See Appendix I, page 534.]

(4) In the special case where two principal tensile stresses are equal in magnitude, the stress can be resolved into three equal shear components plus three equal tensile stresses, by orienting the volume element with a cube diagonal parallel to the third principal stress.

This possibility of various representations for a given stress is important. It is necessary to recognize that a given stress can be described as shear *or* tensile, depending upon the frame of reference. The following is a specific example.

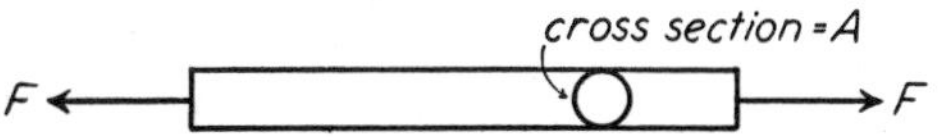

Fig. 6. Tensile stress on a rod or filament.

When a long rod or filament is pulled at the ends, as in figure 6, the stress can be described as a simple tensile stress in a direction parallel to the long axis:

$$\text{stress} = F/A$$

Here the reference volume element has one edge parallel to the long axis of the rod. In this simple problem, the principal stresses are F/A, 0, and 0.

Second, the principal shear stress is $F/2A$. If the differential volume element is oriented with the diagonal of one face parallel to the direction of tensile stress, the shear components acting on this volume element are $F/2A$, 0, and 0.

A third method of resolving a single tensile stress into components is as follows: Consider a differential volume element whose cube diagonal is oriented parallel to the tensile stress. The angular orientation in the plane perpendicular to this direction is arbitrary. The stress now appears in the form of three equal shear components plus a uniform dilatation. These shear components are *not* the principal shear stresses, but are equal to $F/3A$. The isotropic dilatative stress (or negative pressure) is also equal to $F/3A$.

The importance of shear stresses in mechanical problems involving high polymers should be emphasized. All *flow* is a response to shear stresses. The long range elasticity of rubberlike materials is a response to shear stresses. *Unless shear stresses are present, these types of behavior do not occur.* Therefore it is often useful to describe a stress in terms of shear components, rather than in terms of the principal tensile stresses. This is even more clearly brought out in Appendix I.

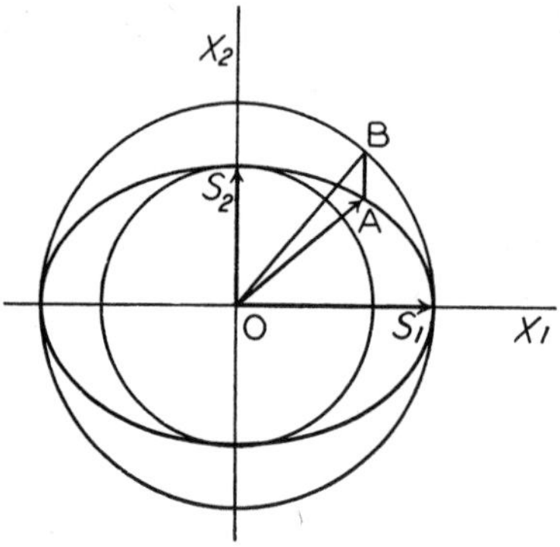

Fig. 7. Representation of a two-dimensional stress by an ellipse.

It can be seen from the complete set of equations represented by equation (3) that the stress components are transformed by a rotation of coordinates in the same fashion as the parameters in the equation of an ellipsoid. Hence the stress at a point is often represented as an ellipsoid whose major axes are oriented parallel to the directions of principal stress, and are proportional in magnitude to the principal stresses. The force per unit area on any oblique surface is indicated by the two-dimensional construction in figure 7. The vector OA represents the force acting on a surface oriented normal to the line OB. Another useful method of representing a stress geometrically is by means of the Mohr stress sphere (7). This method will not be considered here.

2. The Geometry of Small Strains

The result of a balanced set of forces acting on an object is some sort of shape distortion. In the case of an ideal elastic solid, the distortion takes place instantaneously and disappears when the stress is removed. In the case of a viscous liquid subjected to a shear stress, a progressive distortion takes place as long as the stress operates, and remains after the stress is removed. In any case, the particles of the distorted object have a different relative arrangement than they had in the undistorted object. A particle which before the distortion was located at the position x, y, z, is moved to the new position $(x + u)$, $(y + v)$, $(z + w)$. The vector $iu + jv + kw$ is called the *displacement* of the particle. If u, v, and w are known as functions of x, y, and z, then the geometry of the distortion is completely defined.

In order to determine u, v, and w as functions of x, y, and z, it is necessary first to examine the behavior of a small volume element. When the sample as a whole is bent, stretched, or twisted, each small volume element must undergo certain shape changes. The relative shape change of an infinitesimal volume element is called the *strain* at the point in question. A small strain, like the *stress* at the point, can be resolved into six components, which are indicated in figure 8.

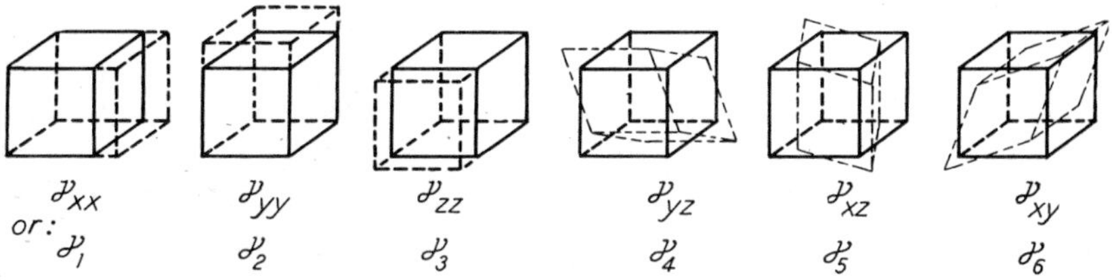

Fig. 8. The six components of strain.

The first component of strain, γ_1 or γ_{xx}, represents a simple extension in the x direction, with the cross dimensions held constant. If a cube with sides 1:1:1 is deformed to a rectangular parallelopiped with sides 1.01:1:1, this represents a pure γ_1 strain, of magnitude 0.01. In the same way, $\gamma_2(\gamma_{yy})$ and $\gamma_3(\gamma_{zz})$ represent the relative elongation of the volume element in the y and z directions, respectively.

The fourth component of strain, γ_4 or γ_{yz}, is a shear strain in the yz plane, *i.e.*, about the x axis. The yz faces of the cubical volume element are deformed into nonrectangular parallelograms. One diagonal is lengthened, the other shortened. The magnitude of the shear strain is simply the angular deformation in radians, *i.e.*, the complement of the acute angle of the deformed parallelogram. The shear strains in the zx and xy planes are γ_5 and γ_6, respectively.

It is clear that the strain components are connected with the manner in which displacement (u,v,w) changes with position (x,y,z). If the displacement of a whole region is constant, the region has simply been moved, with no internal shape change, or strain. A strain denotes a *variation* of displacement with position. The mathematical definitions of the strain components are given below.

$$\gamma_{xx} = \gamma_1 = \frac{\partial u}{\partial x} \tag{4a}$$

$$\gamma_{yy} = \gamma_2 = \frac{\partial v}{\partial y} \tag{4b}$$

$$\gamma_{zz} = \gamma_3 = \frac{\partial w}{\partial z} \tag{4c}$$

$$\gamma_{yz} = \gamma_4 = \frac{\partial v}{\partial z} + \frac{\partial w}{\partial y} \tag{4d}$$

$$\gamma_{xz} = \gamma_5 = \frac{\partial u}{\partial z} + \frac{\partial w}{\partial x} \tag{4e}$$

$$\gamma_{xy} = \gamma_6 = \frac{\partial u}{\partial y} + \frac{\partial v}{\partial x} \tag{4f}$$

In many respects a small strain at a point is analogous to the stress at a point. The strain is a definite quantity—but the components into which it is resolved depend upon the orientation of the reference volume element. Any strain can be expressed in terms only of tensile components, if the volume element is oriented properly. These tensile components are called the *principal strains*, in complete analogy with the principal stresses. It can be shown that in an isotropic elastic material, the directions of principal stress must coincide with the directions of principal strain. The strain, like the stress, can be represented by an ellipsoid (*7*). Both are "second order tensors." (See Appendix I.)

3. Theory of Elasticity (*11*)

Relationship between Stress and Strain in an Ideal Elastic Material

A. Homogeneous Stress

By an ideal elastic material, we mean a material which possesses no time effects of any sort. When a stress is applied, the sample instantaneously deforms to some strained condition. When the stress is removed, the strain instantaneously disappears. Further, only the range is considered in which Hooke's law is obeyed, *i.e.*, where only *linear* relations between stress and strain exist. By choosing the ideal elastic solid, it is possible to isolate the componential aspect of the *stress–strain* relationship and discuss it in detail.

Consider a single crystal, and set up a coordinate system referred to the crystal lattice. The cubical volume elements which are to be used in the specification of the stress and strain at different points are now oriented parallel to this coordinate system. (No attempt is made to make the shear components of stress or strain vanish.)

Although for each of the six stress components there is a "corresponding" strain component, there is, of course, no convenient pairing of variable components in the *stress–strain* relationship. That is to say, a pure s_1 stress does *not* produce a pure γ_1 strain. The first component of stress is a simple tension in the x direction. This results *not only in an elongation in the x direction but also in a contraction in the y and z directions.* In general, *shear* deformations also occur as a result of any kind of stress. Conversely, any type of strain can be produced not only by the *corresponding* stress, but by *any* stress component. If we want to know the total amount of γ_1, we must add up the γ_1 strains caused by each of the six stress components. The same is true for γ_2, γ_3, etc.

$$\gamma_1 = K_{11}s_1 + K_{12}s_2 + K_{13}s_3 + K_{14}s_4 + K_{15}s_5 + K_{16}s_6 \quad (5a)$$
$$\gamma_2 = K_{21}s_1 + K_{22}s_2 + K_{23}s_3 + K_{24}s_4 + K_{25}s_5 + K_{26}s_6 \quad (5b)$$
$$\vdots$$
$$\gamma_6 = K_{61}s_1 + K_{62}s_2 + K_{63}s_3 + \cdots \quad (5f)$$

The K values are the "reciprocal elastic moduli," or the "moduli of compliance." K_{13}, for example, tells how much strain of type 1 is produced by unit stress s_3. K_{25} tells how much γ_2 (elongation in the y direction) results from unit (*shear*) stress component s_5.

The whole set of constants K_{ij} defines the elastic properties of the material in question.

Equations (5) can be written as well in the inverse form:

$$s_1 = k_{11}\gamma_1 + k_{12}\gamma_2 + k_{13}\gamma_3 + k_{14}\gamma_4 + k_{15}\gamma_5 + k_{16}\gamma_6 \quad (6a)$$
$$s_2 = k_{21}\gamma_1 + k_{22}\gamma_2 + k_{23}\gamma_3 + k_{24}\gamma_4 + k_{25}\gamma_5 + k_{26}\gamma_6 \quad (6b)$$
$$\vdots$$
$$\text{etc.} \quad (6f)$$

Here the k values are elastic moduli, rather than reciprocal elastic moduli.

If the set of elastic constants k_{ij} is known, the "reciprocal" constants, K_{ij} for the inverse set of relationships, can be computed by standard algebraic methods.

The *work* per unit volume required to distort a solid to a given strain (γ_1, γ_2, γ_3, γ_4, γ_5, γ_6) depends upon all the elastic constants. This work, the *free energy of deformation*, is given by:

$$W = \mathbf{F} = \sum_i \sum_j \tfrac{1}{2} k_{ij}\gamma_i\gamma_j \quad (7)$$

(In general, **F** may be represented by a power series expansion in terms of the six variables γ_1, γ_2, γ_3, γ_4, γ_5, γ_6.

$$\mathbf{F} = \sum_i a_i\gamma_i + \sum_i \sum_j b_{ij}\gamma_i\gamma_j + \sum_i \sum_j \sum_k c_{ijk}\gamma_i\gamma_j\gamma_k + \cdots \quad (8)$$

The linear coefficients a_i must all be zero, since $\gamma_i = 0$ represents a minimum of **F**. For small values of the strains, the cubic terms can be neglected in comparison with the quadratic terms. The range in which this can be done is the range of Hooke's law.) Among other things, this means that the value of k_{ij} is given by $\partial^2\mathbf{F}/\partial\gamma_i\partial\gamma_j$.

In many discussions of elasticity the work done in a small elastic deformation is spoken of as the "energy of deformation" or the "elastic potential." If one is concerned with the thermodynamic changes occurring in the deformed material, one must identify the elastic potential as a *free energy*. The identification of this elastic potential with the *free energy* of deformation (rather than with the energy of deformation) is particularly significant in the case of high polymers. An unstressed object tends to assume the shape which has a minimum *free energy*, which is not necessarily the shape having the lowest energy. A deformation increases the *free energy*. This may be due either to an increase in energy or a decrease in entropy. In some cases, as for example perfect crystals, the free energy increase during deformation is indeed almost entirely the result of an increase in the potential energy of the lattice. In other cases, as for example rubber, the energy changes hardly at all during a deformation, but instead there is an *entropy decrease* which opposes the deformation. In general, both the energy and the entropy change when an object is deformed, and the elastic constants are given by the expression:

$$k_{ij} = \frac{\partial^2\mathbf{E}(\gamma)}{\partial\gamma_i\,\partial\gamma_j} - T\frac{\partial^2\mathbf{S}(\gamma)}{\partial\gamma_i\,\partial\gamma_j} = \frac{\partial^2\mathbf{F}(\gamma)}{\partial\gamma_i\,\partial\gamma_j} \tag{9}$$

Here **E** represents the internal energy, **S** the entropy, and **F** the free energy of the crystal. T is the absolute temperature.

The 21 Independent Elastic Constants.—It has been pointed out that the relationships between stress and strain in an elastic solid can be written in terms either of the 36 elastic moduli or of the 36 reciprocal moduli.

No matter which method of expression is used, not all 36 constants are independent. It follows from the relation

$$K_{ij} = \frac{\partial^2\mathbf{F}}{\partial\gamma_i\,\partial\gamma_j} \tag{10}$$

that

$$\begin{aligned} k_{12} &= k_{21}, \quad & k_{35} &= k_{53}, \text{ etc.} \quad & k_{ij} &= k_{ji} \\ K_{12} &= K_{21}, \quad & K_{35} &= K_{53}, \text{ etc.} \quad & K_{ij} &= K_{ji} \end{aligned} \tag{11}$$

Therefore, even in the most general case of an anisotropic material, there are only 21 *independent* elastic constants, rather than 36.

The 21 elastic constants which are necessary to describe a completely anisotropic material can be arranged as follows:

$$\begin{matrix} k_{11} & k_{12} & k_{13} & k_{14} & k_{15} & k_{16} \\ & k_{22} & k_{23} & k_{24} & k_{25} & k_{26} \\ & & k_{33} & k_{34} & k_{35} & k_{36} \\ & & & k_{44} & k_{45} & k_{46} \\ & & & & k_{55} & k_{56} \\ & & & & & k_{66} \end{matrix}$$

A single triclinic crystal would require this complete set of 21 constants. However, a crystal possessing symmetry requires fewer constants. For example, for a monoclinic crystal with its two-fold axis of symmetry aligned along the z axis, $k_{14} = k_{15} = k_{24} = k_{25} = k_{34} = k_{35} = k_{46} = k_{56} = 0$, and the following set of constants defines the elastic behavior (7)

$$\begin{matrix} k_{11} & k_{12} & k_{13} & 0 & 0 & k_{16} \\ & k_{22} & k_{23} & 0 & 0 & k_{26} \\ & & k_{33} & 0 & 0 & k_{36} \\ & & & k_{44} & k_{45} & 0 \\ & & & & k_{55} & 0 \\ & & & & & k_{66} \end{matrix}$$

For a rhombic crystal, arranged with axes parallel to x, y, and z, the set of 21 constants reduces to the following (7):

$$\begin{matrix} k_{11} & k_{12} & k_{13} & 0 & 0 & 0 \\ & k_{22} & k_{23} & 0 & 0 & 0 \\ & & k_{33} & 0 & 0 & 0 \\ & & & k_{44} & 0 & 0 \\ & & & & k_{55} & 0 \\ & & & & & k_{66} \end{matrix}$$

For a tetragonal crystal, where the z axis is the four-fold axis of symmetry, the above set of constants applies with the additional condition that $k_{11} = k_{22}$, $k_{13} = k_{23}$, $k_{44} = k_{55}$. For a cubic crystal, $k_{11} = k_{22} = k_{33}$, $k_{44} = k_{55} = k_{66}$, and $k_{12} = k_{13} = k_{23}$. Thus *three* constants will define the elastic behavior of a cubic crystal.

For a completely *isotropic* body, the set of elastic constants depends upon only *two* independent parameters. These are usually represented by the symbols λ and μ. In terms of λ and μ, the fundamental elastic moduli of the isotropic body take on the following form:

$$\begin{aligned} &k_{11} = k_{22} = k_{33} = \lambda + 2\mu \\ &k_{12} = k_{23} = k_{13} = \lambda \\ &k_{44} = k_{55} = k_{66} = \mu \\ &\text{all others} = 0 \end{aligned} \tag{12}$$

The set of 21 elastic constants, in this case, is given below:

$$\begin{matrix} \lambda + 2\mu & \lambda & \lambda & 0 & 0 & 0 \\ & \lambda + 2\mu & \lambda & 0 & 0 & 0 \\ & & \lambda + 2\mu & 0 & 0 & 0 \\ & & & \mu & 0 & 0 \\ & & & & \mu & 0 \\ & & & & & \mu \end{matrix}$$

Hence the general relation between stress and small strain for an isotropic elastic solid is the following:

$$s_1 = (\lambda + 2\mu)\gamma_1 + \lambda\gamma_2 + \lambda\gamma_3 \tag{13a}$$

$$s_2 = \lambda\gamma_1 + (\lambda + 2\mu)\gamma_2 + \lambda\gamma_3 \tag{13b}$$

$$s_3 = \lambda\gamma_1 + \lambda\gamma_2 + (\lambda + 2\mu)\gamma_3 \tag{13c}$$

$$s_4 = \mu\gamma_4 \tag{13d}$$

$$s_5 = \mu\gamma_5 \tag{13e}$$

$$s_6 = \mu\gamma_6 \tag{13f}$$

Alternative Methods of Representation for Elastic Properties of Isotropic Bodies.—The fundamental constants, k_{ij}, relate single stress components and single strain components. Experimentally it is not as simple to determine these fundamental constants as certain combinations of them—Young's modulus, bulk modulus, etc.

When an isotropic body is subjected to a uniform pressure, there results a volume decrease ΔV. The relative volume change, $\Delta V/V$, is directly proportional to the pressure:

$$\Delta V/V = \beta P \tag{14}$$

Here β is the *compressibility* of the body; $1/\beta$ is called the bulk modulus. In terms of λ and μ,

$$\beta = 3/(3\lambda + 2\mu) \tag{15}$$

If an isotropic body is subjected to a simple tensile stress in the x direction, it elongates in this direction and contracts in the two lateral directions. The relative elongation is directly proportional to the tensile stress.

$$\gamma_x = \Delta L_x / L_x = (1/E) S_x \tag{16}$$

E, the Young's modulus of the material, is given in terms of μ and λ by the expression:

$$E = \mu \left(\frac{3\lambda + 2\mu}{\lambda + \mu} \right) \tag{17}$$

In this experiment, the relative lateral contraction, *e.g.* γ_y, is directly proportional to the relative longitudinal extension. The *ratio* between the relative lateral contraction and the relative longitudinal elongation is called Poisson's ratio, and given the symbol ν.

$$\nu = \text{Poisson's ratio} = -\gamma_y/\gamma_x = \lambda/2(\lambda + \mu) \tag{18}$$

A fourth commonly used modulus is the shear modulus, which relates shear stress and shear strain. This modulus is simply equal to μ. The symbol G is used for the shear modulus throughout this book; $G \equiv \mu$.

It is clear that any two independent elastic constants serve to define all the rest. Thus it is possible to express all the elastic constants of an isotropic body in terms of the Young's modulus and the Poisson's ratio, or the shear modulus and the bulk modulus, etc. (see table I).

TABLE I

Constant	Elastic constants expressed in terms of:				
	λ, μ	B, μ	μ, ν	E, ν	E, μ
Lamé's constant, λ	λ	$B - \frac{2}{3}\mu$	$\frac{2\mu\nu}{1-2\nu}$	$\frac{\nu E}{(1+\nu)(1-2\nu)}$	$\frac{\mu(E-2\mu)}{3\mu-E}$
Lamé's constant, μ (shear modulus)	μ	μ	μ	$\frac{E}{2+2\nu}$	μ
Bulk modulus, B	$\frac{3\lambda+2\mu}{3}$	B	$\frac{2\mu(1+\nu)}{3(1-2\nu)}$	$\frac{E}{3}\frac{1}{1-2\nu}$	$\frac{E\mu}{3(3\mu-E)}$
Young's modulus, E	$\frac{(3\lambda+2\mu)}{\lambda+\mu}\mu$	$\frac{9B\mu}{3B+\mu}$	$2(1+\nu)\mu$	E	E
Poisson's ratio, ν	$\frac{\lambda}{2(\lambda+\mu)}$	$\frac{3B-2\mu}{6B+2\mu}$	ν	ν	$\frac{E}{2\mu}-1$

Problems Involving Simple Geometry.—Although in principle six components must be specified in order to define a stress or a strain completely, in many cases a smaller number of explicit parameters may be sufficient. This is particularly true where the geometrical relationships are simple. For example, consider the material which lies between two parallel, infinite plates, which are acted upon by opposite tangential forces. If the sample is not to undergo angular acceleration, the plates must also exert normal forces on the sample. Here the *plane* of the shear stress is apparent, and the second and third shear components are zero. A single explicit variable (together with an implicit recognition of the geometry of the problem) will define the stress. In such a case, little would be gained by setting up the problem in terms of six stress components. Instead, one speaks simply of the shear stress.

In such simple cases, where a single explicit stress variable and a single explicit deformation variable are sufficient to define the stress and strain, the symbols S and γ, without subscripts, will be used. In general the deformation, γ, will not correspond to any one of the six components of strain, but to some combination of them. In the stretching of a thin rod, which is parallel to the x axis, the deformation includes a longitudinal extension and a lateral contraction.

$$\gamma_{xx} = \gamma, \qquad \gamma_{yy} = -\nu\gamma, \qquad \gamma_{zz} = -\nu\gamma, \qquad S = s_{xx} \tag{19}$$

Young's modulus is simply S/γ in these terms.

B. Nonhomogeneous Stresses

When the behavior of an *object*, rather than of an infinitesimal volume element, is considered, it is necessary to "integrate" the strains of a differential volume element over the whole object. (More precisely, it is necessary to solve a set of partial differential equations subject to the proper spatial boundary conditions.) These differential equations will now set up.

First of all, the stress must follow equations (20) in its variation with position (11), where ρ is the density of the material:

$$\frac{\partial s_{xx}}{\partial x} + \frac{\partial s_{xy}}{\partial y} + \frac{\partial s_{xz}}{\partial z} + F_x = \rho \frac{\partial^2 u}{\partial t^2} \tag{20a}$$

$$\frac{\partial s_{xy}}{\partial x} + \frac{\partial s_{yy}}{\partial y} + \frac{\partial s_{yz}}{\partial z} + F_y = \rho \frac{\partial^2 v}{\partial t^2} \tag{20b}$$

$$\frac{\partial s_{xz}}{\partial x} + \frac{\partial s_{yz}}{\partial y} + \frac{\partial s_{zz}}{\partial z} + F_z = \rho \frac{\partial^2 w}{\partial t^2} \tag{20c}$$

Here F_x, F_y, and F_z represent the components of any *body force* (per unit volume) which acts upon the material at the point in question. The above equations are merely the expression of Newton's law of motion, $F = ma$, for a differential volume element at the point x, y, z. If body forces are neglected, and only *equilibrium* elastic deformation is considered, so that accelerations also can be neglected, equations (20) reduce to the form:

$$\frac{\partial s_{xx}}{\partial x} + \frac{\partial s_{xy}}{\partial y} + \frac{\partial s_{xz}}{\partial z} = 0 \tag{21a}$$

$$\frac{\partial s_{xy}}{\partial x} + \frac{\partial s_{yy}}{\partial y} + \frac{\partial s_{yz}}{\partial z} = 0 \tag{21b}$$

$$\frac{\partial s_{xz}}{\partial x} + \frac{\partial s_{yz}}{\partial y} + \frac{\partial s_{zz}}{\partial z} = 0 \tag{21c}$$

Problems involving the propagation of elastic waves demand the general formulae (Eq. 20). Problems of static elastic deformation may be treated by means of the simpler equations (21).

Furthermore, the strain components (in the case of small strains) can vary with position only in accordance with equations (22), which are called the "conditions of compatability" for the strains (*9*, *11*):

$$\frac{\partial^2 \gamma_{xx}}{\partial y^2} + \frac{\partial^2 \gamma_{yy}}{\partial x^2} = \frac{\partial^2 \gamma_{xy}}{\partial x\, \partial y} \tag{22a}$$

$$\frac{\partial^2 \gamma_{yy}}{\partial z^2} + \frac{\partial^2 \gamma_{zz}}{\partial y^2} = \frac{\partial^2 \gamma_{yz}}{\partial y\, \partial z} \tag{22b}$$

$$\frac{\partial^2 \gamma_{zz}}{\partial x^2} + \frac{\partial^2 \gamma_{xx}}{\partial z^2} = \frac{\partial^2 \gamma_{xz}}{\partial x\, \partial z} \tag{22c}$$

$$2\frac{\partial^2 \gamma_{xx}}{\partial y\, \partial z} = \frac{\partial}{\partial x}\left[-\frac{\partial \gamma_{yz}}{\partial x} + \frac{\partial \gamma_{xz}}{\partial y} + \frac{\partial \gamma_{xy}}{\partial z}\right] \tag{22d}$$

$$2\frac{\partial^2 \gamma_{yy}}{\partial x\, \partial z} = \frac{\partial}{\partial y}\left[\frac{\partial \gamma_{yz}}{\partial x} - \frac{\partial \gamma_{xz}}{\partial y} + \frac{\partial \gamma_{xy}}{\partial z}\right] \tag{22e}$$

$$2\frac{\partial^2 \gamma_{zz}}{\partial x\, \partial y} = \frac{\partial}{\partial z}\left[\frac{\partial \gamma_{yz}}{\partial x} + \frac{\partial \gamma_{xz}}{\partial y} - \frac{\partial \gamma_{xy}}{\partial z}\right] \tag{22f}$$

Equations (22) follow from the fundamental definitions of the strain components (Eq. 4). For example,

$$\frac{\partial^2 \gamma_{xx}}{\partial y^2} = \frac{\partial^2}{\partial y^2}\left(\frac{\partial u}{\partial x}\right) = \frac{\partial^3 u}{\partial x\, \partial y^2} \tag{23a}$$

$$\frac{\partial^2 \gamma_{yy}}{\partial x^2} = \frac{\partial^2}{\partial x^2}\left(\frac{\partial v}{\partial y}\right) = \frac{\partial^3 v}{\partial y\, \partial x^2} \tag{23b}$$

$$\frac{\partial^2 \gamma_{xy}}{\partial x\, \partial y} = \frac{\partial^2}{\partial x\, \partial y}\left(\frac{\partial u}{\partial y} + \frac{\partial v}{\partial x}\right) = \frac{\partial^3 u}{\partial x\, \partial y^2} + \frac{\partial^3 v}{\partial y\, \partial x^2} \tag{23c}$$

This immediately gives rise to equation (22a).

It should be emphasized that the above sets of partial differential equations must hold *regardless of the nature of the elastic material concerned.* Equations (20), (21), and (22) are derived from the definitions of stress and strain with no assumptions concerning the *properties* of the continuum. It is therefore necessary to add to these differential equations an additional set of equations which define the properties of the material. The additional information is clearly provided by equations (5) or (6). Considering only the case of *isotropic* elastic solids, we may use equations (13) in place of the more general set of equations (6). Thus equations (13), (21), and (22) together determine the manner in which stress and strain vary throughout an isotropic elastic material in equilibrium. Together with a set of known boundary conditions, these equations therefore determine the elastic deformation of an *object* subject to those boundary conditions.

In the forms given above, however, these equations are not well suited to the problem at hand. Equations (21) are expressed in terms of the *stress*, while equations (22) are expressed in terms of the *strain*. It is therefore useful to unify these equations in either of two ways (11):

(1) Combine the generalized Hooke's law (Eq. 13) with equations (22), and eliminate the strain components. Equations (13), (21), and (22) thus reduce to two sets of partial differential equations, both expressed in terms of the stress; or

(2) Combine Hooke's law with equations (21), and eliminate the *stress*. Now two sets of partial differential equations, both expressed in terms of the *strain*, are obtained. In this case it is useful to go one step further and express both sets of equations in terms of the *displacements*.

The first procedure leads to the following set of equations:

$$(1 + \nu)\left(\frac{\partial^2 s_{xx}}{\partial y^2} + \frac{\partial^2 s_{yy}}{\partial x^2}\right) - \nu\left(\frac{\partial^2 \theta}{\partial y^2} + \frac{\partial^2 \theta}{\partial x^2}\right) = 2(\nu + 1)\frac{\partial^2 s_{xy}}{\partial x\, \partial y} \tag{24}$$

etc.

Here ν is the Poisson's ratio of the isotropic elastic solid. The absolute magnitudes of the constants μ and λ do not appear. The quantity θ is defined as $s_{xx} + s_{yy} + s_{zz}$. Equation (24), for example, may be further condensed and expressed in the form:

$$(1 + \nu)\left[\frac{\partial^2 s_{xx}}{\partial x^2} + \frac{\partial^2 s_{xx}}{\partial y^2} + \frac{\partial^2 s_{xx}}{\partial z^2}\right] + \frac{\partial^2 \theta}{\partial x^2} = 0 \tag{25}$$

The second procedure yields the following set of partial differential equations expressed in terms of the displacements [these equations are obtained from equations (21)]:

$$(\lambda + G)\frac{\partial e}{\partial x} + G\left[\frac{\partial^2 u}{\partial x^2} + \frac{\partial^2 u}{\partial y^2} + \frac{\partial^2 u}{\partial z^2}\right] = 0 \tag{26a}$$

$$(\lambda + G)\frac{\partial e}{\partial y} + G\left[\frac{\partial^2 v}{\partial x^2} + \frac{\partial^2 v}{\partial y^2} + \frac{\partial^2 v}{\partial z^2}\right] = 0 \tag{26b}$$

$$(\lambda + G)\frac{\partial e}{\partial z} + G\left[\frac{\partial^2 w}{\partial x^2} + \frac{\partial^2 w}{\partial y^2} + \frac{\partial^2 w}{\partial z^2}\right] = 0 \tag{26c}$$

Here e represents the relative volume expansion, $\partial u/\partial x + \partial v/\partial y + \partial w/\partial z$. If the equations of compatibility (22) are expressed in terms of the displacements, a set of identities results. This is to be expected, since equations (22) were derived from the definitions of the strain components in terms of the displacements. Thus procedure (2), page 18, results in the single definitive set of equations (26), which, together with the boundary conditions, determine the detailed elastic deformation of an object. If the constraints on the object under consideration are shape constraints, then the spatial boundary conditions are in the form of a defined displacement of every point on the surface. With such boundary conditions, the differential equations (26) offer the most direct approach to the problem of determining the stress and strain throughout the object. If the boundary conditions are in the form of a known stress distribution on the surface, then equations (21) and (25) can be used in the calculation.

The Special Case when $\mu \ll \lambda$.—If an isotropic elastic material has a much higher bulk modulus than shear modulus, then the differential equations governing its elastic deformation become simplified. Physically this means that the material responds easily to shear stresses, but is only slightly compressible. *Rubber* is an example of such a material.

The set of *reciprocal* elastic moduli in this case is particularly enlightening, since these constants indicate directly that the shear modulus determines the elastic deformation. For an incompressible, isotropic material (*i.e.*, one for which $B \ll \mu$), the strains as a function of the stress components are given by the following set of compliance constants:

$$\begin{matrix} \frac{1}{3}J & -\frac{1}{6}J & -\frac{1}{6}J & 0 & 0 & 0 \\ & \frac{1}{3}J & -\frac{1}{6}J & 0 & 0 & 0 \\ & & \frac{1}{3}J & 0 & 0 & 0 \\ & & & J & 0 & 0 \\ & & & & J & 0 \\ & & & & & J \end{matrix}$$

where J, the shear compliance, is equal to $1/G$. This special case will be discussed in detail later.

C. Large Deformations

The whole of classical elasticity theory, as discussed above, deals with the subject of *infinitesimal* strains. The definition of the strain components which we have used cannot be unambiguously applied in the case of finite amounts of strain. This distinction between infinitesimal and finite strains can be illustrated in a number of ways. For example, six (infinitesimal) strain components defines a unique state of combined strain. It does not matter in what order we imagine the different components of strain to be applied. An infinitesimal stretch in the x direction, γ_{xx}, followed by an infinitesimal shear in the xy plane, γ_{xy}, represents a state of strain identical with that obtained by imposing first the shearing strain, γ_{xy}, and then the stretch, γ_{xx}.

When the strains become large, this uniqueness of a combined state of strain disappears. It is clear, for example, that if one first stretches a sample 100% in the x direction ($\gamma_{xx} = 1$), and then subjects it to a unit shear in the xy plane, the resulting state of strain is quite different from the one obtained when one first imposes a unit shear followed by a unit stretch. From a strict mathematical point of view, this difficulty begins to arise as soon as the strain components become finite. From the practical standpoint, it is quite satisfactory to use the classical theory of elasticity for *small* finite strains, but when large strains are involved, a new mathematical framework is demanded for practical as well as theoretical reasons.

A number of attempts have been made to extend the classical theory of elasticity to the general case of finite strains. A satisfactory general theory was provided for isotropic solids by Murnaghan (*35*), who pointed out that there are two possible viewpoints which coincide for an infinitesimal strain but are essentially different for a finite strain; the strain may be described in terms of the co-ordinates of a particle of the medium in the unstrained or initial position, or of its coordinates in the strained or final position. The former method Murnaghan designates as the Lagrangian viewpoint, and the latter as the Eulerian viewpoint.

Consider a three-dimensional medium, regarded as a system of particles, and two positions of this medium—the initial or unstrained and the final or strained position. Let a, b, and c represent the original co-ordinates of a given particle, and x, y, and z the final coordinates. Let u, v, and w represent the *displacement* of the particle.

$$u = x - a, \qquad v = y - b, \qquad w = z - c \tag{27}$$

Murnaghan shows that the tensor *strain* components (in the Eulerian notation) take the form:

$$\epsilon_{xx} = \frac{\partial u}{\partial x} - \frac{1}{2}\left[\left(\frac{\partial u}{\partial x}\right)^2 + \left(\frac{\partial v}{\partial x}\right)^2 + \left(\frac{\partial w}{\partial x}\right)^2\right] \tag{28a}$$

$$\epsilon_{yz} = \frac{1}{2}\left(\frac{\partial v}{\partial z} + \frac{\partial w}{\partial y}\right) - \frac{1}{2}\left[\frac{\partial u}{\partial y}\frac{\partial u}{\partial z} + \frac{\partial v}{\partial y}\frac{\partial v}{\partial z} + \frac{\partial w}{\partial y}\frac{\partial w}{\partial z}\right] \tag{28b}$$

etc.

For very small strains these reduce, of course, to the simple expressions:

$$\epsilon_{xx} = \frac{\partial u}{\partial x}, \qquad \epsilon_{yz} = \frac{1}{2}\left(\frac{\partial v}{\partial z} + \frac{\partial w}{\partial y}\right), \text{ etc.} \tag{29}$$

These expressions are identical with the classical definitions of the strain components (Eq. 4), except for the factor $\frac{1}{2}$ in the shear strains. This factor arises simply because Murnaghan uses a tensor notation throughout (see Appendix I).

When the strain is considered as a tensor, both ϵ_{xy} and ϵ_{yx} retain their identity, instead of being incorporated together as in pages 8–10. Thus the fact that the *tensor* strain components ϵ_{xy} and ϵ_{yx} each have the value $\frac{1}{2}(\partial u/\partial y + \partial v/\partial x)$ is entirely consistent with the fact that the shear strain γ_{xy} as defined in equation (4f) has the value $(\partial u/\partial y + \partial v/\partial x)$.

Murnaghan shows that the components of the stress tensor are given by the equations:

$$s_{ij} = \rho\left(\frac{\partial \phi}{\partial \epsilon_{ji}} - 2\,\Sigma\,\epsilon_{ik}\frac{\partial \phi}{\partial \epsilon_{kj}}\right) \tag{30}$$

Here ρ is the density in the strained state, and ϕ is the free energy of deformation, or "elastic potential," per unit mass. He further shows that for an isotropic material the elastic potential, ϕ, is dependent upon the strain components only through the three quantities I_1, I_2, and I_3, below:

$$I_1 = \text{sum of diagonal elements of strain tensor} \tag{31a}$$

$$I_2 = \tfrac{1}{2} \times \text{sum of principle two-rowed minors} \tag{31b}$$

$$I_3 = \tfrac{1}{6} \times \text{determinant of strain tensor} \tag{31c}$$

Now different materials will differ in the way ϕ depends upon the strain components—*i.e.*, upon I_1, I_2, and I_3. A knowledge of the *properties of the material* now means a knowledge of the function $\phi(\epsilon_{11}, \epsilon_{12}, \epsilon_{13}, \cdots \epsilon_{33})$, or the corresponding function $\phi(I_1, I_2, I_3)$. Once this function is known, the *stress–strain* relations can be computed by means of equation (30). Conversely, experimental *stress–strain* data in the range of finite deformations allow one to compute the definitive function $\phi(I_1, I_2, I_3)$ for the material in question.

It cannot be too strongly emphasized that the classical theory of elasticity, while a very satisfactory approximation in the treatment of *small* finite strains, is a very poor tool in the treatment of *large* finite strains. It is precisely in the field of high polymers, particularly the elastomers, that an extended mathematical framework, valid for strains of any magnitude, is most urgently required. While other treatments (*34, 35*) of finite strains have been made, that of Murnaghan seems to the author to supply the most general framework.

One of the principal aims of this book is to formulate the general phenomenological framework into which should be fitted both the equilibrium elastic behavior and the time behavior of high polymers. Since large deformations are of paramount interest throughout much of the field of high polymers, the formalism of Murnaghan, rather than that of the classical theory of elasticity, should be used whenever possible. This is not done here. Even the problems of equilibrium elastic deformation are couched in terms of the classical theory. The only defence for this neglect is that many of the concepts involved in later chapters are themselves new enough that the additional burden of an unfamiliar geometrical formalism would create hopeless confusion. The author has not hesitated to sacrifice mathematical elegance for physical clarity, but the neglect of the finite theory of strains cannot be justified on this basis. This approach is no mere mathematical nicety; it represents the only proper way to treat the geometrical aspect of the mechanical behavior of high polymers. To use, instead, the classical theory of elasticity definitely detracts from the scientific value of the study made in later sections. The author can only hope that future workers will recognize the importance of the theory of finite strains in connection with high polymers, and will provide the important extensions which he has failed to make here. In particular, it is to be hoped that a general theory of plastoelastic response will be developed, which reduces for small strains to the theory developed on pages 204–218 but which is valid as well for large strains.

4. The Flow of Newtonian Liquids

A. Homogeneous Shear Stress

An incompressible Newtonian fluid (*1*, *2*, *5a*), as well as an ideal elastic solid, responds to stress in such a simple fashion that the *geometric* aspect of the response can be analyzed in detail. In the case of fluids, shear stresses result in viscous flow, rather than elastic displacement. If the fluid is incompressible, uniform compressive stress results in no strain. The term "Newtonian" indicates a direct proportion between shear stress and rate of viscous flow. The "incompressible Newtonian fluid" is, of course, a mathematical abstraction. Every liquid is somewhat compressible, and deviations from a linear relation between stress and flow are extremely common, especially among liquids of high viscosity. Many liquids, it is true, approach the behavior of the incompressible Newtonian fluid very closely over a wide experimental range. Even these liquids, however, possess in reality much more complicated mechanical properties than the idealized model discussed in this chapter. All real liquids, for example, possess an *elastic* character in shear, as well as a viscous character, in spite of the common definition of a liquid as a material which will not support shear stresses except by flow. In a glass, this elastic character is easily observed; in a liquid of low viscosity, special experimental methods are necessary to detect it. The idealized "Newtonian liquid" lacks this elastic character entirely. For this and other reasons, a real liquid can never be said to be Newtonian, without reservation, although it may be essentially Newtonian in a definite experimental range. (In many liquids, the region of essentially Newtonian behavior is quite wide, and indeed covers the entire range of "ordinary" experiments).

If one layer of a Newtonian liquid is held at rest, and a tangential force is applied to a parallel layer (see Fig. 9) the upper layer will move with a constant velocity in the direction of the force. Each successive layer will slip forward relative to the next, so that the velocity of any layer is proportioned to its distance from the stationary layer. It is the frictional or "viscous" drag between parallel layers moving at different velocities, which opposes the applied force. The mechanism of this viscous drag will be discussed in pages 70–75. If y is the distance of a given layer from the stationary layer, v_x its velocity, and F/A the tangential force per unit area, then the following equation governs v_x:

$$v_x = \frac{1}{\eta}(F/A)y \tag{32}$$

The constant of proportionality, η, is called the *viscosity* of the liquid.

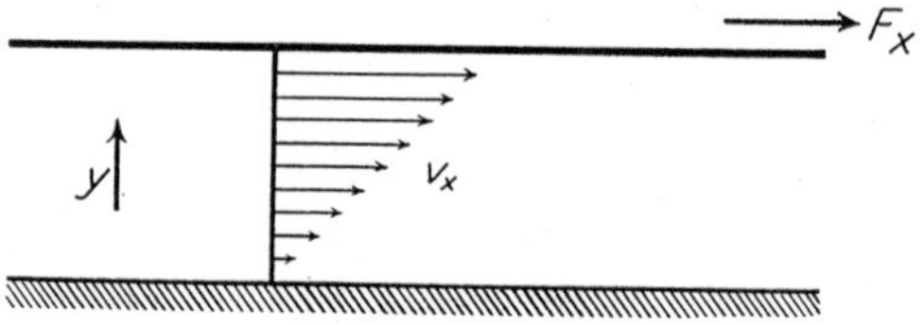

Fig. 9. Velocity distribution in laminar flow.

Although the particle velocity is a function of y, the *relative* motion of any two parallel layers separated by a definite small distance Δ is independent of y. It is thus the *rate at which particle velocity changes with position*, which is the measure of rate of flow—not the particle velocity itself. This is completely analogous with elastic strain, which is connected not with the displacement, but with the rate at which displacement varies with position. Particle velocity is of course the time rate of change of displacement, and in flow plays a role corresponding to that of displacement itself in elastic deformation.

At any point in the liquid in figure 9 there is present a shear stress, $s_{xy} = F/A$. The rate of change of particle velocity (v_x) with position (y), is $\partial v_x/\partial y$, the *velocity gradient*. Hence we may write:

$$\left(\frac{\partial v_x}{\partial y}\right) = \frac{1}{\eta} s_{xy} \tag{33}$$

The essential difference between equations (32) and (33) is that the former describes the behavior of a finite object, whereas the latter relates two "point variables"—quantities which have values at each *point* in the object. Equation (33) is thus in a form which allows it to serve as a starting point in problems involving *nonhomogeneous* stresses.

The "flow rate" at a point can be expressed in slightly different form. If we consider a cubical differential volume element at the time t_0, and observe this volume element for a brief interval, it will be seen to undergo a shearing strain γ_{xy} which increases at a constant rate with time. The rate of increase of γ_{xy} is a measure of the flow at a point, which is completely equivalent to the velocity gradient.

$$\left(\frac{\partial \gamma_{xy}}{\partial t}\right) = \left(\frac{\partial v_y}{\partial x}\right) = \frac{1}{\eta} s_{xy} \tag{34}$$

This expression, $\partial \gamma_{xy}/\partial t$, for the rate of shear obviously will hold only for deformations to which the definition of γ_{xy} is itself applicable, *i.e.*, small deformations. We have seen that large deformations cannot be resolved into six strain components in the fashion of small deformations, and it is clear that any flow will, in the course of time, result in large deformations. However, if a sufficiently short interval of time is considered, even a rapid flow in the xy plane can be represented by a linear increase of γ_{xy} with time. As a matter of fact, in the field of high polymers, viscosities are often so high, and rates of flow so low, that the total flow-deformation during an ordinary mechanical experiment is relatively small. Even when fairly large deformations take place, it may still at times be useful to express the flow rate as instantaneous *rate of change of shear strain*, rather than as *velocity gradient*. In this volume, the *velocity gradient* will be used whenever the *geometric* aspect of flow is under primary consideration, as in hydrodynamics. When the geometry of a problem is simple, and the *time behavior* is under consideration, the rate of deformation will be used, since it most strongly emphasizes the distinctive time behavior of liquids.

In general, although not in the definitive case just treated, v_y will be a function of x, as well as v_x a function of y. Since γ_{xy} includes both rate of change of x displacement with y and rate of change of y displacement with x, the general value of $\partial \gamma_{xy}/\partial t$ must be $[\partial v_x/\partial y + \partial v_y/\partial x]$, so that equation (34) becomes:

$$s_{xy} = \eta \left[\frac{\partial v_x}{\partial y} + \frac{\partial v_y}{\partial x}\right] \tag{35a}$$

In similar fashion, shear stresses in the xz and yz planes can be supported by velocity gradients in those planes:

$$s_{yz} = \eta \left[\frac{\partial v_y}{\partial z} + \frac{\partial v_z}{\partial y}\right] \tag{35b}$$

$$s_{zx} = \eta \left[\frac{\partial v_z}{\partial x} + \frac{\partial v_x}{\partial z}\right] \tag{35c}$$

B. Nonhomogeneous Stresses

Equations (35) apply to the stress and the velocity gradient *at a point*—*i.e.*, to the behavior of a differential volume element. The problem of hydrodynamics is the same as the problem of the theory of elasticity—to predict, from the known properties of a differential volume element, the behavior of a finite sample of the material. Mathematically, hydrodynamics involves the solution of a set of partial differential equations, subject to certain spatial boundary conditions, just as does the theory of elasticity.

The hydrodynamical approach is based upon the fact that even in a complicated flow problem, small volume elements of the liquid behave in a simple fashion, thus:

(1) If a volume element is subjected to a shear stress, it will deform in the manner previously described. This shape change is governed by the *viscosity* of the liquid.

(2) Like any other body, the volume element will accelerate as a whole if acted upon by a net force. This acceleration is governed by the *density* of the liquid.

(3) If the element is subjected to a homogeneous pressure, it will be compressed. This process is governed by the *compressibility* of the liquid.

As we have noted, the compressibility of liquids is so small compared with the deformability in shear that in many cases the third effect is negligible, and the behavior of the volume element can be reduced to:

(1) change of shape resulting from shearing stresses, plus

(2) acceleration resulting from unbalanced forces.

In certain limiting cases, the acceleration effect, (2) above, is the dominant effect. In such cases, the viscosity of the liquid can be neglected, and only the inertia considered. In other cases, effect (1) predominates; that is, the viscosity is much more important than the inertia. When both the viscosity and the inertia are appreciable factors, the prediction of hydrodynamical flow becomes very difficult.

The two special limiting cases are contrasted in the tabulation below.

Inertial case	Viscosity case
Conditions	
Fluid of low viscosity, far from restraining boundaries. (dv/dt) for each particle large.	Fluid of high viscosity, near restraining boundaries. (dv/dt) for each particle small.
Examples	
Water waves, efflux from large hole in side of standpipe.	Flow in capillary tube, flow between infinite parallel plates.
Energy Consumption	
Work done on fluid goes to increase kinetic and potential energy of volume elements of fluid.	Work done on fluid goes to increase random energy of molecules (dissipation as heat).

In order to set up the fundamental differential equations of viscous flow, we must first generalize the relationship in equation (35) between stress and velocity gradient. In the general case, where each velocity component is changing with each position coordinate, the stresses due to *viscous resistance* are given by:

$$s_{xx} = 2\eta \frac{\partial v_x}{\partial x} \tag{36a}$$

$$s_{yy} = 2\eta \frac{\partial v_y}{\partial y} \tag{36b}$$

$$s_{zz} = 2\eta \frac{\partial v_z}{\partial z} \tag{36c}$$

$$s_{yz} = \eta \left[\frac{\partial v_y}{\partial z} + \frac{\partial v_z}{\partial y} \right] \tag{36d}$$

$$s_{xz} = \eta \left[\frac{\partial v_x}{\partial z} + \frac{\partial v_z}{\partial x} \right] \tag{36e}$$

$$s_{xy} = \eta \left[\frac{\partial v_x}{\partial y} + \frac{\partial v_y}{\partial x} \right] \tag{36f}$$

Combining equations (36) with equations (20), the following is obtained:

$$F_x - \frac{\partial P}{\partial x} + k \left(\frac{\partial^2 v_x}{\partial x^2} + \frac{\partial^2 v_x}{\partial y^2} + \frac{\partial^2 v_x}{\partial z^2} \right) = \rho \left[\frac{\partial v_x}{\partial t} + v_x \frac{\partial v_x}{\partial x} + v_y \frac{\partial v_x}{\partial y} + v_z \frac{\partial v_x}{\partial z} \right] \tag{37a}$$

etc. (37b)

Here F_x represents any "body force" in the x direction acting on a volume element. An example of a "body force" is gravitational attraction. This is a force which is not applied at the boundary of the volume element, but rather acts directly upon each part of the interior. In many hydrodynamic problems body forces are of little importance compared with the force which one volume element exerts on another at their common boundary.

The term $(-\,\partial P/\partial x)$ is obviously the force in the x direction (per unit volume) which results from the *pressure gradient* in the liquid. If the pressure on one yz-face of a volume element, dx, dy, dz, is P, that on the opposite face is $P + (\partial P/\partial x)dx$. The pressure difference is $(\partial P/\partial x)dx$, giving a net *force* of $-\,(\partial P/\partial x)\,dx\,dy\,dz$, which is $(-\,\partial P/\partial x)$ per unit volume.

The term $k[\nabla^2 v_x]$ represents the force in the x direction which results from the viscous resistance to flow.

Finally, the term $\rho[\partial v_x/\partial t]$ represents the mass times the acceleration of the volume element.

The above differential equations (37) thus represent Newton's law of motion F = ma, applied to a differential volume element, and expressed in terms of the fluid velocity as a function of position and time.

The general set of differential equations governing the flow of viscous liquids cannot be solved when subject to boundary conditions of any complexity. However, as was pointed out before, in many problems of hydrodynamics either the inertia or the viscosity can be neglected.

In the one case, where only the *inertia* of the liquid is important, the governing differential equation reduces to:

$$\begin{aligned} F_x - \frac{\partial P}{\partial x} &= \rho\left[\frac{\partial v_x}{\partial t}\right] = \rho\left[\frac{\partial v_x}{\partial t} + v_x\frac{\partial v_x}{\partial x} + v_y\frac{\partial v_x}{\partial y} + v_z\frac{\partial v_x}{\partial z}\right] \\ F_y - \frac{\partial P}{\partial y} &= \rho\left[\frac{\partial v_y}{\partial t}\right] = \rho\left[\frac{\partial v_y}{\partial t} + v_x\frac{\partial v_y}{\partial x} + v_y\frac{\partial v_y}{\partial y} + v_z\frac{\partial v_y}{\partial z}\right] \\ F_z - \frac{\partial P}{\partial z} &= \rho\left[\frac{\partial v_z}{\partial t}\right] = \rho\left[\frac{\partial v_z}{\partial t} + v_x\frac{\partial v_z}{\partial x} + v_y\frac{\partial v_z}{\partial y} + v_z\frac{\partial v_z}{\partial z}\right] \end{aligned} \tag{38}$$

In the other case, where *viscosity* is the determining factor, the following equation applies:

$$F_x - \frac{\partial P}{\partial x} + \eta\nabla^2 v_x = 0 \tag{39a}$$

$$F_y - \frac{\partial P}{\partial y} + \eta\nabla^2 v_y = 0 \tag{39b}$$

$$F_z - \frac{\partial P}{\partial z} + \eta\nabla^2 v_z = 0 \tag{39c}$$

Equation (38), which applied to the *inertial* case, gives rise to a still simpler equation if the flow described is known to be nonrotational (devoid of "whirlpools"). In this case, the liquid must obey Bernouilli's principle:

$$V + P + \tfrac{1}{2}\rho v^2 = \text{constant} \tag{40}$$

where V is the potential energy per unit volume, P the pressure, and ρ the density. A great deal of classical hydrodynamics deals with the "ideal liquid," of zero viscosity—*i.e.*, with the inertial special case (see Lamb, *5a*). Bernouilli's theorem is of great practical importance in such problems as the flow of liquids through (large) pipes.

The flow problems which arise in high polymers, however, are of exactly the opposite type. For our purposes, the *viscosity case* is of paramount interest. Equations (39), which govern the viscous flow of a liquid whose *inertial* effects can be ignored, can be simplified still further in problems which have a simple geometry.

When the spatial symmetry is such that the fluid velocity is a function of only one position coordinate, then the flow can be described in terms of a single deformation variable as well as a single stress variable.

If the fluid velocity at the point under consideration is in the direction of the x axis, $v_y = v_z = 0$, and if $\partial v_x/\partial x = \partial v_x/\partial y = 0$, then the equation

$$\eta(\partial v_x/\partial z) = s_{xz} \qquad (41)$$

is useful. This equation not only applies when x, y, z, are an externally fixed set of coordinates, but also when the direction of orientation changes from point to point. In the latter case, $\partial v_x/\partial z$ must be interpreted as meaning only *that part of* the velocity gradient which is due to the flow. The two following examples (flow of viscous fluid in capillary, and between concentric rotating cylinders) will be treated on the basis of this equation. These problems could also be solved by applying the general set of differential equations (39), subject to the boundary conditions obtaining.

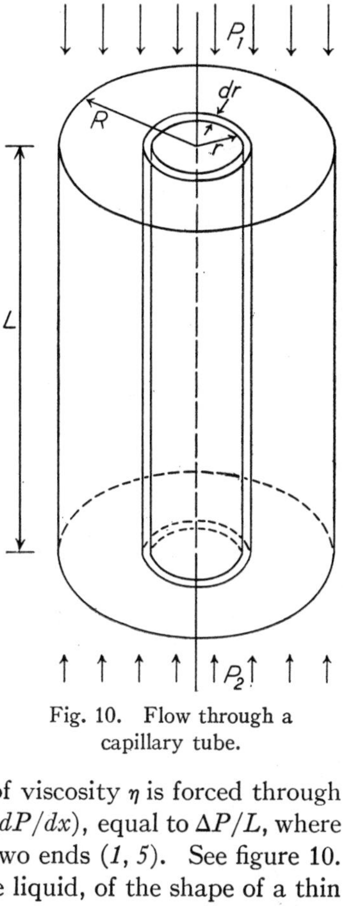

Fig. 10. Flow through a capillary tube.

Flow of a Newtonian Liquid through a Capillary Tube.—Given: a capillary tube of radius R, and length L. A liquid of viscosity η is forced through the tube by means of a pressure gradient (dP/dx), equal to $\Delta P/L$, where ΔP is the pressure difference between the two ends (*1*, *5*). See figure 10.

Consider a small volume element of the liquid, of the shape of a thin cylindrical shell of radius r, thickness dr, and unit length. The forces in the x direction acting on the element are as follows: Normal pressure on the top surface, normal pressure on bottom surface, and tangential drag on the inner and outer cylindrical surfaces. In the steady state, all these forces must add to zero. If dr is indeed a differential, the only finite forces are the two equal and opposite tangential forces, $\pi r^2 \cdot \Delta P/L$, resulting in a shearing stress of

$$\frac{\pi r^2 \dfrac{\Delta P}{L}}{2\pi r} = \frac{(\Delta P)r}{2\,L} \tag{42}$$

Since $d\mathrm{v}_x/dr = (1/\eta)S$, $d\mathrm{v}_x/dr = 1/\eta[(\Delta P)(r)/2\,L]$ at this distance from the center. The actual velocity, v_x, of any given cylindrical layer equals

$$\mathrm{v}_x = \int_R^r \frac{d\mathrm{v}_x}{dr}\,dr = \frac{1}{\eta}\,\frac{(\Delta P)r^2}{4\,L} - \frac{(\Delta P)R^2}{\eta \cdot 4\,L} \tag{43}$$

Thus there is a parabolic distribution of v_x in the capillary.

$$\text{Total rate of discharge} = \int_0^R \mathrm{v}_x \cdot 2\pi r\,dr = \frac{\pi R^4\,\Delta P}{8\,L\eta} \tag{44}$$

The result, which is known as Poiseuille's law, finds wide application in the *determination of viscosity*. A number of viscometers are based upon the capillary tube principle. The simplest is the Ostwald viscometer (*1*, *2*) (Fig. 11). Here the driving pressure difference is obtained by means of the hydrostatic head between the two arms of the tube. This pressure difference depends upon the *density* of the liquid as well as the difference in level. $\Delta P \sim \rho(\Delta H)$. A definite quantity of liquid is inserted into the viscometer. Enough liquid is drawn up into the upper bulb so that the upper reference mark is passed. The liquid is allowed to flow down through the capillary under the influence of the hydrostatic head, and the time is measured for the level to drop from the upper to the lower reference mark. During this experiment, the shear stress and the flow gradient not only are different at different locations in the capillary, but also vary with time at a fixed location. However, since at any point and any time, the local instantaneous velocity gradient is directly proportional to the shear stress,

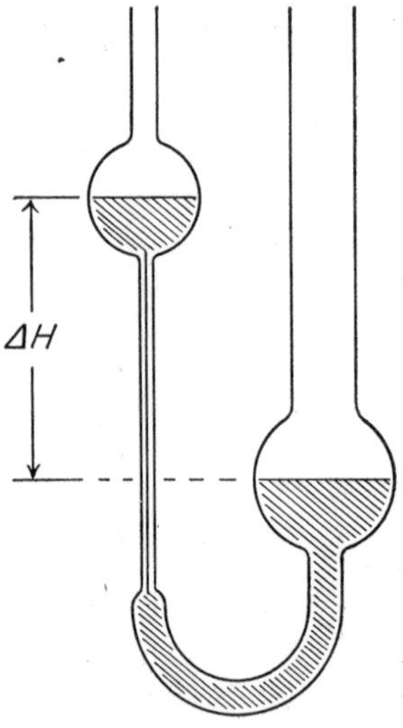

Fig. 11. Schematic representation of a capillary viscometer.

and the same constant of proportionality operates at all points and all times involved, the over-all rate of discharge is directly proportional to density and inversely proportional to viscosity.

$$\text{Time of flow} = K(\eta/\rho) \qquad (45)$$

Here K is the calibration constant for the instrument, which can be determined by means of a liquid of known viscosity and density.

The above entire derivation was made on the assumption that *inertial* effects can be neglected—that the viscosity is the determining factor. This is justified in the capillary itself, but at the ends accelerations are involved. Because of the inertial effect, it turns out that the viscosity is not given by an equation of the form $\eta = K\rho t$, but rather by one of the form $\eta = K\rho t - K'\rho/t$, where K and K' are both constants. Bingham (*1*) has emphasized that the complete calibration of an Ostwald viscometer requires the use of two reference liquids, at the least, rather than one, and has described a two-liquid calibration method.

It is apparent that the kinetic energy correction $(-K'\rho/t)$ will be more important when the conditions fail to conform to those specified for the "viscosity determining" case of hydrodynamics. In the Ostwald viscometer, this means that the kinetic energy correction can be neglected only if the ratio of capillary length to diameter is sufficiently high. The less viscous the liquids to be measured, the higher the necessary *length–diameter* ratio. For a material of high viscosity, the kinetic energy correction can be neglected even with a relatively short, wide capillary.

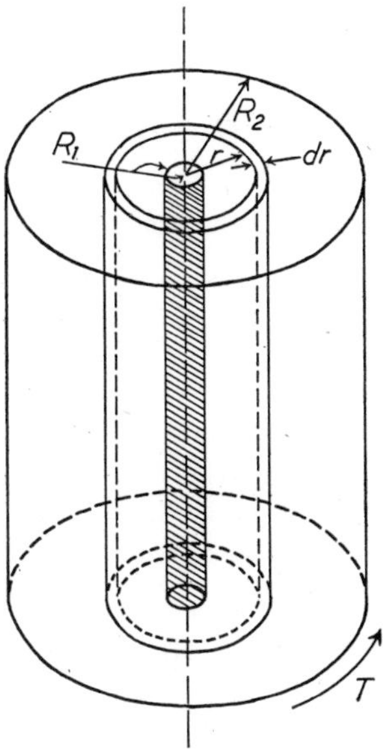

Fig. 12. Flow in concentric cylinder rotational viscometer.

Flow of a Newtonian Liquid between Concentric Cylinders Undergoing Relative Rotation.—Given: a stationary inner cylinder of radius R_1, and a movable, concentric outer cylinder of radius R_2, both cylinders being long enough that end effects may be neglected. A liquid of viscosity η fills the annular interspace. A torque T is applied to the outer cylinder. See figure 12.

Consider a small volume element of the liquid, of the shape of a thin cylindrical shell of radius r, thickness dr, and unit length. In the steady state of flow, the torque T is supported at each cylindrical surface by a force tangential to the surface and perpendicular to the axis of the cylinder. On a surface of radius r (and of unit length), the total tangential force is (T/Lr), and the force per unit area is $(\mathrm{T}/L\,2\pi r^2)$. Thus the liquid at a distance r from the center is subjected to a shear stress of $(\mathrm{T}/L\,2\pi r^2)$, which tends to turn each cylinder surface relative to the next. The gradient of angular velocity, $d\omega/dr$, will be given by the equation:

$$\frac{d\omega}{dr} = \frac{1}{r\eta} S = \frac{1}{\eta} \frac{\mathrm{T}}{L\,2\pi r^3} \tag{46}$$

The actual angular velocity of any layer r will be given by:

$$\omega(r) = \int_{R_1}^{r} \frac{d\omega}{dr}\, dr = \int_{R_1}^{r} \frac{\mathrm{T}}{\eta L\, 2\pi} \frac{dr}{r^3} = \frac{\mathrm{T}}{2\pi\eta L}\left(\frac{1}{2\,R_1^2} - \frac{1}{2\,r^2}\right) \tag{47a}$$

The angular velocity of the outermost layer, R_2, will be:

$$\omega(R_2) = \frac{\mathrm{T}}{4\pi\eta L}\left(\frac{1}{R_1^2} - \frac{1}{R_k}\right) \tag{47b}$$

Thus there is a linear relation between the torque T and the resulting angular velocity ω of the outer cylinder:

$$\omega = \frac{1}{\eta} K\mathrm{T} \tag{48}$$

where K is a calibration constant for the instrument and is determined by the geometry of the instrument.

$$K = \frac{1}{4\pi L}\left(\frac{1}{R_1^2} - \frac{1}{R_2^2}\right) \tag{49}$$

5. Non-Newtonian Fluids and Plasticity

A. Homogeneous Shear Stress

Many materials flow when stressed, and yet do not possess the extreme simplicity of properties characteristic of a "Newtonian" fluid (*1, 2, 5, 7, 8*). Figure 13 shows the displacement which results through time when various constant stresses, s_{xy}, are applied to a typical "non-Newtonian" liquid at t_1 and released at t_2. When the information in figure 13 is plotted as $d\gamma/dt$ *vs*. S, figure 14 results. Such a plot may be called a *flow curve*, and the rate of flow, $d\gamma/dt$, may be represented by the symbol D. The nonlinearity of this curve indicates that, although a stress causes a steady state of flow, the rate of flow is not directly proportional to the shear stress.

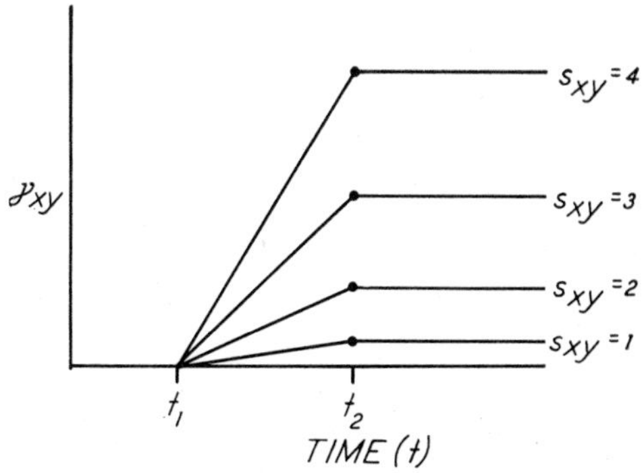

Fig. 13. Shear strain at constant stress for a non-Newtonian fluid.

Knowledge of the rheological properties of such a material implies knowledge of the whole flow curve. Unlike the "straight line through origin" flow curve of a Newtonian fluid, this curve cannot be expressed by a single parameter. The coefficient of viscosity, as defined on pages 23–32, has no precise meaning for a non-Newtonian liquid. At best, a flow curve such as shown in figure 14 can be expressed

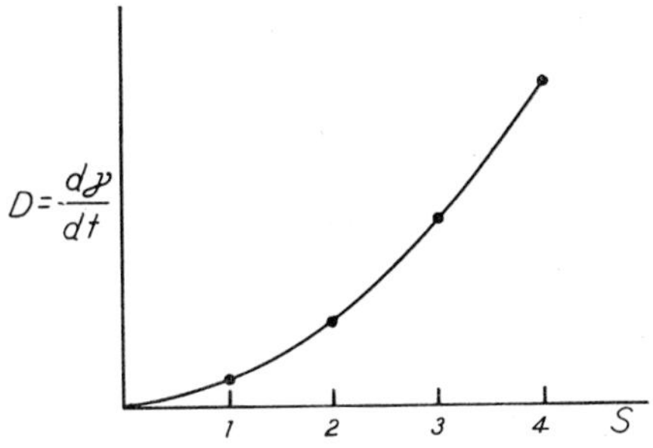

Fig. 14. Rate of shear strain as a function of shear stress for the non-Newtonian fluid of figure 13.

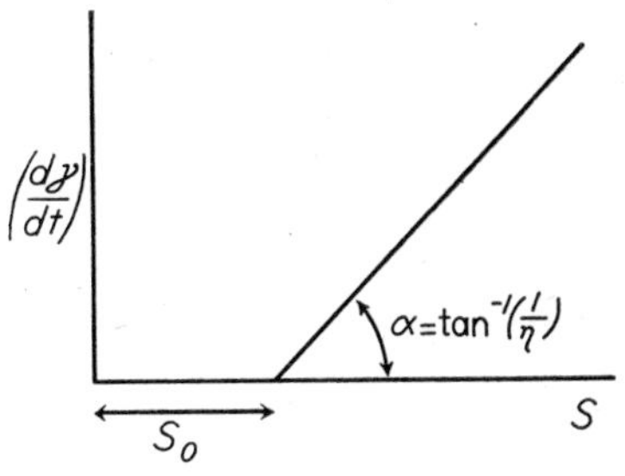

Fig. 15. Rate of shear strain as a function of stress for an idealized plastic material.

by means of two parameters, such as C and r of the empirical equation:

$$d\gamma/dt = CS^r \tag{50a}$$

Bingham (*1*) has emphasized the fact that many non-Newtonian flow curves can be closely approximated by the type of curve shown in figure 15, and the corresponding equation:

$$d\gamma/dt = (1/\eta)\,(S - S_0) \tag{50b}$$

A material whose flow follows this equation is called an ideal plastic material. For stresses smaller than a certain critical value S_0 (called the yield value) the material does not flow at all. For stresses $>S_0$, a steady flow rate is established which is proportional not to the total stress S, but to $(S - S_0)$—the amount by which the stress exceeds the yield value. Most so-called "plastic" materials, however, exhibit a noticeable curvature of the flow diagram. The term "pseudo plastic" is sometimes applied to such a material. Herschel and Bulkley (*23*) have found that some such materials follow the equation:

$$d\gamma/dt = A(S - S_0)^r \tag{51}$$

This means that the information of the flow curve can be condensed into three numerical constants A, S_0, and r. Bingham's equation (50b) is seen to be a special case of equation (51), where $r = 1$, and equation (50a) is the case where $S_0 = 0$.

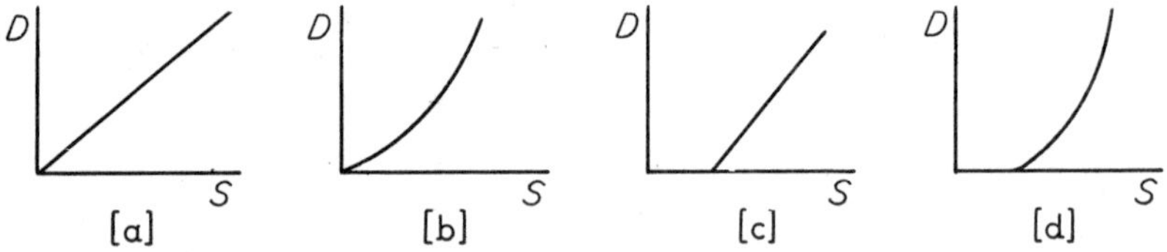

Fig. 16. Rate of shear strain as a function of stress for four types of fluid: (a) Newtonian or viscous liquid; (b) non-Newtonian or quasi viscous liquid; (c) idealized plastic solid, Bingham solid; (d) quasi plastic material.

All these equations are merely empirical formulas which may be used to approximate an observed flow curve in a given range.

Houwink (*5*) groups the general types of flow curves as they are represented in figure 16. These terms, [a], [b], [c], and [d], are by no means generally accepted as precise definitions. In this volume, [a] will be called Newtonian flow, [c] Bingham plasticity, and [b] and [d] merely non-Newtonian flow. Non-Newtonian character is closely associated with high viscosity.

The Question of the Yield Point.—For materials whose flow curves are not too different from type [c] (Bingham plasticity) the usefulness of the term "yield point" is apparent, and hardly needs discussion. The term has been used also to locate singularities in type [d] flow curves. Thus, some authors (compare *1*, *2*, *5*) speak of the "yield point" obtained by extending the linear part of the flow curve (or what seems to be a linear part) (as in Fig. 17) to the point of intersection with the horizontal axis (S_2), and define the "true yield point" as the actual point of intersection of the horizontal axis by the flow curve (S_1). Sometimes, the point at which the flow curve noticeably begins to bend away from a straight line is called an "apparent yield point" (S_3).

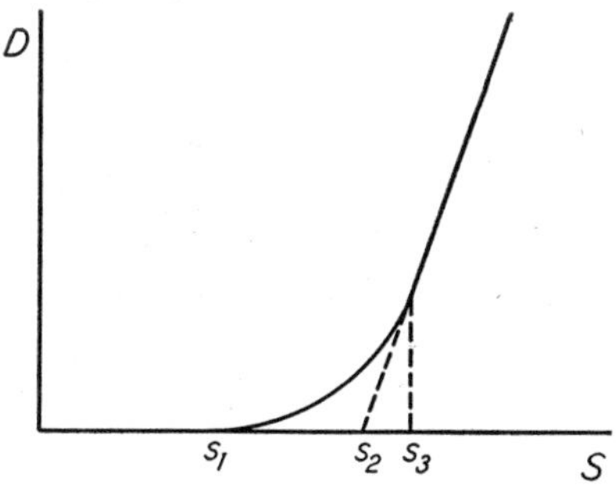

Fig. 17. Yield points which can be defined for a non-Newtonian flow curve.

The arbitrariness of all these "points" is clear. There may be no unique choice of the best tangent to extrapolate to the S axis. Similarly, the "true yield point" is actually the stress at which the flow first becomes *appreciable*, and is therefore also arbitrary. In principle, no flow curve can actually intersect the S axis at a finite value. Real materials which seem to possess "ideal plastic" flow curves actually must have curves of the type [b] (Fig. 16), with the flow at stresses below S_0 being too small to be detectable. The same is true of curves which seem on gross analysis to be of type [d] (Fig. 16).

Thus, the "yield point" or "yield points" of a material have at the best no absolute significance, but merely specify changes in the trend of the flow curve. When these changes are sufficiently abrupt, the "yield points" of the curve may be very useful concepts.

B. Behavior of a Non-Newtonian Liquid Subjected to Nonuniform Stresses

When the flow curve of a material is known, it is possible in principle to predict the response to nonuniform stresses, and to geometrically complex surroundings. In the special case of the Newtonian liquid, this problem has already been discussed in section 4B (pages 25–32).

The more general case of the non-Newtonian liquid may be approached in the same manner—utilizing the fact that *each small volume element* of the liquid behaves in a (relatively) simple fashion. Each such volume element responds to a net force by accelerating as a whole, to a shear stress by flowing (changing shape), and to a uniform pressure by contracting. As in the Newtonian case it is often convenient to neglect this last effect, and consider the material to be incompressible.

The incompressible non-Newtonian fluid possesses inertia and a resistance to flow which is measured by the flow curve. In some problems one or the other of these properties may be of negligible importance in determining the behavior of the fluid. The one special case, when inertia predominates and the viscous resistance to flow can be neglected, is identical with the inertial limiting case for the Newtonian fluid, which has already been discussed.

The second limiting case—where inertia can be neglected—is of more interest for non-Newtonian fluids than is the first case because non-Newtonian liquids usually possess fairly large resistances to flow. A markedly nonlinear flow curve has usually a very small initial slope. As a result, most practical problems involving flow of markedly non-Newtonian liquids depend mainly upon the *flow curve* and hardly at all upon the *inertia*. The range of flow problems of this second limiting type which can be readily solved is less wide than in the case of Newtonian liquids, because of the nonlinear relation between shear stress and velocity gradient. However, in very simple geometrical cases, the method employed in section 4 (pages 29–32) can be used. That is, when the velocity is changing only in one direction, say x, which is normal to the direction of fluid velocity, the following equation holds:

$$dv/dx = f(S) \tag{52}$$

Thus, the nonlinear function $f(S)$ must replace the linear term $(1/\eta)S$ in the treatment of section 4.

When a non-Newtonian fluid of known flow curve is subjected to two simultaneously acting shear stress components, it is not immediately obvious how the material will respond. It is to be expected that the two stress components "interact" so that the total effect of two shear stresses acting in different planes is not simply the sum of the independent effects.

Flow through capillary tubes and between rotating concentric cylinders will be considered in order to illustrate the method and in order to emphasize the difference between the Newtonian and non-Newtonian liquids (*40*).

Flow of a Non-Newtonian Liquid through a Capillary Tube (see Figure 10).

$$S = P\pi r^2 \frac{1}{2\pi r} = \frac{P}{2} r \tag{53}$$

$$\frac{dv}{dr} = f(S) = f\left(\frac{P}{2} r\right) \tag{54}$$

$$v(r) = \int_r^a f(S_r)dr = \int_a^r f\left(\frac{P}{2} r\right) dr \tag{55}$$

$$\text{Rate of discharge} = \int_0^a \mathrm{v}_r\, 2\pi r\, dr = 2\pi \int_0^a r \int_a^r f\left(\frac{P}{2} r\right) dr\, dr \quad (56)$$

For a Newtonian fluid, $f(S) = (1/\eta)S$; rate of discharge $= (\pi P a^4/8\eta)$. This is Poiseuille's law, already derived in the preceding section, pages 29–30. Another special case of interest is that of Bingham plasticity:

$$\frac{d\mathrm{v}}{dx} = 0 \qquad \text{when} \qquad S < S_0 \quad (57a)$$

$$\frac{d\mathrm{v}}{dx} = \frac{1}{\eta}(S - S_0) \qquad \text{when} \qquad S > S_0 \quad (57b)$$

$$\mathrm{v}(r) = \int_a^r \frac{1}{\eta}\left(\frac{P}{2} r - S_0\right) dr \qquad \text{when} \qquad r > \frac{2\,S_0}{P} \quad (58a)$$

$$\mathrm{v}(r) = \int_a^{2S_0/P} \frac{1}{\eta}\left(\frac{P}{2} r - S_0\right) dr \qquad \text{when} \qquad r < \frac{2\,S_0}{P} \quad (58b)$$

$$\text{Rate of discharge} = 2\pi \int_{2S_0/P}^a r \int_a^r \frac{1}{\eta}\left(\frac{P}{2} r - S_0\right) dr\, dr + \pi\left(\frac{2\,S_0}{P}\right)^2 \int_a^{2S_0/P} \frac{1}{\eta}\left(\frac{P}{2} r - S_0\right) dr \quad (59)$$

$$= + \frac{\pi P a^4}{8\eta} - \frac{\pi a^3 S_0}{3\eta} + \frac{2\pi S_0^4}{3\eta P^3} \quad (60)$$

Thus, a given flow curve, $f(S)$, gives rise to a characteristic relationship between velocity of efflux, V, and pressure gradient, P, in a capillary tube. In the special case of a Newtonian liquid, where $f(S)$ is a straight line through the origin with slope $1/\eta$, the V–P curve is also a straight line through the origin, with slope $\pi a^4/8\eta$. In the case of a non-Newtonian fluid, the flow curve transforms in a more complicated fashion into the corresponding V–P curve. Figure 18 indicates the nature of the velocity of efflux *vs* pressure gradient curve for a material exhibiting Bingham plasticity *(20)*.

It is clear that the velocity distribution through the capillary, as well as the over-all rate of efflux, of a Bingham material is different from that of a Newtonian liquid. In the Newtonian case the particle velocity is a simple parabolic function of r. In the Bingham case, there is no motion at all until the pressure gradient, P, exceeds the quantity $2\,S_0/a$. Then flow takes place, but only in the outermost part of the capillary. The central portion moves as a solid cylindrical plug. As P is increased, the size of the central plug is decreased, and the rate of flow in the surrounding annular region is increased. At any value of P, the radius of the plug is given by $2\,S_0/P$. Figure 19 indicates the particle velocity of a Bingham material as a function of r.

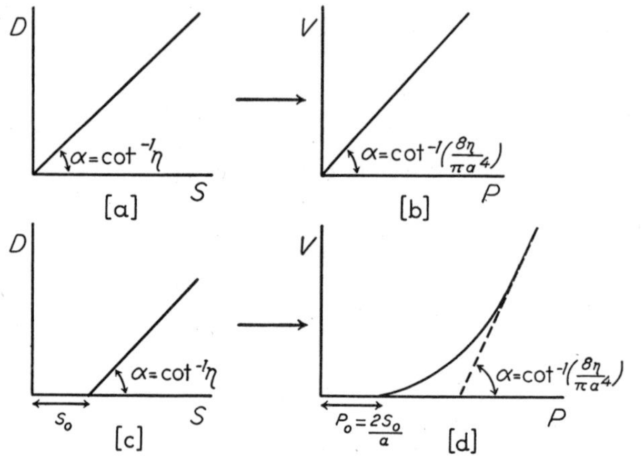

Fig. 18. Relationship between the fundamental flow curve and the rate of efflux from a capillary tube: [a] flow curve for a Newtonian liquid; [b] velocity of efflux *vs.* driving pressure for the above Newtonian fluid; [c] flow curve for a Bingham material; [d] velocity of efflux *vs.* driving pressure for the above Bingham material.

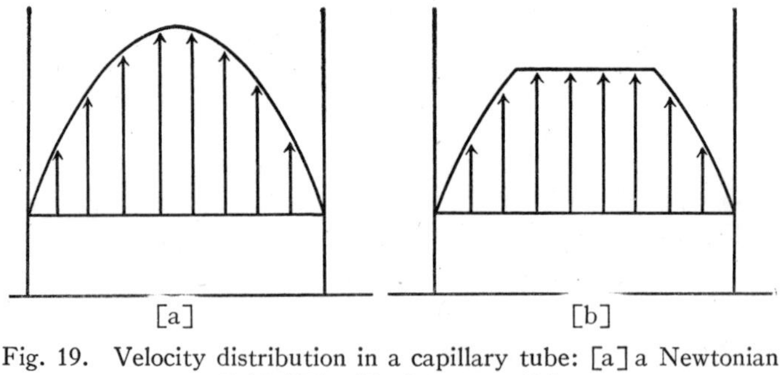

Fig. 19. Velocity distribution in a capillary tube: [a] a Newtonian fluid; [b] a Bingham material.

Rotating Cylinder Viscometer.—Consider the idealized rotating cylinder viscometer of section 4B (pages 31–32). The radii of the inner and outer cylinders, are a and b, respectively. The relative angular velocity of the two cylinders is ω, and T is the torque necessary to sustain this constant relative motion when the space between the cylinders is occupied by a material of flow curve $f(S)$. The radial distribution of shear stress is given by $S(r)$. The length of the cylinders is L.

$$S(r) = \mathrm{T}/2\pi r^2 L \tag{61}$$

$$\omega(a, b) = \int_a^b \frac{1}{r} f\left(\frac{\mathrm{T}}{2\pi r^2 L}\right) dr \tag{62}$$

Where $f(S) = (1/\eta)S$:

$$\omega(a, b) = \int_a^b \frac{1}{r}\frac{1}{\eta}\frac{\mathrm{T}}{2\pi r^2 L}\, dr = \frac{\mathrm{T}}{4\pi\eta L}\left(\frac{1}{a^2} - \frac{1}{b^2}\right) \tag{63}$$

Where $f(S) = 1/\eta\ (S - S_0)$ when $S > S_0$
$f(S) = 0$ when $S < S_0$

$$\omega(a, b) = \int_a^{\sqrt{T/2\pi S_0 L}} \frac{1}{r}\frac{1}{\eta}\left(\frac{\mathrm{T}}{2\pi r^2 L} - S_0\right) dr, \tag{64a}$$

when $\mathrm{T} > 2\pi a^2 S_0 L$
$< 2\pi b^2 S_0 L$

$$\omega(a, b) = \int_a^b \frac{1}{r}\frac{1}{\eta}\left(\frac{\mathrm{T}}{2\pi r^2 L} - S_0\right) dr, \text{ when } \mathrm{T} > 2\pi b^2 S_0 L \tag{64b}$$

Carrying out these integrations, we obtain:

$$\omega(a, b) = 0, \text{ when } \mathrm{T} < 2\pi a^2 S_0 L \tag{65a}$$

$$\omega(a, b) = \frac{\mathrm{T}}{4\pi\eta a^2 L} - \frac{S_0}{2\eta} - \frac{S_0}{2\eta}\ln\frac{\mathrm{T}}{2\pi a^2 S_0 L}, \text{ when } 2\pi a^2 S_0 L < \mathrm{T} < 2\pi b^2 S_0 L \tag{65b}$$

$$\omega(a, b) = \frac{\mathrm{T}}{4\pi\eta L}\left(\frac{1}{a^2} - \frac{1}{b^2}\right) - \frac{S_0}{\eta}\ln\frac{b}{a}, \text{ when } \mathrm{T} > 2\pi b^2 L S_0 \tag{65c}$$

These relationships are shown in figure 20. When the torque is between the limits of $2\pi a^2 S_0 L$ and $2\pi b^2 S_0 L$, there takes place in the rotating cylinder instrument a phenomenon analogous to the plug flow which occurs in the capillary tube. Material between the limits of $r = \sqrt{\mathrm{T}/2\pi S_0 L}$ and $r = a$ does not flow but moves as a solid mass. Flow only takes place in the region $r < \sqrt{\mathrm{T}/2\pi S_0 L}$, which is stressed above the yield point S_0.

C. The Determination of Flow Curves

The fundamental way of expressing the rheological properties of a non-Newtonian fluid is by the flow curve.

In principle, the simplest way of determining the flow curve is by a direct point-to-point investigation. This would mean applying a definite homogeneous shear stress, S_1, and observing the resulting shear rate D_1. This would give one point on the D–S curve. Another determination at a different homogeneous stress would give another point on the curve, *etc.* For any one measurement, the stress would be constant in time and uniform throughout the sample.

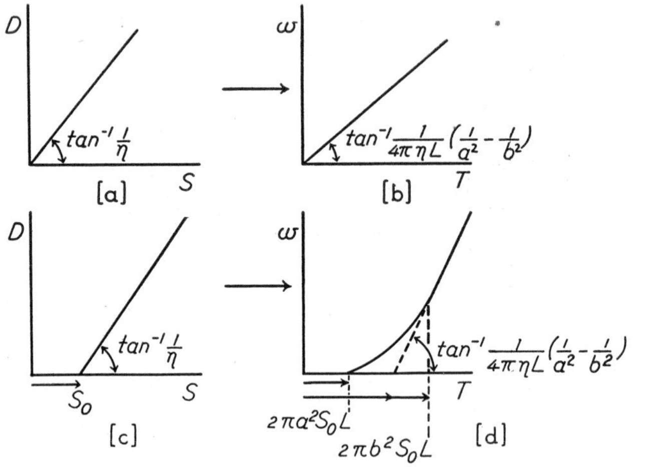

Fig. 20. Relationship between the fundamental flow curve and the behavior in a rotating cylinder viscometer: (a) flow curve for a Newtonian fluid; (b) angular velocity *vs.* driving torque for the above Newtonian fluid; (c) flow curve for a Bingham material; (d) angular velocity *vs.* driving torque for the above Bingham material.

It was seen in section 4 (pages 30–32) that this last requirement was unnecessary in the case of Newtonian liquids. In most viscometers, a liquid is subjected to a nonhomogeneous stress distribution. However, since S/D ratio (or the viscosity) is the same throughout the instrument, two different viscous fluids will have the same flow pattern. The geometry of the measuring instrument thus influences the over-all flow rate by introducing a constant multiplying factor which is the same for all materials (the calibration constant of the viscometer). In such an instrument, the flow curve for a Newtonian material is not determined point by point, but rather the ratio S/D is determined directly.

We have just seen that when a non-Newtonian fluid is subjected to a nonuniform stress, the flow behavior is very complicated. The relation between "over-all flow" and average shear stress cannot be considered as the flow curve. However, it is possible in principle to infer the flow curve from the experimental *rate–driving force* curve. In the concentric cylinder, for example, the problem is to find that function $f(S)$ which, upon insertion into the integral equation (62), will yield the observed *rate–driving force* relation. Instead of deriving curve *d* (Fig. 20) from curve *c*, we proceed in the opposite direction. One way to carry out this inverse process is the following:

(1) Assume some standard form for the flow curve, with as many arbitrary parameters as are felt necessary for a good fit, *e.g.*, assume $d\gamma/dt = aS^b$, where a and b are constants.

(2) Integrate equation (62), using the above function for $f(S)$.

(3) Find the best values of the parameters (here a and b) by fitting the integrated expression for $V(F)$ with the experimentally observed data.

(4) Insert the values for the parameters into the assumed flow curve [step (1) above]. The flow curve is now known.

Rabinowitsch (*38*) has suggested a somewhat different method of deducing the fundamental flow curve from the observed data. Instead of assuming an analytical form for $f(S)$, integrating equation (62), and comparing with experiment, Rabinowitsch suggests the following differentiation method.

The double integration of equation (56) leads to an equation relating the observed variables in the capillary tube experiment. $R = f(P)$, where R is the over-all rate of discharge, and P is the pressure gradient, $\Delta P/1$. In order to proceed from the observed function $f(P)$ to the desired function $f(S)$, replace a, the radius of the capillary in equation (56), by an expression in terms of S_1, the shear stress at the wall of the capillary. ($a = 2\,S_1/P$.) Differentiate both sides of the resulting equation with respect to S_1. This results in an equation of the form below:

$$f(S) = \frac{1}{\pi r^3}\,[3\,F(S) + SF'(S)] \qquad (66a)$$

where the function F is simply the observed function $f(P)$, expressed in terms of S_1. [$R = f(P) = F(S_1)$.] It is seen that equation (66a) contains a term $f(S_1)$, which is the fundamental flow curve function, expressed in terms of S_1, instead of S. If the experimental data are plotted as R *vs.* S_1, instead of R *vs.* P, the derivative on the left can be directly evaluated. When this method is used no assumptions need be made concerning the form of $f(S)$. The method gives $f(S)$ directly if $f(P)$ is known.

It is clear from equation (66a) that if $f(P)$ is rewritten as $G(S_1)$, the rheological function $f(S)$ can be obtained from the expression:

$$f(S) = \frac{1}{\pi r^3} [3\, G(S) + SG'(S)] \tag{66b}$$

Here G' is the first derivative of the function G.

Hersey (*24*) has extended the differentiation method of Rabinowitsch to the case of the concentric cylinder rotation plastometer. The method in this case necessitates certain approximations. The author reports that the method gives satisfactory results when the inner and outer radii are not too different in magnitude.

Only by some such procedure can the results from different instruments be logically compared. A rotating cylinder and a capillary tube will give different V–F curves for the same material, but if one transforms both back into the fundamental form of the *flow curve*, the same result should be obtained.

Van Nieuwenberg (see reference *2*, Volume I, page 241) has emphasized the necessity of actually determining the basic D–S curve for a non-Newtonian material.

"In recent years much experimental work has been devoted to the investigation of the plastic properties of materials, and a great variety of instruments has been developed for this purpose. The greater part of these instruments, however, does not allow unambiguously to obtain the fundamental connection between the rate of shear produced in an element of the substance by a simple shear stress acting uniformly through this element. In most cases a quantity is measured which represents an outward effect of a complicated system of deformations in the interior of the sample investigated, and this quantity is then given as a function of the exterior load, which calls forth a (similarly complicated) distribution of stresses in the sample. It is only in a few cases that methods have been developed for unraveling the character of the actual motion taking place, and that one has succeeded in giving methods which enable to obtain the relation between D and S for the substance from the experimental results."

The interpretation of experimental data becomes very simple if the stress distribution is homogeneous. This condition is attained in the flow between two parallel plates of infinite extension, and approximated by the flow between concentric cylinders which are separated by a small distance. In the limit where $(b - a)/a \rightarrow 0$ equation (62) for the motion of a concentric cylinder viscometer becomes simple:

$$\omega = \frac{2\,\mathrm{T}}{4\pi\eta L} \frac{(b - a)}{a^3} \tag{67}$$

This means that the angular velocity *vs.* torque curve is of the same shape as the flow curve. Figure 21 shows this effect for a Bingham material. The intercept and slope of the flow curve bear a simple relation to those of the ω–T curve. Thus the instrument can be calibrated against a Newtonian liquid of known viscosity, and then used with a non-Newtonian material. The problem of flow curve determination can thus be

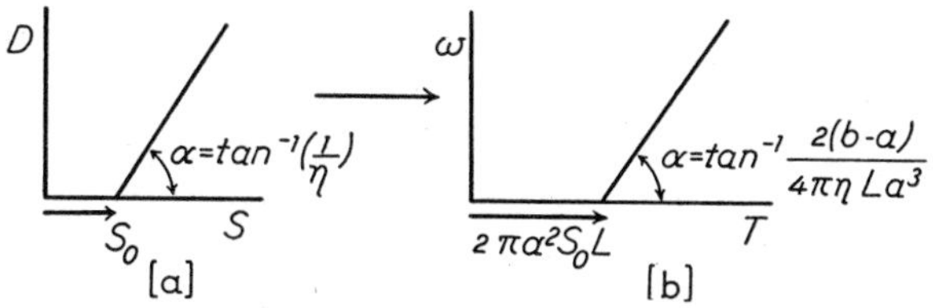

Fig. 21. Relationship between fundamental flow curve [a] and behavior in a rotating cylinder viscometer [b] in the special case of small separation between moving cylinders.

summarized: if the stresses on a material in a viscometer are not homogeneous, then a plot of over-all motion or flow rate against driving force does not have the same shape as the flow curve of the material. The important exception to this is the Newtonian liquid.

If the stress distribution, although nonhomogeneous, varies uniformly and the geometry of the instrument is accurately known, then the *flow curve* can be obtained from the experimental V–*F* curve. In the case where the geometry of the instrument is complex or unknown, the situation is hopeless. (Again the Newtonian liquid is an exception, for even in a very complicated instrument the effects of geometry can be reduced to a single numerical constant—the calibration factor of the instrument.)

D. Extension of the Hydrodynamic Concepts Embodied in the Differential Equations of Viscous Flow

The differential equations of viscous flow, equations (37), are based upon the idea that any work done on a liquid either goes to increase the kinetic energy of the volume elements or is dissipated as heat (work against viscous resistance to flow). It should, however, be considered that the flow process may also result in *entropy* changes within the various volume elements. If a liquid contains anisometric molecules or suspended particles which are arranged at random when the liquid is at rest, but which are oriented by a flow process, then the entropy of the mixture will be decreased by the flow process. Thus in order to establish a given velocity gradient, a certain amount of work must be done to increase the free energy of the suspension by the amount ($-T\Delta\mathbf{S}$, where T = temperature and **S** = entropy).

When a shear stress is suddenly applied to a sample, during the transient period while the velocity gradient is building up to its steady state value, this orientation process opposes the *increase in velocity gradient,* much as the inertia of a volume element opposes the increase in fluid velocity. Once the steady state is reached, the entropy, just as the kinetic energy, remains constant.

In a long capillary tube (or a similar geometrically simple channel), the effect of such orientation changes on the nature of the flow can be handled by the method of the previous section (pages 35–43). That is, because of the orientation at high velocity gradients, the liquid is non-Newtonian in its (steady state) flow curve.

On the other hand, the entropy change accompanying a velocity gradient may have a profound effect on the properties of the liquid. Thus in a capillary tube, the oriented material near the walls has a lower entropy than the unoriented material in the center. If there is any tendency for the material to crystallize, this tendency will be greatest at the wall. The melting point of the material is given by $\Delta\mathbf{H}_{\text{melting}}/\Delta\mathbf{S}_{\text{melting}}$. If the entropy of the liquid phase is decreased, then the entropy increase on melting is also lowered. This results in an *increase* in the melting temperature (assuming the *enthalpy* of melting, $\Delta\mathbf{H}$ to be unaffected by the velocity gradient).

It should be repeated that whereas the kinetic energy of a volume element depends on the velocity of the element, the *entropy* depends upon the *velocity gradient* at the point and not at all upon the actual velocity.

Appendix: Nonlinearity in Stress–Strain Relationships.—Just as a liquid can exhibit a nonlinear relation between velocity gradient and shear stress, necessitating an extension of the hydrodynamics of Newtonian liquids, so an elastic solid can exhibit nonlinearity in its stress–strain relationships, thus necessitating revision of the treatments discussed in section 3.

The relations between stress and strain for an anisotropic material would become extremely complicated if the assumption of linearity were removed. Even the introduction of a quadratic term would expand equation (6) into the following form:

$$s_i = \sum_j k_{ij}\gamma_j + \sum_j \sum_k k_{ijk}\gamma_j\gamma_k \tag{68}$$

Besides the 36 linear coefficients k_{ij} there would be 216 quadratic coefficients k_{ijk}, forming a three-dimensional array. Of course, there would arise necessary relationships among these 216 constants, reducing the number of *independent* parameters, but the situation would still be extremely involved. For an isotropic material, particularly if incompressible, the situation is somewhat less involved. Where the ease of deformation in shear is much greater than the ease of compression, the problem of small elastic deformations becomes analogous to the problem of flow of an incompressible fluid. If the relation between shear stress and shear strain is nonlinear, then the problem is similar to the problem of flow of non-Newtonian liquids, which has been discussed at some length in the sections immediately preceding.

One interesting fact in this connection is that, for small deformations of a material of this type, a linear relation between shear stress and strain necessarily results in a linear relation between tensile stress and elongation. For large deformations this is not true. Mooney (*34*) has shown that a nonlinear tensile stress–strain relation for large deformations is entirely consistent with a linear shear relation.

6. Thixotropy: Flow Accompanied By Structure Changes

In all the cases heretofore considered, the mechanical properties of a material were considered to be dependent only upon prevailing external conditions, and not upon the details of the past history of the material. The viscosity of pure toluene, for example, depends only upon the temperature and pressure at the moment of testing—independent of the condition of the toluene ten minutes before the test. This section will deal with a phenomenon, thixotropy, which cannot be treated from such a point of view (*3*).

A thixotropic material (such as certain clay suspensions, metallic oxide sols, etc.) is one which "gels" on quiet standing, and "liquefies" upon agitation. Freundlich (*3*) speaks of this as an "isothermal reversible sol–gel transformation."

A thixotropic sol, if allowed to stand, builds up a gel structure which may be very rigid or extremely weak depending upon the nature of the suspended material, the concentration, etc. The process of gel formation may take place in a fraction of a second, or in many hours. It is obvious that the rheological behavior of a thixotropic system (*e.g.*, an Fe_2O_3 suspension) depends not only upon temperature, concentration, etc., but also upon the stage in the sol–gel transformation. This, of course, depends upon the recent mechanical history of the system—whether it has been quietly standing or undergoing agitation. It depends, in fact, upon the whole past history in detail since formation of the suspension.

The first aim of a rheological study of a thixotropic material should be the determination of the flow curve for the material at each stage in the sol–gel transformation. This is not easy, since the very act of measuring flow properties necessarily entails a mechanical agitation which will, in general, affect the degree of structure of the thixotropic material. The desired information can, however, be approached in the following manner.

If a sample of definite past history is subjected to a homogeneous shear stress at time t_0, it responds in some manner such as (*a*) or (*b*) in figure 22. The upward sweep of curve (*a*) indicates that the flow breaks down the gel structure, causing the flow rate to increase. The downward

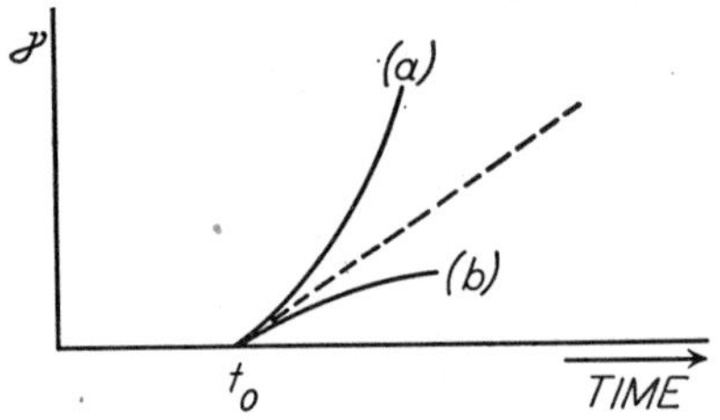

Fig. 22. Change of shear strain at constant stress for a thixotropic material.

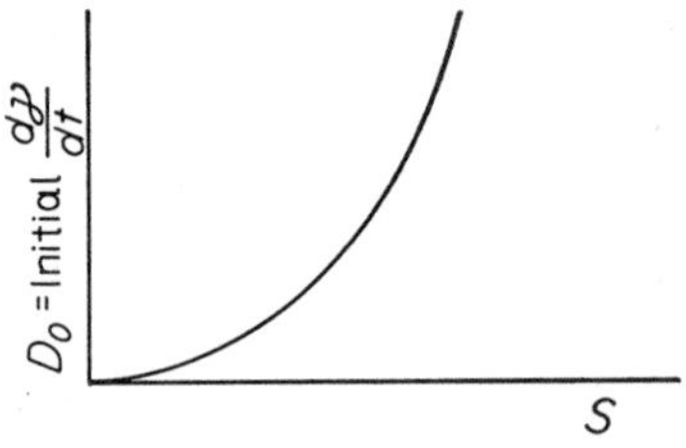

Fig. 23. Flow curve for a thixotropic material at a given stage of gelation.

weep of curve (*b*) indicates that the gel structure is building up, in spite of the agitation. The initial tangent (if well defined) represents the flow induced by the stress S *before the act of measurement has appreciably affected the initial structure.* Let this initial tangent be the measure of $(d\gamma/dt)$ for that value of S. Repeat at different stresses, and plot $(d\gamma/dt)$ *vs.* S (*i.e.*, D *vs.* S) (Fig. 23).

Each of the experimental points in figure 23 should in principle be made with a new starting sample, since the detailed past history has been irrevocably altered by the first measurement. Actually, if the sol–gel transformation is truly reversible, it may be possible to use the same sample over and over, "ironing out" the effects of previous mechanical treatment by thorough agitation, and then producing the desired gelation degree by allowing the suspension to set for a definite time.

The curve in figure 23 represents the flow curve of the material at a given stage of gelation. If such a flow curve determination is made for a series of different setting times (time of quiescence after thorough agitation), the result represents a good start toward an understanding of the rheological changes which accompany thixotropic gelation. A typical result of such a study is figure 24, in which are shown *D–S* curves

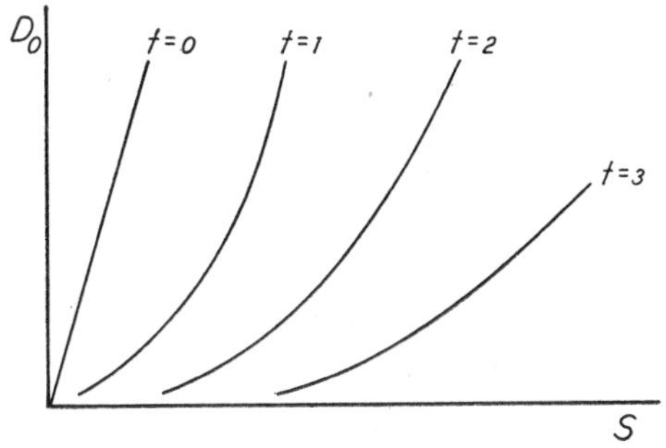

Fig. 24. Set of flow curves for a thixotropic material immediately after agitation and after various setting times.

for a particular bentonite suspension after different setting times. In this case, the completely agitated sol is essentially a Newtonian fluid for small stresses. The gelation process results both in a decrease in slope and in the introduction of an apparent yield point.

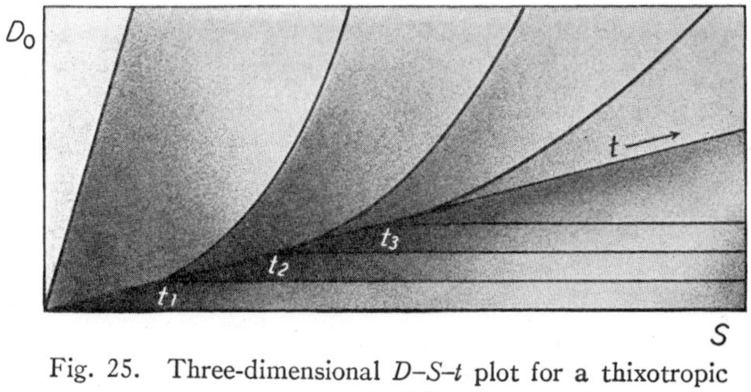

Fig. 25. Three-dimensional *D–S–t* plot for a thixotropic material.

The information contained in a set of curves, such as figure 24, can be conveniently represented as a three-dimensional *D–S–t* plot, where *t* represents the time of setting (Fig. 25). Compare Houwink (*5*, page 13).

From the preceding remarks, it is clear that a measuring device can be used to map out the D–S–t surface for a thixotropic material only if the following conditions are fulfilled:

(1) The shear stress is constant from point to point throughout the sample.

(2) The *instantaneous* rate of shear can be measured—as contrasted to an over-all "time of efflux" or the amount of flow in a large finite period of time.

These conditions can presumably be met in a number of ways. The "torsional pendulum thixotrometer" of Pryce-Jones (*37*) possesses most of the necessary characteristics. A movable bob is suspended in a stationary cup by means of a torsion wire. The bob is turned through a definite angle, and held against the restoring action of the torsion wire. The thixotropic suspension is agitated, then allowed to stand. After a given time t, the bob is released, and begins to rotate through the suspension. If the bob and cup are so designed as to give essential parallel-plane flow, then the *initial* rate of turning and the angular setting are measures of D and S before the measurement can appreciably change the structure. This whole procedure must be repeated at different angular displacements (different stresses) and different setting times.

The data obtained for torsion pendulum thixotrometers are in practice often plotted as scale reading against time. A series of curves are plotted on the same sheet to show the effect of setting time. Gamble used such curves to correlate the thixotropy of paint with other properties such as leveling, brushability, settling, etc. He points out that in order to predict the properties of a paint, the whole series of curves must be known. Neither the viscosity immediately after agitation nor the consistency after long standing will alone define the rheological properties of the system, *or even allow empirical predictions to be made.* For the region of small shear, this method is probably the most informative one yet developed.

As the degree of gelation increases, the *elastic* properties of the gel become more and more important. A thorough study of the rheological changes accompanying gelation should include, in the range of high consistency at least, measurements of the elastic modulus of the gel. A D–S–t relationship by itself is not a sufficient description of the gelation process in the later stages of gelation, although it may be sufficient for the early stages, or throughout gelation in the case of dilute suspensions. In fact, for very firm gels, it may be preferable to describe the mechanical properties in terms of a modulus and an "ultimate strength," since such gels may respond to large stresses by breaking rather than flowing.

Another, less detailed, way of studying the gelation process is the "inverted tube method" (*3*). A sample of the thixotropic suspension is sealed in a glass tube of standard dimensions. The tube is thoroughly shaken, then allowed to stand quietly for a definite time, after which it is inverted. If the suspension is still fluid enough to run down the tube, it is considered not to have set, and the experiment is repeated with a longer time of quiet standing. By trial, the "setting time" of the gel is determined. This is the time for which the suspension must set before it can support its own weight in the inverted tube. This method oversimplifies the problem considerably. The "setting time" as here defined represents merely the time required for an arbitrary degree of structure to be built up, that is, the degree necessary for the gel to support itself in a particular test tube. The gelation process has been going on continuously up to that point, and continues beyond that point. The setting time tells us one point on the complete *D–S–t* surface, and in no respect a unique or cirtical point. The "setting time" depends upon the size of the test tube used, the point to which it is filled, and even the manner in which the tube is inverted.

Even so, if all *D–S–t* surfaces had the same general shape, then the determination of a single definite point (even though arbitrary) might yield useful information concerning the rheological properties of a thixotropic suspension. Unfortunately, this is not the case. One suspension may be extremely fluid immediately after agitation, but may set to a rigid gel very quickly when allowed to stand quietly. Another suspension may be much less fluid after agitation, but may set very slowly. Both may reach a given arbitrary consistency after the same time; and thus, might have the same inverted tube "setting time"; but the two are entirely different in their rheology. This is indicated schematically in figure 26 (page 50).

If the *D–S–t* diagram and the associated elastic properties have been determined, the rheological aspects of the gelation process can be considered to be known. Another question of interest is the nature of the breakdown process which accompanies agitation. When a suspension at any stage of the sol–gel transformation is agitated, the amount of breakdown will be a function of the work done on the suspension, per unit volume, or of the amount of flow during the agitation, or of some such variable or set of variables. The investigation of this problem is much more involved than the study of the gelation process, and will require very careful analysis which up to now has not been made.

An empirical method has been described in which the suspension is placed in a rotating cylinder viscometer (rotating cup, suspended bob), and the cup is turned at constant speed (*30*). The stress (measured by the twist of the bob) changes with time, tending, however, toward a

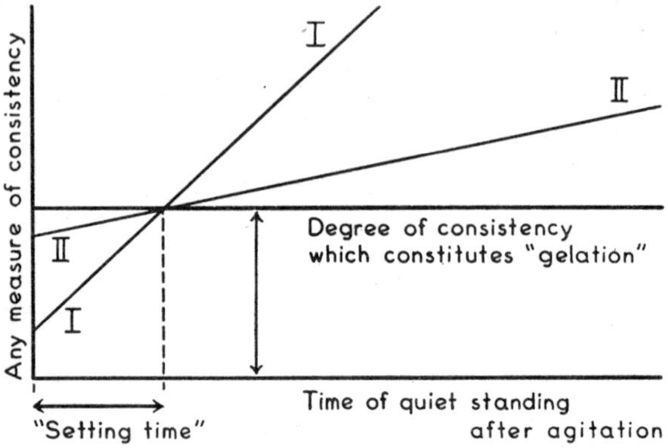

Fig. 26. Example of two materials with the same "setting time" but with markedly different thixotropic properties.

limiting asymptotic value. It has been suggested that the limiting angular reading represents an equilibrium state intermediate between sol and gel, characteristic of the suspension in the given instrument, where the processes of gelation and breakdown just balance each other. This interpretation may be justified when the flow pattern within the viscometer is nearly parallel-plane flow. However, if the flow pattern of the instrument is complex, the above interpretation is somewhat misleading. Those parts of the suspension which are subjected to large stresses flow rapidly, and as a result the gel structure in these parts of the instrument is broken down considerably, so that the flow becomes even greater. In the parts of the instrument where the stress concentration is small, the resulting flow is small, and the gel structure is allowed to build up in these parts, which in turn reduces the flow here still further. The final result in an extreme case is that the material in the instrument is divided into a part which is completely gelled and a narrow channel of fluid sol in which the whole flow is concentrated.

The author believes that the most rational method of investigation involving agitation throughout is that developed by H. Green and R. N.

Weltmann (*22*). These investigators use an instrument in which the shear stress and rate of shear are essentially uniform throughout the sample, and they vary the rate of shear continuously with time, obtaining a *D–S* curve. With a nonthixotropic material the *D–S* curve obtained in this manner is of the same form whether the rate of shear is increasing from zero or decreasing from the maximum value. It is simply the *D–S* curve for the material in question. With a thixotropic material, the curve is not unique. If the rate of shear is first increased, and then decreased to zero, a loop is observed in the *D–S* relationship. The greater the rate of change of *D*, the greater the magnitude of the loop. Sets of such *D–S* curves for a thixotropic material are in a sense analogous to sets of stress–strain curves for an elastic material exhibiting elastic hysteresis. Such data are not susceptible to as direct and quantitative interpretation of a fundamental sort as are the *D–S–t* relationships previously discussed. When carefully analyzed, however, such data can yield much information about a thixotropic system, just as sets of stress–strain loops (which are also complicated from a fundamental standpoint) can yield valuable information about nonideal elastic materials.

It is clear that a complete knowledge of the rheology of a given thixotropic material only begins with the *D–S–t* surface (undisturbed gelation process) and the mechanical breakdown at constant stress or constant rate of flow. It would also be of interest to follow the process of gelation (from the thoroughly agitated state) under the influence of a moderate agitation, etc. Rough studies of this type have been made, and it has been found that some thixotropic suspensions gel more rapidly under the influence of a mild agitation (which presumably helps orient the suspended particles) than when allowed to remain absolutely undisturbed. More completely, the problem is to be able to predict, upon the basis of the complete detailed past history of a thixotropic system, the response it will make to any and all future mechanical situations, and to know, in this sense, the "properties" of gels of all possible variations in past history. Even in the case of a completely reversible sol–gel transformation, this would be a monumental task. Moreover, it seems that many, if not all, thixotropic transformations are at best quasireversible. Superimposed upon the relatively rapid sol–gel change there is often observed a slow, irreversible "aging" process. The properties of a bentonite suspension, for example, depend not only upon the recent mechanical treatment, but also upon the "age" since the preparation of the suspension. A freshly prepared suspension is extremely fluid immediately after agitation, but sets up (gels) very rapidly. The same suspension after a few days of aging will be much less fluid immediately after agitation, but will set up more slowly (see Fig. 26).

7. Coulomb Friction

We have seen that liquids exhibit a resistance to flow which, in the simplest cases, can be described in terms of a coefficient of viscosity. Powdered hard solids can also flow; in some cases they may even be pumped through pipes like liquids. The laws governing the flow of powdered solids are, however, entirely different from those governing the flow of viscous liquids (*26*). This can be seen in a qualitative fashion from the fact that a steep pile of sand will flow downwards and outwards only until a certain critical surface slope is reached, and will thereafter remain stable. On the other hand, a viscous liquid on a flat surface will continue to flow outward until a flat sheet is obtained which is limited in size only by the surface tension of the liquid. It will be shown later that the viscous flow of liquids is based upon the stress-biased molecular diffusion, or Brownian movement, of the liquid. The flow of a powdered solid, on the other hand, arises from the purely mechanical (as contrasted to thermomechanical) motion of macroscopic solid particles, which rub against each other and exert upon each other forces due to sliding friction. This latter type of resistance to motion is termed *coulomb friction,* and should not be confused with *viscous* resistance to flow. The two effects differ in the following important respects:

(1) Dependence of resistive force on *rate* of flow. The resistive force in a viscous liquid is *directly proportional* to the rate of flow. The resistive force in a powdered solid is to a first approximation *independent* of the rate of flow, just as the frictional resistance to the relative sliding of two solid surfaces in contact is independent of the rate.

(2) Dependence of resistive force on external pressure. The viscosity of a liquid increases with external pressure, but only very slowly. As long as only small pressures are concerned, the viscosity can be considered to be a constant. Coulomb resistance, however, is *directly proportional* to pressure, since solid sliding friction is proportional to the normal force.

(3) Dependence of resistive force upon temperature. Since viscous flow is based upon molecular motion, it is extremely temperature dependent. Viscosity decreases rapidly with increasing temperature. Coulomb friction, being a purely *mechanical* effect, is practically independent of temperature.

In the study of the mechanical properties of homogeneous high polymers, viscous resistance plays a much more important role than coulomb resistance. However, in many commercial plastics and rubber formulations, there are incorporated into the polymer solid fillers, the particles of which may well rub against each other mechanically during a deformation, and give rise to forces of coulomb friction. In polycrystalline textile fibers, *crystallites* may rub against each other in the same way. Whenever stresses cause large particles (large compared to atomic dimensions) to slide past one another in a sample, then coulomb resistance to flow is to be expected.

Kennedy (*26*) has discussed the problem of resolving an observed resistance to flow into its viscous and coulomb components.

8. Combinations of Elasticity and Flow, and Inertial Effects

The preceding sections have considered elasticity unaccompanied by flow and flow unaccompanied by elasticity. While many solids exhibit essentially pure elasticity, and while many liquids approximate closely the idealized Newtonian fluid, there are many materials whose mechanical properties cannot be adequately defined unless one simultaneously considers both elastic and viscous effects. In the following passages two of the simpler combinations of flow and elasticity will be discussed, and certain concepts will be defined which will later be of use in the treatment of the complicated plastoelastic behavior of high polymers. The first case is that of Maxwellian relaxation (*33*) in which a material can respond to a stress by means of two different mechanisms—elasticity and flow. In this case the total deformation is the sum of the elastic displacement and the flow. The second case is that of "retarded" elasticity, in which a single elastic mechanism operates, but in which the elastic response is delayed by a viscous resistance to deformation. Furthermore, the role of inertia, which was mentioned briefly in sections 3 (pages 10–23) and 4 (pages 23–32), will be somewhat elaborated. In all these cases—viscous flow superimposed upon elastic deformation, viscous resistance opposing elastic deformation, and inertial effects influencing plastoelastic behavior—it will be shown that the fundamental equations governing the time behavior of the material are differential equations, rather than explicit relationships between stress, deformation, and time. These differential equations can be represented pictorially by equivalent mechanical models. Finally, the role of the experimental "timescale" in the investigation of plastoelastic materials is brought out in these introductory examples.

A. Maxwellian Relaxation

Consider a material which will undergo an instantaneous elastic response when stressed, but which can also flow. The total deformation of such a material under shear stress is the sum of its elastic deformation and its flow. In figure 27[c], the deformation–time curve of such a material in shear is contrasted to that of a simple elastic solid (Fig. 27[a]) and that of a simple liquid (Fig. 27[b]). The elastic deformation is

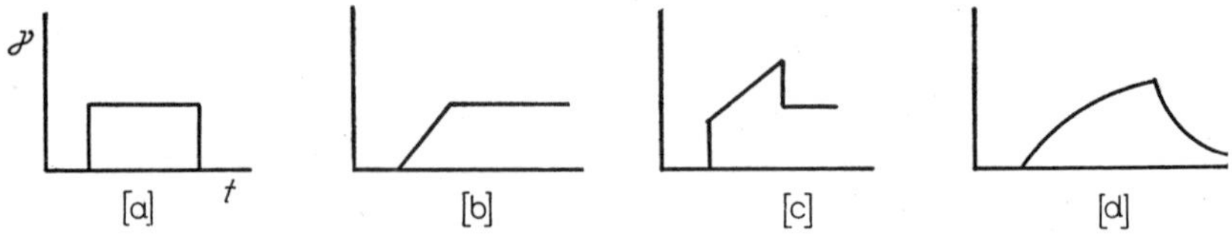

Fig. 27. Strain as a function of time at constant stress for: (a) ideal elastic material; (b) ideal Newtonian fluid; (c) Maxwell element (flow plus elasticity); and (d) the Voigt element (retarded elastic response).

simply $(1/G)S$, where G is the shear modulus. The flow deformation, however, depends not only upon the stress, but upon how long the stress has been acting. All that can be said is that the instantaneous *rate* of flow is given by $(1/\eta)S$ where η is the viscosity. Thus it is not possible to write an explicit expression connecting the deformation with the stress, but only an expression giving the *rate of change* of deformation:

$$\gamma_1 = \text{elastic displacement} = \frac{1}{G}S; \qquad \frac{d\gamma_1}{dt} = \frac{1}{G}\frac{dS}{dt} \tag{69a}$$

$$\gamma_2 = \text{flow displacement}; \qquad \frac{d\gamma_2}{dt} = \frac{1}{\eta}S \tag{69b}$$

$$\gamma = \text{total displacement} = \gamma_1 + \gamma_2; \qquad \frac{d\gamma}{dt} = \frac{1}{\eta}S + \frac{1}{G}\frac{dS}{dt} \tag{69c}$$

This equation merely states that the total rate of change of γ with time is given by the rate of flow, $(1/\eta)S$, plus the rate of change of the elastic part of the deformation, $(1/G)(dS/dt)$. This is the fundamental differential equation, which governs the mechanical response of the material not only to a constant shear stress, but to any sequence of shear stresses and to any sequence of constraints upon the deformation itself.

Consider the following problem. One quickly forces the sample exhibiting both elasticity and flow, to assume a certain deformation, γ_1, and then constrains it so that it must retain this deformed shape. Although the deformation cannot change under these conditions, the internal flow which takes place gradually relaxes the stress, so that smaller and smaller forces are required to keep the sample deformed. Since $d\gamma/dt = 0$, equation (69c) reduces to:

$$\frac{1}{G}\frac{dS}{dt} + \frac{1}{\eta}S = 0 \tag{70}$$

The solution to this differential equation is the following:

$$S = S_0 e^{-G/\eta \cdot t} \tag{71a}$$

Thus the stress relaxes exponentially with time. After a time equal to (η/G), the stress will have decayed to 1/e of its original value. The ratio (η/G) is therefore called the "relaxation time" for the material, and is often represented by the symbol τ. In terms of τ, equation (71a) becomes:

$$S = S_0 e^{-t/\tau} \tag{71b}$$

The behavior of a material exhibiting flow superimposed upon elasticity can be represented by means of the mechanical analog of figure 28. Here the elastic mode of response to stress is indicated by an elastic spring, and the flow mechanism by a dashpot. If the upper end of this mechanical model is fixed, the lower end can move either by a stretching of the spring, or by a flow in the dashpot.

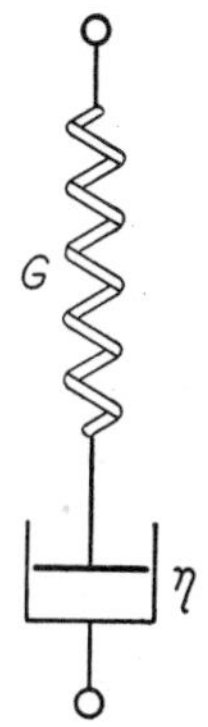

Fig. 28. A Maxwell element; the mechanical model for Maxwellian relaxation.

The response of the material to a constant shear stress can be translated into the corresponding behavior of the model, as follows: when the stress is applied, the spring instantaneously stretches by the amount (S/G), and the dashpot begins to elongate steadily at the rate (S/η). When the stress is removed, the spring instantaneously contracts, but the dashpot remains in its elongated condition. This results in a motion of the lower end of the model of the same form as figure 27[c]. The relaxation of shear stress at constant deformation can also be translated into the corresponding behavior of the model: when the model is quickly stretched, the entire elongation is contributed by the spring, G. If the free end of the model is then constrained, the tension in the spring pulls on the dashpot, causing it to elongate. As the dashpot elongates, the spring is allowed to contract, since the total elongation of the model remains constant. Hence the stress relaxes according to equation (71).

If a material exhibits Maxwell relaxation with regard to its behavior in shear, then it will act in a similar manner in tension. Particularly if the material can be considered as incompressible (shear modulus $\ll$ bulk modulus), the relation between the shear and tensile behavior is very simple. In this case, the tensile behavior can be represented by a Maxwell element composed of a spring with stiffness $3G$, and a dashpot of viscous resistance 3η, where G and η are the shear modulus and the viscosity of the material, respectively. Among other things, this means that the relaxation time for a simple tensile stress is equal to that for shearing stress. This is a special case of the general theorem discussed in Chapter B.

The relative importance of the elastic mechanism of response and the flow mechanism obviously depends not only upon the magnitude of G and η but also upon the *timescale of the experimental investigation.* Consider that the stress S is allowed to act for the time ⓣ. The magnitude of the elastic deformation is (S/G), and that of the flow deformation is (S/η)ⓣ. If ⓣ is very small, compared to (η/G), then the elastic deformation will completely overshadow the flow, and for such short experiments, the material can be considered to be a simple elastic solid. If ⓣ is very large, compared to (η/G), the flow will overshadow the elastic response, and the material can be considered as a simple Newtonian liquid. Only if ⓣ is of the same order of magnitude as (η/G), is the composite nature of the deformation apparent. The critical quantity (η/G) is nothing else than the Maxwell "relaxation time," which appeared in equation (71b). Thus the general nature of the observed behavior of a Maxwell element depends upon the relative magnitudes of τ, the relaxation time, and ⓣ, which is a measure of the timescale of the experimental investigation. τ has a definite value for a given Maxwellian material; it can be thought of as an internal timescale, characteristic of the relaxation of the material. The differential equation (69c) has the character that for *any type of very rapid mechanical test or observation*, where the experimental timescale is much shorter than τ (the "internal timescale" of the material), the material will behave as an ideal elastic body; that for *any type of very slow mechanical test or observation*, where the experimental timescale is much longer than τ, the material will behave as an ideal viscous liquid; and that for any type of mechanical test of intermediate timescale, where ⓣ is of the same order of magnitude as τ, both elasticity and flow are observed.

The "timescale" of an experiment is not a sharply defined value like the relaxation time of a material. It is usually only an *order of magnitude*, although in the case of a sinusoidal stress, the period of the sinusoidal variation serves as a convenient measure of the experimental timescale. In general ⓣ ranges from the shortest time interval which has an experimental meaning up to the complete duration of the experiment. For many experiments, these two extreme values differ only by a factor of 10^2 or less. If ⓣ is defined to the nearest power of 10, that is quite satisfactory. Some experiments may extend over several orders of magnitude in timescale, and cannot be characterized by a ⓣ (*e.g.*, a deformation–time curve which is accurate in the early part to 0.1 second, and which represents a total period of observation of 10^6 seconds).

B. Retarded Elastic Response

The equilibrium (unstressed) shape of an object represents a free energy minimum. Any small distortion must result in a free energy increase. If an external stress is imposed, however, the free energy as a function of object shape is changed, so that the new minimum represents a displacement from the unstressed equilibrium. That is to say, under the action of the stress, a different shape possesses the properties of equilibrium. The original (unstressed) shape is, upon stressing, a displacement from the new equilibrium, and the body tends to diminish its free energy by taking on the new equilibrium shape. If this process is instantaneous, the result is the ideal elasticity already discussed. If the rate of attainment of the new equilibrium is slow, however, the result is an appreciably "damped" or "retarded" elastic response, like that of a spring surrounded by a viscous medium.

A typical molecular mechanism which should be expected to result in such retarded elasticity is the uncurling of long tangled polymer chains. This process takes place by means of diffusion of chain segments, and takes an appreciable time (see Chapter B).

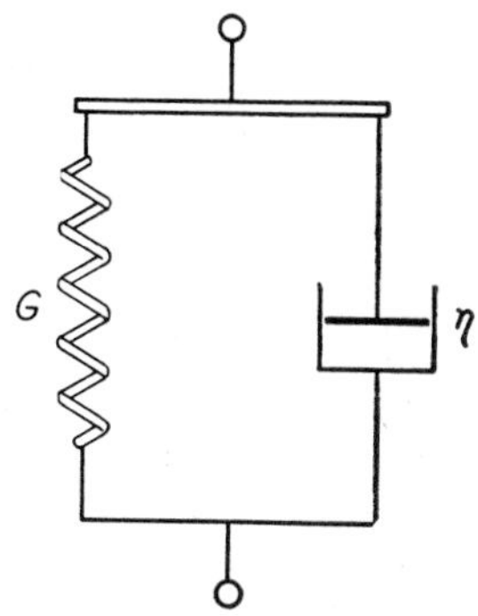

Fig. 29. A Voigt element; the mechanical model for retarded elasticity.

A retarded elastic response may be represented by a mechanical analog of the type shown in figure 29. This device differs from that of figure 28 in that the spring and dashpot are coupled in parallel, rather than in series. The difference corresponds to the fact that in this case the viscous element represents *a damping resistance to the establishment of the elastic equilibrium*, whereas in the Maxwell element it represents an *entirely distinct mechanism of response to stress, the displacement due to which is added to the elastic displacement.*

The following differential equation governs retarded elastic response:

$$\eta \cdot d\gamma/dt + G\gamma = S \tag{72}$$

If a stress is applied at time t_0 and removed at time t_1, the displacement–time curve is of the type indicated in figure 27[d]. If time is measured from the time of application of the stress, the deformation–time relation is given by equation (73a):

$$\gamma = S/G \cdot (1 - \mathrm{e}^{-G/\eta \cdot t}) \tag{73a}$$

The quantity η/G may be called the "retardation time" of the material, and represented by the symbol τ. In terms of the retardation time, equation (73a) can be written as:

$$\gamma = S/G(1 - \mathrm{e}^{-t/\tau}) \tag{73b}$$

Upon removal of stress, the sample slowly returns to its original shape, where $\gamma = 0$, following an exponential curve:

$$\gamma = \gamma_0 \mathrm{e}^{-t/\tau} \tag{74}$$

Thus at constant stress, a retarded elastic element relaxes exponentially into its equilibrium shape at a rate determined by its "retardation time," just as at constant shape a Maxwell element exponentially relaxes its stress, at a rate determined by its "relaxation time."

The experimental timescale is an important factor in the behavior of a retarded elastic element, as well as that of a Maxwell element. If a constant stress is applied for a time which is very short compared with the retardation time τ, then only the first part of the deformation–time curve is observed. This early portion has the slope (S/η); hence the material behaves like a simple fluid of viscosity η. Furthermore, if the recovery is then observed for a period which is also very short compared with τ, it will appear that no recovery at all is taking place. Hence a retarded elastic element behaves, in a very rapid test, just like a viscous fluid of viscosity η. On the other hand, if the experimental timescale is very long compared to τ, the elastic deformation and recovery will appear to be instantaneous. Only if the experimental investigation has a timescale comparable to the "internal timescale" of the material (the retardation time), are both the elastic and the viscous aspects of the behavior observable. Both Maxwell relaxation and retarded elasticity will play important roles in the subsequent discussion of the mechanical properties of high polymers. It may be well, therefore, to point out explicitly the distinction between the two. A Maxwellian material, or a Maxwell element in the mechanical analog, possesses two distinct mechanisms of response to stress. Each mechanism separately is subject to the entire stress; in the model, both the elastic and the viscous element bear the entire load. The deformation of the material, however, is the *sum* of the elastic deformation and the deformation resulting from flow. In the retarded elastic element, the situation is almost exactly reversed. The viscous resistance retards the establishment of elastic equilibrium. The stress is divided between the elastic element and the flow element. Both elements, however, possess the same deformation and the same rate of deformation. In more complicated models this distinction between series and parallel coupling remains. Any two elements coupled in series must individually bear the entire stress, but their deformations are additive. Any two elements coupled in parallel must exhibit the same deformation, but they divide the stress between them. Thus series coupling in a plastoelastic model corresponds to parallel coupling in an electrical circuit, and *vice versa.*

In order not to confuse the physical meaning of the quantity (η/G) for a Maxwell element and the quantity (η/G) for a retarded elastic element, one is given the name "relaxation time," and the other the name "retardation time." In mathematical equations where such confusion cannot arise, each is represented by the symbol τ.

C. Inertial Elasticity and Damped Inertial Elasticity

In the sections on elasticity, inertial effects were neglected. This is a justified procedure when only static problems are concerned, since the volume elements of the object are subject to no accelerations. The *dynamic* behavior of an elastic solid, however, depends upon the inertia as well as the elastic restoring forces. Consideration of inertia in the case of elastic solids leads to the differential equations of solid vibration, which will not be considered here. If a solid elastic rod possessing appreciable inertia is suddenly subjected to tensile forces applied at the two ends, these forces are supported at the beginning by the inertia of the material near the points of application of the forces. The material in the central part of the rod is not stressed at all. Immediately, however, elastic waves begin to run through the rod from the ends. The material in the center of the rod becomes "aware" of the forces after a time which depends upon the distance from the ends and upon the velocity of propagation of the elastic waves. The result of the sudden application of balanced forces is to set up a state of vibration in the rod. The stress at any instant varies throughout the rod, and the stress at any point varies with time. For simplicity we will consider the less general case where only one component of homogeneous stress and one component of homogeneous strain are involved, and where the inertia can be considered as "lumped together," rather than distributed throughout the material. The strain, γ, is no longer given by the static equation $S = G\gamma$, but rather obeys the differential equation

$$\mathrm{m}\frac{d^2\gamma}{dt^2} + G\gamma = S \tag{75}$$

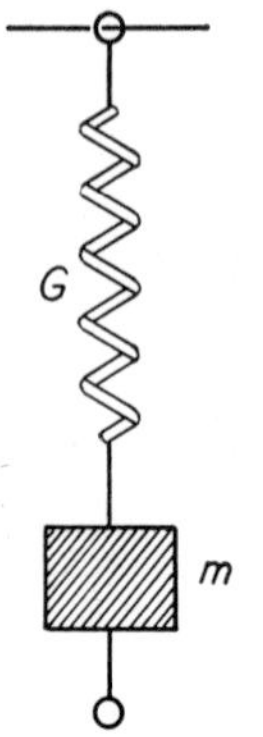

Fig. 30. A mechanical model representing elasticity plus a lumped inertia.

Here m is an inertial term proportional to the density. This differential equation can be represented by the mechanical model of figure 30. If a stress S_1 is suddenly applied at $t = 0$ to a material possessing both elasticity and inertia, it does not jump instantaneously into the equilibrium deformation $\gamma_1 = (1/G)S_1$, but rather oscillates back and forth between the values 0 and 2 γ_1 (Fig. 31[b]). Actually, of course, such an oscillatory motion is *damped out* by an internal viscous-type resistance. A material possessing *damped inertial elasticity* follows the differential equation:

$$\mathrm{m}\frac{d^2\gamma}{dt^2} + \eta\frac{d\gamma}{dt} + G\gamma = S \tag{76}$$

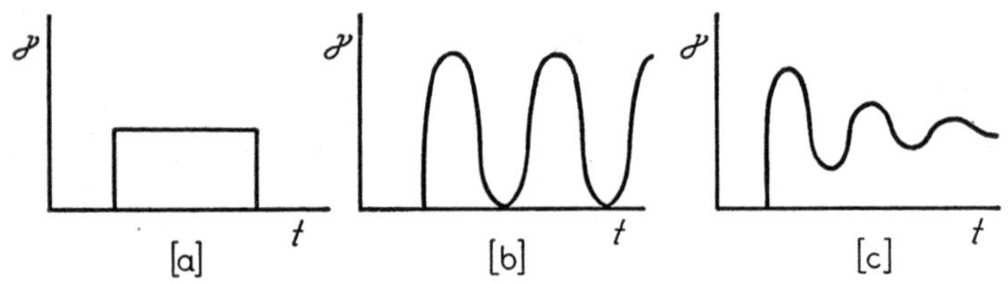

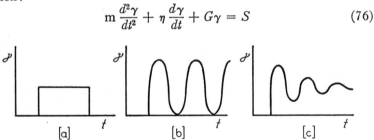

Fig. 31. Strain *vs.* time under the influence of a suddenly imposed stress: [a] elasticity alone; [b] elasticity plus inertia; [c] elasticity plus inertia plus viscous damping.

This differential equation corresponds to the mechanical model of figure 32. The response of such a system to a constant stress S_1, suddenly applied at $t = 0$, is shown in figure 31[c].

Now in many cases, the rate of decay of the oscillation of figure 31[c] is so great that the sample takes on the equilibrium deformation very quickly. For ordinary static and nearly static mechanical experiments, the damped inertial character of the elasticity can then be safely ignored. It is for very rapid experiments that this character cannot be ignored.

(A similar situation was observed in the case of liquid flow. There, too, inertial effects were important under certain experimental conditions. In this volume, the major emphasis will be on problems in which the inertia of the sample plays a negligible role with respect both to flow and to elasticity.)

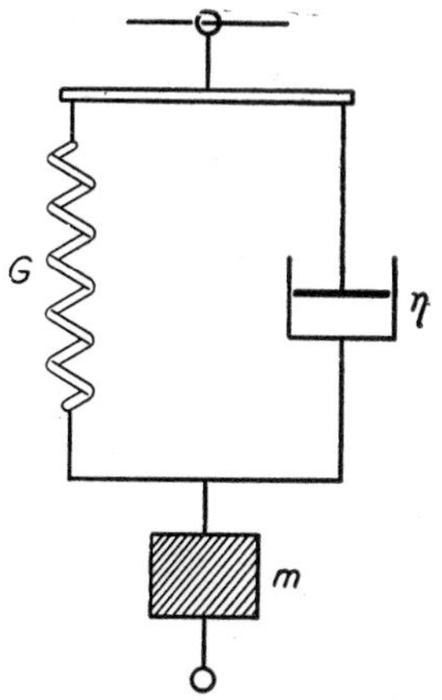

Fig. 32. A mechanical model representing retarded elasticity plus a lumped inertia.

It should be noted that the sudden application of a homogeneous stress by mechanical means is experimentally impossible. One stresses an object by means of forces applied at the surface, and these forces must necessarily set up waves which pass through the object at finite rates. The sudden application of a set of balanced surface forces results in a constant stress distribution only after the time necessary for these elastic waves to be damped out. Equations (75) and (76), and figures 30 and 32 would apply directly only if a homogeneous stress could be instantaneously applied throughout the body of the sample. This would necessarily be by means of nonhomogeneous body forces, rather than surface forces. (It is not correct to include nonhomogeneous *body* forces as part of the "stress." It is done here to obviate a more lengthy discussion of a minor point. The meaning of the paragraph should be clear.) Equations (75) and (76) can, however, be applied in cases where surface forces are involved, if the inertial mass can be considered as localized at one point, rather than distributed throughout the sample. Thus if a large external mass is fastened to a spring of negligible inertia, the resulting mechanical system obeys equation (75) if damping can be ignored, and equation (76) if simple viscous damping is observed. This type of approach to inertial behavior is directly applicable in problems involving mechanical systems composed of large rigid masses and deformable elements of negligible inertia. It can also be used as a first approximation to the mechanical behavior of objects composed of a single deformable material possessing appreciable inertia.

II. SIMPLE MOLECULAR MECHANISMS INVOLVED IN ELASTICITY AND FLOW

The foregoing sections have been purely phenomenological. Phenomenological descriptions have been presented of the mechanical behavior of ideal elastic solids, Newtonian and non-Newtonian liquids, materials exhibiting both elasticity and flow (Maxwell relaxation) or retarded elasticity, etc. Up to this point, however, no mention has been made of the elementary *molecular processes* which give rise to the various macroscopic behaviors. The subject which bears the name of "the theory of elasticity" actually deals with the solution of partial differential equations, and is not in any sense a physical theory of the mechanism of elastic response. The same is true of the subject of hydrodynamics. These subjects are thus analogous to classical thermodynamics, which likewise serves as a phenomenological framework for observed data relating to macroscopic behaviors, and which is not concerned with the molecular mechanisms which give rise to these behaviors.

In the sections which follow, the mechanical properties of simple materials will be approached from the standpoint of the elementary molecular processes which take place when the material is stressed. This approach necessarily involves hypotheses concerning the structure, on an atomic scale, of the material under consideration, and bears the same relation to the phenomenological approach already presented as statistical mechanics bears to classical thermodynamics. The microscopic structures of some materials, notably crystalline solids and ideal gases, are so well established that the mechanical behavior of these materials can be predicted with satisfactory exactness. As one proceeds to materials whose structures are less precisely known, the theoretical prediction of mechanical properties ceases to yield exact quantitative values. Even in such cases, however, it is often possible to predict roughly the values of physical quantities, and to predict very accurately the way in which these quantities vary with temperature, pressure, and other variables.

1. The Mechanism of Elastic Displacement in Crystalline Solids (*9*)

In section 3 (pages 10–15), it was pointed out that, in general, 21 independent elastic constants must be specified in order to define the elastic properties of a crystalline solid. These constants are the coefficients of the set of six linear equations relating stress components s_i and strain components γ_i.

$$s_i = \Sigma_j k_{ij}\gamma_j \tag{77}$$

It was also pointed out that a given constant k_{ij} is given thermodynamically by the relation:

$$k_{ij} = \frac{\partial^2 \mathbf{F}}{\partial \gamma_i \, \partial \gamma_j} \tag{78}$$

Thus if the free energy of the sample is known as a function of the six strain components, the 21 elastic constants can be obtained by differentiation.

The free energy of a crystal can be conveniently divided into two parts: $\mathbf{F}_0$, the free energy at absolute zero, and $\mathbf{F}_v$, the additional free energy which results from the thermal vibrations which are present at all temperatures above absolute zero:

$$\mathbf{F}(T) = \mathbf{F}_0 + \mathbf{F}_v(T) \tag{79}$$

It turns out that the elastic constants are mainly determined by $\mathbf{F}_0$, since $\mathbf{F}_v$ is much less dependent upon deformation than is $\mathbf{F}_0$.

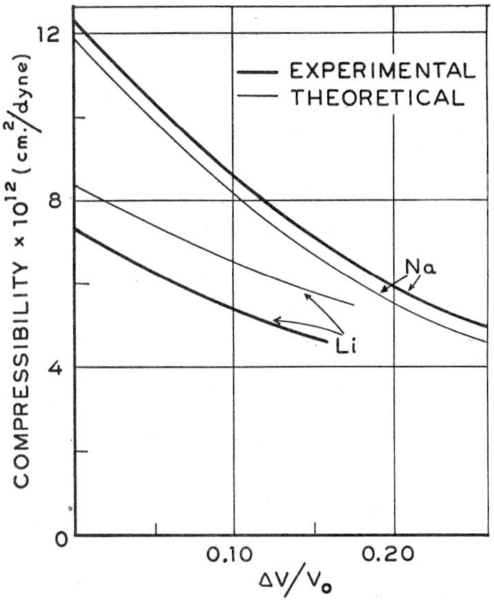

Fig. 33. Compressibility of sodium as a function of the amount of compression (theoretical and observed).

$\mathbf{F}_0$ is completely an *energy* term, since the entropy of a perfect crystal is zero at 0° K. The energy of a crystal at absolute zero is the potential energy of the equilibrium lattice structure plus the zero point vibrational energy, which is very small. $\partial^2 \mathbf{F}_0/(\partial\gamma_i\, \partial\gamma_j)$ will of course give the value of k_{ij} at absolute zero, whereas $\partial^2 \mathbf{F}_v(T)/(\partial\gamma_i\, \partial\gamma_j)$ will give the difference between k_{ij} at the temperature T, and k_{ij} at 0° K.

The zero point constants have been calculated from crystal structures in a number of cases. One simple deformation is a uniform compression. Here $\gamma_1 = \gamma_2 = \gamma_3 = \Delta V/3\ V$, where ΔV is small, and $\gamma_4 = \gamma_5 = \gamma_6 = 0$. Bardeen (*12*) has computed the compressibility β of sodium from the potential energy increase resulting when sodium ions in the metallic lattice are forced closer together. This computation was not limited to the range of linearity between pressure and ΔV. Figure 33 shows the calculated values of β as a function of compression, and also the experimental values as determined by Bridgman (*19*). Similar calculated and experimental values are shown for lithium. These compressibilities were computed directly from the structures of the crystals, taking into account both the coulombic interaction between metallic ions and the noncoulombic interaction.

Similar computations can be made for other simple types of deformation. As a result, several of the constants k_{ij} can be specifically evaluated. Table II lists computed and observed values of several elastic constants

TABLE II

COMPARISON OF OBSERVED AND CALCULATED VALUES OF THE ELASTIC CONSTANTS OF COPPER AND SODIUM (*9*)

(In units of 10^{11} dynes per cm.^{2})

Metal	$1/\beta$	$c_{11} - c_{12}$	c_{44}	c_{11}	c_{12}
Sodium:					
Calculated	0.88	0.141	0.580	0.97	0.83
Observed	0.85	0.145	0.59	0.95	0.80
Copper:					
Calculated	14.1	5.1	8.9	17.5	12.4
Observed	13.9	5.1	8.2	18.6	13.5

for copper and sodium. These zero point elastic constants are calculated on the assumption that the metal ions are spherically symmetrical—that no localized or directed forces, but rather only central forces, act between ions. The close agreement with experiment indicates that the assumption is not too far incorrect. On the other hand, if this were strictly true, the Cauchy-Poisson relation, $k_{12} = k_{44}$, would hold. Since $k_{12} \neq k_{44}$ for the alkali metals, there must be definite noncentral components in the interionic forces.

Similar calculations can be made for ionic lattices, but only the compressibility of sodium chloride has been so evaluated. The calculated value of the bulk modulus is 4.35×10^{12} dynes per cm.^{2}; the experimental value is 4.16×10^{12} dynes per cm.^{2}

A. Change of Elastic Constants with Temperature

The value of k_{ij} at any temperature above absolute zero wi l differ from k_{ij} at 0° K. by the amount $\partial^2\mathbf{F}_v(T)/(\partial\gamma_i\,\partial\gamma_j)$. $\mathbf{F}_v(T)$ depends upon the spectrum of vibrational frequencies possessed by the crystal (Debye theory of specific heat). If the forces between the ions or atoms of the crystal lattice are completely harmonic (*i.e.*, the ions act as though joined by springs which obey Hooke's law over the whole range of extension),

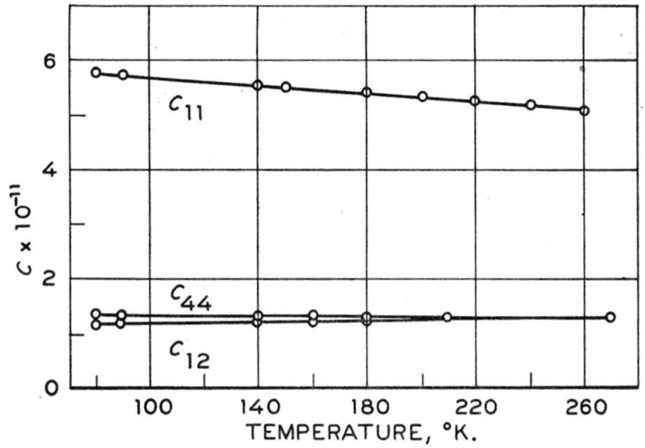

Fig. 34. Effect of temperature on the elastic contents of sodium chloride.

then a small distortion of the lattice increases the potential energy of the crystal, but does not affect the vibration frequencies. Thus $\mathbf{F}_v(T)$ is not a function of γ_1, γ_2, γ_3, etc., but only of temperature. A crystal bound together in such a fashion would have the following properties:

(1) No expansion upon heating. Equilibrium volume at constant pressure independent of temperature.

(2) Elastic constants independent of temperature.

(3) Absolutely no thermal effect accompanying a deformation. An adiabatic deformation would also be isothermal.

If the interionic forces are anharmonic, then $\mathbf{F}_v$ becomes a function of T, γ_1, γ_2, γ_3, γ_4, γ_5, and γ_6. The various elastic k values become temperature dependent, since $\partial^2\mathbf{F}_v/(\partial\gamma_i\,\partial\gamma_j)$ does not vanish.

Expansion coefficients for various materials are: diamond, 1.18×10^{-6}; copper, 16.8×10^{-6}; lead, 29.4×10^{-6}; and paraffin, 130×10^{-6}. For diamond, where the binding forces are very strong, and the atoms light, most of the vibrations take place within the harmonic range. In lead, where the binding forces are weaker and the atoms much heavier, vibrations extend further into the anharmonic range. Note the low expansion coefficient of diamond.

Figure 34 shows the effect of temperature on the elastic constants of a crystal of sodium chloride. This effect is relatively small. A complete thermodynamic theory of crystal elasticity has been made by Born (*17*). The temperature dependence of the elastic constants up to the melting point is derived. Fürth (*21*) has extended the treatment of the elastic behavior of simple crystals to the case of finite deformations.

B. Types of Forces

In short, the macroscopic elastic behavior of a crystal results from the forces acting between neighboring atoms, ions, or molecules. A distortion of the crystal as a whole forces neighboring atoms away from their original equilibrium positions and original relative orientations. In the case of simple metallic and ionic lattices, the macroscopic elastic constants can be computed from the crystal structure and the known properties of the single ions.

In an atomic lattice such as diamond, the interatomic forces are of a different character—covalent valence bonds. These forces possess a pronounced directional character; the four valence bonds of carbon, for example, tend to point toward the corners of a regular tetrahedron. A macroscopic deformation of the diamond lattice can arise from changes in the C—C distances, from deformations of the tetrahedral valence angles, or both. Both types of deformation on the atomic scale are opposed by interatomic forces. This contrasts with the metallic lattice, where the interatomic forces are less sensitive to direction.

In a molecular lattice, several different kinds of interparticle force must be considered. A macroscopic deformation of such a lattice is made up of deformations of the individual molecules and displacement of the molecules as a whole relative to each other. Deformation of individual molecules involves stretching or compression of primary valence bonds and opening or closing of valence angles. Relative displacement of whole molecules is opposed by the intermolecular van der Waals' forces. Mark (*32*) has summarized the various types of forces which must be overcome in the deformation of molecular substances, as given in the following paragraph.

Primary valence bonds and angles within the constituent molecules can be deformed, giving rise to a *compliance* (reciprocal elastic modulus) in the order of magnitude of 10^{-12}. Molecules can be displaced relative to each other against van der Waals' forces, giving rise to a compliance of 10^{-9} to 10^{-11}. Since the "softer" of the two responses will overshadow the more rigid, many molecular crystals can be considered as made up of completely rigid molecules, which change their spatial positions but not their shapes when the crystal is subjected to stress. The precise value of the elastic modulus corresponding to this type of crystal distortion depends upon the size and shape of the "rigid" molecules, as well as the types of forces acting between them. Strong molecular interactions, such as hydrogen bonds, will tend to produce a high elastic modulus. Weak interactions, such as the London forces between saturated aliphatic hydrocarbons, will have the opposite effect. The more closely and perfectly the molecules are able to fit together, the higher the elastic modulus will tend to be. And finally, the larger the rigid molecules (assuming equivalent fitting ability and equivalent specific attractions), the more difficult it will be to deform the crystal as a whole.

2. Liquid Flow—A Mechanism of Response to Stress

Crystal elasticity is an equilibrium phenomenon. Under the action of a stress, an atom, molecule, or segment of a molecule is displaced slightly to a new equilibrium position, *staying within the same potential energy valley*. If a liquid or a gas is subjected to a shear stress, an entirely different sort of response—namely, flow—can take place. (Compare references (*4*) and (*36*).

We have already seen how, phenomenologically, flow differs sharply from elastic displacement. In the latter, *an equilibrium state* of deformation is obtained. Work is done upon the sample by the stress only in the transient period during which the equilibrium deformation is being attained. This work is stored up in the sample as recoverable free energy of deformation. In flow, a *nonequilibrium* "steady state" is established, which is characterized by a constant rate of deformation. Work is done on the sample continuously, as long as the shear stress acts. This work is dissipated as heat.

The *mechanism* by which flow takes place, and by means of which a fluid exhibits "viscous resistance," is closely connected with the process of molecular diffusion, and can be understood only in terms of a detailed knowledge of the structure of the fluid. In the case of gases, such detailed structural information is available. As a result, not only the thermodynamic properties but also the transport properties of gases are well understood. The viscous resistance to flow of an ideal gas arises from the momentum transfer between layers of different stream velocity. In a flowing gas, the stream velocity is ordinarily small in magnitude compared with the mean molecular velocity, and represents a small bias to the random equilibrium distribution of molecular velocities. Molecules in fast layers are continually transferring themselves to slower layers, and *vice versa*, by means of their large transverse velocities. When a molecule from a fast layer enters a slower layer, it will, on the average, tend to speed up the new layer, because it will possess, on the average, a small amount of extra momentum in the direction of streaming. A molecule from a slow layer must, on the average, be speeded up a little upon entering a faster layer. The result is that layers moving at different speeds exert mutual drags on each other. Work must be done constantly upon the gas in order to support a velocity gradient, which by itself would be damped out by the above process of momentum transfer between moving layers. In a liquid, the nature of viscous resistance to flow is somewhat more involved.

A. The Structure of Simple Liquids

The determination of the structure of even the simplest liquid is a very complicated problem. In the case of crystalline solids there exists a simple model—the perfect crystal, with complete regularity of atomic spacings—which serves as a good theoretical starting point. At the other extreme of the order-disorder spectrum is the ideal gas, in which the spatial distribution and orientation of the molecules is completely random. In the liquid state, neither simple extreme is even approximately realized; instead, we have to contend with a rather elusive intermediate state of order and disorder. As a result, the existing descriptions of liquid structure, both theoretical and experimental, cannot be considered to be as satisfactory as the present highly elaborated theories of gases and crystalline solids.

However, in recent years certain light has been thrown on the character of liquid structure (*27*, *39*). The following statements seem to be justified by our present knowledge.

(1) The local or short range structure of a liquid is very similar to that of the corresponding crystalline solid. That is, an individual molecule is surrounded by nearest neighbors whose arrangement is much like that in the crystalline state.

(2) The arrangement of nearest neighbors is not *quite* perfect, and the arrangement of the *next* nearest neighbors is even less definite. The structure at a large distance from any given atom is completely random.

Thus the liquid exhibits *local order* in any small neighborhood, but *long range disorder*. This means that the local crystal-like structures are not correlated with each other. For obvious geometric reasons such a structure is possible only if there are discontinuities or gaps in the molecular packing. To these "holes" can be attributed the increase in volume of all normal liquids upon melting. To these holes also, we shall see, can be attributed the fluidity of liquids. The holes seem to be, on the average at least, about one-fourth as large as a molecule. As a liquid is heated, the number of holes increases, *i.e.*, the crystal-like local order becomes less and less significant.

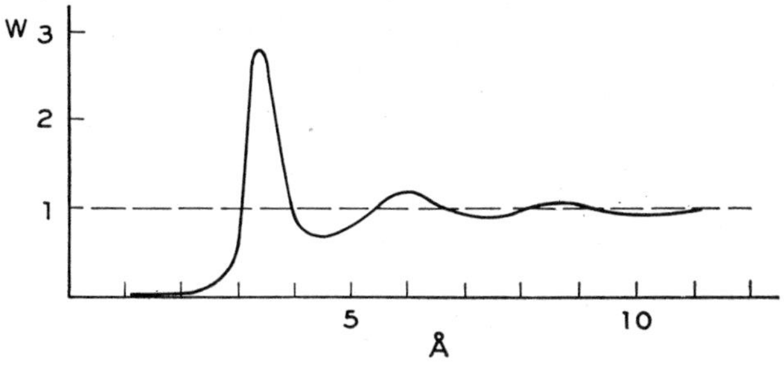

Fig. 35. Typical curve of density distribution about any given molecule in a liquid. *W* measures probability of finding center of another molecule at various distances.

This general picture of liquid structure is supported by much experimental evidence. X-ray diffraction of liquids is one important example. Such studies indicate that the probability of finding a second molecule at any given distance from a chosen molecule is of the type shown in figure 35. The first layer of neighbors is found at a definite distance—as in a crystal. At only a few angstroms distance, however, all such order is "washed out" and there is a random molecular arrangement (referred to the original molecule). If the density distribution curve is determined at various temperatures, it is found that the order becomes less and less pronounced as one approaches the critical temperature.

The device of considering a liquid to be a "mixture" of molecules and holes (although an extreme oversimplification of the problem of liquid structure) goes a long way toward explaining the equilibrium properties of liquids. In the following sections the phenomena of diffusion and viscous flow will be discussed on the basis of this simple model. The concepts in the following sections are due mainly to Eyring and coworkers.

B. Diffusion

Although the molecules in a liquid find themselves in essentially crystal-like surroundings, many will be situated next to holes. See figure 36. All such molecules move in potential energy valleys which are separated by energy barriers from other possible equilibrium positions. If a molecule possesses enough energy it can "jump" into a new equilibrium position, leaving behind it a hole for some other molecule to jump into. The number of such jumps per second will be determined by the number of holes, the height of the energy barriers, and the temperature:

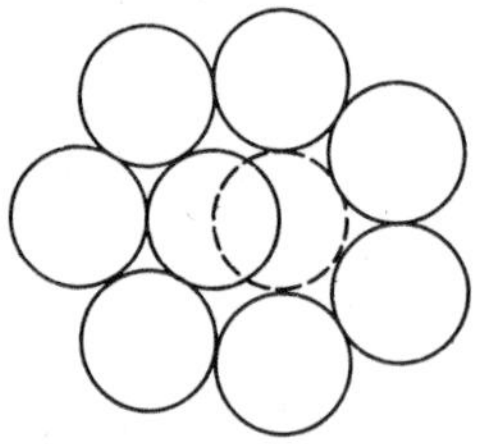

Fig. 36. Molecule in a liquid situated next to a hole.

$$\text{Number of jumps} = \text{number of holes} \times A \times e^{-\epsilon/kT} \qquad (80)$$

These jumps are equally frequent in all directions; together they constitute the *molecular diffusion* of the liquid. (This process is essentially the same as that responsible for diffusion in solids. The difference is in the character and number of the lattice imperfections in the two cases.)

If the temperature of a liquid is increased (at constant free volume) the rate of molecular diffusion is increased. A molecule next to a hole is more likely to have the "activation energy" necessary to surmount the barrier and jump into the hole. If the temperature of a liquid is increased *at constant pressure*, the diffusion rate is increased still more. Not only the rate of jumping into each hole, but also the *number of holes* is increased (thermal expansion). Thus the observed (constant pressure) temperature dependence of diffusion is due to two distinct properties—the activation energy of the actual jumping process, and the coefficient of expansion. It will be seen that a similar situation exists in the case of viscous flow.

C. Viscous Flow

In the process of diffusion, just discussed, the molecular jumps were equally frequent in all directions, and resulted in no net transport of matter in any direction. If, however, the liquid were subjected to an external stress which tended to pull molecules in one particular direction, then the potential valley of figure 37[a] would be deformed as in figure

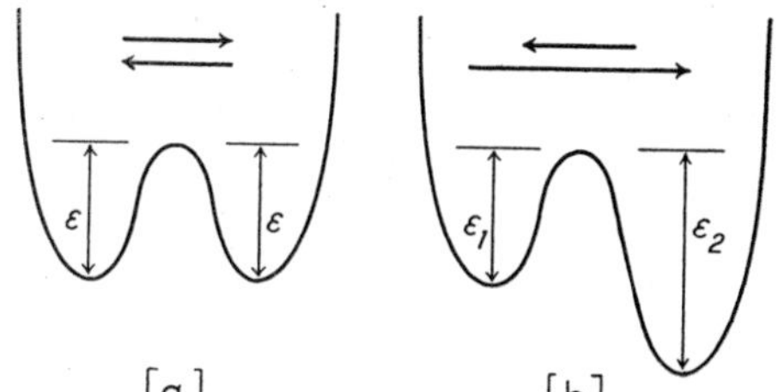

Fig. 37. Potential energy as a function of position for a molecule next to a hole: (a) in the absence of an external force field; (b) in the presence of an external force field.

37[b]. In the potential energy surface of figure 37[b], a jump from left to right is obviously more likely than a jump in the reverse direction, since an energy of activation of only ϵ_1 is required. A material subjected to such a stress would undergo *a biased* molecular diffusion, resulting in a net transport of material from left to right.

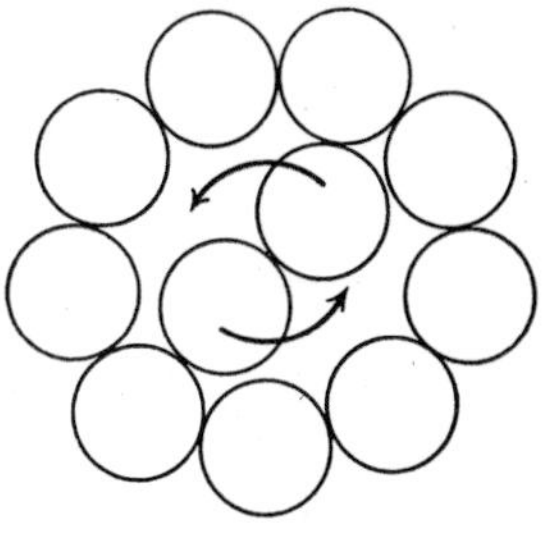

Fig. 38. Pair of molecules in a liquid situated next to two holes so that a rotational jump is possible.

As a matter of fact, this simple mechanism does not quite correspond to the process of viscous flow. In the first place a shear stress (which is the cause of viscous flow) does not result in a unidirectional deformation of the molecular potential energy valley, as in figure 37[b]. Furthermore, the result of a shear stress is the relative motion of each successive molecular layer with respect to the preceding layer. The above simple picture does not explain such *relative* motion of layers. It is therefore necessary to consider a slightly more complicated type of molecular diffusion, namely the rotation of temporary pairs of molecules. Figure 38 shows a molecular arrangement in which two molecules, A and B, can jump at the same time into new positions. The pair AB thus *rotates* to a new position. In the absence of a stress, rotational double jumps of this type are equally frequent in all directions. If a shear stress is imposed, however, the potential energy of the liquid after the jump is different from that before the jump. Since jumps which tend to relieve the stress will be more frequent than the reverse jumps, the result of many jumps will be a net motion of layer *a* relative to layer *b*, etc. If this geometric point is kept in mind, the schematic potential energy curve of figure 37[b] may well be used in the subsequent discussion.

It is to be noted that according to this picture the shear stress on a liquid is supported by elastic restoring forces. For a short time interval, the stressed liquid behaves like an elastically deformed solid. The molecules vibrate many times in their temporary equilibrium positions before jumping to new positions. Because of the jump, each of the molecules gains an amount of energy $\epsilon_2 - \epsilon_1$. In its new equilibrium position it vibrates particularly wildly until the extra vibrational energy is distributed throughout the liquid; hence the conversion of work into heat. It is only after many such jumps (*i.e.*, after the elapse of a time which is quite long compared to the period of molecular vibrations) that this process takes on its character of resultant over-all *flow*.

As the temperature of the liquid approaches the critical temperature, the length of time between molecular jumps becomes shorter and shorter. The liquid resembles more and more a highly compressed gas, becoming less and less crystal-like in its local arrangement. At high temperatures, a different treatment of diffusion and flow should be made. Here the low temperature treatment is emphasized because of the greater applicability to high polymers.

Thus the behavior of a simple liquid in shear corresponds to the phenomenological pattern presented in section 8A (pages 54–57). A liquid possesses two mechanisms of response to shear stress—an elastic displacement and a flow. For low molecular weight liquids (above the melting point) the fluidity is large enough to obscure the elastic response in all ordinary mechanical experiments. The rigidity can be detected only by very rapid experiments which allow no time for flow to take place (*i.e.*, liquids can support transverse as well as longitudinal vibrational waves if the frequency of the disturbance is made high enough). On the other hand, glasses—which are, structurally speaking, supercooled liquids—possess such high viscosities that even at ordinary testing speeds the elastic response is more important than the flow. Such rigid amorphous materials are often considered as solids, in a rheological classification. If the experimental timescale is lengthened sufficiently, flow is observed (see the following section, pages 75–86, for a more detailed discussion of glasses). It is apparent that the higher the viscosity of a liquid, the more relative importance must be assigned to the elastic aspect of its response.

This general picture of flow is supported by the experimentally observed variation of viscosity with pressure. The fluidity ($1/\eta$) is found to be closely related to the *free volume* (or number of holes). Indeed, Batschinski (*14*) has proposed the following equation to relate fluidity with volume changes:

$$1/\eta = c(V_l - V_s) \tag{81}$$

Here V_l is the molar volume of the liquid and V_s is the molar volume of the corresponding crystalline solid, whence $V - V_s$ represents the free volume of the liquid. He finds that this formula gave good agreement with experiment in the case of unassociated liquids, when the volume was changed by raising the temperature at constant pressure. Bridgman (*19*) has made the most exhaustive experimental study of the effects of pressure on the viscosities of liquids. His data indicate that equation (81) is far from being quantitatively correct either at constant pressure or constant temperature. Even so, the close connection between free volume and fluidity strongly supports the mechanism of flow discussed here. For a more complete discussion the reader is referred to the publications of Eyring and co-workers. Compare particularly reference (*4*).

If the temperature of a liquid is increased at constant free volume, it is to be expected that the fluidity will increase. At a high temperature more molecular pairs possess the "activation energy" necessary for their rotational jump than at a low temperature. The temperature dependence of the fluidity under these conditions should be a measure of the activation energy of the jumping process. One would expect this to be of the same order of magnitude as the activation energy for diffusion, but not equal to it.

If the liquid is heated at constant pressure, there is the additional effect of thermal expansion, just as in the case of diffusion. The fluidity will increase more rapidly with temperature at constant pressure than at constant free volume. As to the relative magnitudes of the two temperature effects, the second seems to be of the greater importance. The activation energy of the actual jumping process seems to be fairly small; and most of the increase in fluidity with temperature is due to the expansion of the liquid. Since viscosities are usually measured at atmospheric pressure, it is common to lump the two effects together, and to consider the total temperature dependence of fluidity as due to an over-all "energy of activation of viscous flow." This over-all "energy of activation" is thus mainly the "energy necessary for the creation of new holes in the liquid structure."

Since the temperature dependence of flow and diffusion due to volume expansion overshadows the temperature dependence arising from the activation energy of molecular jumps, it is not surprising that the "over-all activation energy" of viscous flow and diffusion are very closely the same, even though the actual elementary molecular processes are different. For example, E_{vis} of tetrachloroethane is 2995 cal., E_{vis} (calc.) of tetrabromomethane is 3745 cal., mean = 3370 cal., and E_{dif} = 3490 cal.

The use of the term "energy of activation of viscous flow" implies that the viscosity should vary with temperature according to the relationship:

$$1/\eta = Ae^{-E_a/RT}$$

or (82)

$$\eta = A'e^{E_a/RT}$$

As a matter of fact, this equation is widely used as an approximation to the actual behavior of liquids, which is somewhat more complicated. Plots of log η *vs.* $1/T$ for actual liquids are straight lines only over relatively narrow temperature ranges, showing marked curvature over wide temperature ranges. In spite of this fact, equation (82) will be widely used throughout this book to indicate the general nature of the temperature dependence, not only of the true viscosity, but also of the viscous resistances to configurational elastic responses. Such use of equation (82) should not be considered as giving a quantitative picture of the changes of these viscosities with temperature, except in fairly small temperature ranges.

The Question of Momentum Transfer; Relation of Gas Viscosity to Liquid Viscosity. —The origin of viscosity in an ideal gas is well known and is briefly sketched on page 68. It is the following. If one layer of an ideal gas is moving relative to a second nearby layer, then molecules diffuse transversely from one layer to the other. The result is a momentum transfer which tends to destroy the velocity gradient. Molecules moving from a "fast" layer to a "slow" layer impart a little momentum to the layer and tend to speed it up. Molecules moving from a slow layer to a fast layer must be given a little momentum, and thus tend to decelerate the fast layer. Thus the two layers exert viscous drags on one another, and require the presence of an external shear force to maintain the steady state of flow.

Our discussion of liquid viscosity has been couched in different terms from that of ideal gas viscosity. Momentum transfer was not mentioned. The emphasis was rather upon *energy* dissipation. Exactly what role does momentum transfer play in liquid flow, and what correlations can be made between liquid viscosity and ideal gas viscosity?

(*1*) Viscous flow is based upon an underlying process of molecular diffusion, which goes on whether the fluid is stressed or not. A shear stress causes a "bias" or distortion of the normal molecular diffusion. This biased diffusion is viscous flow.

(*2*) During the process of viscous flow, work is converted into heat.

(*3*) During the process of viscous flow, momentum is transferred between layers which are moving relative to one another.

These three statements apply to the viscous flow of both liquid and gas. However, because of the essential difference in nature of diffusion in an ideal gas and in a liquid at low temperature, different aspects of the behavior seem to predominate in the two cases. In a gas which approaches ideal behavior at all closely, the mean free molecular path is large—larger than molecular dimensions. Most of the time, the gas molecules are moving in straight lines at constant velocity, changing speed and direction only during the relatively brief, infrequent collisions. The laws of momentum distribution are known and provide a convenient starting point for a theoretical treatment. In the gas, therefore, statement *3* not only is true, but also has been useful as a theoretical point of attack.

In a liquid at low temperature, the molecules are constantly colliding. The mean free molecular path is small. The motion of a given molecule approximates a sinusoidal vibration more closely than a constant velocity. The distribution of velocities or momenta is not as useful a concept for a liquid as for an ideal gas. Statement *3* does not serve in a liquid as the most fortunate point of attack.

Moreover, momentum transfer in a gas takes place by a simple, easily pictured mechanism. Molecules actually move from one layer to another, "carrying" momentum. In a liquid, it is not necessary for a molecule to move from a fast layer to a slow layer in order to transfer momentum. The neighboring layers are locally coordinated with one another in a solid-like structure. After a "jump" a molecule can transmit momentum to a nearby layer without moving into that layer.

In short, while it may not be factually correct to say that momentum transfer is a less important factor in liquid viscosity than in gas viscosity, it is certainly true that the concept of momentum transfer has not been applied to the problem of liquid viscosity with the same success as to the problem of gas viscosity. At high temperatures—near the critical temperature—momentum transfer by actual molecular motion between layers presumably becomes important, and should be considered in a general theory of liquid flow.

D. The Softening Point and Apparent Second Order Transition Point in Amorphous Materials

At the melting point of a crystalline material, a striking change in mechanical properties takes place within a very narrow temperature range. In the crystalline state, the material is rigid—that is, it responds to shear stress by undergoing a deformation which is predominantly elastic in nature. In the liquid state, the material *flows* when subjected to shear stresses. (Both the crystalline and liquid forms respond elastically to a uniform *compression* stress.) A crystalline material may, in addition, exhibit flow, and a liquid may exhibit elastic effects in shear, but it is fair to say that in an ordinary melting process, a material changes from essentially elastic to essentially viscous mechanical behavior. Associated with this abrupt change in mechanical properties, there are discontinuities in the values of the primary thermodynamic variables—volume, energy, entropy, etc.—and a sudden change from crystalline to amorphous structure.

If a liquid is supercooled below its equilibrium melting point, it retains its characteristic amorphous structure. The viscosity increases with decreasing temperature, roughly following the relationship $\eta = Ae^{B/T}$. At very low temperatures the material is hard and rigid, and in this condition is generally designated as a glass. The transition from rigid glass to viscous liquid occurs in a relatively narrow temperature range which is often represented as a sharp point—the "brittle point" or "softening point." At this point there is no sudden change in structure, and no discontinuity in the primary thermodynamic variables. It has been observed in many cases, however, that at a temperature near the softening point, the *first derivative thermodynamic variables*—coefficient of expansion, heat capacity, etc.—experience rather sudden jumps in value. That is, the *volume–temperature*, *energy–temperature*, and *entropy–temperature* curves exhibit fairly sharp changes of slope in this range (see Fig. 39). This jump in value of the derivative thermodynamic variables will be referred to as an "apparent second order transition" and the temperature at which it occurs as the transition point.

A first order phase transition, such as crystallization or vaporization, is characterized by a discontinuity in the primary thermodynamic variables. A second order phase transition, such as certain order-disorder changes in alloys, is characterized by a sudden change in *slope* of the primary thermodynamic variables, *i.e.*, by a discontinuity in the first derivative variables. The *volume–temperature* curve of a liquid near its softening point exhibits a change in slope which has the appearance of a diffuse second order phase change. It will be shown, however, that this is not a true thermodynamic singularity, and hence should not be called a phase transition. The term "apparent second order transition" is therefore used by the author.

Many authors (*10*, *29*, *42*, *44*) have emphasized that, from a rheological standpoint, the only distinction between a glass and a viscous liquid lies in the *magnitude* of the viscosity. Other authors (*17*, *18*, *25*, *46*) have observed that the change in slope of the *volume–temperature* curve can best be explained on the basis of *rate of approach to equilibrium conditions*. The purpose of this section is to present a more explicit formulation of these accepted points of view, and to state precisely both the connection and the distinction between the "softening point" and the "transition point."

The Softening Point.—We have seen that when a low molecular weight amorphous material is subjected to a shear stress, the first result is an instantaneous elastic deformation which is governed by the shear modulus, G. In a glass at absolute zero this is the only response to stress, but at any finite temperature the material also begins to flow, at a rate which is governed by the viscosity, η. The total response to shear stress can be represented by means of a spring representing the elastic part of the response and a dashpot representing the viscous part. The shear strain, γ, is connected with the shear stress, S, by means of the differential equation:

$$\frac{d\gamma}{dt} = \frac{1}{G}\frac{dS}{dt} + \frac{1}{\eta}S \tag{83}$$

The importance of the relaxation time, τ, equal to η/G, has also been emphasized. The shear modulus, G, does not in general change markedly with temperature. The viscosity, however, is always extremely temperature dependent. In this section it will be assumed that the viscosity follows the relation $\eta = \mathrm{A}e^{\mathrm{B}/T}$, not only at high temperatures, but also through the brittle point into the glassy state. It will be shown in a later section that this is an oversimplification, since the viscosity of a glass is a function of time as well as of temperature, and in any case the exponential relationship holds only over a limited temperature range. However, the later expanded discussion of glass viscosity does not invalidate, but rather extends, the conclusions of this section. Thus the relaxation time τ varies with temperature roughly according to the relation $\tau = \mathrm{A}'e^{\mathrm{B}/T}$, where B is the activation energy for viscous flow divided by the gas constant, R.

The general character of the over-all response to shear stress depends entirely upon the relative magnitudes of the relaxation time of the material and the timescale, ⓣ, of the experimental investigation. If the relaxation time of the material is very long compared with the timescale of the experiment, the elastic response will predominate over the flow and the material will be classified as a glass. If τ is very short, relative to the experimental timescale, the flow will predominate, and the material will be classified as a liquid. The softening range is the temperature range in which τ is of the same order of magnitude as the experimental timescale, ⓣ. In this temperature range, both the elasticity and the flow are important in an experiment of timescale ⓣ, and hence complex time effects are observed in the shear strain, γ.

Consider, for example, an amorphous material which is suddenly given a shear deformarion γ, and then held at constant deformation for the time $\textcircled{t}$.

Here $\textcircled{t}$ is a convenient measure of the experimental timescale. According to equation (84), the stress will decay from the initial value S_0 to the value

$$S = S_0 e^{-\textcircled{t}/\tau} \tag{84}$$

If $\tau \gg \textcircled{t}$, then the stress remains essentially unchanged after the time $\textcircled{t}$, and the material would be considered to be elastic, *i.e.*, a glass. If $\tau \ll \textcircled{t}$, the stress disappears almost completely, and the material would be considered to lack rigidity completely. If $\tau = \textcircled{t}$, the stress relaxes to $1/e$ of its initial value, which means that neither the elastic nor the flow response thoroughly overshadows the other.

As a second example, consider a material which is suddenly subjected to the shear stress, S, which is allowed to act for the time $\textcircled{t}$, and then removed. The elastic part of the deformation is given by $(1/G)S$, and the total flow after $\textcircled{t}$ seconds by $(1/\eta)S\textcircled{t}$. The relative amount of flow as compared with elastic response is $G\textcircled{t}/\eta$ or $\textcircled{t}/\tau$. Thus if $\tau \gg \textcircled{t}$, the elastic response predominates, as in the preceding experiment. If $\tau \ll \textcircled{t}$, the flow predominates. And if $\tau = \textcircled{t}$, the two contributions are equal.

As a third example, consider the response of an amorphous material to a shear stress which varies sinusoidally with time. Here the *period* of the sinusoidal variation is a convenient measure of the experimental timescale. Let $\textcircled{t} = 1/2\pi\nu$, where ν is the frequency.

$$S = S_0 \cos t/\textcircled{t} \tag{85}$$

An ideal elastic material response to such a sinusoidal stress by a deformation which is exactly in phase with the stress:

$$\gamma = S_0/G \cos t/\textcircled{t} \tag{86}$$

An ideal, nonelastic viscous fluid responds to such a stress by a deformation whose *rate* is exactly in phase with the stress:

$$\frac{d\gamma}{dt} = \frac{S_0}{\eta} \cos t/\textcircled{t}$$

Therefore:

$$\gamma = [(\textcircled{t}S_0)/\eta] \sin t/\textcircled{t} \tag{87}$$

An amorphous material of modulus G and viscosity η follows the composite relation given by Equation (88).

$$\gamma = \frac{S_0}{G} \cos \frac{t}{\textcircled{t}} + \frac{\textcircled{t} S_0}{\eta} \sin \frac{t}{\textcircled{t}} \qquad (88)$$

The relative amplitudes of the two components determine the phase of the over-all response. Again the determining quantity is the ratio $\eta/G\textcircled{t}$. If $\eta/G \gg \textcircled{t}$, the first (elastic) term predominates. The over-all response will be in phase with the stress, and the material will be characterized as a glassy solid. If $\eta/G \ll \textcircled{t}$, the flow term will predominate, and the total deformation will be nearly $\pi/2$ out of phase with the stress. If $\eta/G = \textcircled{t}$, the over-all deformation will be exactly $\pi/4$ out of phase with the stress—or midway between the extremes of simple elastic and simple viscous behavior.

The "softening point" then, is in each case the *temperature at which the absolute value of the relaxation time passes through the experimental timescale of the mechanical test used to distinguish a glass from a liquid.* In other words, this is the temperature at which the viscosity passes through the value $G\textcircled{t}$. For an ordinary amorphous material with a shear modulus in the order of magnitude of 10^{11}, and using a mechanical test where timescale is from 1 to 10 seconds, the viscosity which characterizes the softening point will be in the order of magnitude of 10^{11} to 10^{12}. If a test is used which possesses a markedly different timescale, then the critical viscosity and hence the observed softening point will be shifted. If the shear modulus is independent of temperature and the viscosity follows the equation $\eta = \mathrm{A}e^{\mathrm{B}/T}$, then the dependence of the softening point, T_o, upon experimental timescale is given by:

$$T_o = \frac{\mathrm{B}}{\ln G - \ln \mathrm{A} + \ln \textcircled{t}} \qquad (89)$$

Thus in order to shift T_o appreciably, it is necessary to change $\ln \textcircled{t}$ by an amount which is comparable to $\ln G - \ln \mathrm{A}$. This means that $\textcircled{t}$ must be changed to a different order of magnitude, not merely given a slight change in value. A dependence of the softening point upon "rate of testing" has been reported by many investigators, but it is difficult to determine to what extent this dependence follows equation (89). The reported values of T_o for a given amorphous material are generally based on an experimental timescale in the order of magnitude of seconds. In very long tests, "glasses" show appreciable flow at much lower temperatures, and in very short tests (*e.g.*, high frequency sinusoidal stressing) "liquids" exhibit rigidity at much higher temperatures.

Volume Changes.—Liquid structure is characterized by local "crystal-like" order, but by absence of any far-reaching structure. The nearest neighbors of any molecule in a liquid are arranged about it in much the same manner as in the crystalline state, but molecules a few angstroms farther away are arranged practically at random. Such an imperfect packing requires geometrically that there be certain gaps or "holes" in the structure. The greater the disorder of the molecular arrangement, the greater the number of holes. When a normal liquid cools, it takes on a more ordered, and, therefore, a more compact structure. The equilibrium number of holes, and hence the free volume, decreases with decreasing temperature. However, this volume contraction cannot take place instantaneously. The attainment of the more compact structure depends upon molecular diffusion. Furthermore, no *local* rearrangement involving a limited number of molecules can affect the volume of the sample as a whole, but can only change the *positions* of the gaps or holes, and perhaps the manner in which the total free volume is distributed among the different "holes." This could be looked upon as a "diffusion of the holes," in which the identity of individual holes is not necessarily preserved, but only the total free volume. While diffusing, the holes can divide or, upon meeting, combine. If the change of structure is looked upon in this way, it is clear that, in order for the process to yield a volume change, holes must diffuse to the surface of the sample and disappear.

At high temperatures, the diffusion process is rapid enough so that volume expansions and contractions are able to attain equilibrium in a very short time. Hence the large coefficient of expansion of a liquid at high temperatures. At low temperatures, on the other hand, molecular diffusion is slow and holes cannot diffuse to the surface in a reasonable time. The liquid is thus unable to attain its equilibrium structure, but remains "frozen" in a less compact arrangement which is stable only at some higher temperature. Such a liquid can still expand and contract, of course, by the same mechanism that a crystal lattice follows—that is, change in amplitude of anharmonic thermal vibrations. This mechanism of contraction requires no diffusion of matter, and hence volume changes take place as rapidly as the temperature changes.

The volume changes in a glass can thus be divided into two parts: an instantaneous (crystal-like) expansion or contraction which accompanies a temperature change; and a slow drift toward the equilibrium volume, V_0, which takes place even at constant temperature. Assuming a constant instantaneous coefficient of expansion, α_1, and a first order diffusion approach to equilibrium volume, we find that the volume changes are governed by the following equation:

$$\frac{dV}{dt} = \alpha_1 \frac{dT}{dt} - \mathrm{k}[V - V_0(T)] \tag{90}$$

The rate constant k should depend upon temperature according to equation (91), where E_a is the activation energy for diffusion:

$$\mathrm{k} = \mathrm{A}e^{-E_a/RT} \tag{91}$$

At low temperatures, k is very small, and the material exhibits only the small coefficient of expansion, α_1. At high temperatures, k is large, and the material exhibits the larger expansion coefficient (dV_0/dT).* At intermediate temperatures complex time effects are observed.

The *large* expansion coefficient is characteristic of the material at temperatures which are high enough for the time of relaxation into equilibrium volume to be *very short* compared to the time scale of the density measurement. The *small* coefficient of expansion is characteristic at low temperatures where the time of relaxation is *very long* compared to the experimental time scale. The transition from one coefficient to the other occurs in the temperature range where the time of relaxation is of the same order of magnitude as the experimental timescale. The position of the transition temperature is then dependent upon the timescale of the experimental investigation (*i.e.*, rate of temperature change). However, in order to shift essentially the observed transition temperature, the timescale of the experimental investigation would have to be changed to a different *order of magnitude.* Since most experimental investigations have roughly the same timescale, the second order transition point usually appears as a fairly definite reproducible temperature—giving the appearance of a singularity. Near the transition temperature, the time lags in establishment of equilibrium volume are experimentally observable, and in this region rate studies as well as equilibrium studies of volume, energy, etc. are necessary.

By means of this interpretation of the second order transition point as the temperature where the rate of attainment of equilibrium structure fits the ordinary observational timescale, it is possible to explain many apparently anomalous observations in this temperature range. If a

* The "expansion coefficients" used here are the rates of change of specific volume with temperature. The usual definition of expansion coefficient is in terms of *relative* volume expansion $(1/V \cdot dV/dT)$, rather than (dV/dT) as used above. This unconventional definition is used at this point in order to simplify the form of equation 90 very slightly.

sample is cooled at a steady rate, its volume follows a curve such as figure 39, contracting with a large coefficient of expansion at high temperatures and a low coefficient at low temperatures, with the change in slope of the *V–T* curve taking place in a relatively narrow temperature range. The *V–T* curve followed on heating, however, is quite different and depends upon the past history of the sample (*6*).

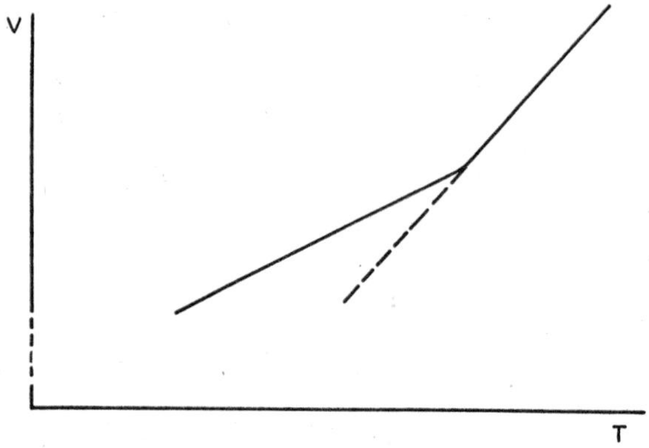

Fig. 39. Volume–temperature relationship in the range of the second order transition point.

It is trivial that the specific heat curve reflects any discontinuities in the expansion coefficient curve. Any structural change in a normal liquid which results in a less compact molecular arrangement requires the introduction of energy.

The point of view taken here coincides in most respects with the interpretation of Berger of the softening point of silicate glasses (*16*). There are the following differences, however. First, it is believed that the observation of a softening *range*, rather than of a sharp transition point, is not the result of a lack of experimental precision, as is sometimes assumed, but rather reflects the fundamental character of the transition. Second, the specific dependency of the *position* of the transition range upon the timescale of the experimental investigation is emphasized.

It is not surprising that the "transformation point," as determined by different methods, lies roughly in the same temperature range and near the softening point, since the timescales for specific heat, density, and mechanical investigations will be at least comparable and since the rate of attainment of equilibrium for all these properties depends upon similar molecular processes of diffusion. Exact definition of a unique sharp temperature is impossible even upon the basis of a single property. Thus, a rapid mechanical test corried out at different temperatures will give a higher "softening point" than a slow mechanical test, and a volume–temperature curve obtained by rapid cooling will give a higher "transition point" than by slow cooling.

Since most ordinary mechanical tests have a somewhat shorter time-scale than most thermal measurements, it might be expected that reported "softening points" are consistently higher than the transition points determined from specific heat or density measurements.

The Viscosity of Liquid and Glass, Detailed Theory.—It was stated that the viscosity of a liquid roughly follows equation (82). It should however be clear that such a simple temperature dependence cannot hold throughout the entire temperature range. It has been established by several authors (*4*, *14*) that the viscosity, which governs behavior in shear, depends markedly upon the "free volume." When the free volume of the sample changes with temperature in a complicated fashion, the *viscosity must necessarily mirror these complications.* At high temperatures, the viscosity, like the specific volume, is an explicit function of temperature. In the temperature ranges where the volume exhibits a slow drift toward V_0, the viscosity also drifts toward its corresponding "equilibrium" value. Lillie (*29*) studied the change of viscosity with time in the region of the transition temperature, and found that the time required to reach the constant viscosity characteristic of a given temperature increased as the temperature was lowered. Figure 40 shows viscosity–time curves for two samples of silicate glass at 486.7° C. The upper curve is that of a sample which had been previously held at 477.8° C. for 64 hours, a period sufficient for its volume and viscosity to approach closely to the equilibrium values for that temperature. The lower curve is that of a sample which had been quenched from a high temperature. At the beginning of the experiment one sample has a larger free volume and lower viscosity than the equilibrium values for 486.7° C. The other sample has too small a free volume and hence too great a viscosity. Both samples slowly drift toward the equilibrium values. At higher temperatures these drifts are more rapid; at lower temperatures they are slower. If a sample is cooled at constant rate, one should expect that the viscosity should roughly follow the Andrade equation at high temperatures, when the volume follows the equilibrium curve, and also at low temperatures, when no appreciable change in structure occurs. At low temperatures, however, the value of E_a should be lower than at high temperatures, since the "number of holes" is no longer changing with temperature. The log η *vs.* $1/T$ plot should show no discontinuity at the transition point, but only a change in slope. This deduced change in slope of the log η *vs.* $1/T$ plot is simply another indication of the "second order transition point," and depends upon the rate of cooling. It is *not* the softening point, which is the temperature at which the viscosity passes through the value $G(t)$, or, as we have seen,

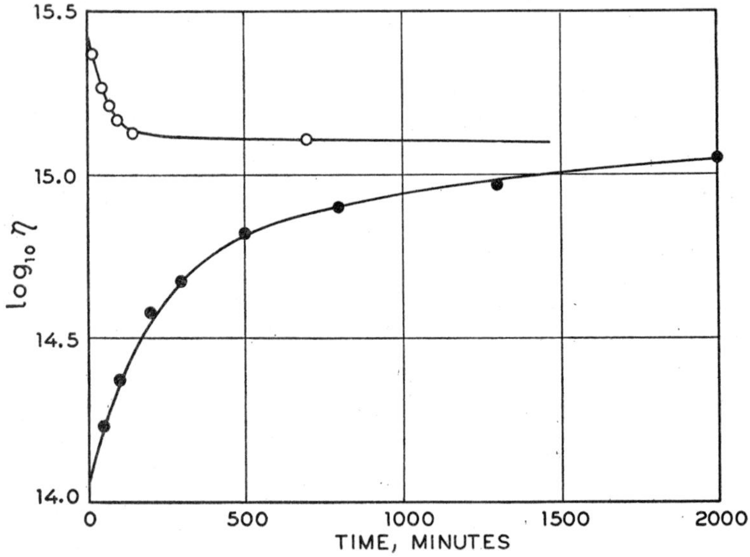

Fig. 40. Viscosity–time curves for silicate glass.

about 10^{12} poises in ordinary cases. If the timescale of the mechanical test is comparable to that of the cooling process, then the change in slope of the log η *vs.* $1/T$ curve will occur at about the same temperature as that for which the absolute value of τ equals $G(t)$, but if this is not the case, the observed softening point may be far from the "transition point." This is indicated schematically in figure 41. If the amorphous material is cooled at a slow steady rate, *e.g.* 1° C. per day, its viscosity will change according to curve a. The break in slope should occur at the same temperature as the transition point in the volume–temperature curve at the same rate of cooling. If, during the slow cooling, mechanical tests are made which have a timescale of about one second, these tests will indicate that the material is essentially fluid at high temperatures. If the shear modulus is about 10^{11}, then the transition from liquid to glass will be observed when the viscosity increases to 10^{11} poises. The mechanical softening point, observed in this way, will appear at the temperature T_1, of figure 41. On the other hand, if a mechanical test with a timescale of about one thousand seconds is used during the slow cooling, the material will appear to be solid only when the viscosity has increased to about 10^{14} poises. This corresponds to a lower temperature, T_2. Furthermore, if the sample is cooled at the rate of one

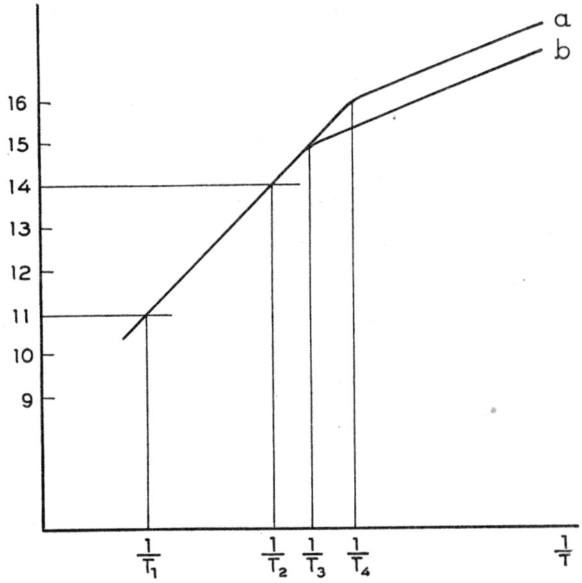

Fig. 41. Change of viscosity with time for glass near its second order transition point.

degree per minute instead of one degree per day, the viscosity should follow curve b instead of curve a. The apparent second order transition now occurs at T_3 instead of T_4. A mechanical test with timescale in the order of magnitude of 1 second will again detect a softening point at temperature T_1.

The process of viscous flow, and hence the viscosity, depends upon the rotational Brownian movement of temporary pairs of molecules (see pages 71–72) whereas the *process of attaining the equilibrium volume and equilibrium viscosity value* depends upon the ordinary Brownian movement of single molecules. It should not be surprising, therefore, if different amorphous substances should show considerable variation in the relative rates of: (*1*) attainment of equilibrium viscosity, and (*2*) viscous flow at unit stress when the equilibrium viscosity has been reached.

It is to be expected that the viscoelastic behavior of an amorphous material may be very complicated in the neighborhood of the transition point and the brittle point. Weyl (*48*), among others, has pointed out that, because of the slow structural change in an incompletely annealed glass, the relaxation of stress at constant temperature should not be expected to be exactly exponential with time. The Maxwell theory of stress relaxation assumes a constant viscosity. As we have seen, the behavior in shear depends upon the extent to which volume equilibrium has been attained, whereas Maxwell's treatment of relaxation of shear stresses applies strictly only to a material whose volume (and hence viscosity) is not changing. If a sample of a well annealed glass, whose density and viscosity are not drifting, is subjected to externally imposed mechanical stresses, the above requirement may be fulfilled. On the other hand, if internal shear stresses are created by rapid and uneven cooling of a hot sample, it is to be expected that this treatment also results in a nonconstant volume and viscosity. The behavior in shear is still governed by the differential equation (69c), but η is not a constant, but rather a function of time, which may in turn be controlled by a differential equation relating volume to time.

In all of this discussion, it was assumed that temperature changes were made so slowly that the entire sample is at the same temperature. If a sample is cooled extremely rapidly, an additional effect occurs. The outer surface is cooled and made hard while the inner mass is still hot. When the inner portion finally cools, it is prevented from contracting by the hardened outer shell. The final sample contains stresses; the outer shell is under compression and the inner part is under tension. Such residual stresses can be removed by viscous flow. This, however, is not a fundamental property of the amorphous material, but rather a complicated effect involving the geometry of the sample, the thermal conductivity, etc.

Force Fields and Stress Fields.—A liquid or a glass, as we have seen, consists of molecules arranged in a pattern of intermediate order, with numerous "holes" interrupting the crystal-like local packings. A given configuration of the sample is rigid for a short period of time, but molecules next to holes can jump into these holes and thus change the configuration of the sample. A single molecular jump of this type can be considered to take place in a rigid matrix of the amorphous material, *i.e.*, the structural change caused by the jump is a *local* change. The molecule moves relative to the other molecules of the surrounding liquid or glass. In the presence of a stress, certain individual jumping processes are favored over the reverse processes, so that the sample continuously deforms. This net transfer of material arises from the distortion of the force fields for molecules adjacent to holes. All this has already been discussed, but the effect of a stress on the molecular force fields was merely schematized, rather than specifically evaluated. The purpose of this section is to present a specific statement of the type of distortion which each kind of stress creates in the molecular force fields.

In the first place, consider the case where there is an external *force* field which acts preferentially on certain molecules tending to pull them in a certain direction relative to the surrounding matrix. For example, if a mixture of two types of molecules, A and B, of markedly different

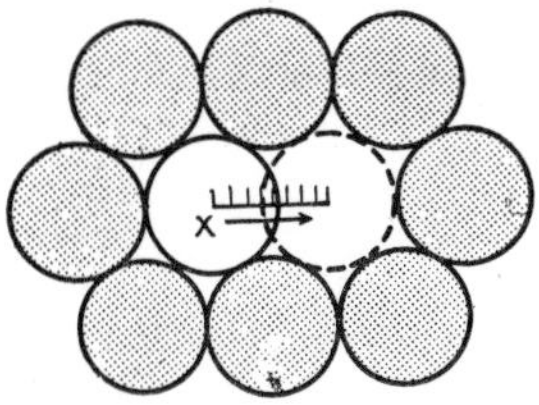

Fig. 42. B molecule moving from its position in a hole along the x axis.

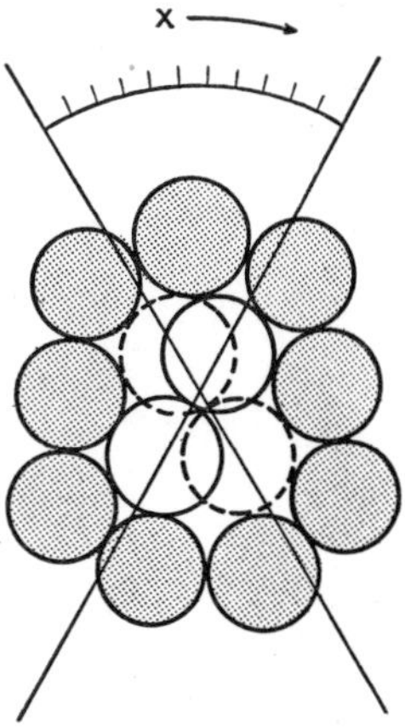

Fig. 43. In a stress field, two B molecules moving in opposite directions.

molecular weight but similar molecular volume, is placed in a gravitational or centrifugal field, there will be a tendency for the heavier, or B molecules, to move in the direction of the field ($+x$), relative to the A molecules. If the A molecules are present in great excess, the motion of the B molecules can be analyzed as follows:

Consider a B molecule situated next to a hole, the line between the center of the molecule and the center of the hole making the angle θ with the $+x$ direction defined by the force field. Let this line be graduated, and taken as a "deformation coordinate," X, for the molecule, so that the process of jumping into the hole can be represented by an increase in the value of X (*cf.* Fig. 42). The potential energy of the molecule as a function of X (in absence of the external field), is of the form shown in 44[a]. In presence of the external force field, the molecular field will be distorted to the form shown in 44[b]. The amount of the distortion $(\epsilon_2 - \epsilon_1)$ will depend upon the orientation of the hole with respect to the field, *i.e.*, upon the angle θ. It seems reasonable that $(\epsilon_2 - \epsilon_1)$ will be proportional to cos θ. Hence in all cases the field will favor a "forward" jump, which moves the molecule in the $+x$ direction, and will oppose a "backward" jump. The over-all effect of the field on the molecular diffusion of the B molecules will be a *net transport* of the B material in the direction of the field. This will continue until a concentration gradient is built up which just balances the extra tendency per molecule for "forward" motion.

It should be emphasized, however, that a *stress* in a homogeneous material does not cause any such unilateral deformation in the force field of an individual molecule. A volume element in a sample subjected

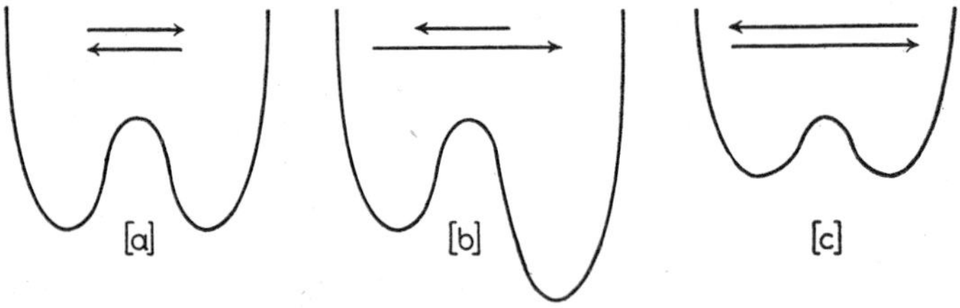

Fig. 44. Potential energy curves: [a] unbiased; [b] unsymmetrically biased; [c] symmetrically biased.

to tensile stress is *not* acted upon by a force tending to pull it in a particular direction. Rather, it is acted upon by a *balanced pair* of opposite forces (*cf.* Fig. 43). *A stress field is geometrically much different from a unilateral force field.* If we consider the stress to be homogeneous down to molecular dimensions, then it is apparent that a stress will cause a different type of bias to the potential energy curve of figure 44[a] than will be caused by a unilateral force field.

A tensile stress, for example, will cause a bias of the type shown in figure 44[c]. The magnitude of this bias will depend upon the angle θ between the direction of the tensile stress and the line of centers of the molecule and hole. The result will be that molecular diffusion will be somewhat more rapid in the direction of the tensile stress than in the cross direction—but it will still be equally rapid in the $+x$ and the $-x$ directions. Since the forward and back diffusion is still balanced along all lines, there will be no *net* transport of material by this mechanism.

Similarly, a *shear* stress s_{xy} will cause a bias of the same type, also depending in magnitude upon the orientation of the line of centers of the hole and the molecule.

Thus no stress, tensile or shear, will cause a unilateral deformation of the molecular field of a molecule which is next to a hole. Consequently, *flow* must take place by some mechanism other than the biased jumping of individual molecules into holes.

In a liquid, however, there will also be found certain places where two neighboring molecules are simultaneously next to holes, so that they can rotate together to a new orientation. This is also true of clusters of three, four, or more molecules. It has been indicated schematically for the case of *two* molecules in figure 38. Let us now consider the angular orientation of the cluster as a "deformation coordinate," X, for the cluster. The potential energy of the cluster as a function of X, in the unstressed sample, can be represented by the curve of figure 44[a]. In the presence of a shear stress, this potential energy field will be distorted to the form in figure 44[b]. The magnitude of the distortion will depend upon the relative orientations of the particular cluster before and after the rotational jump. The stress is best satisfied when the molecular pair is oriented along the diagonal of the square upon whose edges the shear stress gives rise to tangential forces. Hence the rotational Brownian movement of clusters will always be biased by the shear stress in such a direction as to give rise to a shear strain. If the molecular clusters involved in such a jump were permanently joined together, the macroscopic strain arising from this mechanism would be insignificant. However, after a molecule has made a jump as part of a cluster, it can "change partners" and act as part of a completely new cluster. This process of repeated biased rotational motion of temporary pairs or clusters of molecules adds up to give a viscous flow.

A uniform compressive stress distorts all molecular fields in such a way as to change the *rate* of diffusion, but to impart no directional preference. This applies both to the translational jumps of single molecules and to the rotational jumps of clusters. Thus a uniform compressive stress will not cause flow. There will, of course, be an instantaneous elastic compression and a subsequent reduction in the equilibrium number of holes which may be observed as a *retarded* elastic compression. These two effects, however, are relatively small, and can often be neglected alongside the viscous flow effects which result from a shear stress.

A single tensile stress may be regarded as a set of shears plus an isotropic negative pressure. The significant distortion of the molecular force fields by a tensile stress is caused by the shear components of the stress rather than by the isotropic dilatational components. It is often possible to neglect volumetric deformations completely and consider only shear deformations. This will be done many times throughout this book. Both flow and rubberlike elasticity are responses to *shear stress* alone. When no shear stresses are present, these responses are not observed. We shall therefore consider behavior in shear as fundamental, remembering that the behavior in tension for an isotropic material can be calculated therefrom.

BIBLIOGRAPHY

BOOKS

(*1*) Bingham, E. C., *Fluidity and Plasticity*. McGraw-Hill, New York, 1922.

(*2*) *First Report on Viscosity and Plasticity*. Royal Netherlands Academy of Sciences, Noord-Hollandsche, Amsterdam, 1935; 2nd ed., 1939.
Second Report on Viscosity and Plasticity. Royal Netherlands Academy of Sciences, Noord-Hollandsche, Amsterdam; Interscience, New York, 1938.

(*3*) Freundlich, H., *Thixotropy*. Hermann, Paris, 1935.

(*4*) Glasstone, S., Laidler, K. J., and Eyring, H., *The Theory of Rate Processes*. McGraw-Hill, New York, 1941, Chap. IX.

(*4a*) *Handbook of Chemistry and Physics*. Chemical Rubber Pub. Co., Cleveland, 1944.

(*5*) Houwink, R., *Elasticity, Plasticity, and the Structure of Matter*. Cambridge Univ. Press, London, 1937.

(*5a*) Lamb, H., *Hydrodynamics*. 6th ed., Cambridge Univ. Press, London, 1932.

(*6*) Morey, G. W., *Properties of Glass*. Reinhold, New York, 1938.

(*7*) Nadai, A., *Plasticity*. McGraw-Hill, New York, 1931.

(*8*) Prager, W., *Theory of Plasticity*. Lecture notes, Brown Univ., Providence, 1941–1942.

(*9*) Seitz, F., *Modern Theory of Solids*. McGraw-Hill, New York, 1940.

(*10*) Tammann, G., *Der Glaszustand*. Voss, Leipzig, 1933.

(*11*) Timoshenko, S., *Theory of Elasticity*. McGraw-Hill, New York, 1934.

ARTICLES

(*12*) Bardeen, J., "Theory of the Work Function. II. The Surface Double Layer," *Phys. Rev.*, **49**, 653–663 (1936).

(*13*) Barrer, R. M., "The Zone of Activation in Rate Processes," *Trans. Faraday Soc.*, **39**, 237–241 (1943).

(*14*) Batschinski, A. J., "Untersuchungen über die innere Reibung der Flüssigkeiten I," *Z. physik. Chem.*, **84**, 643–706 (1913); "Das Gesetz der Viskosität der Flüssigkeiten," *Physik. Z.*, 1157 (1912).

(*15*) Bennewitz, K., and Rötger, H., "Über den plastisch-elastischen Zustand," *Physik. Z.*, **40**, 416–428 (1939).

(*16*) Berger, E., "Beiträge zur Theorie der Glasbildung und des Glaszustandes," *Kolloid-Beihefte*, **36**, 1–42 (1932); "—Physik des Glases," *Z. tech. Physik.*, **15**, 443–450 (1934).

(*17*) Born, M., *Proc. Cambridge Phil. Soc.*, **39**, 100 (1943).

(*18*) Boyer, R. F., and Spencer, R. S., "Thermal Expansion and Second-Order Transition Effects in High Polymers," *J. Applied Phys.*, **15**, 398–406 (1944).

(*19*) Bridgman, P. W., "The Effect of Pressure on the Viscosity of Forty-three Pure Liquids," *Proc. Am. Acad. Arts Sci.*, **61**, 57–99 (1925); "The Viscosity of Mercury under Pressure," *ibid.*, **62**, 187–206 (1927); "Rough Compressibilities of Fourteen Substances to 45,000 kg/cm^2," *ibid.*, **72**, 207–225 (1938).

(*20*) Buckingham, E., "On Plastic Flow Through Capillary Tubes," *Proc. Am. Soc. Testing Materials*, **21 II**, 1154–1156 (1921).

(*21*) Fürth, R., "On the Theory of Finite Deformations of Elastic Crystals," *Proc. Roy. Soc. London*, **A180**, 285–304 (1942).

(*22*) Green, H., and Weltmann, R. N., "Rheological Properties of Colloidal Solutions, Pigment Suspensions, and Oil Mixtures," *J. Applied Phys.*, **14**, 569–576 (1943); "Analysis of Thixotropy of Pigment-Vehicle Suspensions," *Ind. Eng. Chem., Anal. Ed.*, **15**, 201–206 (1943).

(*23*) Herschel, W., and Bulkley, R., "Konsistenzmessungen von Gummi-Benzollösungen," *Kolloid-Z.*, **39**, 291–300 (1926).

(*24*) Hersey, M. D., "Future Problems of Theoretical Rheology," *J. Rheol.*, **3**, 196–204 (1932).

(*25*) Jenckel, E., and Überreiter, K., "Über Polystyrolgläser verschiedener Kettenlänge," *Z. physik. Chem.*, **A182**, 361–383 (1938).

(*26*) Kennedy, C., "Measuring the Coulomb and Viscous Components of Friction," *Instruments*, **15**, 404–410 (1942).

(*27*) Kirkwood, J. G., "The Structure of Liquids," in Baitsell, G. A., ed., *Science in Progress*, Yale Univ. Press, New Haven, 1942, pp. 208–221.

(*28*) Lark-Horovitz, K., and Miller, E. P., "Structure of Liquid Argon," *Nature*, **146**, 459–460 (1940).

(*29*) Lillie, H. R., "Viscosity–Time–Temperature Relations in Glass at Annealing Temperatures," *J. Am. Ceram. Soc.*, **16**, 619–631 (1933).

(*30*) McMillen, E. L., "Relation between Thixotropy and Leveling Characteristics of Paint," *Ind. Eng. Chem.*, **23**, 676–679 (1931).

(*31*) McMillen, E. L., "Thixotropy and Plasticity. III—The Effect of Thixotropy upon Plasticity Measurements," *J. Rheol.*, **3**, 179–195 (1932).

(*32*) Mark, H., "Intermolecular Forces and Mechanical Behavior of High Polymers," *Ind. Eng. Chem.*, **34**, 1343–1348 (1942).

(*33*) Maxwell, J. C., "On the Dynamical Theory of Gases," *Phil. Trans. Roy. Soc. London*, **157**, 49–88 (1867); *Phil. Mag.*, Ser. 4, **35**, 129–145, 185–217 (1868). (From the *Phil. Trans.* for 1867, Part I, having been read May, 1866.)

(*34*) Mooney, M., "A Theory of Large Elastic Deformation," *J. Applied Phys.*, **11**, 582–592 (1940).

(*35*) Murnaghan, F. D., "Finite Deformations of an Elastic Solid," *Am. J. Math.*, **59**, 235–260 (1937).

(*36*) Powell, R. E., Roseveare, W. E., and Eyring, H., "Diffusion, Thermal Conductivity, and Viscous Flow of Liquids," *Ind. Eng. Chem.*, **33**, 430–435 (1941).

(*37*) Pryce-Jones, J., "Thixotropy," *J. Oil Colour Chem. Assoc.*, **17**, 305–375 (1934).

(*38*) Rabinowitsch, B., "Über die Viskosität und Elastizität von Solen," *Z. physik. Chem.*, **A145**, 1–26 (1929).

(*39*) Raman, C. V., and Venkateswaran, C. S., "Rigidity of Liquids," *Nature*, **143**, 798–799 (1939).

(*40*) Reiner, M., "The General Law of Flow of Matter," *J. Rheol.*, **1**, 11–20 (1929); "The Theory of Non-Newtonian Liquids," *Physics*, **5**, 321–341 (1934).

(*41*) Simha, R., "On Relaxation Effects in Amorphous Media," *J. Applied Phys.*, **13**, 201–208 (1942).

(*42*) Simha, R., "On Anomalies of Elasticity and Flow and Their Interpretation," *J. Phys. Chem.*, **47**, 348–363 (1943).

(*43*) Szegvari, A., "Zur Theorie der Elastizität kolloider Lösungen," *Z. physik. Chem.*, **108**, 175–184 (1924).

(*44*) Taylor, N. W., "Elastic Aftereffects and Dielectric Absorption in Glass," *J. Applied Phys.*, **12**, 753–758 (1941).

(*45*) Taylor, N. W., and Doran, R. F., "Elastic and Viscous Properties of Several Potash–Silica Glasses in the Annealing Range of Temperature," *J. Am. Ceram. Soc.*, **24**, 103 (1941).

(*46*) Überreiter, K., "Über das Einfrieren normaler Flüssigkeiten und Flüssigkeiten mit 'fixierter' Struktur wie Kautschuk und Kunstharze," *Z. physik. Chem.*, **B45**, 361–373 (1940); "Die Ableitung des Begriffes 'Flüssigkeit mit fixierter Struktur' aus einer Betrachtung über die Zergliederung der thermodynamischen Zustandsfunktion bei normalen und hochpolymeren Flüssigkeiten," *ibid.*, **B46**, 157–164 (1940).

(*47*) Weissenberg, K., and Herzog, R. O., "Über die thermische, mechanische und röntgenoptische Analyse der Quellung," *Kolloid-Z.*, **46**, 277–289 (1928).

(*48*) Weyl, W., "Ueber die Konstitution des Glases. I. Deutung der Glasanomalien auf Grund von Dissoziations- und Solvatationsvorgängen," *Glastech. Ber.*, **10**, 541–556 (1932).

(*49*) Wiechert, E., "Gesetzte der elastischen Nachwirkung für constante Temperatur," *Ann. Physik. Chem.*, **50**, 546–570 (1893).

(*50*) Zachariasen, W. H., "The Atomic Arrangement in Glass," *J. Am. Chem. Soc.*, **54**, 3841–3851 (1932).

B. THE PLASTOELASTIC BEHAVIOR OF AMORPHOUS LINEAR HIGH POLYMERS

I. INTRODUCTION

The problem of structure, diffusion, and stress-biased diffusion of amorphous high polymers is fundamentally the same as that for simple liquids. The long chain structure of polymer molecules, however, introduces certain significant new effects. These can be briefly summarized as follows:

(1) Because of the possibility of rotation about single valence bonds, linear polymer molecules are more or less flexible. A wide range of shapes or configurations are possible.

(2) In an amorphous polymer, most molecules are in partially curled configurations, neither tightly curled up nor rigidly extended to maximum length. This is because of the statistical predominance of such intermediate configurations, rather than an energetic preference.

(3) The elementary process in the diffusion of an amorphous polymer is the motion of *chain segments*. In a liquid of low molecular weight, a whole molecule "jumps" to a new equilibrium position; in an amorphous polymer, a segment jumps.

(4) The result of many such elementary processes is twofold: the polymer molecule as a whole wanders about (macro-Brownian movement), and the molecule changes its shape (micro-Brownian movement).

(5) In the presence of a shear stress, the elementary process of diffusion is *biased*, just as in the case of liquids of low molecular weight. Both the micro-Brownian and the macro-Brownian movements are thereby affected.

(6) The stress-biased macro-Brownian movement is a true *flow*.

(7) The stress-biased micro-Brownian movement appears as a *retarded elastic* response (configurational elasticity).

(8) The total response to stress of an amorphous polymer is composed of (a) instantaneous elasticity, (b) retarded (configurational) elasticity, and (c) flow.

(9) A first approximation to the configurational elastic response considers it as an exponential relaxation into the equilibrium deformation. This can be described by a *modulus* and a *retardation time*, and represented by the mechanical analog of a spring and dashpot in parallel.

(10) Although this model indicates the general nature of the plastoelastic behavior of amorphous polymers, further approximations are necessary to explain the behavior in detail. One such refinement is the use of a *distribution of moduli and retardation times*, in place of the single modulus and single retardation time, to describe the configurational elasticity.

(11) Other refinements are also necessary.

II. STRUCTURE AND DIFFUSION OF LINEAR AMORPHOUS POLYMERS

1. Configurations

In a material like benzene, the *shape* of the individual molecule can be considered as fixed, as far as the arrangement or packing of different molecules is concerned. Such a molecule does undergo internal shape changes, but these are small in magnitude and of high frequency so that as far as interaction with other molecules is concerned, they can be neglected. This is not true of high polymers. Because of the flexibility of linear polymers, wide differences in molecular form are possible. The packing together of different molecules is intimately tied up with their individual shapes. Since the flexibility of linear polymer molecules is largely due to the possibility of rotation around single bonds, a few words must be spent on this subject.

Classical organic chemists early recognized an important distinction between the double C═C bond and the single C—C bond, namely, the "free rotation" about the latter. The angular rigidity of the double bond makes possible the phenomenon of *cis-trans* isomerism in substituted ethylenes. Since no analogous isomerism was observed among the substituted ethanes, it was concluded that the methyl groups in ethane were free to turn through 360°.

Modern investigations have revealed that the two halves of the ethane molecule are not *completely* free to spin relative to one another about their joining axis. There seems to be little or no torsional rigidity in the bond itself, *i.e.*, the bonding electrons offer little or no resistance to torsion. The hydrogen atoms of the two methyl groups, however, exert forces on each other. These forces will be most completely satisfied in three equivalent positions—the three "staggered" arrangements of the methyl groups. Potential energy barriers separate these three equilibrium arrangements, as shown in figure 45. At extremely low temperatures, a molecule caught in one of the potential energy minima would remain there a very long time, undergoing torsional vibrations about the equilibrium position. At very high temperatures, the methyl groups would spin freely about their joining axis. At room temperature, neither extreme is observed; the methyl groups of ethane probably make many torsional oscillations within the same energy minimum before jumping over a barrier to the next equilibrium position. Even so, many such rotational changes are made per second. That is, the molecule is trapped within the same energy minimum for a length of time which is long compared to the period of one torsional oscillation, but short compared to a second.

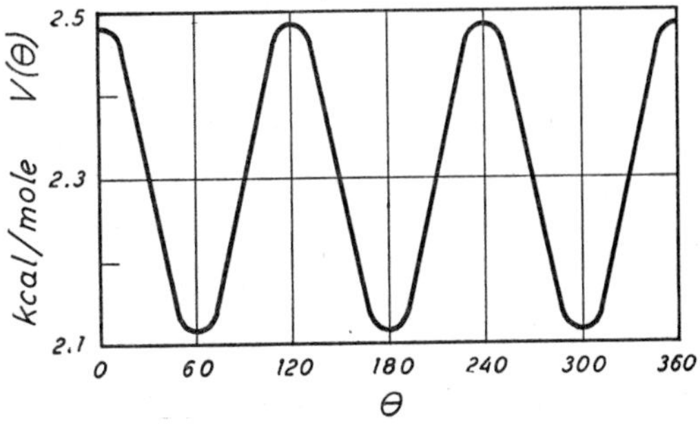

Fig. 45. Energy potential for rotation around single bond.

If one considers an ethane derivative—say, 1,2-dichloroethane—a similar situation is found. The potential energy for such a molecule is no longer triply symmetrical, however, since the close approach of the two large, electronegative chlorine atoms would represent a particularly high energy. Indeed, there may be only one true minimum in the potential energy curve for such a bond, if the interaction of the two substituents is strong enough. The reader is referred to Mark (7), for a more complete discussion of this point.

It is obvious that the possibility of rotation about single valence bonds gives flexibility to a hydrocarbon chain of more than three atoms. Any three successive atoms of a chain form a rigid triangle (subject of course to vibrational deformation). The two extremes of a set of *four* successive chain atoms are nonrigidly connected. The fourth atom is not completely independent of the first by any means, but it does have a certain amount of freedom. The fifth atom is still more independent of the first, since *two* intervening bonds contribute simultaneous torsional freedom (see Fig. 46).

If the rotation about the C—C bond were completely free, then a long hydrocarbon chain would be thoroughly limp—*flexible* in every sense of the word. There would be a continuous range of molecular shapes with the same potential energy. As it is, the potential barrier restricting rotation at each individual bond results in there being a very large, but *discrete*, number of stable molecular configurations. These various stable configurations are *isomers* in precisely the same sense that *cis-trans* isomers of ethylenic compounds are. The only difference is that there is a high potential barrier in an ethylenic compound between the two stable configurations that we call the *cis* and the *trans* isomer, giving each form a definite chemical identity, whereas only small energy barriers separate the various stable configurations of a long chain saturated hydrocarbon. At very low temperatures, such chains are effectively caught in one configuration, but at high temperatures they will move about rapidly from one shape to another. Just how rapid this motion is depends, of course, on the height of the potential energy barriers restricting rotation.

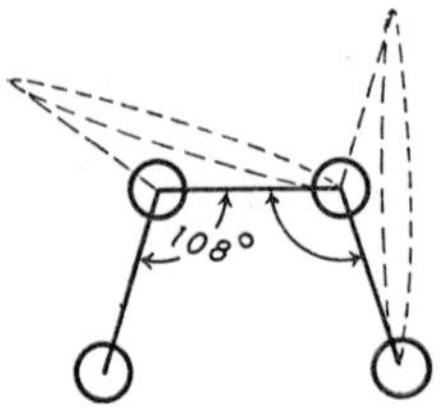

Fig. 46. Chain flexibility arising from rotation about successive single bonds.

If a double or triple bond appears in a hydrocarbon chain, it represents a rigid section, since the potential barriers restricting rotation are very high. On the other hand, the *single bonds adjacent to a multiple bond* are particularly "flexible." Thus the potential barrier restricting relative rotation of the two methyl groups of dimethylacetylene is only a fraction of that encountered in ethane (7). This is presumably a geometrical effect. In dimethylacetylene the two methyl groups are far apart and can interact only slightly. The rubber molecule (isoprene structure) is an example of a "flexible" compound having double bonds within a linear chain.

In the preceding paragraphs, the potential energy of a molecular configuration was considered as a function only of the torsional positions of the chain at the various single bonds (and, of course, any bond angle distortions or bond length variations). Such "internal" forces would alone determine the potential energy of a configuration only if the long chain molecule were surrounded by a *continuous, energetically neutral medium*, which would screen off any forces between different molecular segments. Even in such a hypothetical medium, certain molecular shapes would be prohibited because they would involve interpenetration of two different parts of the polymer molecule. In any *real* environment, each segment of a long chain molecule will be acted upon by "external" forces—originating either from other molecules or from other segments of the same molecule. These forces, which will vary in nature from one environment to another, will affect the energy of a configuration as well as will the intrinsic "internal" forces due to C—C distances, bond angles, and torsional orientation about bonds.

An isolated long chain molecule in a vacuum, for example, will tend to curl up tightly into a compact ball. The van der Waals' forces between different segments are best satisfied by such a configuration. Highly *elongated* configurations will have very large potential energies. This could be considered as a surface tension effect—that is, even a single flexible molecule tends to expose the smallest possible surface.

A polymer molecule in a low molecular weight solvent of similar chemical character, should not be particularly affected by such strong intersegmental attractions. The van der Waals' forces of a given segment should be satisfied by a solvent molecule as a neighbor as well as by another polymer segment as a neighbor. The exposed surface of the polymer molecule no longer tends to a minimum when it is surrounded by a chemically similar solvent. However, even in such an environment external forces affect the energy of a configuration. Some configurations will allow solvent molecules to be packed easily around the polymer; other configurations will necessitate too many gaps and holes. The former configurations, whose geometry facilitates the packing around of solvent molecules, will have low energies,* and will be favored over the configurations which hinder efficient packing of solvent.

If the solvent is not chemically similar to the polymer, the energy may be lowered by polymer–polymer contacts—just as in the case of the isolated polymer molecule, but to a smaller extent. Huggins (*39*) has pointed out that in a poor solvent a flexible polymer molecule should be more compact (making more contacts with itself) than in a good solvent. See Chapter E.

Finally we come to the most important case for our purposes—the "solid" polymer, in which each long chain molecule is surrounded not by small solvent molecules but by the segments of other polymer chains. Here again there is no particular tendency for the individual polymer molecules to expose minimum surface areas. The van der Waals' forces of a segment can be satisfied either by contact with another segment of the same molecule or with a segment of a different molecule. Again the *ease of packing of surrounding molecules* must be considered as well as

* More correctly, *free* energies. The geometry of a polymer configuration will affect both the energy and the entropy of the surrounding solvent. The proper exponential weighting factor for a given configuration in these circumstances is the "internal" potential energy plus the mean free energy of the solvent for the configuration.

the internal strains in the individual molecular chains. If one considers the whole sample, rather than a single polymer molecule, then a "configuration" of the system means a method of packing together of the whole sample, and means perforce a definite shape for each individual molecule. In this wider sense, it is the potential energy which determines the frequency of occurrence of a "configuration."

Different configurations of the sample have different potential energies, both because of "internal" forces and because of packing difficulties. In the low energy configurations, sections of the polymer molecule may be completely straightened out (as in many crystalline polymers), or folded into some definite internal arrangement (as seems to be true especially of proteins).

At low temperatures, the polymer sample will gravitate to the low energy configurations which, because of their necessary regularity, are relatively small in number. At high temperatures, the thermal agitation overcomes the forces which favor particular configurations and the random configurations predominate because of their great number.

This chapter is concerned with the elastic and flow properties of *amorphous* high polymers. Just how random the structure of a polymer must be, in order to justify the use of the term "amorphous," is a matter of definition. The ideal, "completely amorphous" polymer would be completely devoid of specific forces favoring certain ordered configurations. Actual polymers will approach more or less closely to this ideal depending on the temperature and the magnitude of the orienting forces present. Any polymer which exhibits either long range intermolecular order (crystallization) or a decided amount of specific intramolecular curling (Mack elasticity) should not be expected to exhibit the mechanical characteristics discussed in this chapter. Uncrystallized rubber, and polystyrene, are two typical polymers which we can safely call amorphous under "ordinary" conditions. Any linear high polymer will fit into this category at sufficiently high temperatures. To repeat, an amorphous high polymer is one in which random molecular configurations predominate—*specific* forces play only a minor role. As in the case of ordinary liquids and glasses, some local or short range order is always to be expected in the intermolecular packing.

2. Equilibrium Distribution among Configurations (*31*, *88*)

To specify adequately a configuration of a chain molecule would require $(n + 2)$ numbers, where n is the number of bonds which permit rotation. This would define not only the general shape of the molecule, but also its *orientation* in space. (It would *not* define the shape changes arising from actual deformation of bond angles and distances. A *complete* shape and orientation specification would require $(3N - 3)$ numbers, where N is the total number of *atoms* in the molecule). If we are to write down a specific shape distribution function, we must choose a much less detailed specification of a configuration—in which a single quantity gives some idea of the general molecular shape. The separation of the two chain ends is commonly used as such a gross shape factor. (More generally, any two reference atoms of the chain could be used.)

The distance l_0 between two adjacent carbon atoms is 1.54 Å. The angle α between two such carbon bonds is about 109°. If the chain is stretched to its maximum length the distance r_{max} between the first and last carbon atom is $r_{max} = (n - 1)l_0 \sin(\alpha/2)$. This maximum length of the chain can only be realized in one single fashion, namely, if all linkages lie in one plane.

On the other hand, if the maximum possible distance between the first and the last carbon atom is not considered, but rather a shorter distance r, this may be realized in many different ways. Owing to the flexibility of the chain there are many ways to arrange its different chain links so that the distance r between the two ends is always maintained.

For every given r a definite number of configurations exists which can be called the statistical weight for the given distance between the ends of the chains. In order to calculate these weights as a function of r one has to make certain assumptions concerning the constitution of the chain and the mobility of its parts. If l_0 is the length of one chain link, n their number, α the angle between two subsequent links and absolutely free rotation is assumed, then, as shown first by Guth and Mark (*31a*), the probability W that the distance between the two chain ends corresponds to r is represented by:

$$W(n, l_0, \alpha, r)r^2\,dr = 3\sqrt{\frac{6}{\pi}}\frac{1}{l_\alpha^2 n^{\frac{3}{2}}}\exp\left(-\frac{3\,r^2}{2\,nl_\alpha^2}\right)r^2\,dr \qquad (1)$$

where

$$l_\alpha^2 = l_0^2\,\frac{1 + \cos\alpha}{1 - \cos\alpha}$$

The equation (see also Fig. 47) shows that there exists a most probable distance between the chain ends, namely the r by which the function W reaches its maximum value. This r is given by

$$\lambda = l_0\,\sqrt{\tfrac{2}{3}\,n} \qquad (2)$$

and is proportional to the square root of the chain links, as one would expect on the basis of the statistical character of the whole calculation.

We have defined an amorphous polymer as one in which all molecular configurations can be considered as having the same energy. If energy differences among different configurations are neglected, it is simply the statistical weight which determines the frequency of occurrence of a given chain end separation in the equilibrium state of an unstressed polymer. The distribution function D(r) corresponding to the equilibrium unstressed condition will be identical with the probability function W(r).

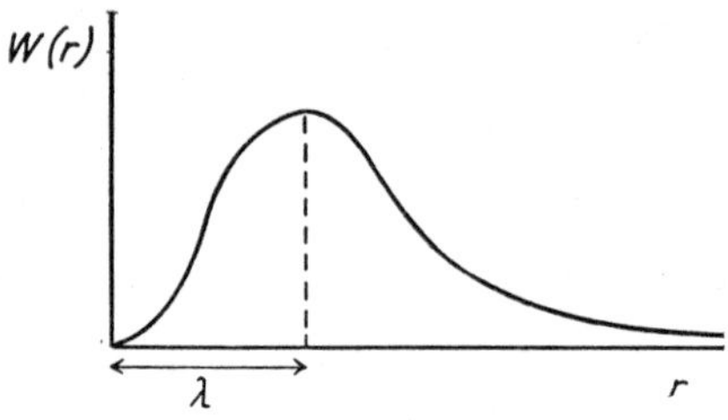

Fig. 47. Statistical distribution of chain-end separations for randomly kinked molecules.

Thus at any instant in a sample of amorphous polymer there will be a few molecules whose ends are very close together ($r \rightarrow 0$), and a few molecules which are almost completely straightened out ($r \rightarrow r_{max}$). Most of the molecules, however, will be curled and kinked so that the distance between the two ends is in the neighborhood of λ.

The *orientation* of the molecule in space is completely random. That is, the vector connecting the two ends of the various polymer molecules points in no preferred direction.

We may describe a molecular configuration by the x, y, and z displacement of the second chain end relative to the first, rather than simply by the total distance between the two ends. It follows from equation (1) and the randomness of orientation that the distribution function of the *vectorial* displacement of chain ends is spherically symmetrical and of the form:

$$W(x, y, z)dx\,dy\,dz = Ae^{-\beta(x^2+y^2+z^2)}dx\,dy\,dz \qquad (3)$$

where A and β are obvious combinations of constants from equation (1). It follows also that the probability that the chain ends are separated by a given x displacement, regardless of the y and z displacements, is given by:

$$W(x)\,dx = A'e^{-\beta x^2}dx \qquad (4)$$

All of these equations refer strictly to the relative number of distinguishable arrangements corresponding to a given value of r or x, *i.e.*, to the statistical weight corresponding to such a value. To the extent that energy differences among configurations can be neglected, these equations will also refer to the actual equilibrium distribution of molecular shapes.

3. Diffusion (*3*)

Diffusion in low molecular weight liquids has been shown (page 70) to proceed by a mechanism involving the jumping of neighboring molecules into "holes" in the liquid structure. It is clear that in an amorphous high polymer, with its tangled, half curled chains, there are many gaps or holes. These holes are not, however, large enough to allow a polymer molecule to shift its position as a whole. Even if such enormous holes existed, the activation energy necessary for an entire polymer molecule to jump to a new equilibrium position would be prohibitive.

On the other hand, if the polymer chain is sufficiently flexible, a *segment* of the chain may shift its position without moving the rest of the molecule. Such a segment may readily find itself next to a hole of reasonable size and in this case can jump to a new equilibrium position without the necessity of crossing an impossibly high energy barrier. It is thus possible to postulate for amorphous high polymers a diffusion process, the unit step of which is the jumping of a polymer segment, rather than a whole molecule, to a new equilibrium position. This hypothesis is supported by a wide variety of experimental evidence. Eyring (*3*) has estimated that the average size of the segments which move in this way is in the order of magnitude of 20 to 30 chain atoms. It is certainly an oversimplification to consider that only segments of one sharply defined size operate in diffusion. No doubt segments containing considerably more than 30 chain atoms occasionally jump as units to new positions and segments of shorter length also contribute to the diffusion. This oversimplification, however, is little more serious than that of considering a low molecular weight liquid as a mixture of molecules and holes of a definite size. The general correctness of this viewpoint will be hereafter assumed, and the results of such segmental jumps will be discussed.

It is clear that although the polymer segments jump into neighboring holes, as do the molecules of a low molecular weight liquid, the former are not as free in their motion as the latter. The polymer segments move always subject to the restriction that they are strung together in chains. The diffusional motion of the segments cannot destroy the identity of the polymer molecules but can only shift the latter from one configuration to another. A single segmental jump will have two effects on the polymer molecule. First, the *shape* of the molecule will be slightly altered by the motion of the segment; and second, the center of gravity of the molecule will be slightly shifted. The result of a large number of successive segmental jumps will likewise be twofold. First, the molecule will wriggle about from one shape to another; and second, the center of gravity will undergo a slow random wandering. Kuhn (*47*) has designated these two effects as the micro-Brownian and macro-Brownian movements, respectively.

In the unstressed state, the micro-Brownian movement carries a polymer molecule through phase space in a completely random fashion. Hence the vectorial separation of the two chain ends will, over a long period of time, follow the distribution laws of equation (3). These distribution laws can be interpreted as giving the fraction of molecules which at a given instant possess a certain chain end separation or, alternatively, as the fraction of its time which a single molecule spends in configurations of a certain chain end separation as it carries out its micro-Brownian motion. This second interpretation is significant, since it specifically negates any static picture of the polymeric structure, and indirectly fixes attention upon the *rate* of the micro-Brownian movement as well as upon the nature of the equilibrium distribution among configurations. It must be recognized that in many cases this micro-Brownian motion is extremely rapid when compared with a timescale of a second. In rubber at room temperature, for example, the segmental diffusion represents a violent molecular activity. This can be seen by the rapidity with which a stretched rubber band (*i.e.*, a sample forcibly held in a nonequilibrium distribution of molecular configurations) snaps back to the unstrained state when released.

The segmental diffusion of high polymers, like the molecular diffusion of low molecular weight liquids, will increase with temperature for two reasons. First, the thermal expansion of the polymer involves the introduction of additional holes, and second, the segments adjacent to holes will more often obtain the activation energy necessary to surmount the intervening energy barrier and jump into the holes. In the low molecular weight case, the total temperature dependence has been resolved quantitatively into these two contributions. It will be remembered that the dominant factor is the introduction of new holes, and the activation energy of the jumping process itself is rather low. In the case of high polymers such resolution has not been made. The activation energy of the jumping process is undoubtedly much larger than in the low molecular weight case, and hence will provide a larger temperature dependence. It may even be true that in the case of high polymers the true activation energy for segmental jumps is more effective than the introduction of new holes in causing the diffusion rate to increase with temperature.

III. EFFECT OF SHEAR STRESS—QUALITATIVE INTRODUCTORY TREATMENT

1. Introduction

In a previous section, the flow of a low molecular weight liquid was interpreted as a stress-biased diffusion process. It is only natural that the segmental diffusion of an amorphous high polymer will likewise be biased in the presence of an external stress. We have seen in the previous section that the segmental diffusion of such a polymer has a double effect on the molecule as a whole—the macro-Brownian motion of the center of gravity and the micro-Brownian wriggling of the molecule from one configuration to another. A shear stress will bias both of these diffusional motions. The biased macro-Brownian movement will carry whole molecules in preferred directions in an irreversible manner; this is a true flow. The biased micro-Brownian movement will cause the polymer molecules to become, on the average, stretched and oriented in certain directions, *i. e.*, in the presence of the stress they will no longer spend in each configuration the fraction of their time demanded by the distribution laws Eq. 3. When the stress is removed, however, they will return to the original equilibrium distribution and any macroscopic strain which resulted from the stretching and orienting of chains will disappear. Hence the strain arising from the biased micro-Brownian motion is an *elastic* strain, which is completely recoverable. This effect will be called "configurational elasticity."

One might consider the amorphous polymer as similar to a liquid, whose *molecules* are the size of the actual polymer *segments*. When a shear stress is applied, this "liquid" begins to flow. Since the "liquid molecules" (polymer segments) are strung together in chains, this "flow," although rapid at first, is slowed down as the polymer molecules are strung out into elongated shapes. Further motion can take place only as whole molecules slowly shift their centers of gravity. When the stress is released, the elongated molecules diffuse back into their statistically abundant half-curled shapes. This represents an elastic recovery of part of the original apparent flow.

It will be remembered that the mechanical behavior in shear of a low molecular weight liquid or glass was made up of two parts—the flow, or biased molecular diffusion, and an instantaneous elastic response which did not involve molecular diffusion at all. In the case of an amorphous high polymer, the biased diffusion alone results in a twofold mechanical result—the retarded "configurational elasticity" which arises from biased *micro-Brownian* motion and the permanent flow which arises from the biased *macro-Brownian* motion. In addition, the amorphous polymer must exhibit the same type of instantaneous elastic response, independent of any diffusion process, as does a simple glass. Even if no polymer segment in the entire sample jumps to a new equilibrium position, the whole structure can be deformed slightly when a stress is applied. Valence bonds are stretched or compressed, valence angles are opened or closed, and near molecular neighbors are moved closer together or farther apart against the action of the intermolecular forces.

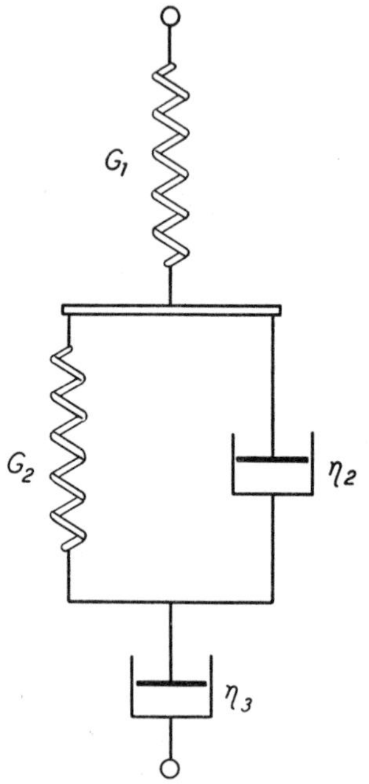

Fig. 48. Mechanical Model A: Instantaneous elasticity, retarded elasticity, and flow.

Thus the very simplest mechanical behavior (in shear) which can be expected from an amorphous high polymer is that represented by the model of figure 48. This model will be referred to throughout as Model A. G_1 represents the instantaneous elastic response. The second mechanism (G_2, τ_2) is the retarded elastic response caused by the uncurling of molecular chains. η_3 is the actual *flow* mechanism, represented here by a *viscosity* term.

If a shear stress is suddenly imposed upon a high polymer whose behavior is governed by Model A, the shear strain will change with time according to figure 49. First there will be an instantaneous elastic response, of the magnitude S/G_1. This will be followed by a retarded elastic response and a flow. The retarded elastic response, caused by the uncurling and orientation of polymer molecules, asymptotically approaches the equilibrium value S/G_2. The flow goes on from the beginning at the rate S/η_3. If, at a later time, the stress is suddenly removed, there results an instantaneous recovery of the first deformation, followed by a retarded recovery of the second. The deformation resulting from flow is not recovered at all.

Figure 50 indicates how the mechanical model reproduces these deformation and recovery effects. If the model is suddenly loaded, the first effect is an instantaneous extension of the spring G_1. This is followed by a retarded elastic extension of the spring G_2 and a steady extension of the dashpot η_3. If the load is removed, the spring G_1 contracts instantaneously. The spring G_2 tends to contract to its original length, but can do so only slowly because of the retarding dashpot η_2. Finally, any extension of the dashpot η_3 remains unchanged after the load on the model is removed.

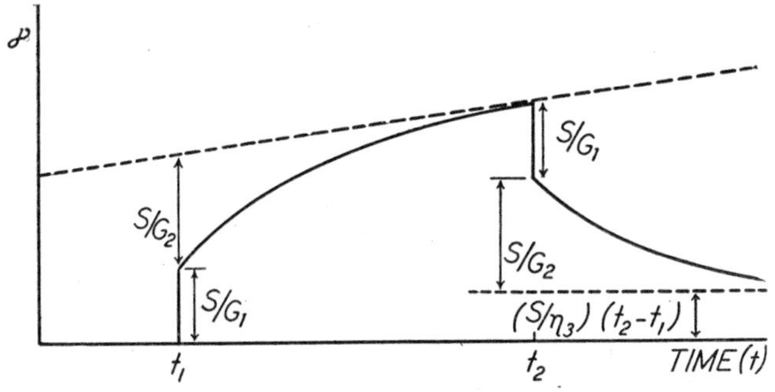

Fig. 49. Strain–time relation at constant stress for material exhibiting instantaneous elasticity, retarded elasticity, and flow (Model A).

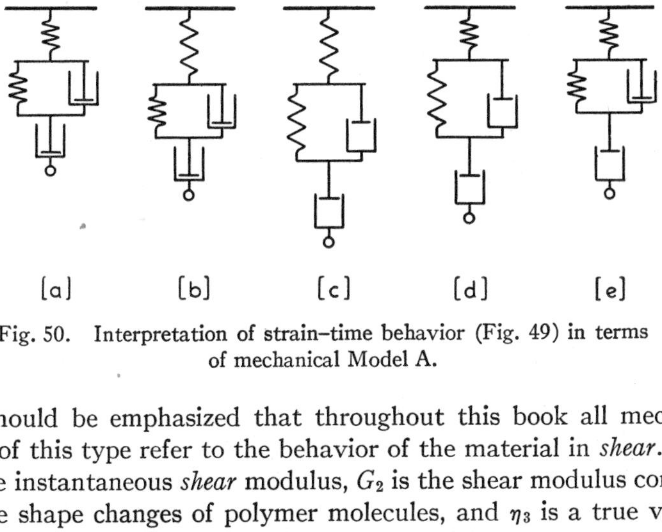

Fig. 50. Interpretation of strain–time behavior (Fig. 49) in terms of mechanical Model A.

It should be emphasized that throughout this book all mechanical models of this type refer to the behavior of the material in *shear*. Thus G_1 is the instantaneous *shear* modulus, G_2 is the shear modulus connected with the shape changes of polymer molecules, and η_3 is a true viscosity term, *i.e.*, it governs the rate of flow caused by a *shear* stress. If the behavior in shear shows such time effects, then the behavior in tension also shows them. Indeed, we could construct a mechanical model of springs and dashpots to represent the behavior in tension, just as Model A, above, represents the behavior in shear. In the tensile model, each spring would represent a Young's modulus instead of a shear modulus, and each dashpot would represent a viscous resistance to tensile deformation instead of to shearing deformation. If the deformations of a high polymer result in no volume changes, then there is a very simple relation between the tensile model and the shear model. For such an "incompressible" material, each element of the tensile model has a numerical value just three times that of the corresponding element of the shear model. That is, each Young's modulus is just three times the corresponding shear modulus, and each "tensile viscosity" is simply three times the corresponding viscosity in the shear model. It would therefore represent a useless duplication if we were always to discuss both types of model. Instead, the behavior in shear will be chosen as the fundamental behavior and used in all discussions. Anyone who prefers to think in terms of tensile behavior can translate the discussion of this chapter into those terms by multiplying every G and η by three to obtain the corresponding Young's moduli and "tensile viscosities."

The condition of incompressibility, upon which the above translation is based, would seem to be well met by the configurational elastic response and the flow of high polymers. It is not met by the instantaneous elastic response. Hence we should recognize the existence of two extreme cases, which require somewhat different treatments. One case is that of the "soft" polymer, where configurational elasticity and flow are important enough to overshadow the instantaneous elasticity. Such polymers are essentially incompressible, and are thus adequately represented by a shear model. The other case is that of a very brittle polymer, where the configurational elasticity and flow are negligible. Such polymers cannot be considered as incompressible. However, in this extreme case no time effects are observed, and the polymer can be treated by the ordinary theory of elasticity. In this chapter we are primarily interested in those aspects of behavior which are specifically associated with high polymers, *i.e.*, we will emphasize the properties of the "soft" polymers, since the extremely "hard" polymers are simply ideal elastic materials and as such require no further discussion here. There is, of course, the intermediate case, where the instantaneous elastic response predominates, but does not completely overshadow the configurational elasticity and the flow. In such a case, the part of the deformation which arises from configurational changes or flow can be considered to occur with no volume change, but the part arising from instantaneous elasticity may involve volume changes.

The above remarks can be restated in different terms. The *instantaneous elastic response* should be characterized by a shear modulus G and a Poisson's ratio ν, rather than by a shear modulus alone. There is no necessity of explicitly providing a Poisson's ratio for the configurational elasticity and the flow, since the assumption of constant volume supplies this information. In this book, mechanical models will be represented by means of shear moduli and viscosities alone—even, for simplicity, the instantaneous elastic response. It should be remembered that in such models the instantaneous elasticity is incompletely specified. If one wishes to translate the shear model into a tensile model, the instantaneous elasticity, G_1, should be multiplied by $(2\nu + 2)$, instead of by 3, to obtain the corresponding instantaneous Young's modulus.

It will be shown later that the model in figure 48 (page 104) is extremely oversimplified, for several reasons. In the first place, there is no reason to expect, *a priori*, that the *flow* element, mechanism 3 (Fig. 48), represents a *Newtonian* flow, characterized by a viscosity coefficient alone. The "internal viscosity," which retards the establishment of elastic equilibrium for mechanism 2 may also be "non-Newtonian." The *elastic* element of mechanism 2 may be "non-Hookian," *i.e.*, the equilibrium elastic strain may not be simply proportional to the stress. And finally, the retarded elastic response of mechanism 2 caused by chain curling and uncurling may require analysis into a series of such terms, each with its own G and τ. However, the simple model of figure 48 gives a great deal of insight into the behavior of amorphous polymers and permits a qualitative description of an enormous range of mechanical behavior. This model will, therefore, be discussed in complete detail in the following sections.

It is apparent that the obvious mechanical nature of a polymer depends strongly upon the relative magnitudes of the constants G_1, G_2, η_2, and η_3. At very low temperatures, for example, η_2 and η_3 are so large that mechanisms 2 and 3 (Fig. 48) are effectively "frozen in" and the material behaves as a simple elastic material of modulus G_1. At higher temperatures, where η_2 and η_3 are smaller, the responses of mechanisms 2 and 3 will completely overshadow the small elastic response of mechanism 1. In such a region, the material will have a "rubbery" character. At still higher temperatures, even mechanism 2 is overshadowed by mechanism 3 and the material will appear to flow as a simple viscous liquid. It is therefore important to understand, from a molecular standpoint, not only the magnitudes of these constants, but also the way in which they depend upon *temperature*.

2. Analysis of Four-Parameter Model

A. Significance of Elements; Magnitude and Temperature Dependence of Parameters

The Modulus G_1.—The modulus G_1 represents the instantaneous elastic response of the amorphous polymer. When a stress is applied, even if no diffusion takes place, the whole structure can be elastically deformed. This deformation involves changes of distance between neighboring molecules and small shape changes within molecules (change of bond distances and angles, etc.). The exact *magnitude* of G_1 is obviously a complicated function of the molecular structure and of both intramolecular and intermolecular forces. However, two semiquantitative statements regarding it can be made. First, as indicated on pages 62–67, this modulus will be very high—in the order of magnitude of 10^{10} to 10^{11} dynes per cm.^{2}. Second, G_1 should exhibit a small decrease in value with increasing temperature.

It will be seen that it is G_1 which dominates the elastic behavior of the polymer at very low temperatures, where mechanisms 2 and 3 (Fig. 48) are "frozen in."

The Modulus G_2.—The magnitude and temperature dependence of G_2 can best be discussed in the case where η_2 can be completely neglected. Physically, this means at a high enough temperature that the configurational elasticity, mechanism 2, is essentially unretarded by internal viscosity—as in rubber at room temperature. Let us consider this case.

When an amorphous polymer undergoes elastic deformation [we consider here only deformation arising from configurational changes (mechanism 2)], the molecules are disturbed from their equilibrium shape distribution, discussed on pages 98–100. The chains are given a *preferential elongation* and *orientation* in the direction of the principal tensile stress. The sample in this distorted condition necessarily has a higher free energy than in the equilibrium shape. If it were possible to calculate the free energy as a function of the degree of shear deformation, the value of the modulus G_2 would follow directly, since any modulus is the second partial differential of the free energy of the sample with respect to the deformation coordinate involved (see page 12):

$$G_2 = \frac{\partial^2 \mathbf{F}}{\partial \gamma^2} = \frac{\partial^2 \mathbf{H}}{\partial \gamma^2} - T\frac{\partial^2 \mathbf{S}}{\partial \gamma^2} \tag{5}$$

Now in our definition of an ideal amorphous polymer, it was postulated that there were present no specific, localized forces tending to make the molecules take on either particular folded or particular elongated configurations. If such is the case, the distortion of the polymer sample, with the attendant elongation and orientation of polymer molecules, cannot change the *energy* of the system. The necessary increase in free energy can be due only to a *decrease in entropy*, and the modulus G_2 must be given simply by $-T(\partial^2 S/\partial \gamma^2)$.

While the assumption of constant energy during a deformation seems reasonable for an "ideal" amorphous polymer, it is far from obvious that any actual polymer will approach this ideal closely enough for its energy to be independent of its degree of deformation. Experimentally, however, this seems to be very nearly true in the case of rubber, which has been more thoroughly investigated in this regard than any other polymer (*31*). It is of course true that a high temperature, which is necessary to make η_2 small (so that G_2 can be observed without complications), also automatically increases the importance of entropy factors relative to energy factors. Thus the fact that the elasticity of rubber (in the early range of extension and at room temperature) is primarily an entropy effect does not necessarily mean that the configurational elasticity of all amorphous polymers can be discussed without considering the energy changes involved. However, the pure entropy effect deserves careful attention, both because of its direct applicability in the case of elastomers and also as a limiting case in all amorphous polymers.

This problem has been discussed in detail by several authors, under such headings as the "kinetic theory of rubber elasticity." The essential problem is to calculate the configurational entropy of the polymer as a function of the strain.

The original treatment of Guth and Mark (*31a*) can serve as the prototype of all theoretical treatments of this subject. This treatment uses a single polymer molecule with completely free rotation about single valence bonds as representative of the macroscopic polymer sample. Guth and Mark assumed that the distance between the two ends of a polymer molecule in an unstretched polymer sample was given by the most probable value of the distribution function, equation (1). When the sample is stretched, the two ends of the polymer molecule are pulled apart. The statistical probability of the new (stretched) separation was considered to be given by the probability function, equation (1). Guth and Mark now applied to the single polymer molecule the Boltzmann entropy equation $S = k \ln W$. The reduced *probability* of the stretched state was thus translated into thermodynamic language as a lowered *entropy*. We already have a relation between the elastic modulus and the free energy of deformation, equation (5). Combining these expressions leads directly to equation (6), which relates the tension σ with the elongation ∂l for a single chain. Mark (*51b*) speaks of this as an "equation of state" of a single polymer molecule, in analogy to the equation of state of an ideal gas:

$$\sigma = 3\,KT\left(\frac{1}{nl_0^2}\frac{1-\cos\alpha}{1+\cos\alpha}\right)\partial l \tag{6}$$

The value G_2 of Model A refers, of course, to the stress–strain ratio in shear for a macroscopic sample, rather than the force–elongation ratio for a single polymer molecule. Kuhn (*47*) and others (*31, 88*) have treated this problem. Kuhn assumed that the entropy of the macroscopic sample was simply the sum of the entropies of the individual chains, and obtained the following relation between tensile stress S and relative elongation γ:

$$S = N^*\,3\,KT\left(\frac{1}{nl_0^2}\frac{1-\cos\alpha}{1+\cos\alpha}\right)\gamma \tag{7}$$

Here N^* represents the number of polymer molecules per unit volume. This gives us for the Young's modulus E the value:

$$E = N^*\,3\,KT\left(\frac{1}{nl_0^2}\frac{1-\cos\alpha}{1+\cos\alpha}\right) \tag{8}$$

N^* is obviously related to the molecular weight and the density; $N^* = \rho/M \times$ Avogadro's number. Inserting numerical values for the parameters, Kuhn obtained the following expression for E:

$$E = 7\,RT\rho\frac{1}{M} \tag{9}$$

The shear modulus, G_2, will be equal to $1/3\,E$. (This simple relation between the shear modulus and Young's modulus holds only if the polymer remains at a constant volume during the deformation, *i.e.*, can be considered as "incompressible." This will be true for all "soft" polymers.)

Two features of this equation are worthy of discussion. First, it is seen that E (and therefore G_2) is directly proportional to absolute temperature. This is not surprising. Indeed, the initial assumption, that stretched amorphous polymer differs from unstretched polymer only in the relative *probability* of the molecular configurations, necessarily leads to this conclusion. The use of a different molecular model, for example, may result in a different absolute value for E, but cannot possibly yield any different temperature dependence.

The second interesting feature of equation (9) is the presence of the molecular weight, M, in the denominator. The implication is that from a measurement of the configurational elastic modulus, G_2, one can compute the molecular weight of the amorphous polymer, and as a matter of fact the calculation actually leads to molecular weight values which are of the right order of magnitude. It is, however, extremely doubtful if a series of monodisperse fractions of the same polymer would exhibit values of G_2 which were inversely proportional to their respective molecular weights. The model which was used by Mark, Guth, and Kuhn—that of a single polymer molecule *whose ends are pulled apart*—is extremely crude from one standpoint. This is the manner in which the macroscopic tensile stress is represented on the molecular scale. Actually, when a tensile stress is applied to a macroscopic polymer sample, the effect on a single polymer molecule is *not* the same as though the molecule were grasped by its two ends by microscopic tweezers and pulled apart. *Every segment* of the molecule is affected directly by the stress, not merely indirectly through the chain by the end segments. The stress tries to straighten out local kinks, and larger convolutions, as well as to separate the end groups. The emphasis upon the chain ends in the Mark-Guth-Kuhn model causes the molecular weight M to enter in the simple fashion of equation (9). A more detailed analysis would necessarily cause M to enter as the upper limit of an integral, and would yield an expression in which G_2 would not in general be exactly proportional to $(1/M)$ (see pages 134–143). Mark (*51b*) speaks of the M of equation (9) as the molecular weight of "the mobile part" of the chain molecules, thus recognizing that it is not identical with the actual (*e.g.*, osmotic) molecular weight.

Several extensions of the "kinetic theory of rubber elasticity" have been made by different authors, but all follow the general pattern of the Mark-Guth-Kuhn treatment. Wall (*88*), for example, quite correctly points out that it is preferable to consider the whole distribution of chain end separations, rather than the most probable value. The single molecule of the original treatment was considered to have in the unstretched state *exactly* the *most probable* value for the distance between its ends. Fluctuation phenomena are neglected, and as Mark points out, a single polymer molecule is not a sufficiently large sample to justify this procedure. Wall (*88*) considers that in the unstretched state the polymer molecules have their ends separated by different distances, according to a distribution function such as equation (3). Upon stretching, this is changed to a different distribution function. Wall calculates the entropy difference corresponding to the difference in probability of the two *distribution functions* and completely dispenses with the entropy of a single molecule. There is no doubt that this represents an improvement in method. The final result, however, is of the same form as equation (9) with a different numerical factor. [Kuhn (*47*) considered the whole distribution of chain end separations, but retained the concept of an entropy of a single molecule.] Bresler and Frenkel (*16a*) attempted to explicitly consider the effects of *hindered* rotation about C—C bonds upon the configurational elasticity. However, as Flory and Rehner (*25a*) point out, some of their results do not seem to agree with experiment, and the latter authors propose an alternative treatment of this problem.

However, the most valid applications of the kinetic theory are those relating to three-dimensional network polymers. Hence a more complete discussion is given in Chapter C. Probably the most satisfactory method of attack yet developed is that of Guth and James (*31*), which is discussed in Chapter C.

For our present purposes, the kinetic theory of configurational elasticity yields the following pertinent information concerning the modulus G_2: (1) G_2 will be much smaller in magnitude than G_1, being of the order of magnitude of 10^6 or 10^7, rather than 10^{11}. (2) G_2 will be directly proportional to the absolute temperature. (3) The mechanism responsible for G_2 permits of very large elastic extensions.

A Note on the "Gaslike" Nature of Rubber Elasticity.—The elasticity of rubber in the early range of extension has been compared to the elasticity of an ideal gas (*52, 53*). This comparison is justified from a thermodynamic standpoint but not from a rate standpoint. A closer analogy, valid kinetically as well as thermodynamically, would connect rubber elasticity with *osmotic* pressure, rather than with gas pressure. All three phenomena (rubber elasticity, osmotic pressure, and gas pressure) are thermodynamically equivalent—all being due, in the ideal cases, to entropy effects. They differ, however, in the nature of the rate processes by which the equilibria are established.

Because the van't Hoff equation for the osmotic pressure exhibited by a dilute solution is identical in form with the equation of state of an ideal gas, it is sometimes implied that the same *molecular mechanism* operates in the two cases, *i.e.*, that solute molecules in a dilute solution move freely through the solution volume, as though they were gas molecules. This picture leads to the correct prediction of osmotic equilibrium but fails to predict the transient phenomena during attainment of osmotic equilibrium. If the solute molecules behaved as gas molecules, and were unaffected by the presence of the solvent, then mixing and dilution would be practically instantaneous processes. Actually, the attainment of osmotic equilibrium is a slow process, since the solute molecules must diffuse through the solvent.

The free energy of dilution of an ideal solution is of the same form as the free energy of expansion of an ideal gas. In both processes $\Delta H = 0$, and the free energy change is purely an entropy change. The equilibrium osmotic pressure must follow the van't Hoff equation, regardless of the mechanism of osmosis. When we consider the *rate of attainment* of osmotic equilibrium, however, the mechanism of diffusion in a condensed phase becomes important.

Similar remarks can be made concerning rubber elasticity. When rubber is slightly deformed, the molecules are forced from their initial, half curled shapes into slightly less curled configurations. This uncurling has been shown to have very little effect on the energy content of the sample but to decrease the entropy. As a result, the *equilibrium* elastic behavior in the range is completely analogous to the elastic behavior of an ideal gas. That is, rubber heats up upon extension and cools down during contraction. The elastic modulus is roughly proportional to the absolute temperature. Rubber can be carried through a "Carnot cycle" of isothermal and adiabatic extensions and contractions. A heat engine (*91*) can be constructed of rubber to operate on such a Carnot cycle, and convert heat into mechanical energy. In brief, as long as we are concerned with the *equilibrium* extension for any tensile stress, this analogy is sound.

However, the model of the rubber molecule as a freely wriggling chain affected only by internal restrictions such as impenetrability of segments, is definitely incorrect. The rubber molecule must carry out its motion in a condensed phase. Any change of molecular shape—curling or uncurling—must take place by means of diffusion of the molecular segments in this condensed phase.

When the rubber is stressed, the final equilibrium deformation is given by the simple kinetic theory of elasticity; but the shape of the early part of the deformation–time curve cannot be understood on this basis. In order to explain the *rate of attainment* of equilibrium deformation, the process must be considered in its true light—as segmental diffusion in a condensed phase. That is, η_2 as well as G_2 must be considered.

In certain cases, the equilibrium deformation is attained in a time which is short in comparison to the timescale of ordinary mechanical tests. In such cases, the rate considerations are not critically significant; only the equilibrium deformation is important. As a result, the analogy between configurational elasticity and gas elasticity is quite satisfactory. In the general case, where the curling or uncurling of molecular chains requires a time comparable to or even longer than the experimental timescale, one should not speak of "gaslike" elasticity. If an analogy in this general case is necessary, perhaps the term "osmosislike" elasticity would be preferable.

Magnitude and Temperature Dependence of η_2 and η_3.—The retarded elasticity and the flow of amorphous high polymers are both due to the same elementary process—the biased thermal diffusion of molecular segments. It is to be expected, therefore, that the magnitudes of η_2 and η_3 should be closely related. At a temperature where the retarded elasticity is essentially "frozen in" by a high η_2, there should also be such a high η_3 value as to reduce flow to a negligible value.

Perhaps η_3, the viscosity factor governing the true flow of the polymer, should be discussed first. This viscosity term has been treated both experimentally and theoretically; Flory (*25*) investigated the melt viscosities of a series of homologous polymers (polyesters). He found that the log of the melt viscosity bore a linear relation to the square root of the polymerization degree:

$$\ln \eta = A + B\sqrt{Z} \tag{10}$$

Eyring has justified this dependency of viscosity upon chain length in the following fashion (*3*):

. . . Although the flow of a long chain is believed to be merely the resultant of the motion of segments of definite size that jump from one equilibrium position to another at a given rate, independent of how many segments are joined together in the chain, it is necessary that there should be some coordination of the movement of the segments if the chain as a whole is to progress. The fraction of successful jumps, which determines the actual fluidity of the polymer, should be independent of temperature but should be a function of the amount of cooperation of the segments constituting the chain, whereas the total number of jumps in unit time depends on the size and nature of the segments and on the temperature and pressure; thus,

$$\phi = \frac{1}{\eta} = F(Z)\,G(p,T) \tag{11}$$

where the function F may be taken as the same for all linear molecules, assuming the same type of cooperation to be necessary, and the function G depends on the nature of the polymer. According to [Flory's results], $F(Z)$ is of the form $e^{-aZ^{\frac{1}{2}}}$, where a is equal to B/R and has approximately the value 0.5/2, *i.e.*, 0.25. Since e^{-x} becomes equal to $[1 - (x/n)]^n$ when n is large and very much greater than x, it follows that

$$F(Z) = e^{-aZ^{\frac{1}{2}}} \approx \left(1 - \frac{a}{n} Z^{\frac{1}{2}}\right)^n \tag{12}$$

The quantity on the extreme right of this equation is, mathematically, the probability that n successive and independent events, each having a probability $(1 - aZ^{\frac{1}{2}}/n)$ of success, shall all be successful. The experimental facts are, therefore, in agreement with the view that the fluidity is related to the probability of the coordinated movement in all the segments constituting a long chain.

"According to the foregoing deduction the probability of failure of any unit to move in coordination with the others is given by Eq. (12) as $aZ^{\frac{1}{2}}/n$, and the following considerations provide a theoretical basis for this result. A freely twisting hydrocarbon molecule containing Z links encloses an average volume of $3.4\,Z^{\frac{1}{2}} \times 10^{-24}$ cc., while the chain itself occupies a volume V_2 of $20\,Z^{\frac{1}{2}} \times 10^{-24}$ cc. Of the total volume enclosed by the freely twisting chain containing n segments, the portion V_1, equal to $(1/n)(3.4\,Z^{\frac{1}{2}})$, is available for each segment. In order that movement may be successful the segment must be located within some definite region of the volume V_2 that the molecule will occupy after moving under the action of the shear force. The probability of failure is the probability that the segment shall be in the portion V_1 of the total space $V_1 + V_2$ in which it might be, and this is given by

$$\frac{V_1}{V_1 + V_2} \approx \frac{V_1}{V_2} = \frac{3.4}{20\,n} Z^{\frac{1}{2}} = \frac{0.17}{n} Z^{\frac{1}{2}} \tag{13}$$

which is in agreement with the result given above. The value of the constant a derived in this manner is 0.17, compared with the experimental result of 0.25 for the linear polyesters. It should be noted that a may be expected to be almost independent of the nature of the straight chain, and the approximation of taking it to be equal to 0.25, *i.e.*, B is 0.5, in other cases will be made.

The *activation energy* for viscous flow, on the other hand, should be nearly the same for all members of a homologous (high polymer) series, since the same elementary process of segment diffusion operates regardless of the number of segments in the chain. The chain length factor enters as an *entropy* of activation, rather than an activation energy. The melt viscosity, η_3, of a high polymeric material may therefore be expressed in the following manner:

$$\eta_3 = A\,e^{BZ^{\frac{1}{2}}}\,e^{E/RT} \qquad (10a)$$

Here A, B, and E are parameters which depend upon the chemical nature of the polymer, but not upon the molecular weight of the sample. This equation is due to Flory.

E will be large for a polymer with strong intermolecular binding forces, and small for molecules which attract each other only weakly.

The "viscous" term of the retarded elastic response, η_2, can be expected to have a much smaller absolute value at any temperature than η_3, since the internal shape change of the polymer molecule can be accomplished by the transport of sections of the molecule, rather than the

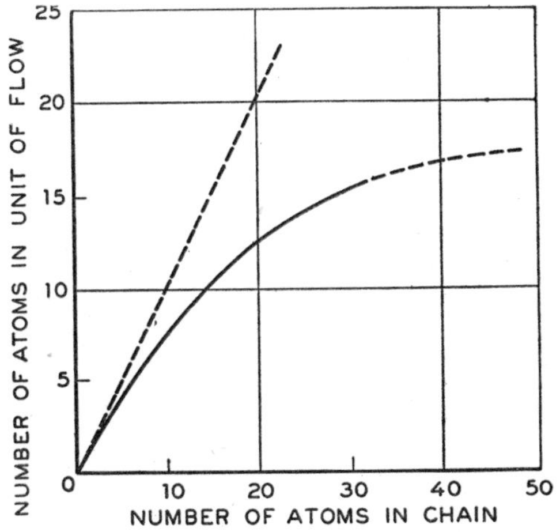

Fig. 51. Dependence of "flow-unit" size upon molecular chain length (after Eyring).

entire molecule. Thus the elementary segment motion needs to be "coordinated" only over a more or less short section of the chain. The *temperature dependence* of η_2, on the other hand, should be governed by an activation energy very close to that of η_3 for the same polymer:

$$\eta_2 = A'e^{E/RT} \qquad (14)$$

If we go to very short polymer molecules, this sort of flow must degenerate into the ordinary flow of low molecular weight liquids. We have seen that the flow of a high polymer is the accumulative result of many segmental jumps and that, for a given chemical type of high polymer, the average size of the moving segments is independent of the molecular weight of the polymer. If we consider a polymer which is shorter than this average segment size, it is clear that the flow of such a polymer cannot consist of jumps by segments larger than the entire molecule. Furthermore, *very* short molecules—monomer and dimer—will behave like the small molecules of section A-II-2 (pages 67–75), that is, the molecule itself will be the unit of flow. Kauzmann and Eyring (*42a*) have computed the average size of the segments which operate in the flow of a series of saturated hydrocarbons as a function of the number of chain atoms in the molecule. Their results are shown in figure 51. It is seen that a chain of 10 atoms already exhibits a small amount of "segmental" flow. While the greater part of the flow of such a hydrocarbon presumably arises from jumps of the whole molecule, jumps of segments contribute also to the flow. The average size of the moving units is about 8, rather than 10, carbon atoms. In the authors' words, "it is evident that with increasing chain length the (average) flow unit becomes a decreasing proportion of the whole chain, and in very long chains the unit attains an average length which is approximately constant and contains 20 to 25 carbon atoms."

B. Range of Behaviors Described by Model A

When a stress is applied to an amorphous polymer, three kinds of deformation result: An instantaneous elastic response, a retarded (configurational) elastic response, and a flow. In our mechanical analog of springs and dashpots, Model A (page 104), these three types of response are represented by the elements G_1, G_2 and η_2, and η_3, respectively. The deformation–time curve at constant shear stress for Model A is of the general form of figure 48.

$$\gamma = S\frac{1}{G_1} + S\frac{1}{G_2}(1 - e^{-\frac{t}{\tau_2}}) + S\frac{1}{\eta_3}t \qquad (15)$$

In special cases, however, one term or another of equation (15) predominates to such an extent that the behavior is essentially reduced to simpler form. At very low temperatures, for example, η_2 and η_3 become so large that only mechanism 1 (Fig. 48) can respond appreciably to an external stress. The polymer behaves as an ideal elastic material of modulus G_1. If the stress is applied for a very long time, a "cold flow" is observed. This, for a truly high polymer, is mainly the slow ***delayed*** *elastic response*, mechanism 2 (Fig. 48), since η_3 can be expected to be much larger than η_2.

At a very high temperature, the material behaves as a simple liquid of viscosity η_3. Mechanisms 1 and 2 still operate, but they are obscured by the extremely large *flow* due to the low value of η_3. At a somewhat lower temperature, the flow [mechanism 3 (Fig. 48)] will be unable to overshadow completely the configurational elasticity (mechanism 2). Over a certain such temperature range, η_2 will still be so small that the elastic response (mechanism 2) will not be appreciably retarded. It will, of course, completely overshadow any elastic response (mechanism 1). The polymer thus behaves as a liquid which exhibits elastic effects. When stressed, it flows steadily; the only anomalies occur at the moments when the stress is *changed*, *e.g.*, small elastic recovery when stress is removed and flow ceases.

As the temperature is reduced further, the *elastic* response plays a relatively greater and greater role, until instead of a "liquid with elastic effects," the polymer becomes an "elastic material exhibiting flow." Raw rubber at room temperature is in this category.

At still lower temperatures, the *retarded* elastic nature of mechanism 2 is apparent. Compare with page 58, where it was pointed out that a retarded elastic element alone represents a wide range of behavior. When the retardation time is extremely large compared with the experimental timescale, the elastic element is essentially "frozen in," and does not appreciably respond to stress at all. When the retardation time is of the same order of magnitude as the experimental timescale, the retarded elasticity appears as such; and when the retardation time is very short compared with the experimental timescale, the element exhibits ideal, apparently unretarded, elasticity.

In the above discussion, the experimental timescale was assumed to be held invariant, and the values of η_2 and η_3 to be changed by going from low to high temperatures. It is clear that a similar shift in the general nature of the behavior of Model A can be obtained by holding constant the temperature (and G_1, G_2, η_2, η_3), but changing the experimental time-scale. Consider the deformation–time curve for a retarded elastic element whose retardation time is five minutes. If this curve is plotted against time, expressed in units of one minute, the retarded elastic character is apparent. (Say 11 points appear, representing the time interval of zero to ten minutes.) If the same curve is plotted against time in seconds, in the corresponding interval of time (ten seconds), only the beginning of the retarded elastic response will be observed. This will be indistinguishable from a flow, since the deformation–time curve will hardly deviate from a straight line in so short a time. On the other hand, if a timescale of *hours* is used, the behavior will appear as an instantaneous elastic response. After an hour, the deformation will, for all practical purposes, have reached its equilibrium value. A similar situation will hold in regard to the recovery curves. If the ten-minute deformation is followed by a ten-minute recovery, that recovery will exhibit its true retarded elastic nature. If the ten-second deformation is followed by a ten-second recovery period, practically no recovery will be observed. This heightens the illusion of *flow* which characterized the deformation curve with the short timescale. Finally, the recovery curve on a very long timescale will have the same form as if an *instantaneous* elastic mechanism were operating. (After one hour, recovery will be essentially complete.)

If the experimental timescale is represented by the symbol ⓣ, the following generalizations apply: When $\tau \ll$ ⓣ, a retarded elastic element (G, η) behaves as an instantaneous elastic mechanism of modulus G, both in deformation and in recovery. When $\tau \gg$ ⓣ, the retarded elastic element appears to be a flow, governed by the viscosity η. Only when τ is of the same order of magnitude as T does the retarded elastic element exhibit its true or complete character. The transition from (pseudo) instantaneous elasticity to retarded elasticity to (pseudo) flow can result either from a change in the retardation time, τ (*e.g.*, by temperature changes) or by a shift in the experimental timescale. See also pages 56 and 58.

By obvious extension of the above considerations, we arrive at the following set of special cases for the complete Model A, made up of (true) instantaneous elasticity (G_1), retarded elasticity (G_2, η_2), and flow (η_3). Assume $G_2 \ll G_1$, $\eta_2 \ll \eta_3$. When $(\eta_2/G_1) \gg$ ⓣ, Model A reduces to elastic behavior, governed by G_1. When $(\eta_3/G_2) \ll$ ⓣ, the behavior is dominated by the flow, with a viscosity η_3. When $(\eta_2/G_2) \ll$ ⓣ, and $(\eta_3/G_2) \gg$ ⓣ, Model A reduces to an instantaneous elastic element governed by the modulus, $1/(1/G_1 + 1/G_2)$, which can be replaced without serious error by G_2.

When (η_3/G_2) is of the same order of magnitude as ⓣ, and $(\eta_2/G_2) \ll$ ⓣ, the behavior reduces to that of a Maxwell element (G_2, η_3). When (η_2/G_1) is of the same order of magnitude as ⓣ, and $(\eta_2/G_2) \gg$ ⓣ, Model A reduces to a Maxwell element (G_1, η_2). The "flow" term here is only a pseudo flow, but this fact cannot be detected under the experimental conditions assumed. When (η_2/G_2) is of the same order of magnitude as ⓣ, the *retarded* elastic nature of the configurational elasticity is apparent.

TABLE III

Conditions			General behavior	Simplified model
$\frac{\eta_1}{G_1}$	$\frac{\eta_2}{G_2}$	$\frac{\eta_3}{G_2}$		
$\gg$ ⓣ	$\gg$ ⓣ	$\gg$ ⓣ	Hard, ideal elastic material. No time effects.	
$\sim$ ⓣ	$\gg$ ⓣ	$\gg$ ⓣ	Hard material (high shear modulus), with some "cold flow" which continues at constant rate.	
$\sim$ ⓣ	$\sim$ ⓣ	$\gg$ ⓣ	High instantaneous modulus, followed by large "cold flow" which reduces in rate as time goes on.	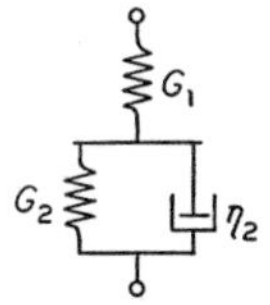
$\ll$ ⓣ	$\gg$ ⓣ	$\gg$ ⓣ	Pseudo Newtonian liquid of viscosity η_2.	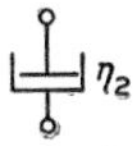
$\ll$ ⓣ	$\sim$ ⓣ	$\gg$ ⓣ	Retarded elastic response.	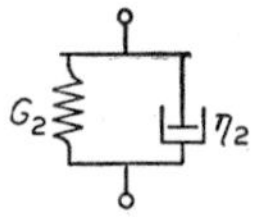
$\ll$ ⓣ	$\ll$ ⓣ	$\gg$ ⓣ	Ideal elastic material of low modulus (elastomer with no flow).	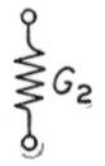
$\ll$ ⓣ	$\sim$ ⓣ	$\sim$ ⓣ	Retarded elasticity plus flow.	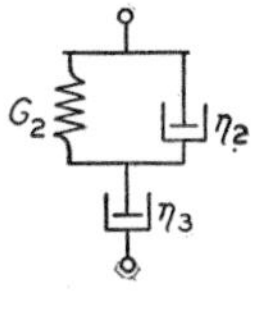
$\ll$ ⓣ	$\ll$ ⓣ	$\sim$ ⓣ	Rapid long range elasticity plus flow (*e.g.*, raw rubber).	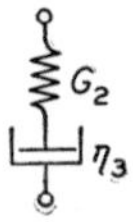
$\ll$ ⓣ	$\ll$ ⓣ	$\ll$ ⓣ	Simple viscous fluid.	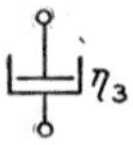

The transition from one special case to another can result either from a change in the various (η/G) ratios or by a shift in the experimental timescale. The various special cases are summarized in table III.

The Apparent Second Order Transition and Softening Point (*16*, *18*, *86*) **of Amorphous Polymers.**—It was pointed out on pages 75–86 that many low molecular weight amorphous materials possess rather definite, narrow temperature ranges in which they change from hard, brittle "glasses" to viscous "liquids." In the same way, many amorphous high polymers possess similar temperature ranges in which they change from glassy resins to softer materials, exhibiting long range elasticity. Furthermore, the "softening point" of a polymer, like that of a low molecular weight liquid, is often characterized by a discontinuity in the values of the first derivative thermodynamic properties—coefficient of volume expansion, specific heat, etc. The mechanical hardening and the thermodynamic discontinuities in the case of low molecular weight materials were interpreted on pages 75–86 in terms of the *rate of attainment* of mechanical equilibrium, including volume equilibrium. The mechanical hardening range was defined as the temperature range in which τ, the mechanical relaxation time, is of the same order of magnitude as the experimental timescale. The phenomenological discussion can be repeated almost exactly for the case of amorphous polymers (*8*).

We have seen that the simplest mechanical behavior in shear which can be expected of an amorphous high polymer is that represented by Model A (Fig. 48). This consists of an instantaneous elastic response, governed by G_1; a retarded elastic response, governed by G_2 and η_2; and a flow, governed by η_3. The instantaneous elastic response (G_1), has the same significance as in the case of low molecular weight amorphous materials. The retarded elastic response, G_2 and η_2, corresponds to the straightening out of curled molecular chains, and the flow, η_3, corresponds to the motion of the centers of gravity of these chains relative to each other. The general nature of the over-all response depends upon the relative magnitudes of the instantaneous elastic deformation, the retarded elastic deformation due to the straightening out of chains, and the flow. When η_2/G_1 of Model A is very large, compared with the experimental timescale, the polymer is hard and inflexible; it behaves as an ideal elastic material of shear modulus G_1. When η_2/G_1 is small, in comparison with the experimental timescale, the elastic deformation, mechanism 1, is completely overshadowed by the much larger deformations arising from configurational elasticity and flow. The material is "soft." The "softening point" is the temperature at which the polymer changes from a "soft" to a "hard" material; it is obviously closely connected with the "brittle point," at which ductile failure changes to brittle failure.

From a molecular standpoint, the mechanical softening point or range represents the temperature range in which segmental diffusion is becoming rapid enough that *biased* segmental diffusion can contribute larger deformations than can the instantaneous elastic mechanism. Just how rapid the diffusion must be in order for this to be true obviously depends upon how long a period of time is allowed for the experimental observation. For example, consider polystyrene. The "softening point" of this material is at about 80° C. for an experimental timescale in the order of a few seconds. However, on a timescale measured in years, polystyrene must be considered as "soft" even at room temperature and below, and on the other hand, polystyrene will give a characteristic "brittle" response to stresses of very short duration, even at 100° C. and above. Just as in the case of a low molecular weight liquid, the softening "point" is actually a softening range. The position of this temperature range has no absolute significance, but depends upon the timescale of the experimental investigation used to determine it.

The same is true of the discontinuity in slope of the thermodynamic variables. This discontinuity is not a sharp break but is spread over a certain temperature range. The position of this range, moreover, depends upon the rate of temperature change used in the investigation. Figure 52 shows in detail the way in which the volume of polystyrene changes with temperature. The line ACD represents the equilibrium volume as a function of temperature. At high temperatures, segmental diffusion is rapid enough for the sample to follow this equilibrium curve strictly and reversibly. If a sample is cooled from A at a constant rate, say 0.1° per minute, it will follow the equilibrium volume curve until the point C. Here the rate of segmental diffusion becomes too slow for the volume contraction to keep up with the temperature lowering. The structure can no longer continue to take on more compact structure, but remains effectively "frozen" in a structure characteristic of the high temperature. Even so, the material can contract, by the same mechanism as a crystal, which also undergoes no change in structure on cooling—that is, by decrease in amplitude of anharmonic thermal vibrations. As the temperature is lowered further, the volume follows curve CE, characterized by the smaller coefficient of expansion. If the temperature is held fixed at any point, the sample will not remain

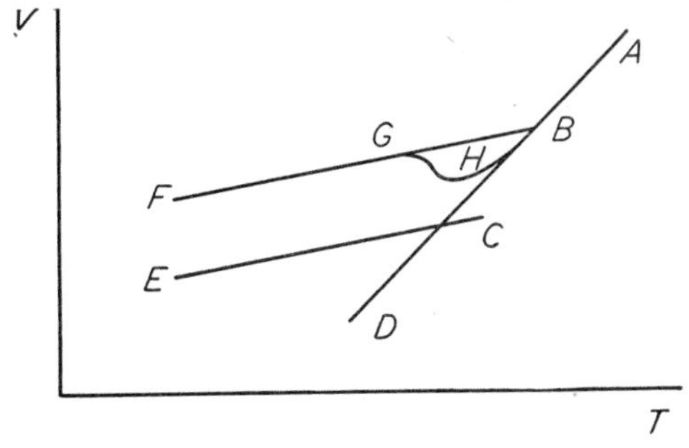

Fig. 52. Schematic diagram of volume–temperature behavior near the transition point.

at constant volume, characterized by a point on *CE*, but will slowly contract toward the equilibrium volume.

At very low temperatures, however, this diffusional contraction becomes so slow as not to be detectable. The lower part of curve *CE* can therefore be followed back and forth reversibly, just as can the upper part of *ABC*. If the cooling from high tem-

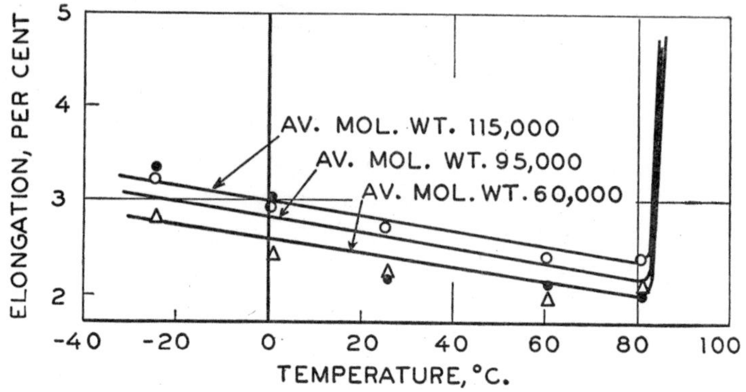

Fig. 53. Variations of ultimate elongation of polystyrene with temperature near the transition point (after Carswell, Nason, and Hayes).

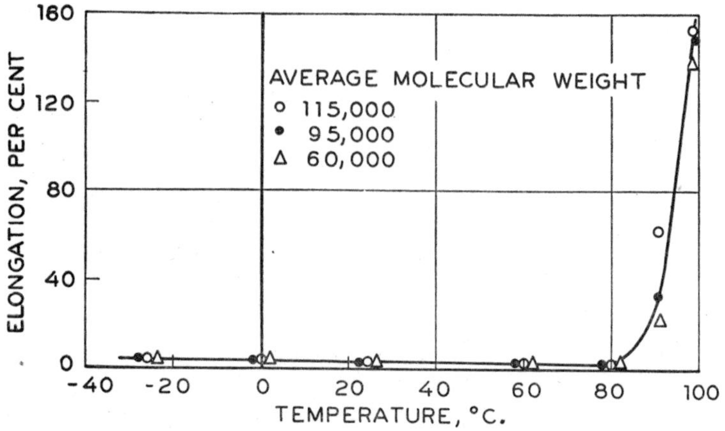

Fig. 54. Variations of ultimate elongation of polystyrene with temperature near the transition point (after Carswell, Nason, and Hayes). Data of figure 53 plotted on the same scale.

peratures is carried out more rapidly, the break away from the equilibrium volume curve appears at a higher temperature (point B). The sample, when cooled rapidly, follows *ABGF*. As before, once a very low temperature is reached, the tendency toward equilibrium volume is too slow to be observed in a reasonable time. Hence the lower part of *GF* can be retraced reversibly, just as the lower part of *CE*. If a sample which has been cooled rapidly to F is heated slowly, it will follow curve FB at low temperatures, that is, it will expand by means of increased amplitude of vibrations, but will undergo no structural change. As the temperature is increased, however, a point G will be reached where the segmental diffusion allows the sample to contract appreciably toward the equilibrium volume. This contraction will be superimposed upon the crystal-like expansion, and may even overshadow it for a while, so that the sample undergoes a net contraction as the temperature is being raised (curve GH). Thus at a high temperature, the volume is an explicit function of temperature. At a low temperature, the absolute magnitude of the volume depends upon how fast the sample was cooled through the critical range but the sample will expand and contract in a simple fashion when small temperature changes are made, exhibiting a lower expansion coefficient than that obtaining at the high temperature. In the intermediate temperature range, neither volume nor coefficient of expansion are explicit functions of temperature, but here complex time effects are observed which arise from the everpresent trend toward the fundamental equilibrium volume, given by $ABCD$.

Carswell, Hayes, and Nason (*18*) have investigated the mechanical properties of polystyrene over a wide range of temperature. They found a marked change in the mechanical properties to occur at about 80° C. Below that temperature, stress–strain curves of polystyrene indicate a hard, inflexible material. Above 80° C. the sample exhibits long range elasticity. Figures 53 and 54, taken from their paper, show how ultimate elongation depends upon temperature and molecular weight. If a much

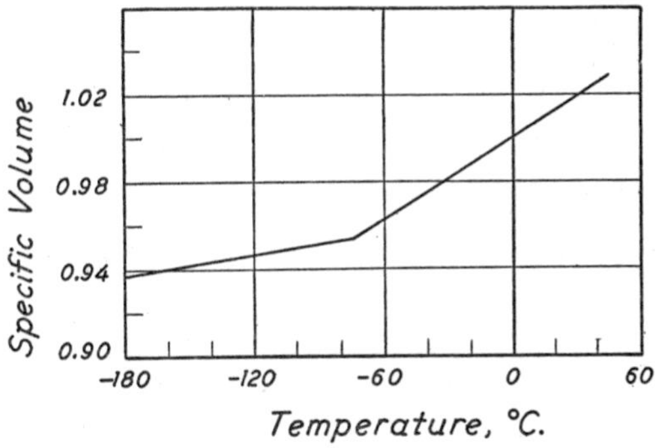

Fig. 55. Dependence of specific volume of rubber upon temperature near the transition point (after Bekkedahl).

slower crosshead speed had been used, presumably the characteristic breaks in these curves would have occurred at lower temperatures.

Similar studies have been made with amorphous rubber. Bekkedahl (*14*) has found a rather sharp change in slope of the volume–temperature curve (Fig. 55) for rubber at about − 70° C. At the same temperature there is a change in slope of the enthalpy–temperature curve. Furthermore, the mechanical properties of rubber undergo a distinct transition at about the same temperature. Mark and Valko (*53a*) found that below a critical temperature which varies from $-65°$ to $-72°$ C., depending on the rate of loading, rubber breaks with little elongation. At higher temperatures, large extensions take place. At a given rate of loading, the transition, measured in this fashion, is quite sharp. The elongation increases four-fold with a 1° increase in temperature.

The recent investigation of Morris, James, and Werkenthin (*59*) is of interest here. Brittle points of natural and synthetic rubber stocks were determined by rapid and slow tests. The rapid test invariably gave a higher observed "brittle point" than the slow test, as shown in table IV.

TABLE IV

COMPARISON OF BRITTLE POINTS DETERMINED WITH RAPID AND SLOW BEND

Vulcanizate	Brittle point, °F.		Difference
	Slow bend	Rapid bend	
Chemigum IV	−106.5	−71	35.5
Smoked sheet	−96.5	−71	25.5
Stanco Perbunan	−71	−29	42
Neoprene E	−64	−29	35
Neoprene GN	−60.5	−31	29.5
Hycar OR-15	−37.5	+5	42.5

The sharpness of the apparent second order transition in both high polymers and ordinary glasses should depend upon the energy of activation of the diffusion process and upon the position of the transition range (which is also partly determined by the activation energy). Of two materials whose transitions come at about the same temperatures, the one with the higher activation energy for diffusion will exhibit the sharper transition. Similarly, of two materials whose activation energies are the same, the one with the lower transition temperature will have the narrower transition range. It will be seen that plasticized high polymers possess smaller energies of activation for diffusion than do pure polymers. It is to be expected, therefore, that such plasticized materials will exhibit broader temperature ranges in which they "soften" than will pure polymers.

C. Model B: an Equivalent of Model A

It can be shown that any material whose plastoelastic properties follow Model A can be described with equal precision by a model of a different type which we will call Model B (Fig. 56). Model B, like Model A, consists of two elastic and two flow elements. The arrangement is different, however. Model B is made up of two Maxwell elements coupled in parallel with one another.

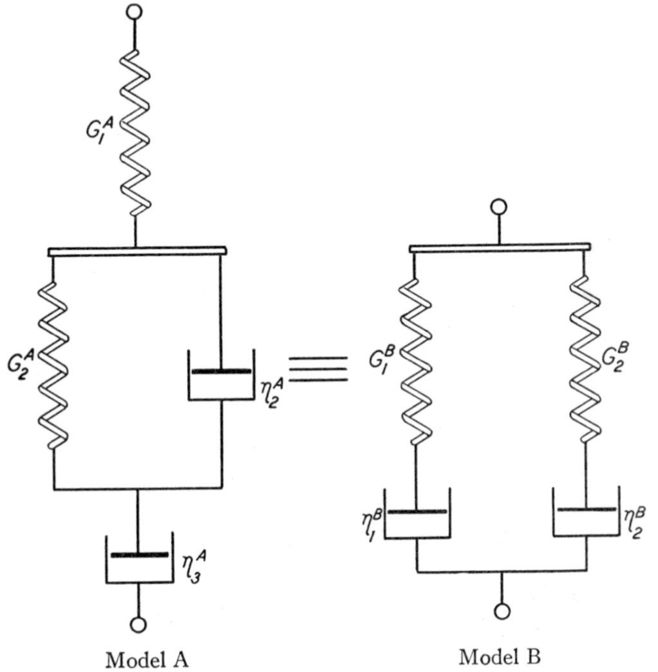

Fig. 56. Two equivalent models A and B, for material exhibiting instantaneous elasticity, retarded elasticity, and flow.

If one knows G_1^A, G_2^A, η_2^A, η_3^A, of Model A, one can calculate G_1^B, G_2^B, η_1^B, η_2^B, of the equivalent Model B, and *vice versa*:

$$G_1^A = G_1^B + G_2^B \tag{16}$$

$$G_2^A = \frac{G_1G_2(\eta_1 + \eta_2)^2(G_1 + G_2)}{(\eta_1G_2 - \eta_2G_1)^2} \tag{17}$$

$$\eta_2^A = \frac{\eta_1\eta_2(G_1 + G_2)^2(\eta_1 + \eta_2)}{(\eta_1G_2 - \eta_2G_1)^2} \tag{18}$$

$$\eta_3^A = \eta_1^B + \eta_2^B \tag{19}$$

In the above equations, the symbols on the right side refer to the elements of Model B—G_1^B, G_2^B, η_1^B, η_2^B—though the superscripts are omitted in the equations for G_2^A and η_2^A. Similarly, in the equations below, all symbols on the right side refer to the elements of Model A—G_1^A, G_2^A, η_2^A, η_3^A—although again superscripts will be omitted:

$$G_1^B = \frac{1}{2\,\beta}\left(G_1\alpha + G_1\beta - \frac{G_1^2}{\eta_2} - \frac{G_1^2}{\eta_3}\right) \tag{20}$$

$$G_2^B = \frac{-1}{2\,\beta}\left(G_1\alpha - G_1\beta - \frac{G_1^2}{\eta_2} - \frac{G_1^2}{\eta_3}\right) \tag{21}$$

$$\eta_1^B = \frac{+1}{2\,\beta}\left(G_1\alpha + G_1\beta - \frac{G_1^2}{\eta_2} - \frac{G_1^2}{\eta_3}\right)\left(\frac{1}{\alpha - \beta}\right) \tag{22}$$

$$\eta_2^B = \frac{-1}{2\,\beta}\left(G_1\alpha - G_1\beta - \frac{G_1^2}{\eta_2} - \frac{G_1^2}{\eta_3}\right)\left(\frac{1}{\alpha + \beta}\right) \tag{23}$$

where

$$\alpha = \left(\frac{G_1^A}{2\eta_3^A} + \frac{G_1^A}{2\eta_2^A} + \frac{G_1^A}{2\eta_2^A}\right) \tag{24}$$

$$\beta^2 = \alpha^2 - \frac{G_2^A G_1^A}{\eta_2^A \eta_3^A} \tag{25}$$

Although Models A and B are mathematically equivalent, Model A has certain advantages from an interpretative standpoint. Each of the terms in Model A has a direct physical significance, and is connected with one particular *mechanism* of response to stress. This has already been discussed in detail. In Model B, on the other hand, the elements have only an *indirect* physical significance. Thus the modulus which corresponds to *instantaneous* elasticity has the value $G_1^B + G_2^B$. The *flow* of the polymer, according to Model B, is governed by a viscosity of the magnitude $\eta_1^B + \eta_2^B$. The retarded elastic mechanism is governed by a still more complex combination of the elements of Model B. For this reason, Model A would seem to be preferable to Model B as a means of correlating macroscopic mechanical behavior with molecular processes.

Which of these models can be applied with the least mathematical effort, depends upon the nature of the application. If one wishes to predict the response of a polymer to constant stress, this can be calculated very simply by means of Model A, but only with difficulty using Model B. On the other hand, if one desires to calculate the stress–strain curve of the polymer at constant *rate* of deformation, then the use of Model B simplifies the task. The use of Model A leads to precisely the same answer, but a more difficult computation must be resorted to in the obtaining of the answer.

In this book models of type A will in general be used instead of the equivalent models consisting of Maxwell elements in parallel.

IV. EFFECT OF SHEAR STRESS—MORE REFINED AND QUANTITATIVE TREATMENT

1. Phenomenological Necessity for Distribution of Retardation Times

In the discussion which led to the formulation of Model A we considered the shape changes of polymer molecules as a single process with a single characteristic retardation time. However, the links and curls of a given molecule are of all sizes. When a stress is applied, presumably the *local* kinkiness of a chain can be straightened out more rapidly than *long range* convolutions. If this is true, one should not speak of the retardation

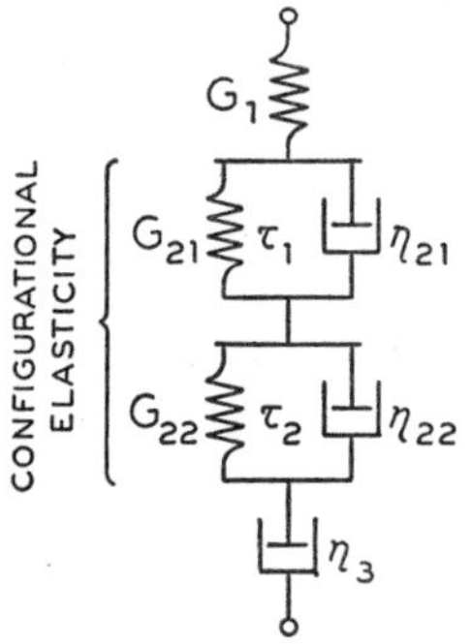

Fig. 57. Mechanical model for material exhibiting two different mechanisms of retarded elasticity, each with its own retardation time.

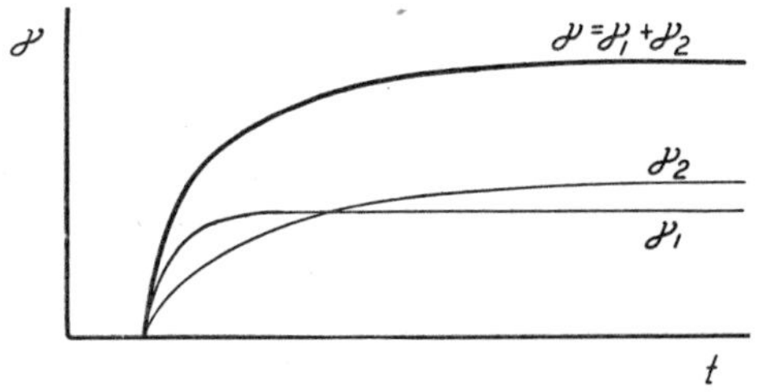

Fig. 58. Schematic creep curve for material exhibiting two mechanisms of retarded elastic response (instantaneous elasticity and flow are not shown). The light curves, each representing a single mechanism, are simple exponential curves; the heavy curve, representing the total deformation, is not exponential in form.

time for molecular shape changes, but rather of the retardation time for the straightening of convolutions of a given size. If the local kinkiness has a retardation time τ_1, and the long bends a retardation time of τ_2, then Model A must be extended to the form indicated in figure 57.

Neglecting the instantaneous elastic response and the true flow, this model results in the deformation–time behavior of figure 58. The configurational elastic response is made up of two exponential curves of different τ. This total response has the same general shape as an exponential curve of intermediate τ. Thus if the *details* of the response can be ignored, it is possible to replace the model of figure 57 with a model of type A, where $(1/G_2) = (1/G_{21} + 1/G_{22})$ of the complete model, and where τ is some sort of average between τ_1 and τ_2. The greater the difference between τ_1 and τ_2, the greater the error involved when $[1/G_{21}(1 - e^{-t/\tau_1}) + 1/G_{22}(1 - e^{-t/\tau_2})]$ is approximated by a single exponential expression $(1/G_{21} + 1/G_{22})(1 - e^{-t/\tau_{Av}})$.

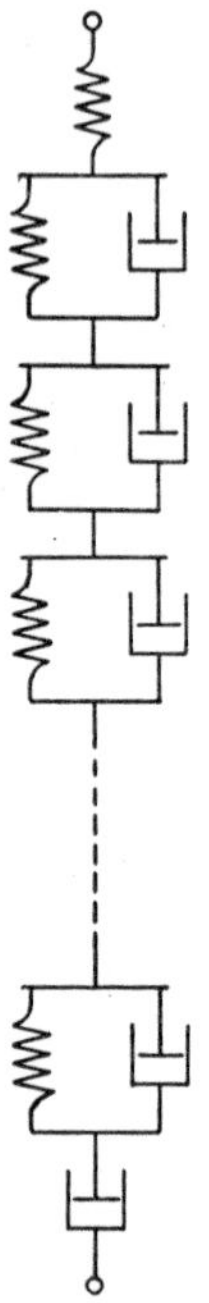

Fig. 59. Model C: mechanical model for material exhibiting a distribution of retarded elastic mechanisms.

The sharp division of configurational elasticity into one part due to "local kinkiness" and one part due to long range curliness is, of course, only a second approximation to the actual situation. One would expect that each different size of molecular segment would exhibit a different retardation time for its shape changes. This would necessitate a continuous distribution of retardation times for the configurational elasticity. The corresponding "model" would have a continuous set of retarded elastic elements in series, as shown in figure 59. If the number of such elements were finite, say n, then the deformation–time curve at the constant stress S would be of the form:

$$\gamma = S \sum_{i=1}^{n} \frac{1}{G_i} (1 - e^{-t/\tau_i}) \tag{26}$$

It would therefore be necessary to know the value of the elastic constant associated with each retardation time τ. This same equation can be expressed in terms of the *reciprocal* moduli, or *compliances*, corresponding to the various retardation times:

$$J_i = \frac{1}{G_i} \tag{27}$$

$$\gamma = S \sum_{i=1}^{n} J_i(1 - e^{-t/\tau_i}) \tag{28}$$

When we go over to continuous distribution of mechanisms, then the deformation–time curve at the constant stress S is given by the *integral* expression:

$$\gamma = S \int_0^\infty J(\tau)(1 - e^{-t/\tau})d\tau \tag{29}$$

where J is now a continuous function of τ. The shape of such a deformation–time curve is compared to a set of simple exponential curves in figure 60.

It is apparent from the nature of such a curve that one would never be driven to a continuous distribution of relaxation mechanisms in order to explain an experimental deformation–time curve. Such a curve could be very closely approximated with a finite number of retarded elastic elements. As long as two elements have roughly the same retardation time they could be combined without major error into a single element of intermediate τ. On the other hand, the use of a continuous distribution of retardation times is much more straightforward and less ambiguous than the arbitrary analysis into a large finite number of retarded elements.

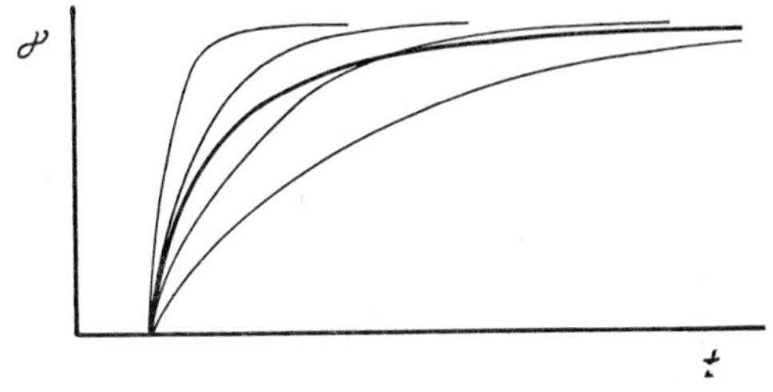

Fig. 60. Deformation–time relationship for a material exhibiting more than one retardation time (heavy curve) compared with a family of exponential curves (light curves).

The dielectric behavior of polar high polymers is in many respects analogous to the plastoelastic behavior. When a polar polymer is placed in an electric field, a force acts upon each dipole, tending to line it up with the field. This force, of an electrical origin, serves to bias the micro-Brownian movement of the polymer, just as does a mechanical shear stress (although not in the same geometric fashion).

A simple polar material such as gaseous hydrogen chloride responds in a relatively simple fashion to an imposed electric field. The instantaneous electronic polarization, resulting from the *polarizability* of the hydrogen chloride molecule, is followed by a retarded *orientation* polarization, as the hydrogen chloride dipoles preferentially line up with the field. This orientation of dipoles can be characterized by a single retardation time. In the actual investigation of a dielectric the steady state response to a sinusoidal field is observed, rather than the transient response to a suddenly applied constant field. At low frequencies, where $\omega \ll 1/\tau$, the dielectric exhibits a high dielectric constant which includes both the electronic and the orientation polarization. The dipoles can follow the field. At very high frequencies, where $\omega \gg 1/\tau$, the dielectric exhibits a low dielectric constant, which includes only the electronic polarization. The field is alternating too rapidly for the dipoles to follow it. At intermediate frequencies, where ω is of the order of magnitude of $1/\tau$, the dielectric constant depends markedly upon the frequency. Furthermore, in this frequency region where the dielectric constant is changing an out-of-phase component of polarization appears giving the dielectric a resistive as well as capacitive character.

When the dielectric constant and the phase angle of a polar high polymer is measured as a function of frequency, the intermediate region of changing constant and of appreciable out-of-phase polarization is found to extend over a much wider frequency range than is consistent with a single time of dielectric retardation. Kirkwood and Fuoss (*26a*, *45a*) have shown that the dielectric behavior of a polar polymer can be understood only on the basis of a *distribution* of retardation times. Furthermore, they show that such a distribution is to be expected from the structures of polar polymers.

A. Complex Phenomena Resulting from a Distribution of Retardation Times

If the configurational elasticity of a polymer actually represents several mechanisms with different retardation times, then the material will exhibit several interesting properties which cannot be explained on the basis of Model A. One such phenomenon is *elastic memory*. For simplicity, consider a specimen which possesses *two* delayed elastic mechanisms rather than a continuous distribution. Let $\tau_1 = 1$ second and $\tau_2 = 100$ seconds. Let the sample be deformed, and held at constant deformation for several hundred seconds. Both retarded mechanisms, 1 and 2, reach their equilibrium displacements. Then remove the stress, and impose a deformation in the opposite direction for several seconds. At the end of this time, the local kinkiness τ_1 will be straightened in the direction of the new stress, but the long range convolutions τ_2 will still be disposed in the manner dictated by the first strain. If the sample is now released, the local kinkiness will quickly return to its equilibrium form, so that $\gamma_1 = 0$. As a result, the sample will recover *beyond* its true equilibrium shape, because of the strain γ_2 still present. In the course of a few minutes, however, the sample will return to its equilibrium shape. A specific example would be the following: twist a rod θ_1 degrees in one direction. Hold for a long time. Then twist it back beyond its equilibrium position to θ_2 degrees in the op-

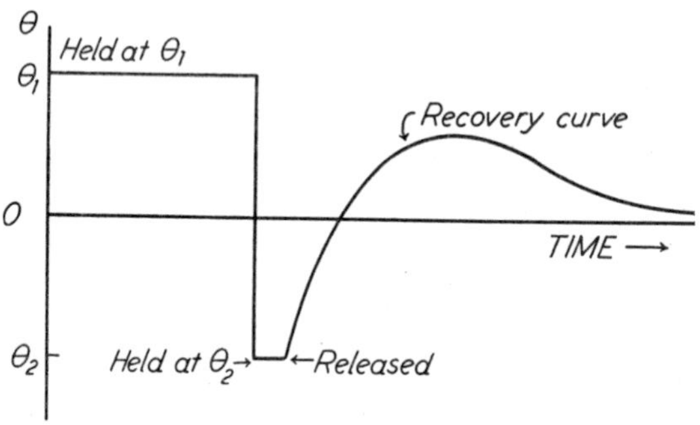

Fig. 61. Memory effect in polymer exhibiting a distribution of retardation times (after Kohlrausch).

posite sense and release rather quickly. The recovery will be of the general nature of figure 61. Such "memory" effects are commonly observed in high polymers.

Thus the experimentally observed properties of high polymers, as well as theoretical deductions from their structures, force the conclusion that configurational elasticity cannot be considered as a single elastic mechanism with a single τ, but must be regarded as a *series* of mechanisms of different τ values. In the limit, a continuous distribution of retarded elastic mechanisms may prove necessary or desirable, in which case the viscoelastic properties are defined by a continuous function $J(\tau)$, which tells the amount of elastic compliance that has the retardation time τ.

In many respects it would be preferable to express the function J in terms of $\ln \tau$, rather than in terms of τ itself. Let us define a new function $K(\tau)$, as equal to $\tau[J(\tau)]$. It is clear that if $K(\tau)$ is plotted against $\ln \tau$, an area under this curve exactly equals the corresponding area under the plot of $J(\tau)$ *vs.* τ:

$$\int_{\tau_1}^{\tau_2} J(\tau)\, d\tau \equiv \int_{\ln \tau_1}^{\ln \tau_2} K(\tau)\, d \ln \tau \qquad (30)$$

It is possible to express the function $K(\tau)$ directly in terms of $\ln \tau$, as follows:

$$\text{Let } \ln \tau = \lambda \qquad (31)$$

$$K(\tau) = \tau[J(\tau)] = e^{\lambda}[J(e^{\lambda})] = L(\lambda) \qquad (32)$$

The distribution function $L(\lambda)$, or $L(\ln \tau)$, is completely equivalent to the original function $J(\tau)$. The distribution of elastic deformability, J, among the various retardation times, can be represented either by a plot of $J(\tau)$ *vs.* τ, or a plot of $L(\lambda)$ *vs.* λ. The total deformability possessing a retardation time in the range between τ_1 and τ_2 is given by the area under either of these curves between the two values of the abscissa.

There are two reasons why the function $L(\lambda)$ may represent a more convenient description of the plastoelastic spectrum than the function $J(\tau)$. In the first place, one is interested in a very wide range of retardation times extending over several orders of magnitude. A graph of $L(\ln \tau)$ against $\ln \tau$ indicates more clearly the nature of a viscoelastic spectrum which extends over several orders of magnitude in τ than does a graph of $J(\tau)$ against τ. In terms of $L(\ln \tau)$, the amount of elastic deformability possessing a retardation time between the limits of τ_1 and τ_2 is given by:

$$[J]_{\tau_1}^{\tau_2} = \int_{\ln \tau_1}^{\ln \tau_2} L(\ln \tau)\, d \ln \tau \equiv \int_{\ln \tau_1}^{\ln \tau_2} L(\lambda)\, d\lambda \qquad (33)$$

A second advantage of such a representation of the viscoelastic spectrum lies in the effect of temperature. If a single energy of activation controlled all "components" of the micro-Brownian motion, and if the temperature variation of the elastic elements could be neglected, then an increase in temperature would simply shift the L(ln τ) curve for a given polymer to lower values of ln τ without changing its shape. We have seen that both of these conditions are approximately fulfilled in a linear amorphous polymer. Since all micro-Brownian, as well as macro-Brownian, molecular motion is built up of unit steps of the same type—segmental jumps—the same activation energy should be involved in all terms. Hence a change in temperature should result in the same proportionate change in τ for the uncurling and orientation of long molecular sections as well as of short ones. On a logarithmic scale this will appear as a simple shift, of magnitude $(E_a/R)(1/T_2 - 1/T_1)$. Furthermore, the elastic deformability, ΔJ, corresponding to a definite set of molecular processes, will be roughly proportional to $1/T$. For a moderate change

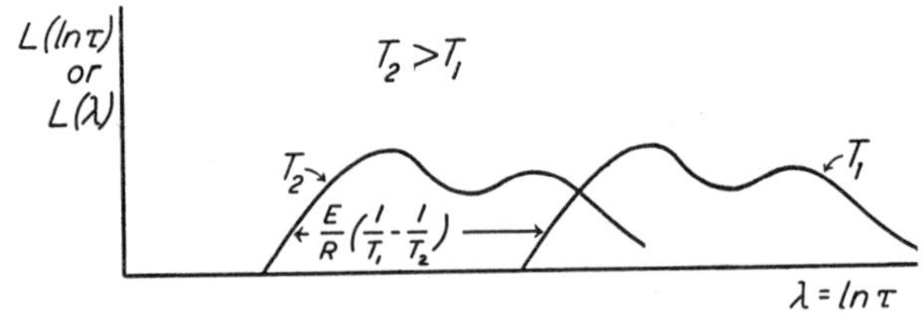

Fig. 62. Effect of temperature on the distribution of retardation times in an amorphous linear polymer (theoretical).

of temperature, the change in ΔJ corresponding to a given molecular process will be small compared to the change in τ for the same molecular process. Thus it seems reasonable to suggest, as a first approximation, the following simple picture of the change of a plastoelastic spectrum with temperature: If the function L(ln τ) is known at one temperature, T_1, the corresponding curve for a nearby temperature, T_2, will have roughly the same shape, but will be displaced horizontally by an amount $(E_a/R)(1/T_2 - 1/T_1)$. This is indicated in figure 62.

B. The Fundamental Partial Differential Equation

It is clear that if the configurational elastic response is distributed continuously over a wide range of retardation times, the configurational behavior in shear is governed by a partial differential equation instead of a set of ordinary differential equations. Let us represent the instantaneous elastic response by γ_1, the configurational elastic deformation by γ_2, and the deformation due to flow by γ_3, and let us further introduce the continuous function $\gamma^*(\tau)$ such that $\gamma^*(\tau)\,d\tau$ represents the configurational strain of elastic elements whose retardation time lies in the range $d\tau$ at the value τ:

$$\gamma_2 = \int_0^\infty \gamma^*(\tau)\,d\tau \tag{34}$$

In general the function γ^* will depend upon the time. Hence we write $\gamma^*(\tau,t)$.

$$\gamma(t) = \gamma_1(t) + \gamma_2(t) + \gamma_3(t) = \gamma_1(t) + \int_0^\infty \gamma^*(\tau,t)\,d\tau + \gamma_3(t) \tag{35}$$

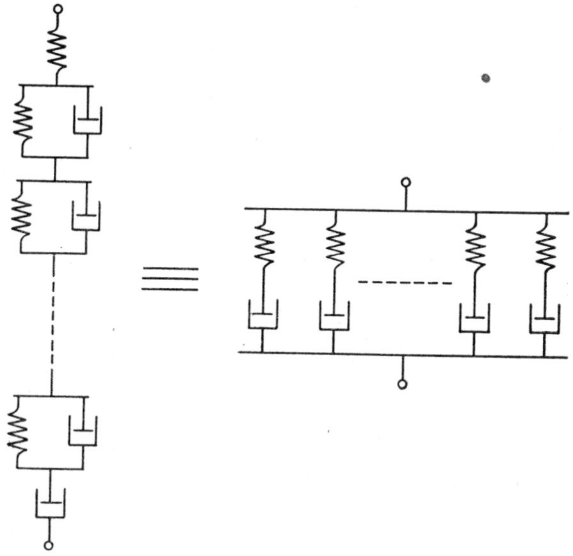

Fig. 63. Model of the Maxwell type, equivalent to Model C. Mathematical Model C represents a distribution of elastic compliance as a function of retardation time while the model on the right represents an equivalent distribution of elastic modulus as a function of relaxation time.

In response to a given stress, $S(t)$, γ_1 and γ_3 behave according to the equations:

$$\gamma_1(t) = \frac{1}{G}S(t) \tag{36}$$

$$\frac{d\gamma_3(t)}{dt} = \frac{1}{\eta}S(t) \tag{37}$$

The function $\gamma^*(\tau,t)$ is governed by the partial differential equation:

$$S(t) = \frac{1}{J(\tau)} \gamma^*(\tau,t) + \frac{\tau}{J(\tau)} \frac{\partial \gamma^*(\tau,t)}{\partial t} \tag{38}$$

The solution of equation (38) yields the desired $\gamma^*(\tau,t)$. *The general solution includes an arbitrary function of* τ, which reflects the fact that at $t = 0$ the sample may possess residual strains from previous deformations.

C. An Equivalent Representation for Model C

Just as the physical properties embodied in Model A can also be represented by an equivalent Model of type B, so also Model C (Fig. 59) (with its group of retarded elastic elements in series) can be represented by an equivalent model (D) made up of a group of Maxwell elements in parallel (Fig. 63).

2. Molecular Theory of the Viscoelastic Spectrum of an Amorphous Linear Polymer

The only well established molecular theory concerning the viscoelastic properties of amorphous high polymers is the kinetic theory of long range elasticity (*13*). This theory has proved very valuable in understanding the magnitude and temperature dependence of the elastic moduli governing configurational changes and has served as a quantitative tool in the study of a series of rubberlike materials (*31*). The kinetic theory, however, has several serious shortcomings, as follows:

(1) The undue emphasis on the separation of the *chain ends* makes it, strictly speaking, unsuitable as a treatment of linear polymers. As we shall see in Chapter C, this objection is largely removed if one considers a net polymer, with mesh points playing the role of chain ends.

(2) In any case, the kinetic theory is purely an *equilibrium* treatment. It predicts the equilibrium elastic deformation in the presence of a stress but does not yield any information concerning the transient conditions during the establishment of elastic equilibrium.

At the present writing, a molecular theory is needed which goes far beyond the kinetic theory of elasticity and predicts the whole viscoelastic spectrum of an amorphous polymer. Qualitatively, we have already done this in section 1 (pages 93–118), where the configurational elasticity was identified as the stress-biased micro-Brownian movement of the polymer. In the presence of a stress, the curled molecular chains are straightened and oriented, the local kinkiness being affected more quickly than the long range convolutions. These qualitative remarks, however, cannot be said to constitute a working theory, since they offer no framework for actually computing the plastoelastic spectrum from molecular structure. In this section, such a computational framework will be presented.

Consider a sample of a monodisperse linear polymer, made up of N molecules, each of which contains n chain atoms. In order to specify the position of every chain atom in the sample, $3\,nN$ coordinates are necessary. A point in $3\,nN$-dimensional phase space expresses this information, and can be considered to represent a molecular configuration of the whole sample. The diffusional motion of the sample, including both the micro- and the macro-Brownian motions, can be represented by a diffusional motion of the point in phase space. Each point in phase space represents some definite macroscopic shape of the sample. In the absence of an external stress, the representative point wanders about through a region in phase space which corresponds to the "unstrained" shape of the sample. In the presence of a stress, the representative point wanders into new regions of phase space, which correspond to finite macroscopic strains. The whole problem of the viscoelastic behavior of such a material would be solved if we were able: (1) to formulate and solve the equations of motion of the point in $3\,nN$-dimensional phase space, and (2) to compute the macroscopic strain from the values of the $3\,nN$ coordinates. The difficulties involved are obviously very great if the $3\,nN$ Cartesian coordinates of the individual chain atoms are chosen as the reference coordinates. The question arises: Can a molecular configuration be described in terms of some other set of parameters than the Cartesian coordinates of the atoms, so chosen as to simplify the mathematical problem projected here?

Such a transformation of coordinates is, of course, common practice in strictly dynamical problems and in statistical mechanics. Consider, for example, the classical motion of diatomic gas molecules. A complete specification of the position and shape of such a molecule involves 6 coordinates. If the Cartesian coordinates of the two atoms are used, the equations of motion are complicated. Each individual atom moves through space along a very complicated path. On the other hand, if the location of the atoms is specified by the Cartesian coordinates of the *center of gravity* of the molecule, the distance between the two atoms, and the angular orientation of the line defined by the two atoms, then the motion can be described much more simply. The center of gravity moves in a straight line at uniform speed; the line defined by the two atoms rotates at constant angular velocity, and the distance between the two atoms varies sinusoidally with time about the equilibrium value. In other words, the molecular motion can be resolved into translational, rotational, and vibrational motions which are individually simple (neglecting interaction between vibrational and rotational degrees of freedom). The Cartesian coordinates of the individual atoms ($x_1, y_1, z_1, x_2, y_2, z_2$) are replaced by 6 new coordinates ($X_1, X_2, X_3, X_4, X_5, X_6$), which follow simpler equations of motion. The new coordinates are more or less complicated combinations of the old. Thus X_1, the x coordinate of the center of gravity, is equal to $(x_1 + x_2)/2$, and X_6, the distance between the two atoms, is given by $\sqrt{(x_2 - x_1)^2 + (y_2 - y_1)^2 + (z_2 - z_1)^2}$, etc. However, the fact that the new coordinates are less simple in definition than the old is more than compensated for by the *increased* simplicity of the equations of motion when expressed in terms of the new coordinates. In the case of a more complicated molecule, such as benzene, the motion of the 12 atoms can be resolved into the translation of the center of gravity, the rotation of the molecule, and 30 distinct modes of molecular vibration. The definition of each of these 36 coordinates in terms of the 36 elementary Cartesian coordinates of the 12 atoms is very complicated, but as before, the equations of motion are much simpler in terms of the new coordinates.

Our problem is one of *diffusion*, rather than vibration, but it may still be helpful to replace the $3n$ atomic Cartesian coordinates for a given molecule by a new set of $3n$ coordinates in terms of which the diffusional motion can be more simply expressed, and more simply connected with the macroscopic strain. It should not be surprising if the new coordinates are complicated functions of the old; indeed, it would be surprising if this were not true.

In order to make an intelligent choice of the $3n$ coordinates which are to replace the Cartesian coordinates of the chain atoms, let us consider how the macroscopic configurational strain is determined by the molecular configuration of the sample. Any definite molecular configuration of the whole sample means a definite set of values of all $3nN$ atomic Cartesian coordinates, and hence a definite *distribution* of values of the $3n$ coordinates defining the configuration of each individual molecule. This can be represented by a density distribution function about a reference point such as an end of the chain. This density distribution is the sum of the density distributions for the individual chain atoms. We already have an approximation for the (equilibrium unstressed) density distribution of the second chain end about the first:

$$D_0(x,y,z) = W(x,y,z) = A\frac{1}{n^{\frac{3}{2}}}e^{-B\cdot 1/n\cdot(x^2+y^2+z^2)} \tag{39}$$

The constant A is here chosen to normalize D_0 to unity. Using this expression for the equilibrium unstressed density distribution of the ith chain atom about the first, whether the ith atom is a chain end or not, we obtain for the total (equilibrium unstressed) density distribution about an end of the chain:

$$^nD_0(x,y,z) = \sum_{s=1}^{n}\frac{A}{s^{\frac{3}{2}}}e^{-B\cdot 1/s\cdot(x^2+y^2+z^2)} \tag{40}$$

This density distribution is spherically symmetrical, and corresponds to the unstrained state. A linear high polymer which possesses configurational strain will have a different distribution among molecular shapes and hence a different density distribution function which will not be spherically symmetrical, but rather ellipsoidally symmetrical at least for small strains. The kinetic theory of high elasticity predicts that in the presence of a tensile stress S (in the x direction), the equilibrium distribution function for the vectorial separation of two chain atoms, which are n units apart in the chain, is given by:

$$D_S(x,y,z) = \frac{A}{n^{\frac{3}{2}}}e^{-\frac{B}{n}\left[\frac{x^2}{\left(1+\frac{nS}{3\rho kT}\right)^2}+\left(1+\frac{nS}{3\rho kT}\right)(y^2+z^2)\right]} \tag{41}$$

It follows that the total density distribution function, including the distribution of each successive chain atom about the reference end, will be given by the equation:

$$^nD_S(x,y,z) = \sum_{s=1}^{n}\frac{A}{s^{\frac{3}{2}}}e^{-\frac{B}{n}\left[\frac{x^2}{\left(1+\frac{nS}{3\rho kT}\right)^2}+\left(1+\frac{nS}{3\rho kT}\right)(y^2+z^2)\right]} \tag{42}$$

The macroscopic strain is connected with the smeared-out molecular shape by equations of the type below:

$$1+\gamma_x = \frac{L}{L_0} = \frac{\int_0^\infty dx\int_{-\infty}^{\infty}dy\int_{-\infty}^{\infty}x\,{}^nD_S(x,y,z)\,dz}{\int_0^\infty dx\int_{-\infty}^{\infty}dy\int_{-\infty}^{\infty}x\,{}^nD_0(x,y,z)\,dz} \tag{43}$$

This compares the mean extension-in-x of a molecule in the strained state to that in the unstrained state. (In the rest of the discussion, other subscripts will appear. In order to avoid double subscripts, it will be assumed that γ refers to γ_{xx}.)

Now equation (43) gives the *total* configurational strain, resulting from the change in short range curliness and long range convolution as well. If it is wished to divide γ into a part which is due to the uncurling and orientation of chain segments which are shorter than some length m, and a part which is due to the uncurling and orientation of longer chain segments, the following procedure can be followed.

Consider the various segments, containing m chain atoms, as though they were complete molecules. There will be a certain density distribution ${}^m\mathrm{D}(x,y,z)$ which will represent the average, or smeared-out, extension in space of these segments, in exactly the fashion that ${}^n\mathrm{D}(x,y,z)$ represents the whole molecule:

$$ {}^m\mathrm{D}_0(x,y,z) = \sum_{s=1}^{m} \frac{\mathrm{A}_S}{s^{\frac{3}{2}}} \, e^{-\mathrm{B}\cdot 1/s\cdot(x^2+y^2+z^2)} \qquad (44) $$

The elastic strain which results from the uncurling and orientation of short segments (containing less than m atoms) may be designated by γ_1, and the strain which results from the uncurling and orientation of long segments by γ_2:

$$ \gamma_1 = \frac{\iiint x\,{}^m\mathrm{D}(x,y,z)dx\,dy\,dz}{\iiint x\,{}^m\mathrm{D}_0(x,y,z)dx\,dy\,dz} - 1 $$

$$ \gamma_2 = \frac{\iiint x\,{}^n\mathrm{D}(x,y,z)dx\,dy\,dz}{\iiint x\,{}^n\mathrm{D}_0(x,y,z)dx\,dy\,dz} - \frac{\iiint x\,{}^m\mathrm{D}(x,y,z)dx\,dy\,dz}{\iiint x\,{}^m\mathrm{D}_0(x,y,z)dx\,dy\,dz} \qquad (45) $$

$$ \gamma = \gamma_1 + \gamma_2 = \frac{\iiint x\,{}^n\mathrm{D}(x,y,z)dx\,dy\,dz}{\iiint x\,{}^n\mathrm{D}_0(x,y,z)dx\,dy\,dz} - 1 $$

Finally, the strain can be resolved into $(n - 1)$ components, each representing the contribution due to the uncurling and orientation of chain segments of a definite length:

$$\gamma_j = \frac{\int dx \int dy \int x\, {}^j\mathrm{D}(x,y,z)\, dz}{\int dx \int dy \int x\, {}^j\mathrm{D}_0(x,y,z)\, dz} - \frac{\int\int\int x\, {}^{(j-1)}\mathrm{D}(x,y,z)\, dz}{\int\int\int x\, {}^{(j-1)}\mathrm{D}_0(x,y,z)\, dz} \tag{46}$$

$$\gamma = \sum_j \gamma_j$$

The form of the above equations suggests a new set of coordinates $(X_1, Y_1, Z_1, X_2, Y_2, Z_2, \cdots X_n, Y_n, Z_n)$ to describe the configuration of a single molecule and thus take the place of the atomic Cartesian coordinates $(x_1, y_1, z_1, x_2, y_2, z_2, \cdots x_n, y_n, z_n)$. Let X_1, Y_1, and Z_1 represent the x, y, and z coordinate, respectively, of the center of gravity of the polymer molecule. Let X_j be defined by the expression:

$$\frac{\overset{\text{[average over all segments of } j \text{ atoms]}}{\left| \sum_{k=2}^{j} |x_k| \right|}}{\int\int\int x\, {}^j\mathrm{D}_0(x,y,z) dx\, dy\, dz} - \frac{\overset{\text{[average over all segments of } (j-1) \text{ atoms]}}{\left| \sum_{k=2}^{j-1} x_k \right|}}{\int\int\int x\, {}^{j-1}\mathrm{D}_0(x,y,z) dx\, dy\, dz} \tag{47}$$

Thus just as γ_j represents the macroscopic x-tensile strain due to the uncurling and orientation of molecular chain segments containing j atoms when a given *distribution* of shapes is present, so X_j represents the relative uncurling and x-orientation of the chain segments containing j atoms in a single polymer molecule of a definite shape.

If the new coordinates X_i, Y_i, etc., were a linear combination of the atomic Cartesian coordinates, $x_1, y_1, z_1, x_2, y_2, z_2, \cdots$ etc., then they would represent an equivalent set of independent variables which together would define the configuration of a polymer molecule. Actually, the *absolute magnitudes* of certain quantities enter in place of the algebraic values. Hence the new "coordinates," $X_1, X_2, \cdots$ etc., do not represent a linear transformation of the original Cartesian coordinates. The X coordinates are not strictly a set of "normal coordinates" for the polymer molecule, although they are introduced for analogous reasons. Just as a given distribution of molecular configurations results in a series of density distributions ${}^j\mathrm{D}(x,y,z)$, so it also results in a series of probability distributions governing the various X values minus ${}^j\mathrm{D}(X_j)$. The strain γ_j is given by:

$$\gamma_j = \int_0^\infty X_j\, {}^j\mathrm{D}(X_j)\, dX_j = \bar{X}_j \tag{48}$$

In particular, the equilibrium unstressed distribution of molecular shapes, which gave rise to the density distributions ${}^{i}\mathrm{D}_0(x,y,z)$, will also give rise to the distributions ${}^{i}\mathrm{D}_0(X_j)$, such that

$$\bar{X}_j = \int_0^\infty X_j \, {}^{i}\mathrm{D}_0(X_j) \, dX_j = 0 \tag{49}$$

In the presence of a stress, there will be a new equilibrium distribution of molecular shapes, and hence a new equilibrium distribution of the values of each of the X coordinates, and new equilibrium values of the macroscopic strain contributions $\gamma_2, \gamma_3, \gamma_4, \cdots \gamma_n$. The local kinkiness, defined by the X coordinates of low index, will take on its equilibrium distribution rather quickly; the long range convolutions, defined by the X coordinates of large index, will assume the new equilibrium distribution more slowly.

However, before discussing the rate of attainment of the equilibrium configurational strains, let us derive explicit formulas for the equilibrium values of $\gamma_2, \gamma_3, \cdots \gamma_n$ in the presence of a stress S, and hence the equilibrium mean values of the new coordinates $X_2, X_3, \cdots X_n$ for a given stress. The total strain, which is produced when the sample diffuses from the equilibrium unstressed density distribution ${}^{n}\mathrm{D}_0$ to the equilibrium stressed distribution ${}^{n}\mathrm{D}_S$ is given by:

$$1 + \gamma = \frac{\displaystyle\int_0^\infty\int_0^\infty\int_0^\infty x \sum_{s=1}^{n} \frac{1}{s^{\frac{3}{2}}} \mathrm{e}^{-\frac{\mathrm{B}}{s}\left[\frac{x^2}{\left(1+\frac{sS}{3\rho kT}\right)^2} + \left(1+\frac{sS}{3\rho kT}\right)(y^2+z^2)\right]} dx\,dy\,dz}{\displaystyle\int_0^\infty\int_0^\infty\int_0^\infty x \sum_{s=1}^{n} \frac{1}{s^{\frac{3}{2}}} \mathrm{e}^{-\mathrm{B}/s\cdot(x^2+y^2+z^2)} dx\,dy\,dz} \tag{50}$$

$$= \frac{\displaystyle\sum_{s=1}^{n} \frac{1}{s^{\frac{3}{2}}} \int_0^\infty x\,\mathrm{e}^{-\frac{\mathrm{B}}{s}\frac{x^2}{\left(1+\frac{sS}{3\rho kT}\right)^2}} dx \int_0^\infty\int_0^\infty \mathrm{e}^{-\frac{\mathrm{B}}{s}\left(1+\frac{sS}{3\rho kT}\right)(y^2+z^2)} dy\,dz}{\displaystyle\sum_{s=1}^{n} \frac{1}{s^{\frac{3}{2}}} \int_0^\infty x\,\mathrm{e}^{-\mathrm{B}/s\cdot x^2}\,dx \int_0^\infty\int_0^\infty \mathrm{e}^{-\mathrm{B}/s\cdot(y^2+z^2)} dy\,dz} \tag{51}$$

$$= \frac{\displaystyle\sum_{s=1}^{n} (s^{\frac{1}{2}} + as^{\frac{3}{2}})}{\displaystyle\sum_{s=1}^{n} s^{\frac{1}{2}}} \sim \frac{\displaystyle\int_1^n (s^{\frac{1}{2}} + as^{\frac{3}{2}})\,ds}{\displaystyle\int_1^n s^{\frac{1}{2}}\,ds} \tag{52}$$

$$= 1 + \frac{3\,a}{5}\frac{(n^{5/2} - 1)}{(n^{\frac{3}{2}} - 1)} \qquad \text{where} \qquad a = \frac{S}{3\rho kT} \tag{53}$$

For large n, this reduces to:

$$1 + \frac{3}{5}\frac{nS}{3\rho kT} = 1 + \frac{nS}{5\rho kT} \tag{54}$$

$$\gamma = S\frac{n}{5\rho kT} \tag{55}$$

Except for the numerical factor, this result agrees with that obtained by the ordinary kinetic theory, where only the distribution of chain *ends* is considered. If we consider only chain ends, we obtain:

$$1 + \gamma = \frac{\iiint x\, e^{-\frac{B}{n}\left[\frac{x^2}{(1+an)^2}+(1+an)(y^2+z^2)\right]}dx\, dy\, dz}{\iiint x\, e^{-B/n\cdot(x^2+y^2+z^2)}dx\, dy\, dz} \tag{56}$$

$$= 1 + an = 1 + S\frac{n}{3\rho kT} \tag{57}$$

$$\gamma = S\frac{n}{3\rho kT} \tag{58}$$

The extended analysis thus yields no significantly new information concerning the equilibrium value of the total strain. The value of the more detailed treatment lies in the fact that we can now resolve the total configurational strain into a series of terms, $\gamma_2, \gamma_3, \gamma_4, \gamma_5, \cdots \gamma_n$, which indicate the contribution to the strain of shape changes in chain sections of different length. This turns out, on the basis of our approximation, to give a very simple result:

$$\gamma_i = S\frac{1}{5\rho kT} \tag{59}$$

Similarly, $\bar{X}_i$, the equilibrium mean value of the "coordinate" X, has the value $S/5\rho kT$. Finally, the contribution to the elastic compliance (in tension) which is furnished by the shape changes of chain sections containing between n and $n + dn$ chain atoms, is given simply by the equation:

$$J_{\text{tension}}(n)\, dn = \frac{1}{5\rho kT}\, dn \tag{60}$$

The corresponding shear compliance, $J(n)$, is given by:

$$J_{\text{shear}} = 3\, J_{\text{tension}}$$

$$J_{\text{shear}}(n)\, dn = \frac{3}{5\rho kT}\, dn \tag{61}$$

Following our usual procedure, we will characterize the polymer by its *shear* compliance, rather than its behavior in tension.

We can now return to the question of the rate of attainment of elastic equilibrium. We have advanced the general hypothesis that the local kinkiness, defined by the X coordinates of low index, will take on its equilibrium distribution rather quickly, while the long range convolutions of the chains, defined by X coordinates of large index, will assume the new equilibrium distribution more slowly.

Let us now specifically assume that each contribution to γ relaxes into its new equilibrium value in a simple exponential fashion, with a retardation time τ which is connected with the chain length of the corresponding segment in the same fashion that the melt viscosity of a linear polymer is connected with the molecular chain length:

$$\tau_i = \mathrm{A}\, e^{b\sqrt{n_i}}\, e^{\Delta \mathrm{E}/RT} \tag{62}$$

This would seem to be a reasonable assumption as long as i is considerably greater than the length of the effective segments which act in flow and diffusion.

If we combine equation (62), which gives the retardation time for the configurational changes of a chain section of size n, with equation (61), which gives the elastic compliance J associated with a range of sizes dn, we can deduce the function $J(\tau)$, which gives the elastic compliance as a function of retardation time. The function so obtained is:

$$J(\tau)\, d\tau = \frac{6}{5\, b^2 \rho k T} \left(\frac{\ln \tau - \ln \mathrm{A} - \Delta \mathrm{E}/RT}{\tau} \right) d\tau \tag{63}$$

In the above form, the dependence on temperature as well as on τ is given. At a definite temperature, the above equation can be expressed in the form:

$$J(\tau)\, d\tau = \frac{\mathrm{C} \ln \tau - \mathrm{D}}{\tau}\, d\tau \tag{64}$$

The equivalent function $\mathrm{L}(\lambda)$, where $\lambda = \ln \tau$, is given by:

$$\mathrm{L}(\lambda)\, d\lambda = (\mathrm{C}\lambda - \mathrm{D})\, d\lambda \tag{65}$$

This latter distribution function is plotted in figure 64.

The theory thus leads to precisely the sort of mechanical behavior discussed in section 1 (pages 127–134), *i.e.*, a distribution of elastic deformability over a wide range of retardation times. While it has not been experimentally tested, the author advances it with some confidence that the general method involved will prove to be the starting point toward a thorough molecular explanation of the nonequilibrium plasto-elastic behavior of amorphous linear polymers, as the Mark-Guth-Kuhn treatment has proved in the equilibrium aspects of long range elasticity. The theory as presented above certainly must fall down in the low τ region, which corresponds to the shape changes of very short segments. In the first place, the equilibrium distribution law, equation (39), should not be applied to very short sections. Furthermore, the assumption that

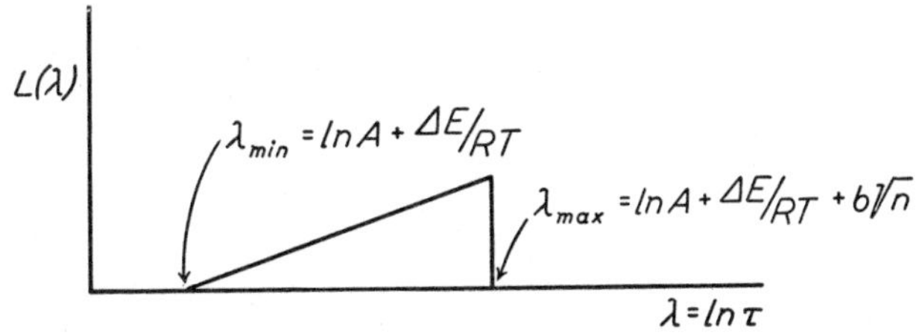

Fig. 64. Distribution of retardation times for a monodisperse amorphous linear polymer (theoretical).

τ_i is given by equation (62) cannot be expected to hold for segments which are not several times as long as the "Eyring segments" which serve as the moving units of flow and diffusion. All assumptions involved in the theory are much more justified in the high τ region of the spectrum. In the case of very high molecular weight polymers, this high τ part of the spectrum should be relatively more important than in the case of a low molecular weight polymer, and therefore the theory as a whole should be most valid for high molecular weight polymers.

A. Different Kinds of "Segments"

Throughout this chapter, and indeed throughout this volume, it often becomes necessary to focus attention upon some portion of a polymer chain, rather than upon the entire molecule. If we describe such portions of polymer molecules by the generic term "segments," then it is clear that there are a number of different kinds of segments to be considered. The "segments" which play a part in the kinetic theory of high elasticity are quite different from the "segments" which appear in the Eyring picture of viscous flow and still a third type of "segment" makes its appearance in the general theory of viscoelastic response. It may be worth while, therefore, to discuss these various types * of molecular segment separately and to make the distinctions among them explicit:

* In view of the many different chain "segments" which are for various reasons considered to have a significance of some kind, it may in the future prove desirable to establish a definite system of nomenclature, in which each type of segment is referred to by a definite word, such as group, segment, section, unit, submolecule, etc. This, however, has not be done here.

(1) In the kinetic theory of high elasticity, we are concerned with the successive orientations of a series of relatively short sections of the chain. In the original theory of Guth and Mark, these elementary sections were considered to be individual valence bonds. Free rotation about each bond was assumed and, hence, the structural unit in the statistical treatment was a single valence bond of definite length, but with a certain orientational freedom. In his extension of this theory to the case of hindered rotation, Kuhn replaced the single bond of the original theory by a larger unit containing several atoms, which unit was considered as a freely orienting segment. "Segments" of this type also enter into statistical-thermodynamic treatments of the thermodynamic properties of polymer solutions (as developed by Huggins and Flory). In all of these statistical theories, the question involved is the number of different configurations possible for the polymer molecules and, hence, the "segments" which appear in these theories have much the same meanings. For convenience we will speak of these as "Kuhn segments."

(2) In Eyring's theory of diffusion and flow of high polymers, a different type of segment appears. We have seen that when a polymer changes from one configuration to another, the motion is made up of many segmental jumps. The "segments" which operate in flow and diffusion seem to be in the same order of magnitude of 20 to 40 chain atoms in length. These "Eyring segments" have no direct connection with the "Kuhn segments," although such structural features as rigidity of the chain, which makes for large "Kuhn segments" might also be expected to result in large "Eyring segments." Actually, the segmental diffusion of a polymer must be made up of the motions of segments exhibiting a wide range of size, but all investigators simplify this problem by choosing an *average* size for the Eyring segments in each case. The Eyring segments are connected with the *rate of flow*, and the *rate of attainment of configurational elastic equilibrium*, but have nothing at all to do with the equilibrium elastic behavior of the polymer.

(3) A third type of molecular "segment" has been encountered in the general molecular theory of viscoelastic response. For the purpose of this paragraph let us denote this third type of section as a "normal segment" since it is connected with a process somewhat analogous to a transformation to normal coordinates. The "normal segments" of a polymer molecule range in size from a single bond to the entire molecule itself. The general theory as developed here assumes, however, that the "normal segment" behaves in a fashion typical of high polymers, *i.e.*, the "normal segment" is distributed among its various possible shapes in the same manner as a high polymer molecule and moves from one shape to another by segmental jumps. This means that a "normal segment" should contain many "Kuhn segments" and many "Eyring segments" in order to justify the mathematical procedure used. However, it is obvious that this requirement is not met by the shorter "normal segments," which is a serious shortcoming of the theory in its present form. The implicit assumption that each "normal segment" contains many "Kuhn segments" is necessary for a simple evaluation of the function $J(n)$, and the implicit assumption that each "normal segment" contains many "Eyring segments" is necessary for a simple evaluation of $\tau(n)$. In order to deduce a viscoelastic spectrum of a polymer which is essentially correct in the low τ region, it will be necessary to remove the assumption that short normal segments follow the same statistical and kinetic patterns as truly "high" normal segments.

(4) A fourth portion of a polymer chain which has a distinct meaning is the monomer unit. The meaning of this type of "segment" is obvious. Closely related is the arbitrary chain section of 5 Å. length, which Mark used in the comparison of molar cohesions.

B. Effect of Molecular Weight on Viscoelastic Spectrum

The theoretical considerations of the previous paragraphs do not, in their present rough form, permit us to predict with any confidence the detailed form of the viscoelastic spectrum of a polymer. Furthermore, the experimental data available today are much too meager to permit the direct empirical calculation of such a spectrum. We should, however, be able to predict roughly the effects of differences in structure upon the viscoelastic spectrum.

The general point of view of section 2 (pages 134–143) leads us to certain conclusions regarding the effect of the molecular weight of a monodisperse higher polymer upon its plastoelastic spectrum. Let us consider two sharp molecular weight fractions of the same high polymer—one of DP 1000 and a second of DP 3000. It seems reasonable to suppose that the low τ portion of the two spectra, representing the uncurling of chain sections of only a few hundred units, will be nearly identical for the two materials. The uncurling of a section of length 200, for example, should not depend very much on the total size of the molecule of which it is a part. The uncurling of a section of 900 units, on the other hand, will presumably be different for molecules of total length 1000 and 3000. The plastoelastic spectra, therefore, will diverge at higher τ values.

Furthermore, the spectrum for the polymer of DP 1000 will be cut off at a lower τ value than that for the DP 3000 sample. (There will be no elements corresponding to the shape changes of sections of more than 1000 units.) Finally, the value of η_3, the viscosity which governs true flow, will be smaller in the case of the polymer of low molecular weight.

By accepting the molecular theory of the previous section without reservation, we could of course be much more specific in our discussion of the effect of polymerization degree upon the viscoelastic spectrum of a polymer. However, in view of the crude nature and the untested status of that theory, it would seem inadvisable to draw such detailed deductions from it at the present time. The general comments of this section, on the other hand, appear to the author to be well grounded and unlikely to be invalidated by future investigations.

To summarize, different molecular weight samples of the same high polymer should exhibit viscoelastic spectra which are identical in the low τ region, diverging in the high τ region, with the most outstanding difference appearing in the viscosity governing true flow. We have seen that this viscosity is an exponential function of $\sqrt{Z}$.

While very little direct experimental confirmation of these results can be offered, the work of Hewitt on butyl rubber is of interest. Creep curves were obtained at temperatures ranging from $-56°$ to $-5°$ C. for four different molecular weights of unvulcanized butyl rubber. The general pattern of the creep behavior for a given sample is shown in figure 64A. The creep curves (on a logarithmic time scale) may be described as consisting of a sigmoidal curve (comprising the retarded elastic response) followed by an exponential rise due to irrecoverable viscous flow.

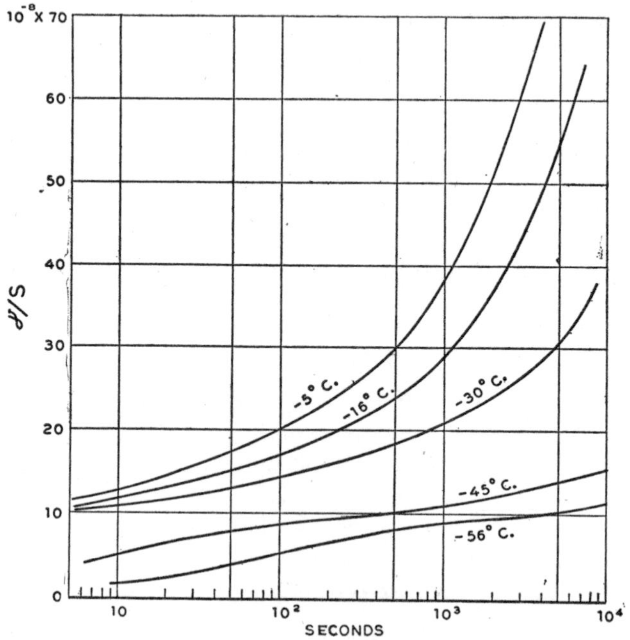

Fig. 64A. Creep curves for an unvulcanized butyl rubber at various temperatures.

As usual, an increase in the temperature shifts the curves to the left. When comparison is made among the four different molecular weights at an extremely low temperature, very small differences were observed among the different samples. The early part of the retarded elastic response is thus, within experimental error, independent of the molecular weight of the rubber. Differences between the different molecular weight samples arise in the long time portion of the creep curve. This is indicated in figure 64B and C.

Our theoretical expectation as to the effect of molecular weight on the creep curves of such materials can be roughly summarized in the following three statements.

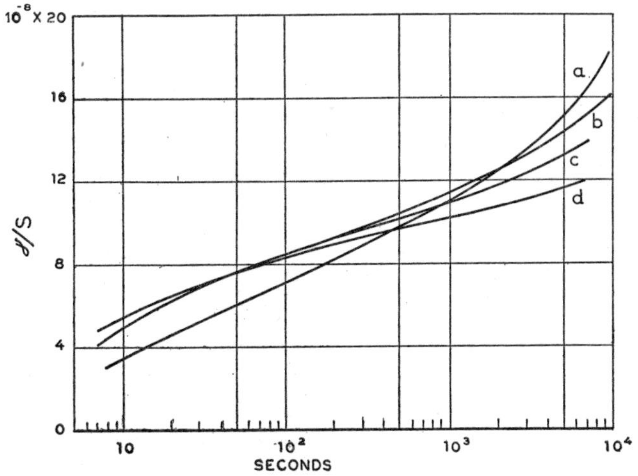

Fig. 64B. Creep curves at −45° C. for four unvulcanized butyl rubbers. Molecular weight increases in the order a, b, c, d.

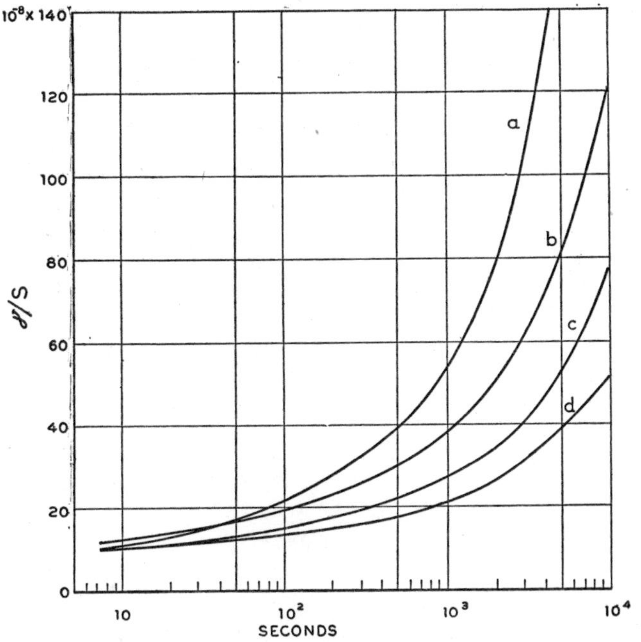

Fig. 64C. Creep curves at −5° C. for the unvulcanized butyl rubber samples of Figure 64B.

(1) The *rapid* part of the retarded elastic response should be independent of molecular weight.

(2) The samples of high molecular weight should exhibit a larger amount of *long time* retarded elastic compliance than the samples of low molecular weight.

(3) The samples of low molecular weight should exhibit a greater amount of irrecoverable flow than the samples of high molecular weight. The data indicated above are in harmony with the first and third of these theoretical conclusions but unfortunately are insufficient to establish the second.

An amorphous polymer of very low polymerization degree is essentially a viscous liquid. The deformation due to actual viscous flow is much greater than that due to configurational elasticity, since the total configurational compliance is small while the fluidity is relatively high. As one proceeds to polymers of longer chain length, the total configurational compliance increases (roughly proportionally with the chain length) while the fluidity decreases very rapidly. Thus the configurational elasticity becomes much more important, compared with the flow, as the chain length becomes greater. Even in the case of a very high polymer, the viscous flow will overshadow the configurational elasticity at very high temperatures or over very long periods of time, but the greater the polymerization degree the higher the temperature and the longer the experimental timescale necessary for this to be true.

C. Effect of Polydispersity upon the Viscoelastic Spectrum

The foregoing discussion of the viscoelastic properties of amorphous polymers has implicitly assumed a completely sharp molecular weight distribution curve. The distribution of retardation times did not arise from a lack of uniformity in molecular weight, but from the configurational changes of different sized *sections* of uniform polymer molecules. Since even a monodisperse polymer exhibits a distribution of retardation times, it might appear at first glance that a polydisperse polymer would exhibit a doubly complicated plastoelastic spectrum. Fortunately, this is not true. If each monodisperse polymer fraction can be adequately represented by a linear model of type C (Fig. 59), with its distribution function $J(\tau)$, then a polydisperse mixture of these fractions can be adequately represented by precisely such a model.

For example, consider a polymer which is a mixture of two molecular weight species, M_A and M_B, each with its individual distribution of elastic retardation times, then presumably the effective model, which is to represent the mechanical properties of the mixture, must be some sort of combination of the separate models for the pure monodisperse polymers A and B. The most logical choice for this combination would seem to be a parallel arrangement, as shown in figure 65. The two individual models should be weighted according to the relative amounts of the corresponding components in the mixture. Presumably the *weight fraction* would serve as the appropriate weighting factor. However, it is always possible to replace a model of this form by a completely equivalent model of the form of Model C. Hence the presence of two different molecular weight components does not increase the complexity of the viscoelastic behavior. If instead of a *binary* polymer mixture, the sample has a continuous molecular weight distribution curve, then the above procedure leads to a continuous set of models, one for each molecular weight, all coupled in parallel. Since each individual model itself contains a continuous distribution of elements in series, this results in a two-dimensional continuous array of retarded elastic elements (see Fig. 66). Such a two-dimensional array is fantastically involved but can always be exactly duplicated by a one-dimensional array such as Model C. Hence, the complicated array of elements in figure 66 actually represents no more complicated a mechanical behavior than does a model such as Model C and, as a corollary, the two-dimensional array of figure 66 introduces no more mathematical parameters and is, therefore, no more "flexible" for fitting to experimental data than the one-dimensional array of Model C in figure 59 (page 128).

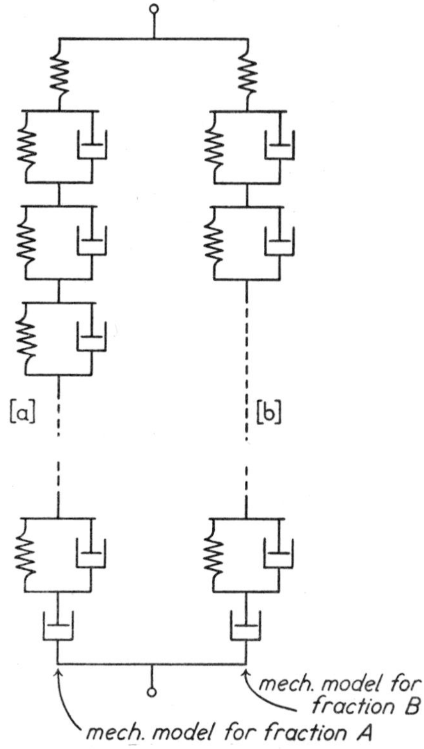

Fig. 65. Mechanical model for a mixture of two molecular weight fractions of an amorphous linear polymer (hypothetical).

If the viscoelastic spectra of several sharp molecular weight fractions of a polymer were known, then it might be useful to represent the properties of a mixture of these fractions by a two-dimensional array of the sort postulated here. Otherwise, the use of such a model would

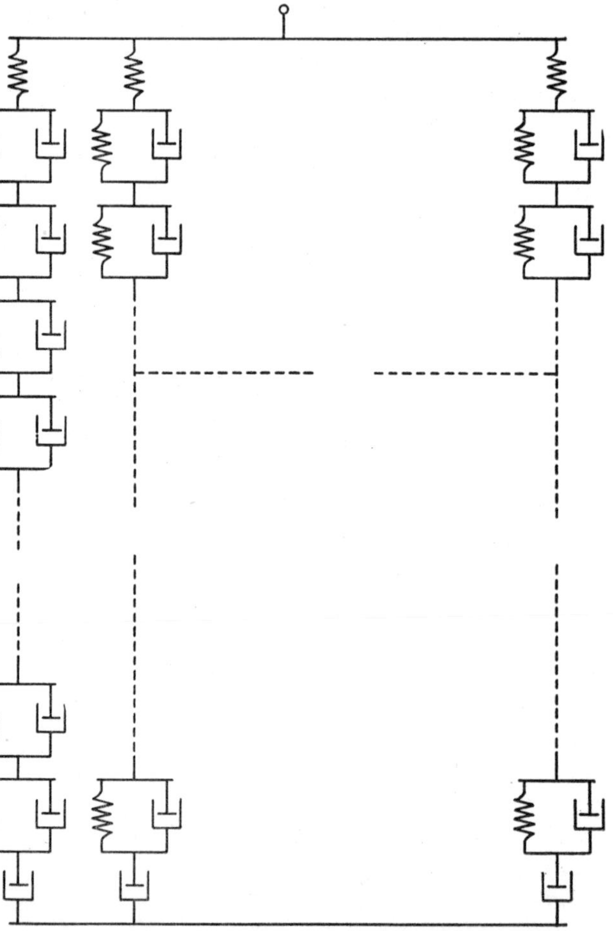

Fig. 66. Mechanical model for a sample containing a distribution of molecular weights (hypothetical).

simply overcomplicate the problem. Since no such data are now available, models such as that in figure 66 have not been used here; the plastoelastic behavior of all amorphous polymers, whether mono- or polydisperse, is represented by one-dimensional arrays such as Model C.

In view of the fact that the detailed nature of the viscoelastic spectrum of each monodisperse polymer is still in doubt, it is only with great caution that we can venture any predictions concerning the viscoelastic spectra of polydisperse mixtures, even expressed in the condensed form of a one-dimensional model, *i.e.*, a function $J(\tau)$. However, a few guesses are now presented, in graphical form, as to such distributions of relaxation time.

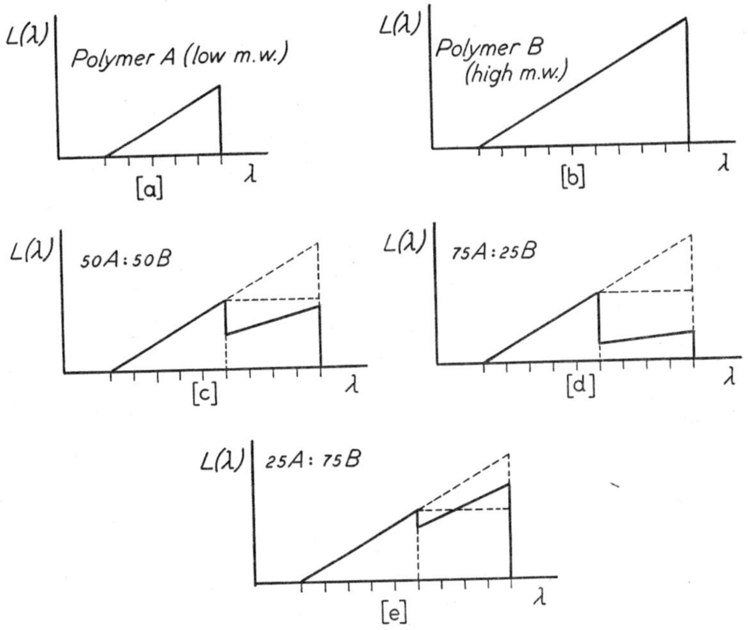

Fig. 67. Distributions of retardation times for various mixtures of a high molecular weight fraction with a low molecular weight fraction (hypothetical).

For this purpose a simple reference shape is temporarily assumed for the curve $J(\tau)$ corresponding to a monodisperse polymer; this causes the variations resulting from polydispersity to show up more distinctly. For want of a better assumption, the spectrum computed theoretically and plotted in figure 64 is chosen as a reference form.

In figure 67[a] the reference distribution $L(\lambda)$ for the monodisperse polymer A is schematized. In [b] the distribution for a monodisperse polymer B of higher molecular weight is shown. In [c] a curve is shown which must indicate the general nature of the distribution $L(\lambda)$ for a 50:50 mixture of the two monodisperse fractions A and B. In [d] a curve is shown which illustrates the distribution for a mixture of the composition 75 A:25 B. Curve [e] should give the general nature of the distribution for a mixture of the composition 25 A:75 B. Besides the differences in the retarded elastic spectra L(λ), the differences in η, the viscosity governing actual flow, must be considered. Flory has found that η depends upon molecular weight according to the relation:

$$\eta = \mathrm{A}\, e^{b\sqrt{Z}}\, e^{\Delta E/RT} \qquad (66)$$

where for a polydisperse sample Z is the weight average polymerization degree. While this relationship has not been extensively tested by comparisons of the viscosity of sharp fractions and various mixtures thereof, it is at least much more definite than the guesses concerning the effect of polydispersity on $J(\tau)$.

D. Effect of Chemical Constitution (*22, 25, 82–85*)

The next question is the relation between the chemical constitution of a polymer (*i.e.*, the structure of the repeating monomer unit) and the viscoelastic spectrum. This is obviously of the greatest importance. If all the contributing factors were thoroughly understood, it would be possible to design polymer structures which would possess desired viscoelastic properties—and even qualitative information regarding the effects of various structural features may be extremely valuable. The present status of this very complicated problem is far from satisfactory, and the following remarks must be considered as but a small step toward a thorough analysis.

In the development of the molecular theory of viscoelastic response, two different functions—$J(n)$ and $\tau(n)$—appeared, and were subsequently combined to give the final viscoelastic spectrum $J(\tau)$. $J(n)$ represents the equilibrium elastic compliance associated with configurational changes of polymer sections containing n chain atoms. This function thus has a thermodynamic significance and is computed from the statistical probability of various molecular configurations. The function $\tau(n)$ represents the retardation time for the configurational changes of polymeric sections containing n chain atoms. An attempt will be made to evaluate the effects of various structural features on each of these two functions as well as upon the composite function $J(\tau)$.

The significant structural differences involved among different amorphous linear polymers may be divided into two types: differences in internal flexibility and differences in intermolecular forces. Each of these features can be further subdivided. Thus the internal flexibility of a polymer chain can be reduced either by the presence of high energy barriers restricting rotation about each bond or, alternatively, by the presence of rigid sections between the links about which relatively free rotation occurs. Similarly, the magnitude of the forces acting between adjacent polymer molecules depends both upon the polarity and polarizability of each group and upon such geometrical factors as bulkiness and regularity of shape. Each of these structural factors will be discussed in turn.

Consider first a high polymer in which there is a high energy barrier restricting rotation about the valence bonds of the chain. Eyring and coworkers have shown that, if the potential barrier restricting rotation is symmetrical, the equilibrium distribution among configurations (chain end separations, etc.) is the same as in the case of completely free rotation. This is independent of the *magnitude* of the potential barrier. It follows that such symmetrical potential barriers have no effect upon the function $J(n)$. However, the presence of a large restricting potential barrier will necessarily reduce the *rate* of segmental diffusion and hence will increase the retardation times for all configurational changes. The introduction of high symmetrical potential barriers restricting rotation will increase $\tau(n)$ and hence $J(\tau)$ will be shifted to larger values of τ, without changing the total configurational compliance $\int_0^\infty J(\tau)\, d\tau$.

Flory and Rehner (*25a*) have presented a cogent survey of the effect of *unsymmetrical* hindering potentials upon the distribution among configurations, as follows:

Steric effects in long polymer molecules are certain to disrupt the symmetry of the bond rotation hindrance potential. This dissymmetry is likely to be accentuated when large substituent groups are attached to the chain. Recently Bunn has called attention to the tendency in long-chain molecules (*e.g.*, polyethylene, rubber, and polyesters) for the bonds to assume a "staggered configuration," the equivalent of the planar zig-zag structure having θ equal to zero. In other words, $\theta = 0$ frequently represents the lowest minimum in the bond rotational potential. Sequences of bonds in the planar zig-zag form should occur in such cases. The average length of these sequences will depend on the depth of the potential minimum for $\theta = 0$, and on its depth as compared with minima for other values of θ. Such a chain would consist of numerous straight (planar zig-zag) sequences of bonds joined together in an essentially haphazard fashion.

The above analysis represents an oversimplification. In any actual case, the hindrance potential for any given bond will depend on the arrangement of its neighbors in a complicated manner. Without attempting any detailed analysis, Kuhn considers that hindrance of rotation about chain bonds necessitates replacement of the single bond of length l by a larger unit composed of s bonds as the freely orienting segment. Z must then be decreased by the factor $1/s$ and l must be replaced by the length of the average freely orienting segment. There is no apparent necessity for abandoning equation (3′) or for changing its form...

$$W(r)\,dr = A\,e^{-\beta(r^2)}r^2\,dr \qquad (3')$$

...Only β requires revision. Since it depends on the inverse first power of the length of the segment and on the inverse square root of the number of segments, β should decrease somewhat with a decrease in flexibility of the chain. The average displacement lengths will increase approximately as the square root of the average equivalent segment length. This segment length remains a rather indefinite quantity.

Bresler and Frenkel have attempted a quantitative treatment of the effects of hindered rotation on chain configuration. They assume a potential given by ...:

$$U = U_0(1 - \cos n\theta)/2 \qquad (67)$$

... with $n = 1$, which is sufficiently great to limit the average rotation angle $\bar{\theta}$ to moderately small values, *i.e.*, $U_0 \gg RT$. They derived an expression that may be written

$$\overline{r^2}/l^2 = 3\,Z(1 - \cos\omega)^2/(1 + \cos\omega)(1 - \cos\bar{\theta}) \qquad (67a)$$

and showed that the value of $\bar{\theta}$ is related to the potential U_0 according to

$$\cos\bar{\theta} = L(U_0/2\,RT) \qquad (68)$$

where L is the Langevin function. Substituting equation (68) in (67a) and recalling that $\cos\omega \cong -\frac{1}{3}$, the following is obtained:

$$\overline{r^2} = 8\,l^2Z/[1 - L(U_0/2\,RT)] \qquad (69)$$

TABLE V

U_0^*, cal. per mole	U_0, cal. per mole	$\left(\frac{\overline{r^2}\text{ (hindered rotation)}}{\overline{r^2}\text{ (free rotation)}}\right)^{\frac{1}{2}}$
9000	1000	5.48
3600	400	3.49
1800	200	2.67

The ratio of r calculated for hindered rotation using equation (69) to r for free rotation using [$\overline{r^2} = 2\,l^2\,Z$] is shown in table V for several values of the hindrance potential U_0. In drawing comparisons between these potentials and those for simple molecules such as ethane (3600 cal.), propylene and acetone (600–2000 cal.), it must be borne in mind that Bresler and Frenkel used a potential function with a single minimum, *i.e.*, $n = 1$ in equation (67). These simpler molecules possess three potential minima ($n = 3$). For the small displacements from $\theta = 0$ assumed by Bresler and Frenkel in the development of their theory, the shape of the potential curve near its minimum is approximately the same regardless of whether $n = 1$ or 3. But in order to make the two curves coincide in the vicinity of $\theta = 0$ it is necessary to let U_0^* for $n = 3$ equal 9 U_0 for $n = 1$. Both U_0 and U_0^* values are included in table V. In the case of natural rubber, the hindrance potential should be of the order of 1000 cal. or less, in analogy with propylene. The corresponding $U_0^* = 9000$ cal. leads to a considerable increase in r over the free rotation value. However, if other minima, possibly a few hundred calories above the lowest, were taken into account, this length would be appreciably decreased.

We conclude, therefore, that hindrance to rotation about bonds of the chain will generally increase the mean displacement length of the chain over that which would prevail for free rotation. However, this increase will not be manyfold. If the chains are very long the mean displacement length will remain only a small fraction of the chain contour length. The expansion of the configuration with increasing hindrance to free rotation should exert a noticeable effect on the viscosities of dilute solutions of the polymer; the more extended the configuration the greater will be the viscosity of the solution for a given chain contour length at the same concentration.

As to the effect of an unsymmetrical hindering potential upon $J(n)$, this would appear to be small, at least in the case where there are three minima of unequal energy. In Kuhn's theory, the bond length must be replaced by the length of the "freely orienting segment," but this effect is compensated by the corresponding reduction in the number of freely rotating units in the polymer molecule. (This is not true in the extreme case treated by Bresler and Frenkel.)

Consider next the case of a polymer molecule in which rigid sections occur and are connected by bonds about which rotation is essentially free. Here the treatment of Kuhn is most obviously applicable; the rigid section enters in place of the single bond in the kinetic theory. Again, $J(n)$ will not be markedly affected, but $\tau(n)$ will presumably be increased.

Many molecules possess a composite structure as far as freedom of rotation is concerned. The bonds in the chain of rubber, for example, are of three types. The double bond in each isoprene unit represents a completely rigid link, since the barrier restricting rotation is extremely high, with only one accessible minimum. The two single bonds adjacent to this double bond, on the other hand, exhibit a particularly large freedom of rotation. Finally, the single bond which is not adjacent to a double bond is intermediate in torsional freedom. In spite of this composite character, the rubber molecule seems to fit the statistical pattern of the kinetic theory very closely.

The general conclusion to which we come in regard to the effect of flexibility upon the viscoelastic spectrum is the following: high potential barriers restricting rotation will increase the retardation time τ for shape changes within chain sections of a given size. If the barriers are symmetrical, there will definitely be no marked effect upon the compliance $J(n)$, however. If the barriers are unsymmetrical, with three accessible minima of different energy, a first approximation theory predicts again that $J(n)$ will be unaffected. A more detailed theory might well introduce a change in $J(n)$ for such cases. Finally, when the restricting potential barriers are extremely steep, with only one minimum, $J(n)$ will be markedly affected. In all cases, of course, a decrease in flexibility results in a shift of the spectrum to higher retardation times.

Strong intermolecular forces also lead to high retardation times. When the van der Waals' forces between neighboring chain sections are strong, the potential barriers preventing a segment from jumping into an adjacent hole will be high. This will increase the energy of activation for segmental diffusion and, hence, the retardation time for each configurational elastic response. In a truly amorphous polymer, however, the strength of the intermolecular forces will have no effect on the function $J(n)$, but will affect $J(\tau)$ only through $\tau(n)$.

The magnitudes of the intermolecular forces are dependent both upon the specific attracting powers of the groups and upon the geometry of the molecule. Mark (*52, 53*) has estimated the relative magnitudes of the specific attracting powers of various polymers, expressed as the "specific molar cohesion," in calories per 5 Å. of chain length. These figures, listed in table XIII (page 358) are based upon the assumption that the molecular shape is such as to allow efficient packing of the chains. Thus differences among the cohesion values in table XIII originate from differences in polarity or polarizability, rather than from geometric differences. It can be seen that the specific cohesion of a saturated hydrocarbon chain is low, while the presence of polar groups increases the cohesion. Those polymers which have high cohesion will, in the amorphous state, exhibit larger retardation times for configurational response than the polymers of low cohesion.

Mark has emphasized the fact that the crystallization tendency of a polymer depends not only on the specific cohesion as defined above but also upon geometric factors. The properties of *amorphous* polymers are also influenced by both types of factor. We may divide these geometric factors into two effects—bulkiness and regularity.

The presence of large rigid substituent groups, rigidly attached to the chain, increases the bulk of the chain. This should increase the amount of configurational elastic compliance $J(n)$, since the number of chain atoms per unit volume is decreased. Furthermore, when a segment jumps into an adjacent hole, the moving chain must drag along the large substituent groups. This should result in an increase in the retardation time, $\tau(n)$. This latter effect is partially accounted for in the computation of the specific cohesion value, since the substituent groups will furnish a contribution to this cohesion.

The presence of bulky substituents is also likely to destroy the smooth contours of the polymer molecule. The phenyl groups in polystyrene, for example, give the chain a "bumpy" shape. As a result, it may not be possible to pack the adjacent chains as efficiently as if the bumps were not present. If certain parts of two adjacent chains are forcibly held apart by the protruding side groups, then the intermolecular forces will not be able to satisfy themselves completely. The polymer molecules will be (internally) somewhat strained. In such a case, the actual specific molar cohesion will be somewhat less than that computed on the assumption that the intermolecular forces are completely satisfied. This will tend to lower the retardation time for a given configurational response, $\tau(n)$, below the value one would expect by merely consulting a table such as XIII.

Our general conclusion, then, is that variations in chemical structure should primarily influence the viscoelastic spectra of amorphous linear polymers through the *rate* function $\tau(n)$, rather than through the equilibrium function $J(n)$. If this be true, the general over-all effect of chemical structure can be roughly assessed by an observation of the "softening point" or the apparent second order transition point of the polymer. Such assessment can be made because these transition points do not depend very much upon the polymerization degree or the degree of polydispersity (assuming that no appreciable fraction of extremely low polymer is present) but are rather determined by the *chemical* structure of the polymer, *i.e.*, by the internal flexibility of the chains and the intermolecular forces acting between chains. Indeed, one is inclined toward the formulation of some rough rule of "corresponding temperatures" which would state that the viscoelastic spectrum of polystyrene at 100° C. would be roughly the same as that of unvulcanized rubber of the same DP at some "corresponding" temperature a few degrees above its brittle point (− 70° C.) and that the viscoelastic spectrum of rubber at room temperature would be roughly reproduced by polystyrene at some elevated temperature. Whether this concept would be of any quantitative value cannot be determined until more experimental data have been obtained than are now available. However, some such rule must be adopted temporarily if we are to be able to discuss specific polymers. In the case of most linear amorphous polymers, the only available facts concerning viscoelastic properties are the softening points, qualitative discussions of the "hardness," "rubberiness," or "viscosity" or similar information, of the polymer at room temperature. In the following discussion, we shall attempt to utilize such information and draw specific deductions concerning the relation between various structural features and the viscoelastic spectrum. The rule of corresponding temperatures will be implicitly assumed for the purpose of this discussion.

It should be recalled that it was assumed in the discussion of intermolecular forces that strong forces merely increase the *depth* of the potential energy valleys, so that the unit process of segmental diffusion is slowed down, without influencing the distribution among configurations. If the intermolecular and intersegmental forces favor certain specific molecular shapes, then the requirements for perfectly "amorphous" behavior are no longer met. These cases will be discussed in chapter *D*. It will be seen that many of the structural features which tend to cause a high brittle temperature also tend to favor crystallization and Mack elasticity. Thus strong forces between polymer molecules will tend to cause the material to be hard and inflexible for two reasons; both a high second order transition point and a high crystalline-amorphous melting point will be favored. These two effects should not be confused. In this section it is assumed that no crystallization occurs.

The simple hydrocarbon polymers such as polyisobutylene and rubber possess small specific molar cohesions and, hence, soften to elastomeric materials at low temperatures. The introduction of polar groups results in an increase in softening point. Thus polychloroprene, which is geometrically very similar to polyisoprene, has a somewhat higher softening point, although this is still well below room temperature. Further introduction of polar C—Cl bonds progressively raises the softening temperature. Thus polyvinyl chloride, highly chlorinated rubber, and poly-2,3-dichlorobutadiene are all hard, inelastic materials at room temperature, softening only at elevated temperatures.

TABLE VI

PROPERTIES OF POLYACRYLATES

Material	Description
Polymethylacrylate	Tough, elastic, celluloid-like
Polyethylacrylate	Less tough, softer, elastic
Polybutylacrylate	Soft, sticky
Polyisobutylacrylate	Hard, crumbling
Cyclohexylacrylate	Hard, crumbling
n-Hexylacrylate	Soft, sticky

The reverse effect—the screening or destruction of polar groups by the introduction of nonpolar substituent groups—can also be observed. Thus polyacrylic acid, with strongly polar acid groups, can be softened by esterification. In table VI are listed the properties of a series of polyacrylate esters.

It can be seen that the longer is the normal alkyl side chain of the polyester, the more the material is softened, *i.e.*, the lower the brittle point is made. The nonpolar hydrocarbon chain acts as a sort of lubricant by screening the polar ester groups. A branched or cyclic alkyl group, on the other hand, has much less softening effect than a normal alkyl group of the same molecular weight. Both polyisobutylacrylate and polycyclohexylacrylate are hard, whereas the *n*-butyl and *n*-hexyl polyesters are soft and sticky. A similar sequence can be observed in the polymethacrylates, as shown in table VII.

TABLE VII

PROPERTIES OF POLYMETHACRYLATES

Material	Softening point, °C.	Description
Polymethylmethacrylate	125	Hard, tough
Polyethylmethacrylate	65	Tough
Poly-*n*-propylmethacrylate	38	Tough, flexible
Polyisopropylmethacrylate	95	Solid
Poly-*n*-butylmethacrylate	33	Flexible, tough
Polyisobutylmethacrylate	70	Rather brittle
Poly-*sec*-butylmethacrylate	62	Rather brittle
Poly-*tert*-amylmethacrylate	76	Brittle
Polydiisopropylcarbinolmethacrylate	60	Very brittle
Polyoctylmethacrylate	Below 20	Jellylike
Polylaurylmethacrylate	—	Viscous liquid
Polyphenylmethacrylate	120	Very brittle
Polycyclohexylmethacrylate	105	Rather brittle
Poly-*p*-cyclohexylphenylmethacrylate	145	Hard, brittle
Polyglycoldimethacrylate	—	Not melting

It can be seen that a given polymethacrylate tends to be harder (*i.e.*, possesses a higher softening point) than the corresponding polyacrylate but that various alkyl side groups have much the same effect in both series. Thus the softening point goes down steadily as one proceeds from polymethylmethacrylate through the ethyl, *n*-propyl, *n*-butyl, and octyl derivatives. Each branched or cyclic alkyl group gives a much higher softening point than the corresponding normal side chain. It has been suggested (*82*, *88*) that the high softening points of the polymethacrylates, as compared with the acrylates, result from increasing resistance to torsional motion about the C—C bonds of the chain, due to the presence of the bulky methyl group in place of the smaller hydrogen atom. This seems very reasonable.

In view of the importance of the general question of chemical constitution as related to viscoelastic properties, it seems desirable at this point to introduce a number of direct quotations from several different investigators. The author feels that the following passages, taken from the recent paper of Tuckett (*82*) and from the discussions of those papers, succeed in conveying a clear idea of the present status of the problem.

The next stage is to see whether there is any general qualitative connection between molecular structure and elastic properties. In a vinyl polymer of the type $(—CH_2—CXY—)_n$ or in one based on butadiene, the ease of rotation depends on the nature of X and Y and their interaction with adjacent similar groups, both on the same chain and on neighbouring ones. In this treatment, only the free rotation of a single chain is considered, and it will be affected by two main factors—one of these is purely steric, due to the bulk size of the substituent groups, the other is electrical and is caused by the existence of dipoles on them. In general, the latter effect will be much larger, a fairly large bulk size of X or Y being necessary before free rotation is appreciably affected.

A considerable amount of insight can be obtained into the problem by a study of Fischer-Hirschfelder models of the polymers concerned. Polymers based on butadiene will first be considered, then the vinyl types. For a natural rubber composed of isoprene units, free rotation is possible about all the C—C single bonds, the same being true for a butadiene chain (Buna rubber). In polychloroprene, free rotation is still possible as the adjacent halogen atoms, although strongly polar, are too far apart to affect each other, and this substance will have approximately the same elastic range as natural rubber, in agreement with experience...

The various copolymers of butadiene and styrene (Buna S) or acrylonitrile (Perbunan) will still have rotational freedom over a large proportion of C—C links as "blocking" will occur only if two hindering groups are adjacent. If x is the proportion of "blocking" constituent in the co-polymer, the fraction of C—C bonds which are hindered can easily be calculated from the work of Wall; it works out as x^2 of the whole. For the 2:1 styrene:butadiene co-polymer ($x = 0.66$) studied by Ueberreiter, the fraction comes, to 0.43, so a large proportion of the C—C bonds is still free, in spite of the high percentage of styrene. This is borne out by the T_F values of Ueberreiter. (Styrene = + 81°C. Styrene:Butadiene 2:1 polymer = − 70°C.)

In pure vinyl polymers, the X and Y substituents are much closer together in adjacent groups, and hindrance effects become much more pronounced. A model of a polyisobutene chain $(—CH_2—CMe_2—)_n$ gives very little clearance for the side-chain methyl groups but, owing to their essentially non-polar character, it seems likely that their interaction will be small and rotation not impeded. This would explain why high molecular polybutenes have essentially the same elasticity range as natural rubber. If, however, the size of the substituent group is increased much, a purely steric effect enters, as with polystyrene (Y = H, X = C_6H_5). Hence, in this case, free rotation is not possible until a much higher temperature is reached (T_F = +81° C., as opposed to −66° C. for polyisobutenes).

If we now consider the effect of a single polar group (Y = H, X = polar), the general result will be to raise T_F, the extent depending on the dipole interaction. For polymers such as vinyl acetate and methyl acrylate, rotation is still comparatively free; the former polymer is elastic above ~40° C., and the latter still has rubber-like properties at room temperature. For both these molecules, the corresponding models show comparatively free rotation, but for a polyvinyl chloride molecule, the hindrance to rotation is very much more severe, owing to the strong C—Cl dipoles. This also corresponds to its behaviour in practice, as it does not acquire elastic properties until ~ 100–110°C. without a plasticiser.

These ideas can now be extended to cover polymers of the type $(CH_2—CXY)_n$; if Y = H and rotation is partially restricted by the polar nature of X, hindrance can be very sharply increased by replacing the hydrogen atom at Y by a very slightly larger group such as methyl. This is seen most strikingly if models of methyl acrylate and methacrylate are compared: the former is fairly free, while in the latter, rotation is badly hindered. The elastic properties of these two polymers are, moreover, in agreement with this observation, there being a very great contrast between their T_E values (methyl acrylate $T_E <$ room temperature; methyl methacrylate $T_E \sim 90$°C.). A similar contrast is found with polymers from methyl vinyl ketone and methyl isopropenyl ketone.

Rotation of the long-chain molecule will also be cut down if parts of it are linked up internally; this occurs in the process of acetalation, *i.e.*, in the formation of polyvinyl formals, acetals and butals from acetates. [Rotation about two of the bonds is] completely suppressed by this reaction so that for a highly substituted polyvinyl formal, the elastic transition only occurs at $\sim +115$°C. (Part of this effect is, however, due to cross-linking, which is considered later.) For a less highly substituted acetal, a number of free links still remain, and hence the elastic transition will be nearer to that of the pure acetate, as considerations similar to those discussed for the butadiene–styrene polymer apply here also.

In the discussion of the above paper (*82*), a number of significant points were raised. The following remarks from this discussion seem particularly worthy of quotation:

DR. R. M. BARRER (Bingley) said:... It is also advisable at this point to summarise the main features which contribute to rubber-like elasticity. From the molecular viewpoint elasticity requires or is favoured by:

(1) Relative apolar chains;
(2) Very long chains;
(3) Relatively apolar side chains (—Cl, CH_3—, C_2H_5—, C_6H_5—);
(4) Special kinks in chains introduced, for example, by double bonds;
(5) No cross-linking, or not too extensive cross-linking, by chemical bonds.

Referring to (1) and (2), the chains must be sufficiently long to become thoroughly entangled, and must not interact strongly enough to crystallise. The rubber is then a fluid in one sense, but the great chain length immobilises the chain as a whole, though intermeshing. In shorter chains, onset of rotation is not enough to produce elasticity. Above certain temperatures long chain hydrocarbons rotate in their crystals, but develop no rubber-like or even fluid properties.

At least two effects may be ascribed to (3):

(*a*) There is the steric hindrance to rotation discussed by Tuckett, which decreases fluidity.

(*b*) The side chains help to prevent easy crystallisation by making close packing more difficult. They therefore increase fluidity which, coupled with the intermeshing of coiled very long chains, renders the polymer elastic. The double bonds, by introducing unavoidable special kinks in the chains, also reduce the ease with which they may pack together and crystallise and so favour elasticity. For example, of the polymers: polyethylene $(—CH_2—CH_2—)_n$, polyisobutene $[—C(CH_3)_2—CH_2—]_n$, and polybutadiene ($—CH_2—CH=CH—CH_2—)_n$, the first is inelastic and wax-like at ordinary temperatures; the two latter are elastic. Similarly, "Nylon" polymers without side chains are inelastic, but when suitable side chains are introduced a rubber-like polymer may be obtained.

MR. C. W. BUNN (Northwich) said: In considering the "freezing points" T_F of different high polymers and their relation to the flexibilities of the molecules, it does not appear to be sufficient to take into account only the interaction of the side chains on each other. This is shown by the fact that polyethylene, which has no side chains, has a high freezing point (115°C.) while polyisobutene, which has a pair of methyl groups on every other chain carbon atom, has a very low freezing point (−65°C.). Evidently, there must be some other factor, and I suggest that this other factor is the potential barrier associated with the preferred (staggered) position of the bonds themselves. At any rate, by assuming that both these factors play a part, it is possible to explain some otherwise puzzling phenomena, such as the low freezing point of polyisobutene—for the two factors may sometimes act in opposition and so cancel each other out. If a model of the polyisobutene molecule is made, it will be found that, if the configuration is such that the bonds of linked carbon atoms are staggered, then the methyl side groups are overcrowded, while if (by rotation round the chain bonds) the methyl side groups are given greater clearance, then the bonds of linked carbon atoms are no longer staggered; thus the bonds prefer one configuration, while the methyl side groups prefer another, the net result being that all configurations have much the same energy, the barriers to rotation are small, and the freezing point low.

MR. D. J. CRISP (Cambridge) said: It has been suggested that in rubbers and rubber-like substances the flexibility of the main chain is considerably influenced by the nature and position of side groups. I would like to mention some work on surface films of certain polymeric substances which support this view.

Polymers of the acrylate and polyvinyl series are found to spread uniformly on aqueous substrates giving monomolecular films at low pressures. The properties of these films depend on: (*a*) the interaction of the polar group with water, causing spreading and expansion. Substances with only weak polar groups such as polystyrene, rubber, chloroprene do not spread.

(*b*) The flexibility of the chains, which is evidenced by finite pressures, due to kinetic agitation, at relatively large areas of the order of 100–150 (A^2.) per residue.

(*c*) The interaction of chains with each other, due to non-polar forces, leading to condensation of the films. This can be reduced at an oil–water interface.

Thus polyvinyl acetate and acrylates give fluid expanded films, whose force–area relation follows a curve asymptotic to the area axis; while the presence of a methyl group opposite the side chain, as in methacrylates, reduces the flexibility and increases the cohesion. This makes spreading less perfect, and the resulting films are coherent and show a sharp rise in pressure at a fairly definite limiting area.

It is interesting to recall that Adam, using films of cellulose ethers and esters, obtained a similar result, the presence of benzene rings in the side groupings precluded freedom of movement from the cellulose units.

Experiments show also that the length of the alkyl radical in the side chain of a polyester reduces cohesion to a minimum at 3 or 4 carbon atoms. Thus propyl acrylate gives a more expanded film than either ethyl or butyl acrylates, and in the methacrylate series expansion occurs progressively to the butyl member, while octadecyl methacrylate gives films more closely resembling ethyl and methyl methacrylates. Presumably the alkyl radical first reduces cohesion by separating the main chains from each other, but long aliphatic chains will introduce strong attractive forces which counteract the initial effect.

Both in physical properties and in their effect on phase boundary potential, the films closely parallel those of long chain ester compounds.

DR. R. F. TUCKETT (Cambridge) in reply said:...The paper, as originally presented, put forward two main suggestions. The fundamental hypothesis was that there existed a close connection between the onset of high elasticity in a polymer and the extent of free rotation in the chain molecule, the latter being determined by steric and inter-chain effects; this was deduced from a variety of other physical data and the discussion has not diminished my faith in its essential validity. The second point, namely, the connection between molecular structure and free rotation, was admittedly a bit more speculative, and here it may be that the picture is not so simple as was first suggested. I would be the first to admit that simple concepts based on steric considerations are not in themselves sufficient to explain the various high elasticity temperatures encountered, but they do correlate a number of diverse facts, *e.g.*, the acrylate-methacrylate differences and the low T_E value of a 2:1 styrene butadiene co-polymer.

On the other hand, some molecules do not fit very well into the scheme. Polyethylene is difficult to explain on any general theory, though the ease with which it crystallises makes the assessment of its elastic properties difficult—polyisobutene also seems to be an awkward case to some people...

The case of the various acrylates and methacrylates shows that a simple steric theory may not be adequate, and that here the determining factor is the interaction between different chains. From the discussion, several points arise; the first is that softening temperatures which fall progressively as the methacrylate series is ascended must not be confused with high elasticity (T_E) values—it will be shown elsewhere that softening points essentially represent iso-viscous states and hence depend on molecular size; T_E values above a minimum chain length are independent of it; for the range of molecular weight over which this is true, Ueberreiter gives 33,000 to 484,000 for polystyrenes.

The effect of changing the side chain length in the acrylates and methacrylates is certainly not a simple steric one, and in this connection the complementary lines of investigation initiated by Coumoulos and Crisp seem to be extremely promising. Mr. Crisp's work indicates clearly the importance of the interaction between different chains in determining elastic properties, a point which was emphasised in my original paper in the plasticiser section—a large side chain such as butyl may, in this respect, almost function as an internal plasticiser...

It can be seen from the previous discussion that very little has been accomplished in the direction of a *quantitative* prediction of the visco-elastic behavior of a given polymer from its chemical structure. Mark's estimation of "molar cohesions" represents an exception, but even the predictions deduced from these cohesion values must be qualified by qualitative geometrical considerations. Qualitatively, however, a number of investigators have shown beyond question that it is possible to correlate mechanical behavior with chemical structure. This leads to the hope that an extension of Mark's energy considerations which considers geometric factors in an equally quantitative fashion may lead to a completely satisfactory picture. It is true that even the qualitative deductions of various workers are now not always in exact agreement, but the writer feels that this is largely due to the fact that different investigators concentrate their attentions upon different aspects of the problem rather than that any deeply rooted differences of opinion exist.

Two-Phase Theories of Polymer Structure.—The plastoelastic properties of high polymers are sometimes explained on the basis of a two-phase structure. Ostwald's "net theory" of rubber structure (*5, 61*), for example, pictures natural rubber as made up of an elastic netlike structure imbedded in and containing a viscous fluid. In such a theory, the elastic component of the mechanical response is more or less localized in one part of the material and the viscous component is localized in another part. A given atom either is a part of the elastic network or of the viscous fluid, but not of both. There are without doubt many materials which possess such a polyphase structure, particularly among crosslinked polymers. It should be emphasized, however, that such a structure is not necessary in order for a polymer to exhibit complex viscoelastic properties. In the ideal amorphous linear polymer, now under discussion, it is not possible to divide the *material* into an elastic component and a viscous component. The elasticity is simply *one aspect* of the mechanical behavior of the material and the viscous effects represent another aspect of the behavior. The different retarded elastic elements do not refer to different kinds of material but to different mechanisms of response of a single homogeneous material. In the last analysis, the macroscopic mechanical behavior of a material can be resolved into the motions of the individual atoms. A chain atom in a linear amorphous polymer acts as a member of a series of chain segments of different size. It is this membership of individual atoms in a series of different collective groups of atoms which results in a complex time behavior rather than the existence of regions of different properties.

When a sample *does* contain more than one type of material, this results in additional complications. If the plastoelastic spectrum of each component material is completely linear, then the spectrum for the heterogeneous mixture will also be linear. This means that the *observed* macroscopic properties of the material may not be essentially more complicated and may even be simpler than those of a homogeneous linear amorphous polymer. The problem of correlating the macroscopic behavior with molecular processes, however, is inevitably complicated in the case of a "polyphase" material. This is true whether the system is actually heterogeneous from a thermodynamic standpoint (*e.g.*, polycrystalline polymers, polymers with fillers, etc.) or whether the system is thermodynamically homogeneous but consists of structural material of more than one kind (*e.g.*, a three-dimensional cross-linked network interspersed with polymer molecules which are not chemically bound to the network). Again, this statement must be qualified if we are interested only in the equilibrium elastic deformation.

For these reasons, a multiphase structure should not be assumed merely to account for the existence of complex plastoelastic properties in a material. The fundamental origin of such properties lies in the possibility of different *modes of response*, rather than the presence of different types of material each possessing simple mechanical properties. A multiphase structure can be established by various direct methods of structure analysis, or by a *detailed analysis* of the plastoelastic spectrum of a material. This latter method assumes a rather intimate knowledge of the types of plastoelastic spectra exhibited by various "homogeneous" amorphous polymers. At the present time, established knowledge concerning this point is only beginning to be obtained. Hence, it is rather difficult to establish a multiphase structure on the basis of mechanical tests alone. In this book, in general, such structures will be considered only in those cases where independent corroborative evidence exists.

The Concept of "Internal Stress."—Even when there are no external forces acting on a material, the springs of the representative model obviously may be under tension, or compression, and this may be looked upon as an "internal stress." In the model such a term has a very definite meaning, since one part of the model pulls against another part, and the individual elements are subjected to stresses which are just as real as if an external force were being applied to the model as a whole.

Within the plastoelastic material itself, the internal stresses are mathematical fictions. Consider a linear polymer which has been elongated and released; γ_2 is now different from zero, and tends slowly to approach zero (delayed recovery). During this process, the stress (as defined on pages 1–4) is zero. The sample is in a state of low probability and, as it carries out its (unbiased) Brownian movement, it simply tends to drift toward the state of maximum probability—maximum number of distinct molecular configurations. The sequence of macroscopic states which is followed can be "explained" in terms of a driving force, or "internal stress," opposed by a resistance, or "internal viscosity." The very use of mechanical models, such as Model A (page 104), to represent the mechanical behavior of a plastoelastic material, tends to objectify the concept of internal stresses. Since the various elements in the mechanical model are spatially separated, the stress borne by a given element is a measurable quantity, and has a physical as well as a mathematical significance. The equivalent "internal stress" in the actual plastoelastic material is by its very nature an unmeasurable quantity and should be considered as a mathematical abstraction. Specifically, a straightened out linear polymer molecule in an unstressed amorphous sample is not under tension in any physical sense. Such a molecule tends to contract, merely because as it carries out its random Brownian movement it tends to spend equal portions of its time in each equivalent volume of phase space, and most of the volume of phase space corresponds to the contracted state.

This does not mean that an object which is not subjected to external surface forces is necessarily unstressed. It does mean that such an object cannot possess a *homogeneous* stress. If an unstressed metal ring has a section removed and the separated ends are brought together and welded, the reduced ring contains real stresses. If a glass sphere is suddenly quenched from a high temperature, the outer shell hardens while the inner core is still hot, and prevents the core from fully contracting. In the final cooled state the outer shell is in a state of compression, and the inner core in a state of tension. These are real stresses. One part of the object pulls or pushes against another part and, because of the geometry of the system, these forces cannot be relieved. On the other hand, if a plastoelastic material, whose properties are represented by Model A, is subjected to a *homogeneous* tensile stress, which slowly builds up a homogeneous configurational strain γ_2 and then the external stress is removed, the situation is quite different. The true stress within the sample is now zero. *A volume element in the strained sample is subject to no surface forces exerted by its neighboring elements.* The configurational strain slowly disappears and it is possible to represent this process in terms of a homogeneous "internal stress" opposed by an internal viscous resistance, but the "internal stress" does not have the physical significance of a true stress as defined in chapter A (pages 1–4).

With this qualification, the concept of "internal stress" will be used at times in this book. In order to avoid confusion, however, the unqualified term "stress" will invariably refer to actual stress as defined in chapter A.

3. The Empirical Four-Parameter Model

If a material possessing a wide distribution of retardation times is investigated by means of experiments whose timescales are all of the same order, some of the retarded elastic mechanisms will appear as (pseudo) ideal elastic responses, and some will appear as (pseudo) flow. Only those having retardation times in the same order of magnitude as the experimental timescale will exhibit their true retarded elastic character. This continuous set of elements may be represented with reasonable precision by a single retarded elastic element of intermediate τ. Thus the continuous model can be represented by a four-parameter model of the same general form as Model A (Fig. 48, page 104). The two should not be confused, however.

Model A is a qualitative picture of the plastoelastic response of a polymer over a wide range of temperature and of experimental timescale. It is useful as an introductory model because each element has a single physical significance and a reasonable temperature dependence and because it does explain, qualitatively, the plastoelastic behavior of an amorphous polymer over a wide range of conditions—from hard brittle solid, to obvious retarded elasticity, rubbery behavior, and finally viscous flow.

A four-parameter model of the type shown in figure 68 is a semiquantitative condensation of a whole plastoelastic spectrum. It describes the material only in one range of experimental timescale and only at one definite temperature—but in this limited range of conditions it may describe the material very well. Such a model is necessarily empirical. *It is the model obtained by fitting to experimental data.* The separate elements of such a model are not identified with specific molecular mechanisms. Furthermore—and this is of extreme significance—for a given timescale, the *temperature dependence of the elements of the best empirical four-parameter model is not necessarily simple in nature.*

The precise theoretical significance of the empirical four-parameter model will be discussed at some length, and this model will be given a separate designation, that of "Model E," in order to distinguish it from Model A. For the purpose of the discussion, let us assume that the function $J(\tau)$ is known for the material under consideration and that this distribution of elastic moduli changes with temperature according to the previous descriptions, *i.e.*, the viscous resistance of each retarded elastic element exhibits a simple exponential dependence upon $1/T$ and the activation energy is the same for all these elements. Let the experimental timescale lie in the range between $ⓣ_1$ and $ⓣ_2$.

G_1 of Model E represents all elastic response which experimentally appears to be instantaneous—not only the "crystal-like" elasticity but also all retarded elasticity whose retardation time is too small to be detected ($\tau < ⓣ_1$). η_3 of Model E represents not only the true flow but also all flowlike response from retarded elastic elements of very long retardation time $\tau > ⓣ_2$. The retarded element G_2^E, η_2^E of Model E lumps together all retarded response of $ⓣ_1 < \tau < ⓣ_2$. It should be clear that, to the extent that the timescale limits $ⓣ_1$ and $ⓣ_2$ have sharply defined values, G_1^E will be given by the following expression:

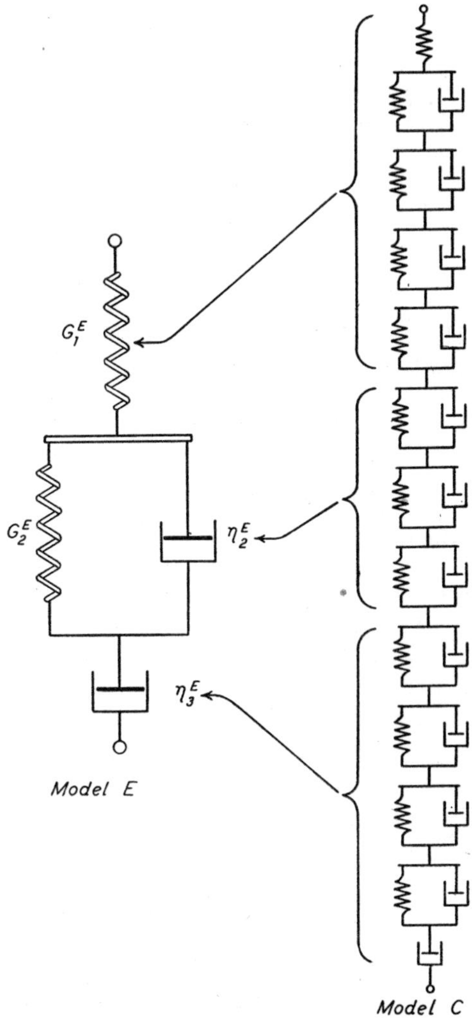

Fig. 68. Model E: An empirical four-parameter model giving an approximation to the behavior described exactly by Model C.

$$\frac{1}{G_1^E} = \int_0^{ⓣ_1} J(\tau)\, d\tau \qquad (70)$$

Further, G_2^E should be given by:

$$\frac{1}{G_2^E} = \int_{ⓣ_1}^{ⓣ_2} J(\tau)\, d\tau \qquad (71)$$

The retardation time, τ_2, of Model E would presumably be given by a weighted mean value, as below:

$$\tau_2 = \frac{\int_{ⓣ_1}^{ⓣ_2} \tau\, J(\tau)\, d\tau}{\int_{ⓣ_1}^{ⓣ_2} J(\tau)\, d} \qquad (72)$$

However, if $J(\tau)$ is a smooth function, and the range $ⓣ_1$ to $ⓣ_2$ is small, the last two equations may well be replaced by the approximations:

$$\frac{1}{G_2^E} = J(ⓣ_m)(ⓣ_2 - ⓣ_1) \qquad (73)$$

$$\tau_2 = ⓣ_m$$

whence $$1/\eta_2 = J(ⓣ_m)(ⓣ_2 - ⓣ_1)/ⓣ_m \qquad (74)$$

where $ⓣ_m$ is the mean of $ⓣ_1$ and $ⓣ_2$.

The empirical viscosity, η_3, corresponding to all response which appears to be true flow, can likewise be computed from the fundamental distribution function $J(\tau)$ or the corresponding $L(\ln \tau)$. All retarded elastic elements for which $\tau > ⓣ_2$ appear to contribute true flow response. The total apparent fluidity, $1/\eta_3$, is equal to the sum of the fluidities of all these elements plus the true fluidity of the polymer. The viscosity term accompanying a given element of elastic deformability, $J(\tau)\, d\tau$, is given by the expression:

$$\eta = \frac{\tau}{J} = \frac{\tau}{J(\tau)\, d\tau} \qquad (75)$$

$$\phi(\tau)\, d\tau = \frac{J(\tau)\, d\tau}{\tau} \qquad (76)$$

The total pseudo fluidity is obviously:

$$\int_{ⓣ_2}^{\infty} \phi(\tau)\, d\tau = \int_{ⓣ_2}^{\infty} \frac{J(\tau)}{\tau}\, d\tau \qquad (77)$$

The total fluidity incorporated in the flow element of the empirical four-parameter model is the total pseudo fluidity plus the true fluidity, $1/\eta$:

$$\varphi_3 = \int_{Ⓣ_2}^{\infty} \frac{J(\tau)\,d\tau}{\tau} + \frac{1}{\eta} \tag{78}$$

$$\eta_3 = \frac{1}{\dfrac{1}{\eta} + \displaystyle\int_{Ⓣ_2}^{\infty} \frac{J(\tau)\,d\tau}{\tau}} \tag{79}$$

In terms of $\mathrm{L}(\lambda)$, rather than $J(\tau)$, the apparent viscosity η_3 is given by:

$$\eta_3 = \frac{1}{\dfrac{1}{\eta} + \displaystyle\int_{\ln Ⓣ_2}^{\infty} e^{-\lambda}\,\mathrm{L}(\lambda)\,d\lambda} \tag{80}$$

$$1/G_{\mathrm{E}} = \mathrm{L}(\ln Ⓣ_m)\ln(Ⓣ_2/Ⓣ_1) \tag{81}$$

$$\tau_2 = Ⓣ_m$$

$$1/\eta_2 = \mathrm{L}(\ln Ⓣ_m)\cdot 1/Ⓣ_m \cdot \ln(Ⓣ_2/Ⓣ_1) \tag{82}$$

An increase of temperature shifts the whole spectrum to lower retardation times. Thus G_1 may change rapidly with temperature—not because any individual elastic mechanism is strongly temperature dependent but because certain mechanisms are essentially instantaneous at high temperatures which were noticeably retarded at low temperatures. G_1 describes *different sets* of mechanisms at different temperatures. In the same way, the temperature dependence of G_2 does not signify a change in any contributing modulus, but rather the net gain or loss in the amount of response for which τ falls between $Ⓣ_1$ and $Ⓣ_2$. τ_2, by definition, cannot be markedly affected by temperature since the experimental timescale is held constant. η_3 varies with temperature for two reasons: (1) Each viscous element is strongly temperature dependent, and (2) the number of retarded mechanisms which appear as pseudo flow changes with temperature. See figure 69.

Thus it is incorrect to interpret the temperature dependence of the various elements of an empirical four-parameter mechanical model as the *activation energies of fundamental* molecular processes. Each parameter—G_1^{E}, G_2^{E}, and η_3—represents the cumulative result of a whole set of molecular processes. Almost all the temperature dependence of G_1 results from the fact that at high temperatures G_1 describes additional molecular processes rather than from changes in the moduli of the processes already within the group.

It should be emphasized that while the individual elastic moduli, corresponding to the biased configurational diffusion of chain sections of various sizes, change only slowly with temperature, and while this small temperature dependence is in the direction of an increase of modulus with temperature, the empirical modulus, G_1^E, in general, *decreases* with temperature—and in some ranges very rapidly. Furthermore, the empirical modulus, G_2^E, increases with temperature in some ranges and de-

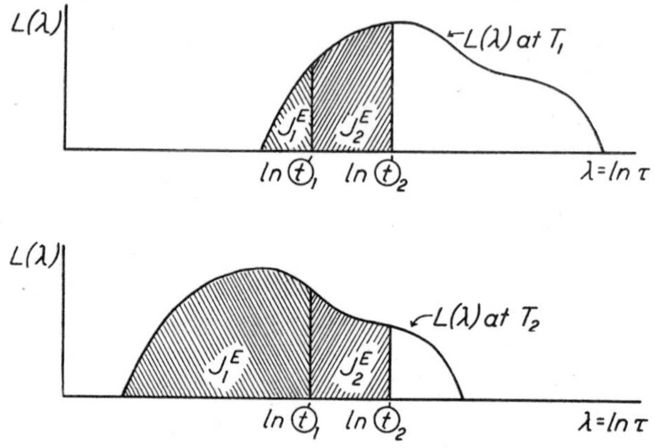

Fig. 69. Effect of temperature on the parameters of the empirical four-parameter model of Figure 68.

creases in others. Also implicit in the above equations, but worthy of explicit recognition, is the fact that the empirical viscosity, η_3^E, may either increase or decrease with temperature, although the various individual viscosity terms in the "true," or continuous, model all decrease rapidly with increasing temperature. The empirical viscosity element, η_3^E, changes with increasing temperature for three reasons:

(1) As the elastic spectrum shifts to lower retardation times, certain molecular processes which at a low temperature are classified as flow shift into the second element of the empirical model, leaving a smaller number of processes classified empirically as flow.

(2) The viscous resistance to configurational elastic changes within the group classified as flow decrease.

(3) The true flow viscosity, η, decreases.

The first of these changes tends to decrease the apparent fluidity, *i.e.*, to *increase* η_3^E. The second and third effects will be in the direction of decreasing viscosity. The net change in η_3^E with temperature, of course, depends upon the nature of the viscoelastic spectrum, $J(\tau)$.

More Detailed Empirical Models

By the introduction of more elements, it is possible to construct empirical models which will approximate the behavior of the precise (continuous) model more closely than is possible with the four-parameter model. That is to say, more elaborate sets of ordinary differential equations will represent closer approximations to the basic partial differential equation (38) (page 134). In figure 70 there is indicated an empirical six-parameter model, which will serve to approximate the continuous model over a wider range of experimental timescale than the best four-parameter model can do. By an obvious extension one could construct an eight-parameter model, etc. Such models are often worked out by investigators whose studies cover so wide a range of experimental conditions that a simpler model would not serve to represent their data with desired accuracy.

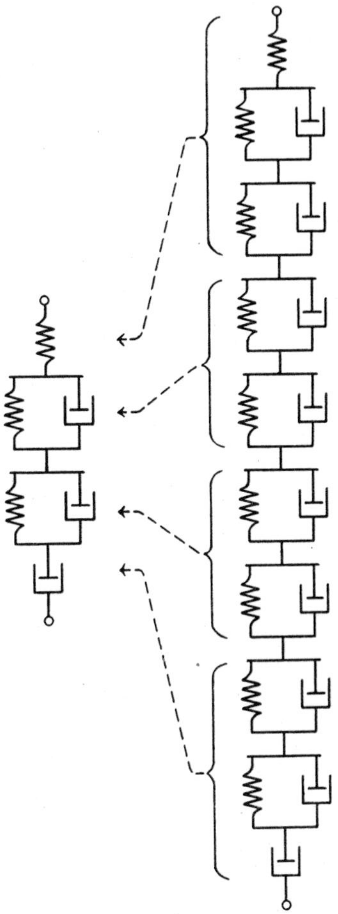

Fig. 70. An empirical six-parameter model.

Many of the remarks concerning the empirical four-parameter model can be repeated here. For example, the temperature dependence of the elements of an empirical eight-parameter model must be interpreted with caution. A change of temperature changes the number of elementary molecular processes which are lumped together in each empirical element. This is indicated in figure 71. In the case schematized here, an increase in temperature results in a large increase in J_1, the apparently instantaneous deformability; J_2 remains much the same, but J_3 and J_4 are reduced by the increase in temperature. The viscosity, η_5, governing all response which appears to be true flow, is calculated exactly as in the case of the four-parameter model:

$$\eta_5 = \frac{1}{\dfrac{1}{\eta} + \displaystyle\int_{\ln \text{Ⓣ}_4}^{\infty} e^{-\ln \tau}\, L(\ln \tau)\, d(\ln \tau)} = \frac{1}{\dfrac{1}{\eta} + \displaystyle\int_{\text{Ⓣ}_4}^{\infty} \frac{J(\tau)}{\tau}\, d\tau} \quad (83)$$

4. Interdependence and Nonlinearity of Plastoelastic Elements

The elastic and flow elements which entered into Model A (Fig. 48, page 104) and Model C (Fig. 59, page 128) were assumed to be linear. For large deformations and large rates of deformation this is not to be expected.

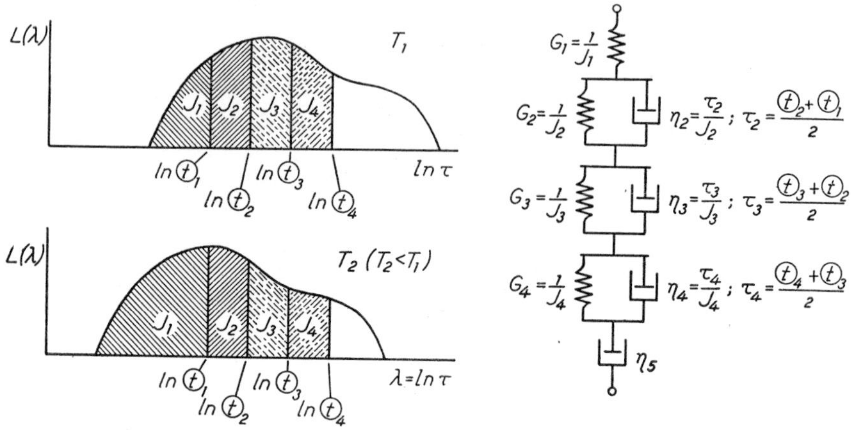

Fig. 71. An empirical eight-parameter model, and the effect of temperature upon its parameters.

We have seen that a given shear modulus G_i, corresponding to the ith retarded elastic element, has a magnitude given by:

$$G_i = \frac{\partial\ ^2\mathbf{F}}{\partial\ ^i\gamma^2} \tag{84}$$

This is based on the assumptions that the various mechanisms of response are independent, and that a single deformation variable $^i\gamma$ measures the extent of response of this mechanism.

If the free energy as a function of $^i\gamma$ is a power series, the first degree term must have a zero coefficient, leading to

$$\mathbf{F}(^i\gamma) = \mathrm{A}_2\ ^i\gamma^2 + \mathrm{A}_3\ ^i\gamma^3 + \mathrm{A}_4\ ^i\gamma^4 + \cdots \tag{85}$$

For small values of $^i\gamma$, only the quadratic term will be significant. The free energy *vs.* $^i\gamma$ curve will be a simple parabola. As a result, the elastic modulus, $(\partial\ ^2\mathbf{F}/\partial\ ^i\gamma^2)$, will be a constant, independent of $^i\gamma$. For large deformations, the higher order terms will result in a nonlinearity of the equilibrium stress—$^i\gamma$ relation. Likewise, at large rates of deformation, it is to be expected that the viscous resistance to deformation is non-Newtonian in character.

The convention will be adopted of representing nonlinear elastic elements by the symbol [a] of figure 72, and nonlinear flow elements by the symbol [b].

A mechanical network composed entirely of linear elements can easily be distinguished from a nonlinear network. If deformation–time curves

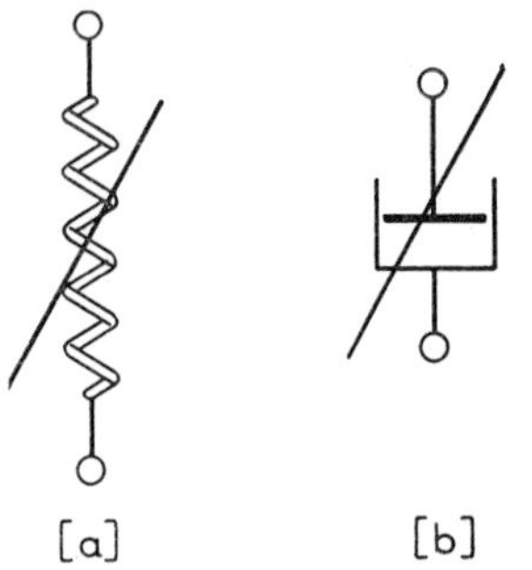

Fig. 72. Symbols representing nonlinear elastic and viscous behavior.

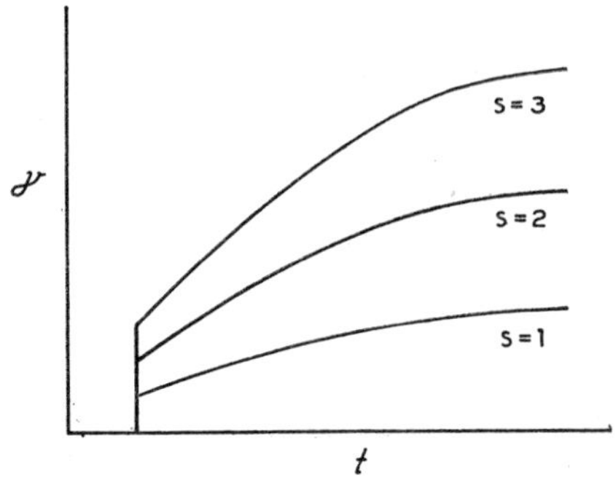

Fig. 73. Deformation–time curves at different stresses for a material with "linear" viscoelastic properties.

at constant stress are run, at a series of different constant stresses, the curves for a linear network must be simply proportional to the stress (see Fig. 73).

If the network contains nonlinear elements, then a change in stress does not result in a uniform magnification, but in a shape distortion as well. It would seem that nonlinearity of elastic or dissipative elements is very frequent among high polymers. Haward (*34*), for example, reports for cellulose acetate (containing 40% of an unspecified plasticizer, cut into strips across the line of extrusion) at 26° C. the set of extension curves shown in figure 74. (In these curves, the instantaneous elastic response has been subtracted. This instantaneous response was found to be ideal Hookean, with a Young's modulus of 24,000 ± 1000 kg. per cm.^{2}.) The extension curves of figure 74 represent retarded elastic deformations. It is clear that the behavior is far from linear—the four curves for stresses of 37.5, 43.0, 48.9, and 53.9 kg. per cm.^{2}, respectively, are not even approximately proportional to those stresses. The slope of the third curve (48.9 kg. per cm.^{2}) is over six times that of the first curve (37.5 kg. per cm.^{2}). Hence a mechanical model which duplicates the behavior of the cellulose acetate used in this experiment must necessarily contain non-Newtonian flow elements.

Haward also recorded the retraction curves at 26° C. of the samples after about 25% and 53% extension (Fig. 75). The form of these curves indicates that more than one retarded elastic mechanism with nonlinear

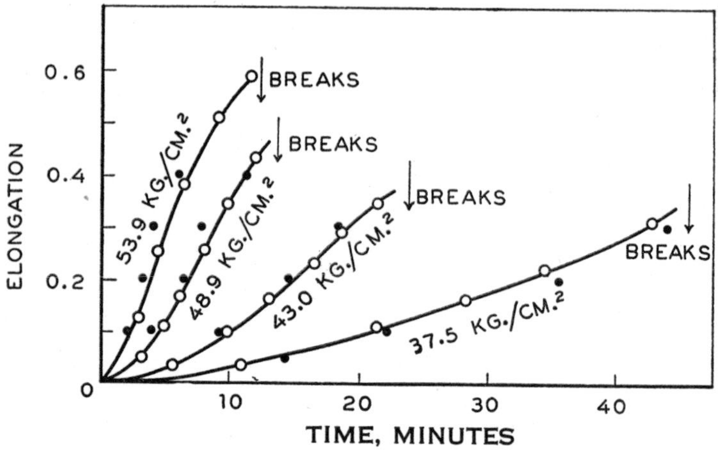

Fig. 74. Creep curves for cellulose acetate at different loads (after Haward).

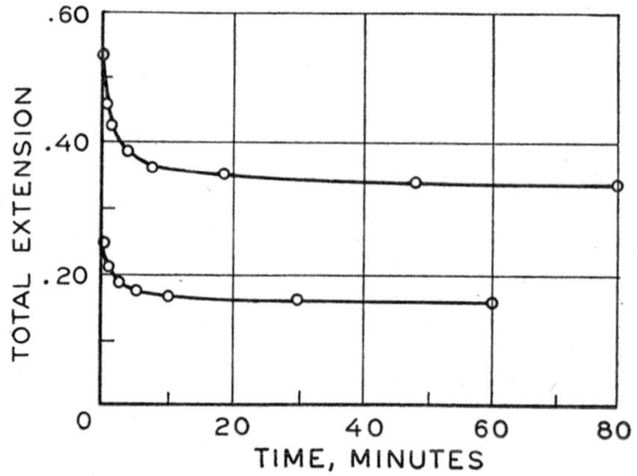

Fig. 75. Creep recovery curves for cellulose acetate (after Haward).

dissipative elements must be operating. It is not possible on the basis of these extension and retraction curves to determine whether the *elastic moduli* of the retarded elastic elements are linear or not. Further, these data are perfectly consistent with the possibility that true flow is taking place, since at 26° C., the deformations do not spontaneously disappear even after a very long time. However, Haward found that if the samples were heated to 70° C. the original shape was restored in a few minutes, which precludes flow.

Haward's experiments represent extreme conditions of stressing since stresses were used which would lead to actual failure in a reasonable time. Furthermore, Haward determined that during the extension experiments the samples were being irreversibly weakened. Hence the deformations involved cannot be expected to fit into the category of simple viscoelastic response. The true viscoelastic response of amorphous polymers seems to be more closely connected with a linear mechanical model than does the above response to very large stresses.

The nonlinearity of elastic or viscous elements introduces a mathematical difficulty. Instead of the linear differential equations which are the symbolic counterpart of a linear mechanical model such as Model A (Fig. 48, page 104), a nonlinear network corresponds to a set of nonlinear differential equations. A nonlinear retarded elastic element, for example, obeys the differential equation:

$$S = f_1(d\gamma/dt) + f_2(\gamma) \tag{86}$$

where $f_1(d\gamma/dt)$ and $f_2(\gamma)$ represent nonlinear functions of the rate of deformation and the deformation, respectively. Shohat (*70*) has pointed out the difficulties involved in the solution of nonlinear differential equations. These equations possess *movable singularities*, depending upon *initial conditions*. For example, the simple nonlinear equation $dy/dt = y^2$ has for its general solution $y = 1/(c - t)$, which approaches infinity as t approaches the value of c. But c, the constant of integration, depends upon the initial conditions, y_0 and t_0. $c = t_0 + 1/y_0$. Thus the singularity of the function appears at a time which depends upon the initial conditions. This mobility of singularities makes it difficult to apply rigorously and effectively the ordinary methods of solution. In special cases, however, it is possible to predict the behavior of a material with a nonlinear plastoelastic spectrum, or, conversely, to determine the proper nonlinear model from the observed behavior.

Not only the *linearity*, but also the assumed *independence* of the various mechanisms of response, cannot be expected to hold if large stresses and deformations are present. As an example, consider the true flow, governed in the various models by the term η_3. It is only reasonable to suppose that the rate of flow will be different for a polymer in which the molecules are straightened out than for a polymer where the molecules are curled. That is, η_3 is not a completely independent quantity but rather depends upon the magnitudes of the various deformations due to the configurational elasticity. In the steady state, at constant stress, where the retarded elastic elements have reached their equilibrium values, this variation of η_3 can be expressed simply as a non-Newtonian flow, *i.e.*, flow $\neq$ constant $\times$ shear stress. The transient phenomena, during the period when the molecules are changing their shapes, however, cannot be explained in this fashion; rather, the resistance to flow must be considered to be a function of the various γ values. This sort of analysis is too involved to be practicable at the moment. The independence of mechanical elements cannot be dispensed with if any actual calculations are to be made. In this book, therefore, interdependence of elements is not considered. As a result, all the models presented, from Model A to Model E, should be considered to be applicable quantitatively only for relatively small deformations.

No model which consists of independent linear elements should be expected to fit, without error, experimental data involving deformations of several hundred per cent or stresses which are comparable to the ultimate strength.

V. SHEAR STRESS: THE DYNAMICS OF VISCOELASTIC BEHAVIOR

The previous sections of this chapter have been devoted to the problem of assessing the viscoelastic *properties* of linear amorphous high polymers. We have seen that, if viscoelastic deformation is accomplished with no volume change (which seems to be true except for the small instantaneous elastic response), then the behavior in shear is sufficient to define the properties of the material. Furthermore, the behavior in shear (in the range of stresses which are not too large) is characterized by a distribution of elastic compliance $J(\tau)$ plus a viscosity which governs true flow. If the function $J(\tau)$ and the physical constants η and G_1 are known for a given amorphous polymer, the viscoelastic properties of the polymer can be considered as known.

However, this information alone cannot be considered to represent a satisfactory understanding of the viscoelastic *behavior* of such materials. There remains the important question: "Assuming the properties of the material to be known, how will the material behave in various situations?" Indeed, the most ambitious question which we desire to answer is: "If an *object* of some known shape is constructed from a polymer of known properties and is subjected to a known sequence of surface forces or constraints, what will be the detailed response of this object?"

This question will be answered in stages. In this section we shall ignore spatial complications and discuss the response of a viscoelastic medium of known properties to a homogeneous shear stress which is a known function of time. All the formulae of this section can also be directly applied to the case of a homogeneous *tensile* stress which varies with time, by the simple expedient of replacing each shear compliance by a tensile compliance one third as large, and each viscosity term by a "tensile viscosity" three times as large. The extension to nonhomogeneous and combined stresses is made in section VI (page 204).

Knowledge of the properties of a linear amorphous polymer (*i.e.*, knowledge of the viscoelastic spectrum) means essentially that we know the *differential equations* governing the time behavior of the material in shear. The problem of this section is the *solution* of these differential equations in various special cases which happen to be of practical interest.

The differential equations governing the time behavior of some idealized materials are listed in table VIII.

TABLE VIII

DIFFERENTIAL EQUATIONS GOVERNING TIME BEHAVIOR OF SOME IDEALIZED MATERIALS

Nature of behavior	Equation
Instantaneous, linear, elasticity	$S = G\gamma$
Newtonian flow	$S = \eta \cdot d\gamma/dt$
Non-Newtonian flow	$S = f(d\gamma/dt)$
Maxwell element	$d\gamma/dt = 1/\eta \cdot S + 1/G \cdot dS/dt$
Retarded elasticity	$S = G\gamma + \eta \cdot d\gamma/dt$
Instantaneous elasticity plus retarded elasticity	$\gamma = \gamma_1 + \gamma_2$ $G_1\gamma_1 = G_2\gamma_2 + \eta_2 \cdot d\gamma_2/dt = S$
Model A	$\gamma = \gamma_1 + \gamma_2 + \gamma_3$ $G_1\gamma_1 = G_2\gamma_2 + \eta_2 \cdot d\gamma_2/dt = \eta_3 \cdot d\gamma_3/dt = S$
Model B	$S = S_1 + S_2$ $d\gamma/dt = 1/\eta_1 \cdot S_1 + 1/G_1 \cdot dS_1/dt$ $= 1/\eta_2 \cdot S_2 + 1/G_2 \cdot dS_2/dt$
Model C. Continuous distribution of retardation times	$\gamma(t) = \int_0^\infty \gamma^*(\tau,t)\, dt$ $S(t) = 1/J(\tau) \cdot \gamma^*(\tau,t) + \tau \cdot 1/J(\tau) \cdot \partial\gamma^*(\tau,t)/\partial t$
Model D. Continuous distribution of relaxation times	$S(t) = \int_0^\infty S^*(\tau,t)\, d\tau$ $d\gamma/dt = 1/G(\tau) \cdot \partial S(\tau,t)/\partial t + 1/\tau G(\tau) \cdot S(\tau,t)$

Since these equations are formulated in terms of *stress and strain, as functions only of time*, they apply by definition to samples of homogeneous *spatial* distribution of stress and strain, and the boundary conditions to which these equations are subject in various special physical problems are temporal rather than spatial. This is important, since it indicates that the solutions presented in this section represent only *part* of the answer to the fundamental mechanical question: "How will an object of known dimensions, constructed of a material of known properties, respond to a known mechanical situation?"

The general problem before us is the computation of the response of a viscoelastic material (of known properties) to any sequence of homogeneous shear stresses, or the stresses set up by any sequence of enforced homogeneous strains. The most interesting special cases, perhaps, are the following:

(1) Constant stress or constant load—the deformation changes with time.

(2) Constant deformation—the *stress* changes with time.

(3) Constant rate of deformation—the stress and strain change with time (stress–strain curve).

(4) Stress varying sinusoidally with time—the strain also changes with time, not necessarily sinusoidally; or strain varying sinusoidally with time—the stress changes with time, not necessarily sinusoidally.

1. Case (1)—Constant Stress

This case has already been discussed in previous sections, subject to the implicit assumption that at the beginning of the experiment, the sample was in complete elastic equilibrium. Thus if a stress S is suddenly imposed at $t = 0$, a material governed by a four-parameter model such as Model A or Model E responds as follows:

$$\gamma = S\left[\frac{1}{G_1} + \frac{1}{G_2}(1 - e^{-t/\tau}) + \frac{1}{\eta_3}t\right] \tag{87}$$

A material possessing a finite number, n, of retarded elastic mechanisms responds as follows:

$$\gamma = S\left[\frac{1}{G_1} + \sum_{i=1}^{n}\frac{1}{G_{2,i}}(1 - e^{-t/\tau_i}) + \frac{1}{\eta_3}t\right] \tag{88}$$

A material possessing a continuous distribution of retardation times, $J(\tau)$, will respond as follows:

$$\gamma = S\left[\frac{1}{G_1} + \int_0^\infty J(\tau)(1 - e^{-t/\tau})d\tau + \frac{1}{\eta_3}t\right] \qquad (89)$$

If at the time of application of the stress ($t = 0$), the sample contains residual configurational strains, γ_i, from previous deformations, then the deformation-time curve of the material is not so simple. Let $\gamma_2(0)$ represent the configurational strain present at $t = 0$, for a material governed by a four-parameter model. Upon application of the stress S at $t = 0$, the sample responds as follows:

$$\gamma = S\left[\frac{1}{G_1} + \frac{1}{G_2}(1 - e^{-t/\tau}) + \frac{t}{\eta_3}\right] + \gamma_2(0)\, e^{-t/\tau} \qquad (90)$$

The material possessing a finite number n of retarded elastic mechanisms of response responds to the constant stress S in the following manner, if $\gamma_{2,i}(0)$ represents the value of $\gamma_{2,i}$ at $t = 0$:

$$\gamma = S\left[\frac{1}{G_1} + \sum_i^n \frac{1}{G_{2,i}}(1 - e^{-t/\tau_i}) + \frac{1}{\eta}t\right] + \sum_i^n \gamma_{2,i}(0)\, e^{-t/\tau_i} \qquad (91)$$

Finally, the material possessing a continuous distribution of retardation times responds as follows:

$$\gamma = S\left[\frac{1}{G_1} + \int_0^\infty J(\tau)(1 - e^{-t/\tau})d\tau + \frac{1}{\eta}t\right] + \int_0^\infty \gamma_\tau^*(0,\tau)\, e^{-t/\tau}d\tau \qquad (92)$$

In this last equation, the function $\gamma^*(0,\tau)$ represents the initial value of the strain function $\gamma^*(t,\tau)$, *i.e.*, the value for $t = 0$.

The initial configurational strain, $\gamma_2(0)$, in equation (90) clearly depends in value upon the previous stress–strain history of the sample. If the sample is allowed to rest with zero stress for a long time before the stress S is applied at $t = 0$, then the configurational strain γ_2 is able to relax. In this case $\gamma_2(0)$ is equal to zero, and equation 87 is applicable (in the case of a material which can be represented by a four-parameter model). If, however, the constant stress experiment is begun soon after the material has experienced some other stress sequence, then γ_2 has a value different from zero at $t = 0$ and the decaying of the residual strain $\gamma_2(0)$ must be considered, as in equation (90). The effect of residual strains in more complicated materials is much the same. Thus in a material exhibiting a continuous distribution of retardation times, the configurational strain function $\gamma^*(\tau)$ decays to zero after a time which is long compared to the greatest retardation time. In such an unstrained state, the effect of a constant stress beginning at $t = 0$ is given by equation (89). If, however, the sample has been subjected in the near past to some stress sequence, there are residual strains at $t = 0$. That is, $\gamma^*(0,\tau)$ is a nonvanishing function. When the stress is applied at $t = 0$, we must consider the decaying away of these residual configurational strains, as in equation (92).

At a later stage of the discussion, the response of a viscoelastic material to any arbitrary stress sequence $S(t)$ is computed by resolving the stress sequence into a series of step functions. For this analysis, it is necessary to know how the strain changes with time when a constant stress S is imposed at some time other than zero. The following equations give this information. The sample is presumed to be unstrained initially and at the time t_1 a stress S is imposed. Equations (93), (94), and (95) give the response of the three typical materials which we have been considering.

$$\gamma(t) = 0 \quad \text{for } t < t_1;$$

$$\gamma(t) = S\left[\frac{1}{G_1} + \frac{1}{G_2}(1 - e^{-(t-t_1)/\tau}) + \frac{t - t_1}{\eta_3}\right] \quad \text{for } t > t_1 \tag{93}$$

$$\gamma(t) = 0 \quad \text{for } t < t_1;$$

$$\gamma(t) = S\left[\frac{1}{G_1} + \sum_{i=1}^{n} \frac{1}{G_{2,i}}(1 - e^{-(t-t_1)/\tau_i}) + \frac{t - t_1}{\eta_3}\right] \quad \text{for } t > t_1 \tag{94}$$

$$\gamma(t) = 0 \quad \text{for } t < t_1;$$

$$\gamma(t) = S\left[\frac{1}{G_1} + \int_0^\infty J(\tau)(1 - e^{-(t-t_1)/\tau})d\tau + \frac{t - t_1}{\eta}\right] \quad \text{for } t > t_1 \tag{95}$$

If only *linear* elastic and flow elements operate in the plastoelastic response of a material, as here assumed, then the effect of changing the magnitude of the stress from one constant value to another is only to make a proportional change in the whole deformation–time curve. For example, the deformation–time curve for $S = 5$ will be identical to that for $S = 3$, except that every deformation value will be just 5/3 as large. A *single* deformation–time curve thus suffices in principle to define a completely linear plastoelastic spectrum. On the other hand, if nonlinear elements operate, a change from one stress to another distorts the whole form of the curve. In this case, the family of deformation–time curves at different constant stresses are not simply proportional to the respective stresses. Further, no single deformation–time curve can, even in principle, define the plastoelastic spectrum. Rather, the whole set of curves at different stresses are necessary.

2. Case (2)—Constant Deformation

The relaxation of stress at constant strain is the second special case of interest. An ideal elastic solid, of course, does not relax at all, while a liquid exhibiting only viscosity without rigidity can support no shear stress at constant shape (*i.e.*, relaxes instantaneously). We have seen that, if a Maxwell element is deformed, and then held at constant deformation, the stress relaxes exponentially:

$$S = S_0\,e^{-(G/\eta)t} \quad \text{or} \quad S_0\,e^{-t/\tau} \quad \text{where} \quad \tau = \eta/G \tag{96}$$

A retarded elastic element does not relax its stress at constant deformation. However, a retarded elastic element in series with an instantaneous element (material exhibiting both instantaneous and retarded elasticity) relaxes according to equation (97).

$$S = \frac{G_1G_2}{G_1 + G_2}\gamma + A\,e^{-(G_1+G_2)t/\eta_2} \tag{97}$$

Here A is an arbitrary constant which depends upon the past mechanical history of the sample.

The relaxation at constant deformation of Model A (instantaneous elasticity, retarded elasticity, and flow) follows a still more complicated equation:

$$S = A\,e^{-\alpha t} + B\,e^{-\beta t} \tag{98}$$

where
$$2\alpha = \left[\frac{\eta_2^2}{G_1\eta_3} + \frac{G_2}{\eta_2} + \frac{G_1}{\eta_2}\right] + \sqrt{\left[\frac{\eta_2^2}{G_1\eta_3} + \frac{G_2}{\eta_2} + \frac{G_1}{\eta_2}\right]^2 - \frac{4\,G_2G_1}{\eta_2\eta_3}}$$

$$2\beta = \left[\frac{\eta_2^2}{G_1\eta_3} + \frac{G_2}{\eta_2} + \frac{G_1}{\eta_2}\right] - \sqrt{\left[\frac{\eta_2^2}{G_1\eta_3} + \frac{G_2}{\eta_2} + \frac{G_1}{\eta_2}\right]^2 - \frac{4\,G_1G_2}{\eta_2\eta_3}}$$

Here A and B, like A of equation (97), are arbitrary constants which depend upon the *deformation route* by which the sample is brought to the deformed state under consideration. If the sample is quickly deformed from the equilibrium state to the deformation γ_1, at $t = 0$, and then held at γ_1, the constants A and B take the values:

$$A = \gamma\,\frac{G_1^2\left(\dfrac{1}{\eta_2} + \dfrac{1}{\eta_3}\right) - \beta G_1}{\alpha - \beta} \tag{99}$$
$$B = G_1\gamma - A$$

This physical problem can be handled with much simpler mathematical methods if instead of Model A, we use the equivalent Model B. At constant deformation the two Maxwell elements each relax simply, and since their stresses are additive,

$$S = \mathrm{A}\,e^{-(G_1/\eta_1)t} + \mathrm{B}\,e^{-(G_2/\eta_2)t} \tag{100}$$

As above, A and B are arbitrary constants depending upon past history. For the special case chosen above,

$$S = G_1\gamma\,e^{-(G_1/\eta_1)t} + G_2\gamma\,e^{-(G_2/\eta_2)t} \tag{101}$$

It can be seen from inspection that equation (100) is of exactly the same form as equation (98), and the arbitrary coefficients A and B are of the same form in these two equations. The parameters are simply more complicated combinations of the quantities E_1^A, E_2^A, η_2^A, η_3^A, than of the complementary quantities E_1^B, E_2^B, η_1^B, η_2^B. That the equations are actually identical can be shown by substituting into equation (100) the values of the B quantities in terms of the A quantities (section III. C, pages 125–126).

For a material possessing a distribution of relaxation mechanisms, represented by a continuous set of Maxwell elements coupled in parallel with each other, the stress relaxation is given by the integral expression:

$$S(t) = \int_0^\infty \varphi(\tau)\,G(\tau)\,e^{-t/\tau}\,d\tau \tag{102}$$

Here $G(\tau)$ is the distribution function of elastic modulus over the continuum of relaxation times and $\varphi(\tau)$ is an arbitrary function which depends upon the past history [corresponding to A and B in Eq. (100)]. The only necessary constraint on $\varphi(\tau)$ in the general case is that the integral $\int_0^\infty \varphi(\tau)d\tau$ must be equal to the initial stress. When an initially unstrained sample is quickly given the deformation γ at $t = 0$, equation (102) takes on the specific form:

$$S(t) = \gamma \int_0^\infty G(\tau)\,e^{-t/\tau}\,d\tau \tag{103}$$

Equation (102) can be converted into a form which is similar to that of equation (92):

$$S(t) = \gamma \int_0^\infty G(\tau)\,e^{-t/\tau}\,d\tau + \int_0^\infty S_0^*(0,\tau)\,e^{-t/\tau}\,d\tau \tag{104}$$

Here the first term gives the stress which results from quickly deforming the sample to the extent γ, while the second term gives the effect of residual "internal stresses" which are present at $t = 0$ because of previous stressing operations.

Any material which can be represented by a distribution of relaxation times (*i.e.*, a model of type D) can also be represented by an equivalent model of type C and a distribution of retardation times. A given distribution of "internal stresses" in one terminology corresponds to a definite distribution of strain contributions in the other terminology. Hence a given residual internal stress $S^*(0,\tau)$ corresponds to a definite set of residual strains $\gamma^*(0,\tau)$. It should, in principle, be possible to compute the residual "internal stresses," $S^*(\tau)$ of Model D from the known residual strains $\gamma^*(\tau)$ of the corresponding Model C. This will not be done here, but the possibility is mentioned to emphasize the close connection between *strain memory effects*, as observed in constant stress experiments, and *stress memory effects* as observed in constant strain experiments.

3. Case (3)—Constant Rate of Deformation

It is a common procedure to test even so complex a material as an organic high polymer by placing it in a tensile machine and determining the "stress–strain" curve, or "load–elongation" curve. During such a test, the stress is not constant, but increases up until the time when the material begins to yield. Instead of the stress, the *rate of elongation* is usually held constant (by constant crosshead speed). The early slope of the "stress–strain" curve is often interpreted as a measure of the Young's modulus of the material.

Because of the common use of such tests, it seems worthwhile to analyze the mechanical behavior of plastoelastic materials under the imposed condition of constant rate of deformation. The form of the "load–elongation" curve will thus be correlated with that of the more direct elongation–time curve. The importance of the *rate* of elongation will become apparent.

If the elongation proceeds to high values, then the cross-sectional area of the piece is appreciably reduced. As a result, the stresses calculated on the basis of actual cross section and on the basis of original cross section are different. The "stress–strain" curve (based on actual cross section) has a different shape from the directly observed "load–elongation" curve. The stress–strain curve is comparable to elongation–time curves at constant *stress;* the load–elongation curve to elongation–time curves at constant *load.* The following equations, however, refer only to small strains. Furthermore, in accordance with our usual procedure, they are formulated in terms of shear stress and strain. They can be converted to the case of tension by introducing the factor 3.

An ideal elastic material responds to a stress by instantaneously taking on a new equilibrium shape. The shear strain, γ, is related to the shear stress, S, by the equation:

$$S = G\gamma \tag{105}$$

When such a material is distorted at constant *rate*, the stress again follows equation (105). The stress–strain curve is thus a simple straight line through the origin.

As long as the elastic response is instantaneous, even though it be nonlinear, the stress–strain curve is simple. The initial slope, for example, gives the Young's modulus in this case. The stress–strain curve is *independent of the rate of straining* for an object exhibiting only (linear or nonlinear) instantaneous elastic behavior.

Let us now consider a material possessing both instantaneous elasticity and a superimposed flow, represented by the model of a Maxwell element (G,η). If we impose upon this system the condition of constant rate of deformation, we obtain the stress–strain relation:

$$S = \eta \mathrm{R}(1 - e^{-G/\mathrm{R}\eta\gamma}) \tag{106}$$

where R represents the rate of increase of strain, $d\gamma/dt$. The stress–strain curve of such a material is thus a more complicated function than is that of a simple elastic material. The importance of R, the imposed rate of strain, is evident.

In the limiting case, where $\mathrm{R} \gg G/\eta$, the stress–strain equation (106) reduces to the simple form $S = G\gamma$. This is, of course, necessary, since the condition means that the test is made so rapidly that only elastic response is possible; the amount of flow can be neglected.

As long as $\mathrm{R} \gg G/\eta$, *the stress–strain curve* is not affected by the precise value of R. When $\mathrm{R} \sim G/\eta$, the stress–strain curve is not only different from the above case, but is strongly dependent upon R. When $\mathrm{R} \ll G/\eta$, the deformation is entirely the result of flow, and the stress at every point is simply $\eta\mathrm{R}$.

A *retarded* elastic element follows the differential equation:

$$S = G\gamma + \eta(d\gamma/dt)$$

If we impose the condition of constant rate of deformation, we obtain stress–strain equation (107):

$$S = G\gamma + \eta\mathrm{R} \tag{107}$$

Here again the *rate of deformation* is important. The simple equation $S = G\gamma$ is followed in the limiting case of small R, rather than large R.

Consider now a material possessing both instantaneous and retarded elasticity, but no flow (Model A, without the element η_3). If the condition is imposed that $d\gamma/dt = \mathrm{R}$, where R is a constant, the following stress–strain relation results:

$$S = \frac{G_1G_2\gamma}{G_1 + G_2} + \frac{RG_1^2\eta_2}{(G_1 + G_2)^2}\left(1 - \mathrm{e}^{-(G_1+G_2)/\eta_2\cdot\gamma/\mathrm{R}}\right) \qquad (108)$$

Several limiting cases are of interest. When R is very great, equation (108) reduces to $S = G_1\gamma$. When R is very small, equation (108) reduces to:

$$S = \left[\frac{1}{1/G_1 + 1/G_2}\right]\gamma \qquad (109)$$

that is, the effective reciprocal modulus is the sum of the two contributing reciprocal moduli. It is of interest that in both of these limiting cases, the stress–strain curve is not dependent upon the precise value of R. At high testing rates, the material behaves like an ideal elastic material of modulus G_1; the second mechanism is "frozen in." At very low rates, it acts as an ideal elastic material of lower modulus; both mechanisms contribute ideally. When R is intermediate in magnitude (*i.e.*, when the retarded elastic mechanism has time to respond *partially* to the stress at any instant), the curve is strongly dependent upon R.

A material which follows the behavior of Model A (instantaneous elasticity, retarded elasticity, and flow) can better be expressed in terms of Model B if the condition of constant rate of deformation is to be considered. The expression for the stress is simply the sum of the expressions for the two Maxwell elements:

$$S = \mathrm{R}[\eta_1 - \eta_1\,\mathrm{e}^{-(G_1/\mathrm{R}\eta_1)\gamma} + \eta_2 - \eta_2\,\mathrm{e}^{-(G_2/\mathrm{R}\eta_2)\gamma}] \qquad (110)$$

Because of the importance of the stress–strain relationship at constant rate of deformation and the emphasis we have given to Model A itself, it may be interesting to write the above equation in terms of the equivalent Model A with α and β as defined in equation (98).

$$S = \eta_3\mathrm{R} + \left(\frac{G_1\mathrm{R} - \eta_3\beta}{\beta - \alpha}\right)\mathrm{e}^{-\alpha(\gamma/R)} + \left(\frac{\eta_3\alpha - G_1\mathrm{R}}{\beta - \alpha}\right)\mathrm{e}^{-\beta(\gamma/\mathrm{R})} \qquad (111)$$

This equation is perhaps too complicated to permit of any direct use. One would probably not try to fit this equation to a set of stress–strain data and thus determine the parameters G_1, G_2, η_2, η_3, of Model A or E. Under certain limiting conditions, equation (111) becomes very simple.

For example, if $R \gg G_1/\eta_2$, equation (111) reduces to the simple form $S = G_1\gamma$. At such a high rate, the configurational elasticity is frozen in and the material behaves as an elastic body of modulus G_1. If $R \ll G_2/\eta_2$, but at the same time $R \gg G_2/\eta_3$, equation (111) reduces to equation (109). At such an intermediate rate the configurational elasticity is able to follow the stress with no time lag, and yet too small a time is allowed for any appreciable flow to develop. Finally, for very slow speeds of testing, where $R \ll G_2/\eta_3$, the entire response is the result of flow, and the stress–strain curve is a horizontal line at $S = R\eta_3$.

A material exhibiting a continuous distribution of relaxation times, $G(\tau)$, gives a stress–strain curve of the following form:

$$S = R\int_0^\infty \tau G(\tau)(1 - e^{-\gamma/R\tau})d\tau \tag{112}$$

It is apparent that the general nature of the plastoelastic behavior depends upon the timescale of the stress–strain experiment in relation to the "internal timescale" of the material, *i.e.*, the relaxation times or retardation times. When the imposed deformation rate is very high, mechanisms 2 and 3 (see page 104) are unable to operate to any significant extent. They are "frozen in." Hence the material behaves as an ideal elastic material of modulus G_1. If the imposed deformation rate is extremely slow, the sample simply flows. At intermediate rates, both elastic and viscous elements may contribute to the stress–strain curve.

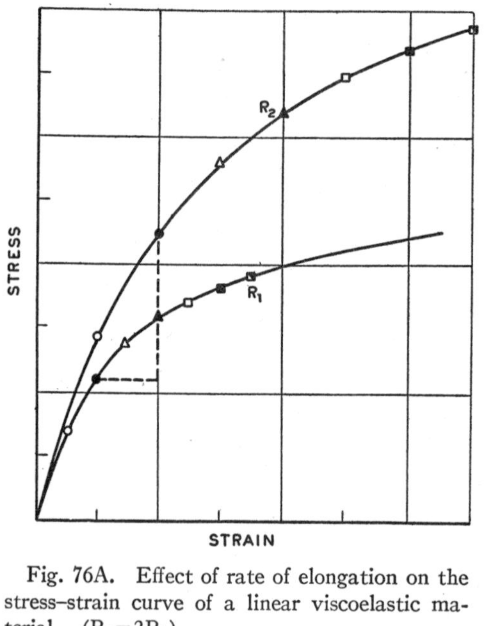

Fig. 76A. Effect of rate of elongation on the stress–strain curve of a linear viscoelastic material. ($R_2 = 2R_1$)

In a range of crosshead speed where the material exhibits truly elastic behavior—where none of the work done on the sample is absorbed by dissipative elements—

moderate *changes* in crosshead speed should not change the initial part of the stress–strain curve. On the other hand, in a range where the response is "plastoelastic," and the stress must work against dissipative as well as elastic elements, changes in crosshead rate will result in changes in the stress–strain curve. In the former case, the interpretation of the initial slope as a measure of the Young's modulus is justified, if it be remembered that this Young's modulus applies only to a definite experimental timescale. In the latter case, the calculation of a Young's modulus leads to confusion.

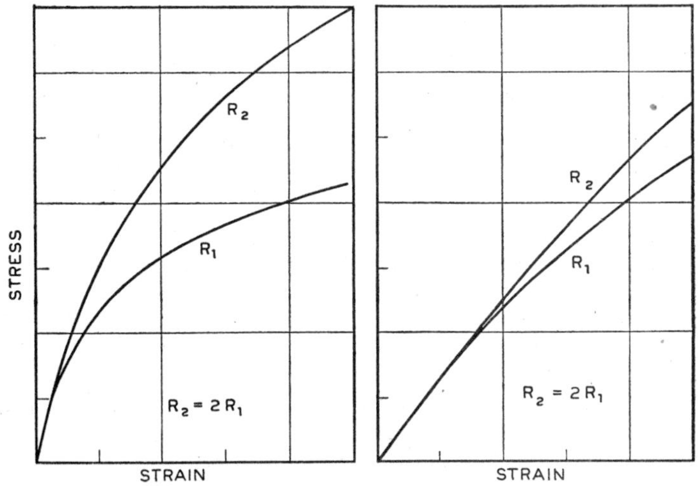

Fig. 76B. Correlation between curvature of stress–strain curve and sensitivity to testing speed. The curve on the left is markedly curved and hence a change in rate of testing causes a lower displacement. The curve on the right is nearly straight, and as a result is only slightly affected by changes in testing speed.

It is not to be expected that the stress–strain curve of any polymer will be independent of crosshead rate over the whole range of rate from zero to infinity. However, in some ranges the dependency upon rate will be more marked than in others. The ranges where the dependency is small correspond to timescales for which the mechanical response of the polymer is essentially elastic; the ranges where the dependency is large correspond to timescales for which the mechanical response of the polymer is largely governed by its dissipative elements.

The "apparent modulus"—or initial slope of the stress–strain curve—will always *increase* with R, the rate of deformation. That is, the faster the test, the "stiffer" the material will appear to be. In some ranges of

R, the dependency will be small, in other ranges it will be very large—but whether large or small, it will always be in this direction.

This dependence of the stress–strain curve on the rate of testing is governed in a quite explicit fashion by equation (112). If the stress–strain curve is known for one rate, R_1, the curve for another rate, R_2, can be computed as follows. To obtain a point on the new stress–strain curve, choose a point on the original curve and multiply both abscissa

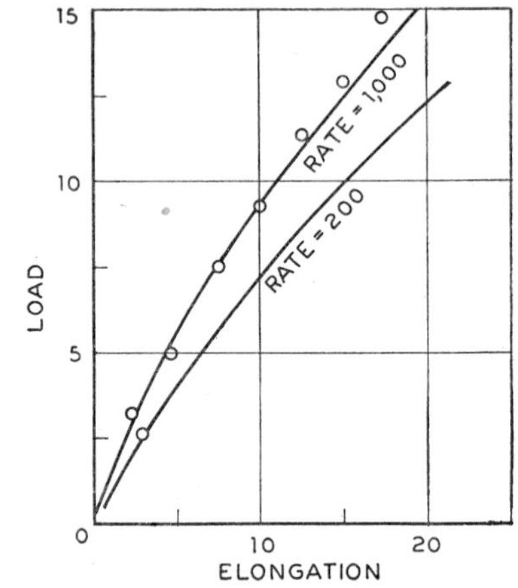

Fig. 77A. Stress–strain curves at two rates of testing for plasticized polyvinyl butyral. The upper curve was calculated theoretically from the stress–strain curve at the lower rate of testing. It agrees satisfactorily with the experimental points, which are also shown.

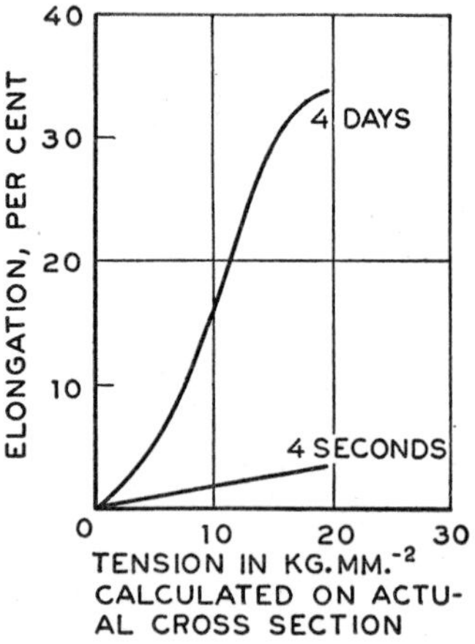

Fig. 77B. Effect of testing speed on the stress–strain curve of cellulose acetate.

and ordinate by the factor R_2/R_1. This procedure is illustrated in figure 76A, where the ratio of testing rates is chosen as 2:1. It is clear that there is a close connection between curvature and dependence upon rate of testing. If the stress–strain curve is nearly a straight line at rate R_1, it will be only a little steeper at the higher rate, R_2. On the other hand, if the stress–strain curve at rate R_1 is far from straight, the curve at the higher rate, R_2, will be *much* steeper. This correlation between the *shape* of the stress–strain curve and the sensitivity to changes in testing rate is illustrated in figure 76B. In the limiting case of a non-relaxing material the stress–strain curve is a straight line and is completely unaffected by change in testing rate.

While it is not usual to vary the crosshead speed in a tensile test over wide ranges, this has been done in a few cases. Figures 77A and B show the effect of rate of straining upon the stress–strain curves of plasticized polyvinyl butyral and cellulose acetate.

Perhaps a word of warning should be appended to this discussion. In an ordinary stress–strain experiment the straining is continued until the sample fails. It is shown, in the discussion of ultimate strength (see chapter F), that permanent and irreversible changes in the *structure* of a material begin long before actual failure occurs. If the stress S_1 causes failure after a time t_1, then this stress will cause an appreciable permanent change in the material if it is applied for a time which is an appreciable fraction of t_1. In the early part of the stress–strain experiment, the stresses are not present for an appreciable part of their breaking times. Here the above analysis would be most applicable. In the later stages of a stress–strain experiment, the stresses cause permanent damage to the material, which accumulates until failure occurs. The later parts of the stress–strain curve should therefore be analyzed with this in mind and should not be expected to follow the pattern of this section.

4. Case (4)—Response to Stresses Varying Sinusoidally with Time (*11*, *23*)

Consider a material which exhibits the behavior predicted by Model A, under the action of a sinusoidal stress.

$$S = S_0 \cos(\omega t) \tag{113}$$

In the steady state, the sample undergoes a *sinusoidal deformation* which has the same frequency as the stress, which in general is out of phase with the stress and which depends in amplitude upon both the magnitude and the frequency of the stress. Mathematically, this problem is completely analogous to the steady-state response of an electrical network (Fig. 79), containing both resistance and capacitance, to an alternating voltage source. If the stress at any time is given by equation (113), the deformation of the sample is governed by the equation:

$$\gamma = S_0 \left[\frac{1}{G_1} \cos(\omega t) + \frac{\sin(\omega t - \alpha)}{\sqrt{\omega^2 \eta_2^2 + G_2^2}} + \frac{1}{\omega \eta_3} \sin(\omega t) \right] \tag{114}$$

where $\alpha = \tan^{-1}(-G_2/\omega\eta_2)$. The first term represents the response of the instantaneous elastic mechanism, and is completely in phase with the applied stress. The third term represents flow and is out of phase with the stress by exactly $\pi/2$. The second term represents the retarded elastic response and is intermediate in phase between the first and third terms.

The periodic deformation represented by the first term absorbs no net energy during a cycle. Since the deformation itself is in phase with the stress, the rate of deformation is $\pi/2$ out of phase with the stress. This is analogous to the current–voltage relation in a purely capacitive electrical circuit. The flow deformation, on the other hand, continuously absorbs mechanical energy, which is dissipated as heat, just as the resistance element of figure 79 absorbs electrical energy. The energy absorption of mechanism 2 depends strongly upon the frequency, which determines the phase angle α as well as the amplitude of the periodic deformation. At extremely low frequency, $\alpha = -\pi/2$, and hence the second term, like the first, is exactly in phase with the stress. Hence there is no net energy loss during a cycle. At extremely high frequency, $\alpha = 0$, and hence the second mechanism is in phase with the flow rather than with the instantaneous elastic response. At intermediate frequencies, where $1/\omega$ is of the same order of magnitude as τ_2, the sinusoidal deformation due to mechanism 2 is intermediate in phase between these two extremes.

In many cases, particularly with cross-linked polymers, the flow can be neglected, since if η_3 is large and ω is appreciable, the third term becomes very small. (At extremely low frequency, of course, this is not true.) If flow is not considered, equation (114) reduces to the following:

$$\gamma = S_0 \left[\frac{1}{G_1} \cos(\omega t) + \frac{\sin(\omega t - \alpha)}{\sqrt{\omega^2\eta_2^2 + G_2^2}} \right] \tag{115}$$

It is interesting to follow in detail the mechanical response of such a flowless specimen as a function of frequency. It is evident that equation (115) can be rewritten in the form:

$$\gamma = S_0[\mathrm{A} \cos(\omega t) + \mathrm{B} \sin(\omega t)] \tag{116}$$

Here A could be called the "real" and B the "imaginary" reciprocal modulus of elasticity, analogous to the "real" and "imaginary" components of polarizability. The amplitude of the deformation which is in phase with the stress is given by $\mathrm{A}S_0$; $\mathrm{B}S_0$ gives the amplitude of the deformation which is out of phase by $\pi/2$. Figure 78 is a plot of A and B *vs.* frequency for this case:

$$\mathrm{A} = \frac{1}{G_1} + \frac{1}{G_2(\omega^2\tau^2 + 1)} \qquad \mathrm{B} = \frac{\omega\tau}{G_2(\omega^2\tau^2 + 1)} \tag{117}$$

At very low frequency, both mechanisms 1 and 2 give ideal elastic response. The phase angle α for mechanism 2 is $(\pi/2)$, which makes γ_2 stay exactly in phase with S. In other words, at low frequency, the molecular uncurling can keep up with the changes in stress. Thus the material behaves as a simple elastic solid, with a reciprocal modulus equal to $(1/G_1 + 1/G_2)$. As long as the period of the stress cycle is long, compared with the retardation time of mechanism 2, this same reciprocal modulus applies. Note that at these low frequencies (in the absence of flow) the *out-of-phase* component is zero. Thus all energy stored in the sample during one part of the mechanical cycle is exactly regained during the other part of the cycle. There is no net energy absorption—no heat loss.

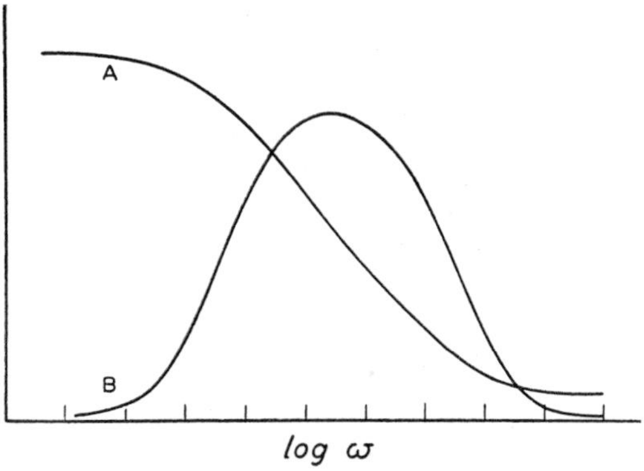

Fig. 78. Real (A) and imaginary (B) reciprocal modulus of elasticity as a function of frequency.

As the stress frequency increases, the molecular curling and uncurling are no longer able to follow the stress, α becomes smaller in magnitude, and γ_2 is no longer exactly in phase with S. This has two results. First, the "real" reciprocal modulus decreases and second, the "imaginary" one becomes noticeable. In this region, where the period of S is of the same order as τ, A is markedly a function of ω, and there is an appreciable *heat loss.*

At still higher frequencies, the molecular curling is unable to follow the stress at all. Again B = 0 and again A is independent of ω. The high frequency value of A is simply $1/G_1$. Thus a material governed by Model A will respond to a high frequency alternating stress (period $\ll \tau$) as an ideal elastic material of modulus G_1.

It is significant that at high frequency ($\omega \gg G_2/\eta_2$) the deformation γ_2 takes on the form:

$$\gamma_2 = \frac{S_0}{\omega\eta_2}\sin(\omega t)$$

since $\alpha = 0$. This is of exactly the same form as the expression for the flow response, $\dot{\gamma}_3$. Thus at very high frequency the retarded elastic mechanism behaves just like a flow mechanism. The heat loss per cycle is proportional to the out-of-phase component of strain, and hence decreases toward zero as the frequency increases toward infinity. The heat loss *per unit time*, however, includes the frequency as a factor and hence approaches a constant limiting value as the frequency approaches infinity.

It is apparent that the above results constitute a special case of the generalizations of previous sections. The behavior of Model A (without flow) depends upon the retardation time of mechanism 2, τ, as compared with the timescale of the experimental investigation. When τ is small, compared with the experimental timescale, the material behaves as an ideal elastic material of modulus $1/(1/G_1 + 1/G_2)$. When τ is large, the material exhibits the deformation typical of an ideal elastic material of modulus G_1. When τ is of the same order of magnitude as the experimental timescale, the modulus has an intermediate value, and complex time effects (here, an intermediate phase angle) are observed. In the case of sinusoidal stresses, the *period* of variation is the obvious measure of the experimental timescale.

The previous discussion pertains only to the *steady-state* response to sinusoidal stresses. If the stress, $S = S_0 \cos(\omega t)$, begins suddenly at $t = 0$, it is clear that the strain can immediately begin to follow equation 116 only if there is a residual configurational strain at $t = 0$ which just equals the value predicted for $t = 0$ by equation 116. This value is $1/G_2 \cdot (\omega^2\tau^2 + 1)$. If at $t = 0$, the configurational strain, $\gamma_2(0)$, has some other value than this, the *difference*, $\gamma_2(0) - 1/G_2 \cdot (\omega^2\tau^2 + 1)$, will decay away exponentially with time. Thus the complete strain–time function, including this transient part, is given by:

$$\gamma(t) = S_0 \left[\frac{1}{G_1} + \frac{1}{G_2(\omega^2\tau^2 + 1)} \right] \cos \omega t + \frac{S_0 \omega \tau}{G_2(\omega^2\tau^2 + 1)} \sin \omega t + e^{-t/\tau} \left[\gamma_2(0) - \frac{S_0}{G_2(\omega^2\tau^2 + 1)} \right] \quad (118)$$

When $S(t) = 0$ for $t < 0$, $S(t) = S_0 \cos \omega t$ for $t > 0$. In the special case where the stress is imposed suddenly upon an unstrained sample, this reduces to:

$$\gamma(t) = S_0 \left[\frac{1}{G_1} + \frac{1}{G_2(\omega^2\tau^2 + 1)} \right] \cos \omega t + \frac{S_0 \omega \tau}{G_2(\omega^2\tau^2 + 1)} \sin \omega t - \left[\frac{S_0}{G_2(\omega^2\tau^2 + 1)} \right] e^{-t/\tau} \quad (119)$$

The steady-state response of a material exhibiting n mechanisms of retarded elastic response is given by:

$$\gamma(t) = S_0 \cos \omega t \left[\sum_i \frac{1}{G_i(\omega^2\tau_i^2 + 1)} \right] + S_0 \sin \omega t \left[\sum_i \frac{\omega\tau_i}{G_i(\omega^2\tau_i^2 + 1)} \right] \quad (120)$$

If the transient behavior is included, we obtain:

$$\gamma(t) = S_0 \cos \omega t \left[\sum_i \frac{1}{G_i(\omega^2\tau_i^2 + 1)} \right] + S_0 \sin \omega t \left[\sum_i \frac{\omega\tau_i}{G_i(\omega^2\tau_i^2 + 1)} \right] \sum_i e^{-t/\tau_i} \left[\gamma_i(0) - \frac{S_0}{G_i(\omega^2\tau_i^2 + 1)} \right] \quad (121)$$

Finally, for a material possessing a continuous distribution of retardation times, the steady state and total response functions are, respectively, the following:

$$\gamma(t) = S_0 \cos \omega t \int_0^\infty \frac{J(\tau)\, d\tau}{\omega^2\tau^2 + 1} + S_0 \sin \omega t \int_0^\infty \frac{\omega\tau\, J(\tau)\, d\tau}{\omega^2\tau^2 + 1} \quad (122)$$

$$\gamma(t) = S_0 \cos \omega t \int_0^\infty \frac{J(\tau)\, d\tau}{\omega^2\tau^2 + 1} + S_0 \sin \omega t \int_0^\infty \frac{\omega\tau\, J(\tau)\, d\tau}{\omega^2\tau^2 + 1} + \int_0^\infty e^{-t/\tau} \left[\gamma^*(0,\tau) - \frac{S_0\, J(\tau)}{\omega^2\tau^2 + 1} \right] d\tau \quad (123)$$

5. Analogy with Electrical Networks

It has already been emphasized that knowledge of the *differential equations governing the mechanical behavior of a material* constitutes, in principle, a complete knowledge of its properties. In order to predict the response of an object to various situations, it is necessary to solve these basic differential equations subject to the proper boundary conditions.

Now many other physical phenomena are governed by differential equations of precisely the same form as those we have been discussing. One of the most thoroughly studied examples is furnished by the linear *electrical network*. If we consider electromotive force to be equivalent to stress, and current to be equivalent to $d\gamma/dt$, then a capacitance is equivalent to a reciprocal elastic modulus and a resistance is equivalent to a viscosity. To each simple type of mechanical response there corresponds a simple electrical network with precisely analogous properties. These are tabulated in figure 79.

It should be noted that when elements are coupled in *parallel in the mechanical* model, the equivalent electrical network has a corresponding

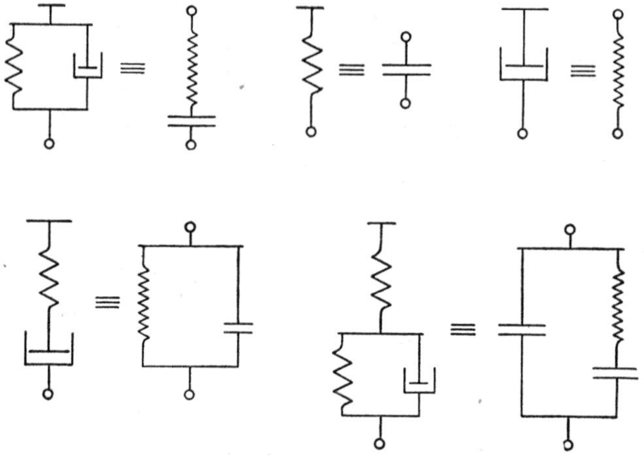

Fig. 79. Equivalence of mechanical and electrical networks. In each equivalent pair the mechanical network is shown on the left.

series coupling. Likewise, a series coupling in the mechanical model goes over into a parallel coupling in the analogous electrical network. The reason for this is obvious.

Burgers (*2*) has pointed out that a given plastoelastic model can be identified with a corresponding electrical network in a somewhat different fashion. Let a spring in the mechanical model be represented by a resistance and a dashpot by a capacitance. Couple the electrical elements in exactly the same fashion as the mechanical elements. Now the difference of electrical potential at the terminals of the electrical network corresponds mathematically to the *displacement* of the mechanical model and the current flowing through an element to the *stress* on the corresponding mechanical element. This is mathematically correct, but is not physically as satisfactory an analogy as the one presented here. In our model, the role of elasticity is played by capacitance and that of viscosity by resistance, which is obviously to be preferred. Furthermore, stress is represented by difference of potential (electrical driving force) and flow by electric current. In the electrical network, electrical work done on capacitances is stored up and that done on resistive elements is dissipated as heat, just as mechanical work done on elastic springs is stored up and that done on flow elements is dissipated as heat. For these reasons, we prefer the electrical analog presented in the previous paragraph to that of Burgers.

The steady-state response of electrical networks to alternating electromotive forces is a subject which is treated in every sophomore physics book. The simplified methods which have been developed to handle this problem can be used directly in the mechanical case. We can consider the stress to be represented by the horizontal component of a rotating vector, whose length is S_0 and whose angular velocity is ω. The deformation γ will be given by the horizontal component of a rotating γ vector, which in general will be out of phase with S. The S vector and the γ vector will be thus rigidly fixed to each other as they rotate, separated by the phase angle α.

Just as the vectorial relation between current and voltage depends upon the resistance and the reactance of the network, so will the relation between S and γ depend upon corresponding mechanical quantities. We can define an "elastic reactance," X, which is analogous to a capacitive reactance in the electrical case:

$$X = -G/\omega = -1/J\omega \tag{124}$$

The viscoelastic "impedance," Z, would be given by the obvious formula:

$$Z = \mathrm{R} + iX \tag{125}$$

where R, of course, corresponds to η.

$$|Z| = \sqrt{\mathrm{R}^2 + X^2} \tag{126}$$

Now, if we were content with a relation between $d\gamma/dt$ and S, the problem would be exactly the familiar current–voltage problem:

$$\begin{aligned} S &= S_0 \cos(\omega t) \\ d\gamma/dt &= \mathrm{A} \cos(\omega t - \alpha) \end{aligned} \tag{127}$$

where $\mathrm{A} = S_0/|Z|$ and $\alpha = \tan^{-1}(X/\mathrm{R})$. That is, if the stress is represented by a rotating vector of length S_0, the rate of strain, $d\gamma/dt$, can be represented by a vector of length A, leading the stress vector by the angle α. However, in the mechanical case we would generally prefer to know γ as a function of time, rather than $d\gamma/dt$. Hence some slight changes in the familiar electrical equation are necessary.

If a vector γ is rotating at the angular velocity ω, the corresponding *rate-of-change vector*, $d\gamma/dt$, has an amplitude of $\gamma_0\omega$ and leads γ by $\pi/2$. Conversely, γ lags behind $d\gamma/dt$ by $\pi/2$, and has an amplitude equal to $1/\omega$ times the amplitude of $d\gamma/dt$. Hence equations (127) become:

$$\gamma = \gamma_0 \cos(\omega t - \beta) \tag{128a}$$

where $$\gamma_0 = S_0/\omega Z_{(\omega)} \tag{128b}$$

$$\beta = [\tan^{-1}(X/R) + \pi/2] \tag{128c}$$

This can be written as:

$$\gamma = \gamma_0 \sin(\omega t - \alpha)$$

By this method, the steady-state solution of a given mechanical problem can be found without writing down a single differential equation. One merely combines the "viscous resistances" and "elastic reactances" to determine the total mechanical impedance of the mechanical model, and then substitutes into equations (127). These combinations are made exactly as in the electrical case, keeping in mind the inversion of series and parallel coupling.

As an example, let us consider the "impedance" of the model in figure 79. First G_4 and η_4 must be combined to give Z for this Maxwell element:

$$Z_4 = \frac{1}{1/\eta_4 + 1/iX_4}$$

where $X_4 = -G_4/\omega$. X_3, η_3, and Z_4 can now be combined by simple addition to give Z_3, the impedance of this subnetwork:

$$Z_3 = \eta_3 + iX_3 + Z_4$$

where $X_3 = -G_3/\omega$. The impedance Z_2 of the retarded elastic element G_2, η_2, is simply:

$$Z_2 = \eta_2 + iX_2$$

where $X_2 = -G_2/\omega$. Z_1 is obviously $(-i \cdot G_1/\omega)$. Now Z_1, Z_2, Z_3, and η_5 can be combined as follows:

$$Z = \frac{1}{\dfrac{1}{Z_1} + \dfrac{1}{Z_2} + \dfrac{1}{Z_3} + \dfrac{1}{\eta_5}}$$

This resultant Z will be a complex number, the real part of which is the "resistive" part of the impedance and the imaginary part of which is the "elastic" part of the impedance. Extending this method to the case of a continuous distribution of retardation times, $J(\tau)$, we obtain for the mechanical admittance:

$$\frac{1}{Z(\omega)} = \int_0^\infty \frac{\omega^2\tau\, J(\tau)\, d\tau}{(\omega^2\tau^2 + 1)} + i\int_0^\infty \frac{\omega\, J(\tau)\, d\tau}{(\omega^2\tau^2 + 1)} \tag{129}$$

If the instantaneous elastic modulus, G_1, and the true flow, η, are included, as well as the retarded elastic spectrum, the admittance becomes:

$$\frac{1}{Z(\omega)} = \frac{1}{\eta} + \int_0^\infty \frac{\omega^2\tau\, J(\tau)\, d\tau}{(\omega^2\tau^2 + 1)} + \frac{i\omega}{G_1} + i\int_0^\infty \frac{\omega\, J(\tau)\, d\tau}{(\omega^2\tau^2 + 1)} \qquad (130)$$

The impedance function, $Z(\omega)$, is in each case the reciprocal of the above. In a similar manner, a continuous distribution of *relaxation* times, following Model D (Fig. 63, page 133), gives rise to a corresponding impedance function:

$$Z(\omega) = \int_0^\infty \frac{\tau}{(\omega^2\tau^2 + 1)} G(\tau)\, d\tau - i\int_0^\infty \frac{\omega\tau^2\, G(\tau)\, d\tau}{(\omega^2\tau^2 + 1)} \qquad (131)$$

If in addition to the elastic and viscous effects, there is a lumped inertial effect, we must include an inertial reactance X_m, which is analogous to an inductive reactance in the electrical case. If m is the lumped mass,

$$X_m = \omega m \qquad (132)$$

General Use of Impedance Function

While the method just discussed applies only to the *steady state* response to *sinusoidal* stresses, it can be extended to cover the response to any arbitrary stress as a function of time, by the use of Fourier integrals. This method is described in detail in works on electrical networks and will be merely outlined here. For any function of time, say $S(t)$, which obeys certain broad conditions, there exists a "transform," $T_s(\omega)$, which is a function of the parameter ω, and which is related to $S(t)$ by:

$$T_s(\omega) = \frac{1}{2\pi}\int_{-\infty}^\infty S(t)\, e^{-i\omega t}\, dt \qquad (133a)$$

Conversely:

$$S(t) = \int_{-\infty}^\infty T_s(\omega)\, e^{i\omega t}\, d\omega \qquad (133b)$$

The physical problem at hand is the following: given the mechanical impedance as a function of frequency, $Z(\omega)$, and the stress function $S(t)$, to find the resulting *rate of deformation* as a function of time, $\gamma'(t)$. The answer is given very simply in terms of the *transforms* of $\gamma'(t)$ and $S(t)$ in terms, that is, of $T_{\gamma'}(\omega)$ and $T_s(\omega)$. *The transform of $S(t)$, divided by the impedance function, $Z(\omega)$, is the transform of $\gamma'(t)$*:

$$T_{\gamma'}(\omega) = \frac{1}{Z(\omega)}\frac{1}{2\pi}\int_{-\infty}^\infty S(t)\, e^{-i\omega t}\, dt \qquad (134a)$$

and
$$\gamma'(t) = \int_{-\infty}^{\infty} T_\gamma(\omega)\, e^{i\omega t}\, d\omega \tag{134b}$$

The deformation, is γ, of course given by $\gamma_0 + \int_0^t \gamma'(t)\, dt$.

Conversely, if $\gamma'(t)$ is known, the transform of $S(t)$ is given by the impedance function multiplied by the transform of $\gamma'(t)$.

Simha (*72*) has applied this general method to the special problem of evaluating the distribution of relaxation times of the model of figure 59 from the known deformation–time curve.

The viscoelastic properties of a polymer can thus be expressed in several completely equivalent ways—as a distribution of elastic retardation times $J(\tau)$, as a distribution of relaxation times $G(\tau)$, or as an impedance function $Z(\omega)$. Which of these methods of representation should be chosen as the "standard" method is largely a question of convenience. The writer has already expressed the opinion that the function $J(\tau)$, corresponding to a mechanical model of the type C (Fig. 59, page 128), is most easily correlated with molecular processes and is most likely to be derived from a rational molecular theory of viscoelastic response. On the other hand, the impedance function $Z(\omega)$ offers certain computational advantages in many problems. At the present stage of development, it is doubtful if these computational advantages are sufficient to outweigh the interpretative advantages of the function $J(\tau)$. Finally, the use of Maxwell elements coupled in parallel—giving rise to a function $G(\tau)$—seems to be a more or less artificial conception in the case of an amorphous linear polymer (although it possesses real physical significance in the case of cross-linked structures). The inclination of the writer is therefore to choose the function $J(\tau)$ as the standard method of representing the viscoelastic spectrum of an amorphous polymer and to consider both $G(\tau)$ and $Z(\tau)$ as derived forms which may be used in special cases for mathematical convenience.

6. The Principle of Superposition

One of the characteristics of a linear mechanical (or electrical) network is that it obeys Boltzmann's superposition principle (see Fig. 80). Leaderman (*6*, *48a*), has presented an excellent discussion of this principle and methods of testing its validity. His discussion is repeated here (*48b*).

The superposition principle may be stated as follows: We assume that when a load, P, is applied at zero time to a previously unloaded body, an instantaneous deformation occurs first, proportional to load P. This subsequently increases by the delayed deformation, which is assumed to be again proportional to load P and to a function, $\psi(t)$, of the time under load t. Thus if F is a form factor and E is the appropriate instantaneous modulus, the instantaneous deformation is given by (FP/E) and the deformation, x_t, at time t by:

$$x_t = (\mathrm{FP/E})\{1 + \beta\psi(t)\} \qquad (1)$$

where β = a constant
$\psi(t)$ = the creep function

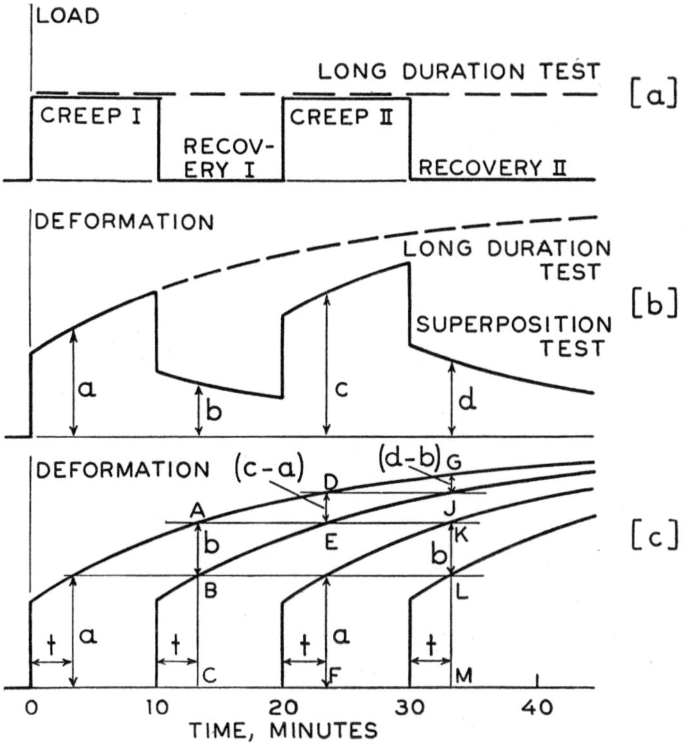

Fig. 80. Illustration of the Boltzmann superposition principle (after Leaderman).

Now let us assume that various loads, P_θ, are applied at times θ previous to a given instant, t. According to Boltzmann's principle, the deformation at time t due to the several previously applied loads is assumed to be equal to the simple summation of the deformations which would have been observed at that instant if each of the loads had been independently applied. The deformation x_t at time t due to all the previously applied loads is thus assumed to be given by:

$$x_t = \sum_{\theta=-\infty}^{\theta=t} (\mathrm{FP}_\theta/\mathrm{E})[1 + \beta\psi(t - \theta)] \qquad (2)$$

Equation 2 is one form of the superposition principle.

Leaderman has found experimentally that the superposition principle is obeyed satisfactorily by plasticized polyvinyl chloride (*48a*). It is clear that any polymer exhibiting a "linear" viscoelastic spectrum must obey the principle in the region of small stresses.

7. Hysteresis and Heat Loss in Cyclic Elastic Deformations

An important characteristic of the ideal elastic solid is the exact *reversibility* of its stress–strain curve. If an ideal elastic solid is progressively distorted, and then returned to its original shape, the stress–strain curve followed on the return is identical with that followed during the distortion. This means, among other things, that there is no (net) work done during a cyclic operation.

There are materials which follow this simple behavior very closely, *e.g.*, certain types of steel. However, it is more common for a material to exhibit a certain amount of "elastic hysteresis," or nonreversibility, of the stress–strain curve. This phenomenon is particularly common among high polymers, both natural and synthetic, and in some cases is a very important factor in the practical performance. In rubber, for example, stress–strain hysteresis is quite pronounced.

Stress–strain hysteresis is always closely connected with heat losses on cyclic deformation. The area of the hysteresis loop for one mechanical cycle is a measure of the net work done on the sample during the cycle. Since this net work is entirely dissipated as heat energy, the area of the hysteresis loop also measures the heat generated during one stress–strain cycle.

Hysteresis is always an indication of *departure from equilibrium* during the extension and recovery. The nonequilibrium condition present may refer to any of the following equilibria:

(1) Mechanical equilibrium (flow hysteresis and plastoelastic hysteresis).
(2) Thermal equilibrium ("Carnot cycle" hysteresis).
(3) Phase equilibrium (crystallization hysteresis).

In case (1), the timescale of the cyclic operation is of the same order of magnitude as the time necessary to establish mechanical equilibrium (retardation times). In case (2), it is of the same order as the time necessary for establishment of *thermal* equilibrium and, in case (3), of phase equilibrium. When the timescale of the cyclic operation is either very slow or very fast compared to the times necessary for all equilibria to be established, there is no hysteresis.

A. Mechanical Nonequilibrium

Consider a single retarded elastic mechanism (G,τ), acted upon by a stress which increases linearly with time ($S = at$), until a maximum stress S_m is reached, after which the stress is removed at the same rate, ($S = 2\,S_m - at$). If the timescale of the experiment is comparable to the elastic retardation time, the deformation will lag behind the stress on both halves of the cycle. Before sufficient time elapses for the system to come to elastic equilibrium at any stress, the stress is changed to a new value.

During deformation: $$G\gamma + \eta \cdot d\gamma/dt = at \tag{135a}$$

During return: $$G\gamma + \eta \cdot d\gamma/dt = 2\,S_m - at \tag{135b}$$

If these equations are solved and expressed as stress–strain relations, the two stress–strain curves are not identical. The area of the "hysteresis loop" is a measure of the net work and therefore of the heat loss during the cycle. This dissipated energy represents work which was done against the damping element of the retarded elasticity, rather than against the elastic element.

In the limiting case of extremely high viscosity and low modulus this sort of hysteresis can hardly be distinguished from a true flow, which results in a permanent set. Perhaps stress–strain irreversibility due to actual flow should not be considered as "hysteresis." When flow takes place, the sample never returns to its original condition and a true mechanical cycle is never completed. If by hysteresis is meant only that the stress–strain curve during retraction is not identical with that during deformation, then of course flow results in hysteresis. If, however, hysteresis is taken to mean a *closed* loop in the stress–strain curve, then flow is distinct from hysteresis, although both have the effect of dissipating mechanical energy as heat.

Hysteresis arising from mechanical nonequilibrium is especially pronounced at temperatures near the "brittle point" of a polymer. The retardation time of an elastic response involving the uncurling of molecular chains is strongly temperature-dependent. At low temperatures, the diffusion of segments (micro-Brownian movement) is extremely slow. As a result, the retardation times of elastic responses involving molecular shape changes are very high. In an ordinary mechanical experiment there is no time for any appreciable response from these mechanisms. They do not, therefore, result in much stress–strain hysteresis. At high temperatures, the retardation time becomes so small that complete mechanical equilibrium can be maintained throughout the experiment. Again there is no hysteresis, but for the opposite reason than before; at high temperatures the shape responds instantaneously to the stress, whereas at low temperatures it does not respond at all.

It is at intermediate temperatures that hysteresis of this type occurs—when the elastic retardation time is neither effectively zero nor infinite, but is of the same order of magnitude as the timescale of the mechanical cycle.

Presence of plasticizers and swelling agents of course shifts the temperature range in which hysteresis of type (1) is likely to be encountered.

Hysteresis of this type can be summed up in the following way: as the stress goes through a complete cycle, the deformation or strain follows but always lags behind. This lagging of the strain behind the stress results in a net work input and heat loss for the cycle.

B. Thermal Nonequilibrium

In the preceding section, it was implicitly assumed that *thermal* equilibrium was maintained, although mechanical equilibrium was not. This meant that at every step in the cycle, the specimen was at the same temperature as its environment; the cycle was strictly isothermal.

Even when mechanical equilibrium is maintained, a departure from *thermal* equilibrium can result in hysteresis and heat loss. Consider an elastic response mechanism whose retardation time is so small that it can take on its equilibrium displacement in a negligible time. When the specimen is deformed, it will always be in a condition of elastic equilibrium. However, there will, in general, be a heat effect of some type during the deformation. This may manifest itself as a temperature change, as a heat interchange with the environment, or both. (This heat effect during deformation does not necessarily denote hysteresis. If the heat effect during recovery is just equal and opposite to that during deformation, then there is no hysteresis. Hysteresis means a *net* heat effect during a complete mechanical cycle.)

The heat effect will be very small during the distortion of a crystal, since the process is only very slightly endothermic. However, if the elastic element is governed by an *entropy* factor (the free energy increase on distortion being due to an entropy decrease) then the heat effect is relatively large. An entropy mechanism (gaslike elasticity) results in an *exothermic* deformation. The heat of deformation may be either dissipated to the environment (isothermal distortion), retained within the sample increasing the temperature (adiabatic distortion), or partly dissipated and partly retained. The stress–strain curves for the different cases are not identical. During an adiabatic distortion, the temperature rises and the elastic constant increases (being proportional to absolute temperature).

If a perfectly isothermal extension is followed by a perfectly isothermal return, the stress–strain curve is retraced and the *net* heat interchange with the surroundings is zero. There is no hysteresis. If a perfectly *adiabatic* extension is followed by a perfectly *adiabatic* return, the net temperature change is zero. Again there is no hysteresis. If, however, a specimen is deformed adiabatically and returned isothermally, or *vice versa*, a different stress–strain curve is followed during the return; there will be a hysteresis loop for such a cycle. This isothermal-adiabatic hysteresis is exactly comparable to the Carnot cycle for an ideal gas. Indeed, a heat engine can be constructed from a rubber band, operating on isothermal and adiabatic stress–strain curves (*91*).

If the extension is neither slow enough to permit thermal equilibrium to be maintained nor rapid enough to prevent completely heat interchange with the environment, then the process is neither perfectly isothermal nor perfectly adiabatic. The stress–strain curve followed is intermediate between the two ideal curves. A complete cycle under such intermediate conditions necessarily results in hysteresis and heat loss.

C. Phase Nonequilibrium

The importance of phase changes such as crystallization which take place during a distortion is emphasized in Chapter D.

During the extension of rubber, for example, the process of crystallization serves to increase the orientation and, thus, to assist the external stress. The middle range of "easy extensibility" coincides with the range in which the crystallization mainly takes place—as indicated by X-ray patterns, volume changes, and heat of crystallization. The crystalline-amorphous equilibrium is dependent upon stress and temperature. The attainment of the phase equilibrium is a rate process which may not be as fast as the rate of the mechanical cycle.

A quasi equilibrium between the amorphous and crystalline phases is set up rather quickly when a rubber sample is extended and held at a definite length. That this quickly reached degree of crystallization does not represent a true equilibrium is indicated by the fact that the crystallization curve is not retraced exactly during retraction, *i.e.*, a *crystallization hysteresis* accompanies a stress–strain cycle. The result of the hysteresis in the crystallization cycle is a corresponding hysteresis in the stress–strain curve. This correlation is made still more certain if we consider the effect of *successive cycles* of extension. During a second extension the crystallization begins at a lower elongation (presumably because of crystal nuclei from the first cycle). The second crystallization

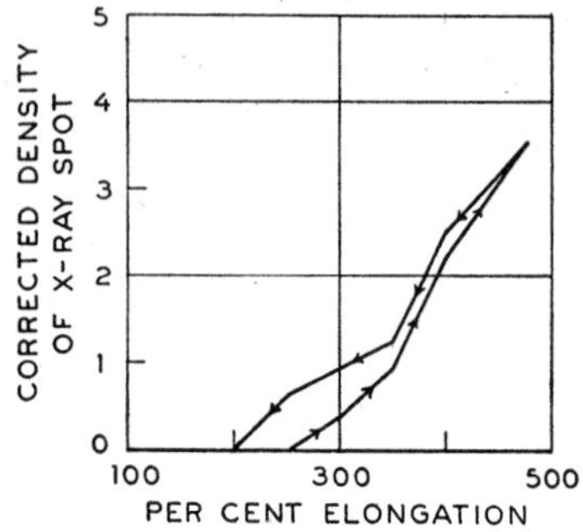

Fig. 81. Hysteresis in the crystallization curve of rubber (after Gehman and Field).

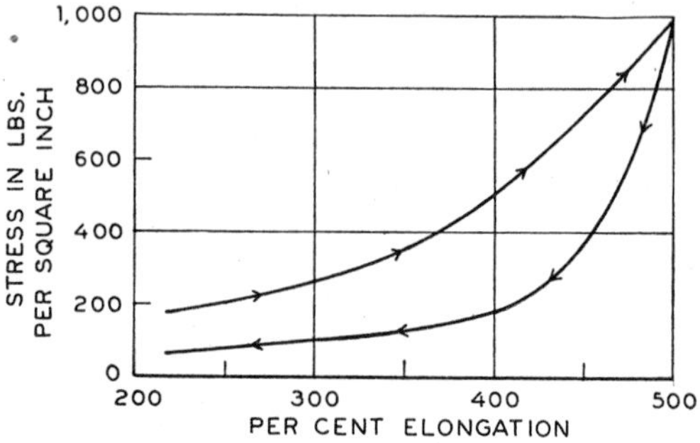

Fig. 82. Hysteresis in the stress–strain curve of rubber.

cycle is also more nearly reversible than the first. These effects are closely paralleled in the corresponding stress–strain curves (see Figs. 81 and 82).

VI. NONHOMOGENEOUS AND COMBINED STRESSES (*10, 12*)

1. Introduction

The purpose of this section is the extension of the theory of elasticity to include viscoelastic materials. Only isotropic, incompressible materials possessing linear viscoelastic spectra will be considered. Furthermore, as in the classical theory of elasticity, only small strains will be treated. Body forces and accelerations will be neglected throughout.

In subsections 1 and 2 a dual notation for the components of stress and strain will be used for convenience. Thus the six stress components will be designated as s_{xx}, s_{yy}, s_{zz}, s_{yz}, s_{xz}, s_{xy}, or, alternatively, as s_1, s_2, s_3, s_4, s_5, s_6. The six strain components will be represented by γ_{xx}, γ_{yy}, γ_{zz}, γ_{yz}, γ_{xz}, γ_{xy}, or by γ_1, γ_2, γ_3, γ_4, γ_5, γ_6.

No matter what the properties of the material of which an object is composed, the stress within the object must follow differential equations

(136) in its variation with position:

$$\frac{\partial s_{xx}}{\partial x} + \frac{\partial s_{xy}}{\partial y} + \frac{\partial s_{xz}}{\partial z} = 0 \tag{136a}$$

$$\frac{\partial s_{xy}}{\partial x} + \frac{\partial s_{yy}}{\partial y} + \frac{\partial s_{yz}}{\partial z} = 0 \tag{136b}$$

$$\frac{\partial s_{xz}}{\partial x} + \frac{\partial s_{yz}}{\partial y} + \frac{\partial s_{zz}}{\partial z} = 0 \tag{136c}$$

Furthermore, the infinitesimal strain components must obey equations (137):

$$\frac{\partial^2 \gamma_{xx}}{\partial y^2} + \frac{\partial^2 \gamma_{yy}}{\partial x^2} = \frac{\partial^2 \gamma_{xy}}{\partial x\, \partial y} \tag{137a}$$

$$\frac{\partial^2 \gamma_{yy}}{\partial z^2} + \frac{\partial^2 \gamma_{zz}}{\partial y^2} = \frac{\partial^2 \gamma_{yz}}{\partial y\, \partial z} \tag{137b}$$

$$\frac{\partial^2 \gamma_{zz}}{\partial x^2} + \frac{\partial^2 \gamma_{xx}}{\partial z^2} = \frac{\partial^2 \gamma_{xz}}{\partial x\, \partial z} \tag{137c}$$

$$2\frac{\partial^2 \gamma_{xx}}{\partial y\, \partial z} = \frac{\partial}{\partial x}\left(-\frac{\partial \gamma_{yz}}{\partial x} + \frac{\partial \gamma_{xz}}{\partial y} + \frac{\partial \gamma_{xy}}{\partial z}\right) \tag{137d}$$

$$2\frac{\partial^2 \gamma_{yy}}{\partial x\, \partial z} = \frac{\partial}{\partial y}\left(\frac{\partial \gamma_{yz}}{\partial x} - \frac{\partial \gamma_{xz}}{\partial y} + \frac{\partial \gamma_{xy}}{\partial z}\right) \tag{137e}$$

$$2\frac{\partial^2 \gamma_{zz}}{\partial x\, \partial y} = \frac{\partial}{\partial z}\left(\frac{\partial \gamma_{yz}}{\partial x} + \frac{\partial \gamma_{xz}}{\partial y} - \frac{\partial \gamma_{xy}}{\partial z}\right) \tag{137f}$$

Equations (137) follow from the fundamental definitions of the six strain components and are called the *conditions of compatability*.

When a set of boundary conditions are specified, the states of stress and strain within the object are still not completely fixed by equations (136) and (137). The final definitive set of equations are those relating the values of the various stress components and the various strain components in the general case of combined stresses and combined strains. It is through these equations that the *properties of the material* enter the problem. For an ideal elastic material these equations are (138) and its inverse from (139).

$$s_i = \sum_j k_{ij}\gamma_j \tag{138}$$

$$\gamma_i = \sum_j k'_{ij}s_j \tag{139}$$

In the case of an incompressible, isotropic elastic solid, the set of 36 reciprocal elastic moduli in (139) can all be defined in terms of the shear modulus G, as follows:

$$k'_{11} = k'_{22} = k'_{33} = \frac{1}{3G}$$

$$k'_{12} = k'_{13} = k'_{21} = k'_{23} = k'_{31} = k'_{32} = -\frac{1}{6G}$$

$$k'_{14} = k'_{15} = k'_{16} = k'_{24} = k'_{25} = k'_{26} = k'_{34} = k'_{35} = k'_{36} = k'_{41}$$
$$= k'_{42} = k'_{43} = k'_{51} = k'_{52} = k'_{53} = k'_{61} = k'_{62} = k'_{63} = 0$$

$$k'_{44} = k'_{55} = k'_{66} = \frac{1}{G}$$

Hence (139) can simply be written as:

$$\gamma_i = \frac{1}{G}\sum_j a_{ij}s_j \tag{140}$$

where the matrix (a) is composed of the elements:

$$\begin{pmatrix} \frac{1}{3} & -\frac{1}{6} & -\frac{1}{6} & 0 & 0 & 0 \\ -\frac{1}{6} & \frac{1}{3} & -\frac{1}{6} & 0 & 0 & 0 \\ -\frac{1}{6} & -\frac{1}{6} & \frac{1}{3} & 0 & 0 & 0 \\ 0 & 0 & 0 & 1 & 0 & 0 \\ 0 & 0 & 0 & 0 & 1 & 0 \\ 0 & 0 & 0 & 0 & 0 & 1 \end{pmatrix} \tag{141}$$

The term "incompressible" has the same meaning here as in hydrodynamics; an incompressible material is one which can be deformed much more easily in shear than in compression. In the elastic case, this means that the bulk modulus is much greater than the shear modulus.

If the equations of compatability (137) are now rewritten in terms of the stress components by combining (137) and (140), there is obtained a set of six partial differential equations of which the following, taken from (137a), is typical (for clarity we use here the symbols s_{xx}, s_{yy}, s_{zz}, s_{yz}, s_{xz}, s_{xy}, instead of $s_1, s_2 \cdots s_6$ for the six stress components):

$$\frac{1}{3}\frac{\partial^2 s_{xx}}{\partial y^2} - \frac{1}{6}\frac{\partial^2 s_{yy}}{\partial y^2} - \frac{1}{6}\frac{\partial^2 s_{zz}}{\partial y^2} + \frac{1}{3}\frac{\partial^2 s_{yy}}{\partial x^2} - \frac{1}{6}\frac{\partial^2 s_{xx}}{\partial x^2} - \frac{1}{6}\frac{\partial^2 s_{zz}}{\partial x^2} = \frac{\partial^2 s_{xy}}{\partial x\,\partial y} \tag{142a}$$

or:
$$\left(\frac{1}{3} + \frac{1}{6}\right)\left[\frac{\partial^2 s_{xx}}{\partial y^2} + \frac{\partial^2 s_{yy}}{\partial x^2}\right] - \frac{1}{6}\left[\frac{\partial^2 \theta}{\partial y^2} + \frac{\partial^2 \theta}{\partial x^2}\right] = \frac{\partial^2 s_{xy}}{\partial x\,\partial y} \tag{142'a}$$

Here θ has the meaning of $(s_{xx} + s_{yy} + s_{zz})$.

In the case of an ideal elastic body in elastic equilibrium, the boundary conditions may be given by a function $f(\sigma)$, which defines the surface forces acting on the object as a function of position on the surface, σ. $f(\sigma)$, in conjunction with equations (136) and (142) define the state of stress distribution within the object and, hence, also the strain distribution and the displacement as a function of position.

2. Extension to Viscoelastic Materials

We wish to extend this treatment to the case of isotropic, incompressible viscoelastic materials. The first step in this direction is the proper formulation of the equations governing viscoelastic response to homogeneous *combined stresses*, corresponding to equation (140) in the ideal elastic case. The question involved is: "If the viscoelastic properties of the material in pure shear are given, what is the response to a general stress, where all six components must be considered?" That is, if the (linear) relation between *shear stress* and *shear strain* is known, what is the form of the general equation connecting the six components of stress and the six components of strain?

First let us consider the subcase of a material whose behavior in shear is governed by a Maxwell element. When only a single shear component is concerned, equation (143) relates the stress and strain:

$$\frac{d\gamma}{dt} = \frac{1}{G}\frac{ds}{dt} + \frac{1}{\eta}s \tag{143}$$

Since we now plan to consider simultaneously more than one component of stress and strain, we must identify the components explicitly. For the single shear components in the xz plane—s_5 and γ_5—we must write:

$$\frac{d\gamma_5}{dt} = \frac{1}{G}\frac{ds_5}{dt} + \frac{1}{\eta}s_5 \tag{144}$$

We are now in a position to proceed to combined stresses and strains.

Simha (*71*) has published an interesting and provocative treatment of this problem, based on the assumption that the governing equations in the case of combined stresses are of the form:

$$\frac{ds_i}{dt} = \sum_j k_{ij}\frac{d\gamma_j}{dt} - \frac{1}{\tau}s_i \tag{145}$$

This equation reduces to the correct form for any special case where only one component of stress acts. In the general case of *combined* stresses, however, equation (145) is incorrect. The equation implies that a given stress is supported by elastic forces and at constant deformation decays exponentially with a relaxation time τ, *which is independent of the geo-*

metric nature of the stress. This treatment ignores the fact that viscous flow, which is the cause of relaxation, is a response to *shear* stresses only. A uniform pressure does not produce viscous flow and, hence, does not tend to relax. *The tendency toward relaxation is not a fundamental attribute of a stress in a Maxwellian material, but is a secondary effect arising from the fundamental process of viscous flow.* A pure shear stress causes a certain amount of flow in a given time interval. This tends to cause a slight increase in the shearing deformation, γ. If the total shearing deformation is to remain constant, the stress must be relaxed somewhat so that an elastic recovery which just counterbalances the flow can take place. A *single* tensile stress, which can be considered as a set of equal shear stresses plus an isotropic negative pressure, relaxes in the same fashion. The flow response to the shear stresses tends to elongate the sample—hence the tensile stress must be relaxed if the total elongation is to be held constant. Relaxation is not a fundamental characteristic of a tensile stress, however. If three equal components of tensile stress are acting, the result is a simple negative pressure. No shear components are present and the stresses *do not relax.* If equation (145) were correct, a uniform pressure would result in a continuous increase in density and a negative pressure would result in a continuous expansion which would never reach a limit. No real materials possess these properties. The following discussion is modeled after that of Simha, but includes the distinction between shear stresses and isotropic compressive stresses.

The simplest formulation of the rigorous equations connecting combined stresses and combined strains for a Maxwellian material is the following:

$$\frac{d\gamma_i}{dt} = \frac{1}{G} \sum_j a_{ij} \frac{ds_j}{dt} + \frac{1}{\eta} \sum_j a_{ij} s_j \tag{146}$$

Here the a values are geometric factors which depend upon the particular components of stress and strain which are being related. Remembering always that we are concerned only with incompressible, isotropic, Maxwellian materials, the matrix (a) is identical with (141). The six equations (146) can obviously be solved for the quantities (ds_j/dt).

The resulting equations, however, are more complicated than equation (145). Specifically, the *rate of relaxation of a given tensile stress component depends not only on the magnitude of that component, but also upon the magnitudes of the other two tensile components.*

When equations (146) are combined with the equations of compatability (137), there is obtained a set of equations involving only the stress and the rate of change of stress with time. For the sake of clarity let us revert from the symbols s_1, s_2, s_3, s_4, s_5, s_6 to the corresponding symbols s_{xx}, s_{yy}, s_{zz}, s_{yz}, s_{zx}, s_{xy} for the six stress components.

A typical member of this set of equations, obtained from equation (137a) and hence comparable with equation (142a), is given below:

$$\frac{1}{\eta}\left[\frac{1}{3}\frac{\partial^2 s_{xx}}{\partial y^2} - \frac{1}{6}\frac{\partial^2 s_{yy}}{\partial y^2} - \frac{1}{6}\frac{\partial^2 s_{zz}}{\partial y^2}\right] + \frac{1}{G}\left[\frac{1}{3}\frac{\partial^3 s_{xx}}{\partial y^2 dt} - \frac{1}{6}\frac{\partial^3 s_{yy}}{\partial y^2 \partial t} - \frac{1}{6}\frac{\partial^3 s_{zz}}{\partial y^2 \partial t}\right]$$
$$+ \frac{1}{\eta}\left[\frac{1}{3}\frac{\partial^2 s_{yy}}{\partial x^2} - \frac{1}{6}\frac{\partial^2 s_{xx}}{\partial x^2} - \frac{1}{6}\frac{\partial^2 s_{zz}}{\partial x^2}\right] \tag{147}$$
$$+ \frac{1}{G}\left[\frac{1}{3}\frac{\partial^3 s_{yy}}{\partial x^2 \partial t} - \frac{1}{6}\frac{\partial^3 s_{xx}}{\partial x^2 \partial t} - \frac{1}{6}\frac{\partial^3 s_{zz}}{\partial x^2 \partial t}\right] = \frac{1}{\eta}\frac{\partial^2 s_{xy}}{\partial x\, \partial y} + \frac{1}{G}\frac{\partial^3 s_{xy}}{\partial x\, \partial y\, \partial t}$$

The similarity of equations (147) (for the Maxwellian material) to the corresponding equations (142) (for the elastic material) is clear. It is also clear that the actual application of equations (147) is much more difficult than the application of equations (142). In any specific problem, there will be given a certain set of boundary conditions, *e.g.*, $f(\sigma,t)$, which defines the external forces acting on the object as a function both of (surface) position σ and of time t. The boundary conditions, $f(\sigma,t)$, the differential equations (147), and the differential equations (136), together define the stress and, hence, the strain and displacement, as functions of x, y, z, and t. In the general case, however, the actual solution of these equations will be involved.

Let us now consider a material which exhibits retarded elastic response to a single shear stress and which is incompressible and isotropic. Such a material responds to a single shear stress according to the equation: $s = G\gamma + \eta \cdot d\gamma/dt$. As before, the first problem is the proper formulation of the relations between the components of stress and the components of strain in the case of combined stress. These equations are:

$$\sum_j a_{ij}s_j = G\gamma_i + \eta \cdot d\gamma_i/dt \tag{148}$$

If equations (148) are combined with the equations of compatability for the strains and the equations of compatability for the time derivatives of the strains, there results a set of equations analogous to (147) and (142). As a matter of fact, these equations turn out to be *identical* with those of an ideal elastic body (142). That is, the *stress distribution in a retarded elastic material (with a single retardation time) is identical with that in an ideal (incompressible and isotropic) elastic material under the same instantaneous boundary conditions.* The stress distribution does not depend upon the past stressing history although, of course, the strain distribution does. This simplicity in the general equations disappears, however, if we consider a material possessing more than one retarded elastic mechanism of response. Since no material can be accurately described in terms of one retarded elastic mechanism, the relative simplicity of this case is not particularly helpful.

As one proceeds to materials possessing more than one Maxwellian relaxation time or more than one retardation time in shear, the equations governing the response to homogeneous combined stresses become much more complicated. As a result, this general method of approach becomes mathematically involved. For this reason, a special treatment has been developed which does not necessitate the explicit formulation of the partial differential equations corresponding to (147), or even of the equations—such as (146)—which govern the response to homogeneous combined stresses. The properties of the medium are introduced in the convenient and elementary form of the equations governing the response to a single component of shear stress.

In subsection 3 this method of treatment is developed for the special case where the boundary conditions $f(\sigma,t)$ can be resolved into a product of two functions, one dependent only upon position and one only upon time. In subsection 4 the treatment is extended to cover completely arbitrary boundary conditions, by means of an expansion of the boundary function into a series of such products. In subsection 5 the relation between this method and the straightforward approach of subsection 2 is shown. Finally, in subsection 6 the method is applied to specific problems.

3. Case in which $f(\sigma, t)$ Can Be Factored

Consider an isotropic, incompressible material whose behavior in simple shear can be represented by a known function $J(\tau)$, which gives the distribution of elastic compliance as a function of retardation time. An object of definite initial shape, constructed from this material, is subjected to a set of external forces which are a function both of surface position σ, and of time t. $f = f(\sigma,t)$. Consider further that the boundary function $f(\sigma,t)$ can be factored into the form of a function of position alone multiplied by a function of time alone.

$$\vec{f}(\sigma,t) = \vec{f}(\sigma)\, T(t) \tag{149}$$

The response of the viscoelastic object to this sequence of surface forces can be calculated as follows:

(1) Consider the geometric response of an ideal (incompressible, isotropic) elastic body of shear modulus $(1/\lambda)$, possessing the equilibrium shape of the object under consideration, to the set of external forces $f = \vec{f}(\sigma)$. The displacement as a function of position can be calculated for this simplified problem by the ordinary theory of elasticity and is of the form:

$$\vec{\mathrm{D}}(x,y,z) = \lambda\vec{\delta}(x,y,z) \qquad (150)$$

(2) Then write the differential equations that govern the *time* behavior of the material in *simple shear*, replacing γ by λ and $s(t)$ by $T(t)$. Solve these differential equations with the proper initial conditions, obtaining λ as a function of time. Simply insert λ as a function of time into the geometric equation (150), where λ was originally considered as a constant. The resulting equation gives the displacement as a function of both time and position.

As a corollary, it is possible to calculate the stress as a function of position and time if an object is forced to conform to surface geometric constraints which vary uniformly with time. $\vec{\mathrm{D}}(\sigma,t) = \vec{f}(\sigma)T(t)$. This is done as follows:

(1) Calculate the equilibrium stress distribution for an elastic material of shear modulus λ, subjected to the constraint $\vec{\mathrm{D}}(\sigma) = \vec{f}(\sigma)$. This will be of the form:

$$\mathrm{S}(x,y,z) = \lambda\phi(x,y,z) \qquad (151)$$

(2) Write the differential equations governing the time behavior of the material in shear, replacing $\gamma(t)$ by $T(t)$ and the unknown $s(t)$ by λ. Solve these differential equations subject to the proper boundary conditions, obtaining λ as a function of time. Insert $\lambda(t)$ into equation (151). The resulting equation gives s as a function of time and position.

4. General Case

A. The method of subsection 2 can be generalized to apply to cases where the boundary conditions $f(\sigma,t)$ can be resolved into a sum of functions each of which can be factored.

$$f(\sigma,t) = f_1(\sigma)\,T_1(t) + f_2(\sigma)\,T_2(t) + f_3(\sigma)\,T_3(t) + \cdots \qquad (152)$$

We may determine the strains, displacements, etc., which result from each of these terms by means of the method outlined in subsection 3, above. According to the principle of superposition, the *total* strains, displacements, etc., are simply the sums of these individual solutions.

It is clear that each spatial function $f_n(\sigma)$ must represent a balanced, or nonaccelerating, distribution of surface forces, if a treatment involving only deformations is to apply.

In many physical problems the boundary conditions may be analyzed into a small finite set of terms of the form (152). In such cases this method represents an obvious means of attack.

B. Even in the general case, $f(\sigma,t)$ can be resolved into various *infinite* series of the form $\sum_{i=1}^{\infty} f_i(\sigma)\, T_i(t)$. By introducing various types of time functions for the expansion, a group of closely related approaches can be developed. Thus the $T_i(t)$ may be sinusoidal functions, impulse functions, step functions, etc. In this introductory survey only the step function will be developed in detail. This development follows. Let the function $T(\xi,t)$ be defined in the following fashion:

$$\begin{aligned} T(\xi,t) &= 0 \quad \text{for} \quad t < \xi \\ T(\xi,t) &= 1 \quad \text{for} \quad t \geqq \xi \end{aligned} \tag{153}$$

An arbitrary continuous function $f(\sigma,t)$ can now be expanded in the form:

$$f(\sigma,t) = f_0(\sigma) + \int_0^\infty f(\xi,\sigma)\, T(\xi,t)\, d\xi \tag{154}$$

Here $f(\xi,t)$, the expansion coefficient for a given step function $T(\xi,t)\, d\xi$ is given by:

$$f(\xi,\sigma) = \left[\frac{\partial f(\sigma,t)}{\partial t} \right]_{t=\xi} \tag{155}$$

[If *sudden* changes are made in the surface distribution of forces at certain times, a sum of discrete, finite step terms must be added to the integral of (154).] The method of subsection 3 can now be applied to the general term in the expansion—$f(\xi,\sigma)\, T(\xi,t)\, d\xi$—to obtain the corresponding displacement as a function of position and time:

$$\vec{\mathrm{D}}(x,y,z,t,\xi)\, d\xi \tag{156}$$

The *total* displacement is given by the integral:

$$\vec{\mathrm{D}}(x,y,z,t) = \int_0^\infty \vec{\mathrm{D}}(x,y,z,t,\xi)\, d\xi \tag{157}$$

Specifically, the analysis proceeds as follows:

(1) Analyze the boundary force $f(\sigma,t)$ into a continuous set of step functions. That is, determine the general expression for the expansion

coefficients $f(\xi,\sigma)$:

$$f(\xi,\sigma) = \left[\frac{\partial f(\sigma,t)}{\partial t} \right]_{t=\xi} \quad (158)$$

(2) Consider the geometric response of an ideal elastic body, of shear modulus $1/\lambda$, to the surface distribution of forces $f(\xi,\sigma)$. In this geometric analysis, ξ can be considered as a constant parameter. The displacement as a function of position will be of the form:

$$\vec{D}(x,y,z) = \lambda\vec{\delta}(x,y,z,\xi) \quad (159)$$

(3) Set up the differential equations for the time behavior in simple shear of the viscoelastic material under consideration. For $S(t)$ substitute the infinitesimal step function $T(\xi,t)\,d\xi$, and replace γ by λ. Again ξ can be considered as a constant parameter. Solve these differential equations subject to the proper initial conditions, obtaining λ as a function of the variable t and the parameter ξ. For a material exhibiting a distribution of elastic compliance J as a function of retardation time given by $J(\tau)$, this equation is of the form:

$$\lambda(t,\xi)\,d\xi = T(\xi,t) \left[\int_0^\infty J(\tau)(1 - e^{(\xi-t)/\tau})d\tau \right] d\xi \quad (160)$$

(4) Substitute λ as a function of t and ξ into equation (159) for the displacement. The resulting equation gives the displacement as a function of x, y, z, t, and ξ, and is of the form:

$$\vec{D}(x,y,z,t,\xi)d\xi = \lambda(t,\xi)\,\vec{\sigma}(x,y,z,\xi)\,d\xi \quad (161)$$

(5) Integrate the above equation over all values of ξ to obtain the total displacement as a function of x, y, z, and t.

5. "Accessible" and "Inaccessible" States of Strain

A. The state of strain in a viscoelastic medium possessing n mechanisms of deformation is incompletely defined by a specification of the total strain at each point. A completely detailed specification must give the values of the strain contributions arising from *each mechanism of deformation.* Thus, if ${}^k\gamma_i$ represents the contribution of the kth mechanism of response to the ith component of strain, the total γ_i component of strain is given by $\sum_{k=1}^{n} {}^k\gamma_i$. A detailed specification of the strain at a given point involves not only the values of the six total strain components, $\gamma_1, \gamma_2, \cdots \gamma_6$, but the values of all the contributing terms ${}^k\gamma_i$. It is clear that while a given displacement function, $\vec{D}(x,y,z)$, corresponds to a definite distribution of *total* strain, there are an infinite number of ways this strain can be divided among the n mechanisms of deformation. That is, a given geometric deformation is consistent with many different molecular arrangements. This is implicit in all elastic memory effects. Henceforth the expression "detailed strain distribution" will be taken to imply a definite molecular arrangement and hence a definite distribution of each contributing strain term ${}^k\gamma_i$. The expression "total strain distribution" will mean a definite distribution of the total strains γ_i. A single "total strain distribution" will thus correspond to an infinite number of different "detailed strain distributions."

B. Of all the multiple infinity of possible detailed strain distributions, only a certain minor set are physically accessible by means of stressing operations alone, starting from the state of zero strain (where all ${}^k\gamma_i$ are zero). An "accessible" state of strain is defined here as one which can be reached by some sequence of stressing operations, starting from a state of zero strain.

C. Any detailed strain distribution is "accessible" if the individual strains, ${}^k\gamma_i$, resulting from each mechanism of deformation, follow the equations of compatability (137). In particular, any completely homogeneous strain distribution (where the individual ${}^k\gamma_i$ as well as the total strain, are homogeneous) is an accessible state. (If the material exhibits a *continuous* set of mechanisms of response—a continuous distribution of elastic compliance as a function of τ—then it must also be true that the strain ${}^k\gamma_i\, dk$ at each point is a continuous function of $k\, dk$).

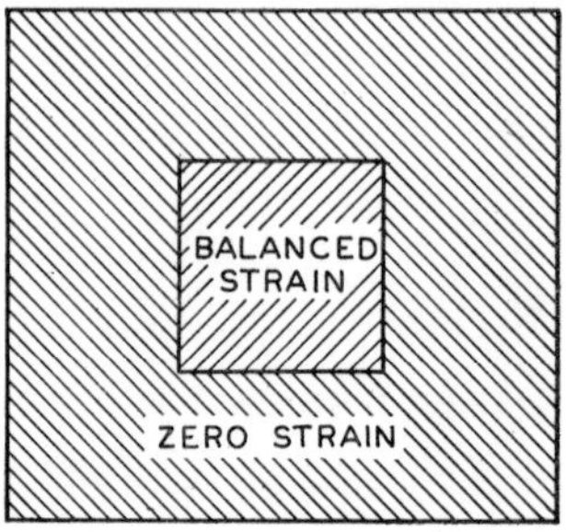

Fig. 83. Example of a "non-accessible" state of strain.

D. Other types of detailed distribution exist—where the total strain, γ, follows the equations of compatability but the individual strains, ${}^k\gamma$, do not. Such states of strain are not accessible by means of stressing operations alone. An example of an inaccessible state of strain is given in figure 83. The *total* strain in the object shown is zero throughout. The outer region is completely strain-free. The inner region is in a state of "balanced" strain, where various ${}^k\gamma_i$ have nonzero values, which add up to a total of zero for each component γ_i. An object can be brought into such a state of strain as follows: Start with one sample in a state of zero strain and cut out a square hole. Bring a second sample into the desired state of (homogeneous) balanced strain and cut out a square of this sample to fit the hole above. Insert the plug of strained material into the hole and fuse together. The result is a single sample with the desired nonhomogeneous distribution. This detailed strain distribution could not have been obtained by taking a single unstrained object and subjecting it to a sequence of stressing operations. It is thus a nonaccessible distribution by our definition.

E. An object in an "accessible" state of strain, upon release of all boundary forces, reverts immediately to a state of zero *stress*. More generally, the stress distribution in a viscoelastic medium (in an accessible state) is determined entirely by the *instantaneous* boundary conditions and is identical with the stress distribution in an ideal elastic material under similar loading.

A sample in a nonaccessible state of strain possesses residual true stresses.

F. The special treatment of subsections 3 and 4 applies only to accessible states of strain. The simplicity of the special treatment arises from this limitation. On the other hand, the general approach outlined in subsection 2 applies to nonaccessible as well as accessible states.

G. In the special case of a retarded elastic material with only one retardation time, *all* possible detailed states of strain are accessible. Hence, for such a material, the general theory reveals the significant features of the stress distribution directly. In all other viscoelastic materials, the general theory is more inclusive and hence more complicated than our special treatment.

6. Special Cases

A. Use of method 4A (see page 211).—Consider a thin cantilever beam, of length L, and cross-sectional moment I, about the neutral axis, fixed rigidly at one end ($x = 0$). The beam is composed of an isotropic, incompressible material which possesses a continuous distribution of elastic compliance J in shear as a function of retardation time τ. This distribution is expressed as a known function $J(\tau)$. The beam is loaded with a vertical force distribution which varies with position and time:

$$f(x,t)\,dx = a\,dx + bt\,dx + c\left(1 - \frac{x}{L}\right)t\,dx + \mathrm{P}_L \cos\omega t \qquad \text{for } 0 \leqq x \leqq L \quad (162)$$

$$f(x,t)\,dx = 0 \quad \text{for} \quad x < 0 \quad \text{or} \quad x > L, \quad \text{and/or} \quad t < 0$$

Here P_L represents a concentrated load at the end of the beam ($x = L$). Thus the beam is subject to a steady, evenly distributed load plus an even load which increases linearly with time plus a load which varies both with time and position plus a concentrated load which varies with time. We desire the deflection Y as a function of x and t.

The deflection $Y_1(x)$ of an elastic cantilever beam loaded uniformly is given by:

$$Y_1(x) = \frac{Px^2}{24\ EI}(x^2 + 6\ L^2 - 4\ Lx) \tag{163}$$

For an incompressible elastic material, $E = 3\ G$. Hence:

$$Y_1(x) = \frac{Px^2}{72\ GI}(x^2 + 6\ L^2 - 4\ Lx) \tag{164}$$

The deflection $Y_2(x)$ of an elastic beam loaded according to

$$Fdx = P\left(1 - \frac{x}{L}\right)dx$$

is given by:

$$Y_2(x) = \frac{Px^2}{360\ GLI}(10\ L^3 - 10\ L^2x^2 + 5\ Lx^2 - x^3) \tag{165}$$

The deflection $Y_3(x)$ of an elastic beam loaded at the end with a force P is given by:

$$Y_3(x) = \frac{Px^2}{18\ GI}(3\ L - x) \tag{166}$$

These three functions are also the necessary solutions of the spatial part of the problem at hand.

Furthermore, a viscoelastic medium possessing the distribution of elastic compliance $J(\tau)$ responds to a homogeneous shear stress which is constant in time as follows:

$$\gamma(t) = S\int_0^\infty J(\tau)(1 - e^{-t/\tau})d\tau \tag{167}$$

The same viscoelastic medium responds as follows to a shear stress which increases linearly with time *i.e.*, $S = \alpha t$:

$$\gamma(t) = \alpha\int_0^\infty (t - \tau + \tau e^{-t/\tau})J(\tau)d\tau \tag{168}$$

Finally, the viscoelastic medium responds as follows to the homogeneous shear stress $S = S_0 \cos \omega t$:

$$\gamma(t) = S_0 \left[\int_0^\infty \frac{J(\tau)\, d\tau}{(\omega^2\tau^2 + 1)} \right] \cos \omega t + \omega S_0 \left[\int_0^\infty \frac{\tau\, J(\tau)\, d\tau}{(\omega^2\tau^2 + 1)} \right] \sin \omega t - S_0 \int_0^\infty \frac{J(\tau)\, e^{-t/\tau}\, d\tau}{(\omega^2\tau^2 + 1)} \quad (169)$$

These three solutions represent the temporal aspect of the solution to the problem at hand. Combining the spatial and temporal solutions as in subsection 3 and summing over the four individual terms, we obtain for the desired $Y(x,t)$ the following:

$$\begin{aligned} Y(x,t) &= \frac{ax^2}{72\, I} (x^2 + 6\, L^2 - 4\, Lx) \int_0^\infty J(\tau)(1 - e^{-t/\tau}) d\tau \\ &+ \frac{bx^2}{72\, I} (x^2 + 6\, L^2 - 4\, Lx) \int_0^\infty (t - \tau + \tau e^{-t/\tau}) J(\tau) d\tau \\ &+ \frac{cx^2}{360\, IL} (10\, L^3 - 10\, L^2 + 5\, Lx - x^3) \\ &\times \int_0^\infty (t - \tau + \tau e^{-t/\tau}) J(\tau) d\tau \qquad (170) \\ &+ \frac{P_L x^2}{18\, I} (3\, L - x) \left[\int_0^\infty \frac{J(\tau)\, d\tau}{\omega^2\tau^2 + 1} \right] \cos \omega t \\ &+ \frac{P_L x^2}{18\, I} (3\, L - x) \omega \left[\int_0^\infty \frac{\tau\, J(\tau)\, d\tau}{\omega^2\tau^2 + 1} \right] \sin \omega t \\ &- \frac{P_L x^2}{18\, I} (3\, L - x) \int_0^\infty \frac{J(\tau)\, e^{-t/\tau}\, d\tau}{(\omega^2\tau^2 + 1)} \end{aligned}$$

B. Use of method 4B (page 212). Consider a thin cantilever beam of length L, moment I, etc., as in the previous example. The beam is loaded with a vertical force distribution which varies with time and position as follows:

$$F(x,t)dx = c\left(1 - \frac{x}{L}\right) t\, dx \quad \text{for} \quad 0 \leqq x \leqq L \quad \text{and} \quad t > 0 \quad (171)$$

This function can be directly factored in the fashion of subsection 3 and hence can be solved directly. It has already been used as part of a more general problem, in the preceding example. However, it is now attacked by means of method 4B, in order to illustrate that method.

$$f(\xi,\sigma) = \left[\frac{\partial F(\sigma,t)}{\partial t} \right]_{t=\xi} = c\left(1 - \frac{x}{L}\right) dx \tag{172}$$

This leads to the following equation for the geometric part of the problem:

$$Y(x) = \frac{\lambda c x^2}{360\ LI} (10\ L^3 - 10\ L^2 x + 5\ L x^2 - x^3) \tag{173}$$

The time variation for a single step function is given by equation (140). Combining equations (140) and (173) we obtain the following:

$$Y(x,t,\xi)\ d\xi = T(\xi,t) \frac{cx^2}{360\ LI} (10\ L^3 - 10\ L^2 x + 5\ L x^2 - x^3) \times \left[\int_0^\infty J(\tau)(1 - e^{(\xi - t)/\tau} d\tau \right] d\xi \tag{174}$$

When this is integrated over all values of ξ, we obtain the complete solution which agrees with that obtained by the method of subsection 3.

$$Y(x,t) = \frac{cx^2}{360\ LI} (10\ L^3 - 10\ L^2 x + 5\ L x^2 - x^3) \times \int_0^\infty (t - \tau + \tau e^{-t/\tau}) J(\tau)\ d\tau \tag{175}$$

7. Large Strains

Practically all of the mathematical relationships developed in this chapter apply only to small deformations. Below are listed reasons for the failure of these relationships in the range of large deformations:

(1) The treatment of this chapter has been couched in terms of the classical theory of elasticity. The classical definitions of the six strain components is unsatisfactory for purely geometric reasons as soon as large deformations are encountered. This failure was discussed in chapter A.

(2) The (small strain) behavior in pure shear and in pure tension of an isotropic, incompressible, viscoelastic material are very simply related to one another. When the viscoelastic spectrum in shear is known, the corresponding spectrum in tension can be computed by replacing every shear modulus G in the shear model by a Young's modulus equal to $3G$ in the tensile model and each viscosity element η by a viscous resistance to tensile deformation equal to 3η. This simple relationship has been used throughout this chapter and has obviated much unnecessary duplication. It holds only in the range of small strains, however. When large

deformations are involved, the relation between shear and tensile behavior must be approached much more cautiously (*57*).

(3) Indeed, the whole problem of combined stresses and strains has been developed in a simple fashion from the behavior in pure shear. This treatment also holds only in the range of small strains.

(4) The emphasis in this chapter has been placed upon materials possessing linear viscoelastic spectra. We can confidently expect real amorphous polymers to exhibit linear behavior in the region of small strains and small rates of strain, but there is no reason at all to expect a linear model to be satisfactory for large strains (or large rates of strain).

(5) Not only the phenomenological framework but also the mechanistic theories of this chapter fail when applied to large deformations. These mechanistic theories have been mathematically formulated in a fashion which limits them to the range of small strains.

As far as incompressible, isotropic, linear, amorphous polymers are concerned, then, we are in the following position: for the range of small strains we have a satisfactory phenomenological framework and a good start toward a satisfactory molecular theory. Many details of the molecular theory must be considerably improved, and a great deal of experimental data must yet be gathered before a thoroughly satisfactory unity can be reached, but the following important steps have been made. We can predict confidently, reasoning entirely from the molecular structure of high polymers and the fundamental laws of statistical mechanics and kinetics, that even a monodisperse linear polymer will exhibit a distribution of retarded elastic responses, as well as instantaneous elasticity and flow. We have at out disposal a molecular theory which, with proper refinement, can be expected to yield a good approximation to the retarded elastic spectrum of a given material. From the phenomenological standpoint, the subject is even more completely developed. From any one type of time test in either shear or tension, we can compute the viscoelastic "spectrum" in shear or tension and thence the response to any other type of time test. Still further, from the basic viscoelastic spectrum for pure shear we can compute the response to combined stresses —and even nonhomogeneous combined stresses. In contrast to this happy situation in the range of small strains, we have at this stage absolutely nothing in the way of a treatment applicable to large strains. This defect is not remedied in this book; instead, we simply list below several methods of approach which can be used for large deformations:

(1) We may employ the "small strain" treatments of this chapter as an approximation in the range of moderate deformations. This is

out of the question when deformations of several hundred percent are concerned.

(2) We may abandon the attempt to treat combined and nonhomogeneous stresses and strains and focus our attention upon one special type of deformation after another. By adopting such a frankly empirical point of view, we may, for example, study the tensile deformations of a sample up to any point, relating relative elongation or some function thereof to stress, or total load, and to time. The determination of "stress-strain" curves for elastomers is an example of this approach.

(3) There is no reason why the molecular theories of this chapter cannot be extended to deal with any desired amount of deformation, if only one special type of deformation is considered at a time. As a matter of fact, Guth and James (*31*) have done just this in connection with the equilibrium elastic properties of a cross-linked polymer. Treloar (*80*) has also contributed very significantly to this problem.

(4) The writer feels that the only completely satisfactory approach to the phenomenological problem of large strains would consist of a rigorous extension of Murnaghan's theory of finite elastic strain (or of some equivalent theory) to the case of viscoelastic materials. This would presumably be extremely difficult—particularly since the restriction to linear systems should also be removed at this point. A widespread usage of the rigorous treatment of large *equilibrium elastic* deformations would act as an impetus in this direction, however. It should be remembered that it is out of the question to hope for a phenomenological treatment of large plastoelastic deformations which is at once rigorous and simple.

(5) It follows that a completely satisfactory molecular theory of large plastoelastic deformations must discard classical definitions of strains and embrace Murnaghan's definitions, or some equivalent thereof. Whether it will ever be practicable to develop such theories is a question which the writer is unable to answer.

VII. OPTICAL EFFECTS IN STRAINED AMORPHOUS POLYMERS—PHOTOELASTICITY (*1a*)

An optically isotropic material has the same index of refraction in all directions. The structural requirements for optical isotropy are less extreme than for mechanical isotropy. (A cubic crystal, for example, is optically isotropic but mechanically anisotropic.) This is because the electrical polarizability, which relates the three-vector polarization with the three-vector electric field, possesses the symmetry properties of an ellipsoid; and if the three major axes of the polarizability ellipsoid are equal, the ellipsoid necessarily reduces to a sphere. In the mechanical case, the stress and strain may each be resolved into *six* components and the elastic moduli together constitute a physical property considerably more complicated than the electrical polarizability. Thus the fact that three mutually perpendicular directions in a cubic crystal are mechanically identical does not insure that the properties in any *oblique* direction will also be the same.

A completely unstrained amorphous material is isotropic, both mechanically and optically. It has long been known, however, that (when stressed) amorphous materials exhibit double refraction, *i.e.*, become optically anisotropic. This was first observed by Brewster (*16b*) with glass. In recent years mechanical-optical effects have been extensively investigated and have proved a valuable tool in the engineering field.

If one wishes to know the stress distribution in an elastic object of given shape, loaded in a given fashion, one method of procedure is to solve the differential equations of elasticity subject to the proper boundary conditions. If the object has a complicated shape (*e.g.*, with holes, notches, corners, etc.), this may prove difficult. It has proved helpful to construct models from some transparent, isotropic material, load these models in the desired manner, and determine the essential features of the stress distribution from the photoelastic pattern. Various amorphous high polymers have found such widespread use in photoelastic studies that a few paragraphs should be devoted to the mechanical-optical properties of these materials.

The photoelastic behavior of an ideally elastic amorphous material is relatively simple. Under the action of a tensile stress in the x direction, for example, the molecules will be somewhat pulled away from each other in this direction. The electronic clouds surrounding the various molecular skeletal frames will interact differently than in the unstressed condition. Even though the material was isotropic before the stress was imposed, it is anisotropic in the presence of the stress. A light ray normal to the direction of the stress will suffer a phase retardation which depends in magnitude upon the orientation of the plane of polarization relative to the direction of the stress. Two such rays, one polarized in the direction of the stress and the other across the direction of the stress, will thus suffer a relative shift in phase during passage through the sample. The magnitude of this relative phase retardation can be related either with the *stress* or with the *strain*. If we choose the stress, the following relation may be written:

$$\mathrm{r} = CS\mathrm{d} \tag{176}$$

Here r is the distance a wave front polarized parallel to the stress is in advance of a wave front polarized across the stress, d is the thickness, and C is the stress-optical coefficient of the material. The dimensions of C are $cm.^2$ per dyne; the usual unit is the Brewster, which is defined as 10^{-13} $cm.^2$ per dyne. If we wish to connect the relative phase retardation of the two polarized rays with the strain, it must be remembered that there are two components of strain in the plane normal to the ray—a positive elongation γ_{xx} and a lateral contraction, with $\gamma_{yy} = -\nu\gamma_{xx}$. Assuming the retardation to be a linear function of the strains, we may write:

$$r = C'(\gamma_{xx} + \nu\gamma_{xx})d = C''\gamma_{xx}d \qquad (177)$$

Here C' is a strain-optical coefficient. If Hooke's law is obeyed, C' must be equal to $C \cdot E/(1 + \nu)$. Thus in the range of Hooke's law equations (176) and (177) are completely equivalent. If the relative retardation is directly proportional to the tensile stress, it must necessarily be proportional to the strains and even to the elongation. The author, however, has a strong predilection toward the latter type of treatment, in which strain is considered as the determining factor. This is partly due to the fact that in the case of materials with more complex mechanical properties —*e.g.*, organic high polymers—it *is* possible to resolve the question experimentally and here the facts point strongly toward a strain-optical effect, rather than a stress-optical effect. It is partly due to the *a priori* consideration that a strained material is no longer structurally isotropic, and the structural anisotropy of a strained sample would seem to offer the simplest and most direct explanation of the optical anisotropy.

Neumann developed the mathematical theory of double refraction of a medium possessing any combination of strain components, the strains being assumed to be small. Coker and Filon (*1a*) have extended this treatment to the case of finite strains. Maxwell, on the other hand, formulated the general theory of double refraction in a medium subjected to any combination of stress components. It is clear that in the range of Hooke's law these treatments are equivalent, just as in the special case of simple tensile stress already discussed (pages 220 *et seq.*). The results of such treatments may be summarized in terms of Neumann's two derived laws:

(1) The directions of polarization of any given ray are parallel to the directions of principal strain in the plane normal to the ray, *i.e.*, they are parallel to the principal axes of the section of the strain quadric which is cut by a plane parallel to the optical wave front.

(2) The difference in velocity of propagation of the two perpendicularly polarized colinear rays is proportional to the algebraic difference between the principal strains in the plane defined in (1) above.

According to Coker and Filon, these two laws have received very satisfying experimental verification for ideal elastic materials.

In the case of an amorphous linear polymer, the mechanical effect of a stress is less simple. Besides the instantaneous elastic response there is a series of *retarded* elastic effects. The total elastic strain is a function of time as well as stress. On pages 134–143 it was shown how the configurational elastic strain can be resolved into a series of terms connected with the uncurling and orientation of molecular segments of different lengths. It would seem reasonable that to each of these terms there should correspond a distinctive strain-optical coefficient. Consider for simplicity a simple tensile stress. When the stress is applied, the first effect is an instantaneous elastic strain, γ_1. This strain is similar to the elastic strain in glass; neighboring atoms are pulled slightly apart or pressed together, with no change in the general structure of the packing arrangement. This small deformation entails a slight anisotropy and, hence, double refraction, just as in the case of glass. As time goes on, biased segmental diffusion results in an uncurling and orientation of the polymer chains. This gives rise to the configurational strains, γ_2, γ_3, γ_4, etc. The additional strains entail additional anisotropy, with additional double refraction effects. Since the configurational strains are physically distinct from the instantaneous strain, there is no reason to expect the same strain-optical coefficient to operate. Instead, equation (177) should be generalized to the form:

$$\mathrm{r} = \mathrm{d}[C_1\gamma_1 + C_2\gamma_2 + C_3\gamma_3 + \cdots] \qquad (178)$$

(Since the electrons, which give rise to polarizability and hence determine the refractive index, are in most molecules essentially localized in definite chemical bonds or on definite atoms, it would seem reasonable that the most significant aspect of the configurational strain is the orientation of relatively *short segments* of molecular chains. Indeed, if the angular distribution of each type of valence bond were fixed, the optical retardation due to configurational strain should be fairly definitely fixed as well. In a conjugated structure, the orientation of larger sections of the chain would presumably be significant.)

The important thing is that a high polymer under stress exhibits an *optical creep* which parallels the mechanical effect of retarded elasticity. The same is true of the elastic recovery. Whereas in an ideal elastic material the artificial double refraction disappears as soon as the stress is removed, in a high polymer only *part* of the double refraction disappears instantaneously and the rest decays only slowly. If we divide the total double refraction simply into two parts—r_1 connected with the instantaneous elastic strain and r_2 with the configurational strain—then these two parts behave quite differently. Since the instantaneous strain follows the stress with no time lag, r_1 is proportional to the stress as well as to the instantaneous strain. On the other hand, r_2 does not depend at all upon the stress acting at the moment. Furthermore, the magnitude of the configurational strain in general is much greater than that of the instantaneous strain. Therefore, the natural tendency is to relate r_1 with the stress (rather than with the instantaneous elastic strain which is overshadowed by the configurational strain) and to relate r_2 with the total strain (which does not appreciably differ from the configurational part of the strain). This mathematical convenience does not invalidate the point of view that double refraction is fundamentally a function of the strains, but rather strengthens it. Coker and Filon report that the double refraction in celluloid can be reasonably described by an equation of the form:

$$r = C_1 S + C_2 \gamma \qquad (179)$$

where C_1 is a stress-optical coefficient and C_2 is a strain-optical coefficient. They emphasize that such a "mixed" law cannot be readily accepted as a fundamental physical representation of the phenomenon. In order to avoid this, they postulate a two-phase structure and are thus able to express these results in terms of the *stresses* on the two phases. This corresponds to explaining the *plastoelastic* properties of the polymer in terms of a two-phase theory. Certain objections to this procedure have already been raised in section D (pages 164–165), and these apply here as well. It is very likely that celluloid is far from a simple homogeneous amorphous polymer and different regions may have different physical properties. However, as is emphasized in section D (pages 164–165), any such heterogeneity should be considered as an additional complication, rather than as the fundamental source of complex mechanical time effects. It can be safely stated that a strained amorphous polymer, even in the absence of stress (other than the "internal stress" of section D (pages 165–166), exhibits double refraction. If the polymer chains are oriented, so that the valence bonds are not randomly disposed in direction, the material can hardly be optically isotropic.

If the polymer is far above its brittle point (*e.g.*, rubber at room temperature) then the double refraction connected with configurational strain follows the stress practically instantaneously and, in this case, r_2 as well as r_1 can be related with the stress if this is desired. Coker and Filon report that double refraction in India rubber is simply proportional to the stress (in simple tension). The author confidently predicts that if the mechanical-optical characteristics of rubber are investigated in the region of the brittle point, this will no longer be true, but that an equation of the type of (179) will be necessary. Furthermore, if measurements are made *far below* the brittle point, where the configurational elasticity is essentially "frozen in," a simple relation with stress alone is again applicable, but with a markedly different stress-optical coefficient than that which governs the room temperature behavior. At these low temperatures only r_1 appears, whereas at room temperature both r_1 and r_2 appear.

It is clear that in a photoelastic study where a stress distribution is to be determined from birefringence data, time effects involving retardations which are not simply related to the stress must be avoided or corrected for. This can be done by working well below the brittle point of the material or, presumably, by using a cross-linked polymer well *above* its brittle point.

One technique which has been used in certain stress distribution problems involves heating a cross-linked polymer above its brittle point, imposing the stress and allowing elastic equilibrium to be established, and then cooling while under the stress. The configurational strain is frozen in; the stress can be removed and the sample removed for observation. In such a case, it is to be expected that a different optical coefficient will govern the double refraction than if the sample were observed under stress without heating, in the usual fashion. In an ordinary photoelastic test well below the brittle point, the retardation is of the type of r_1. In the heat-stress, cool-under-stress test, the frozen-in birefringence is of the type of r_2 (configurational effect). These two effects are different in origin and are only accidentally equal in magnitude for the same stress.

Having discussed briefly the complications involved in the photoelastic behavior of organic high polymers in certain temperature ranges, we can now describe in more detail the nature and significance of the birefringence patterns in stressed objects. The following discussion applies only to materials and conditions for which the optical phase retardation is a linear function of the stress components. For simplicity, furthermore, only planar stress distributions are considered here.

Referring back to Maxwell's two laws (page 222), we find that the directions of principal polarizability at a point in a stressed sheet coincide with the directions of principal stress at the point and, further, that the relative retardation of the two plane polarized components of a transmitted ray is proportional to the difference between the two principal stresses. In figure 84 a sheet of transparent amorphous material is pictured oriented parallel to the xy plane. A ray of monochromatic light, directed parallel to the z axis and polarized in the xz plane, passes through the sheet at the point P and thence to a Nicol prism which allows only

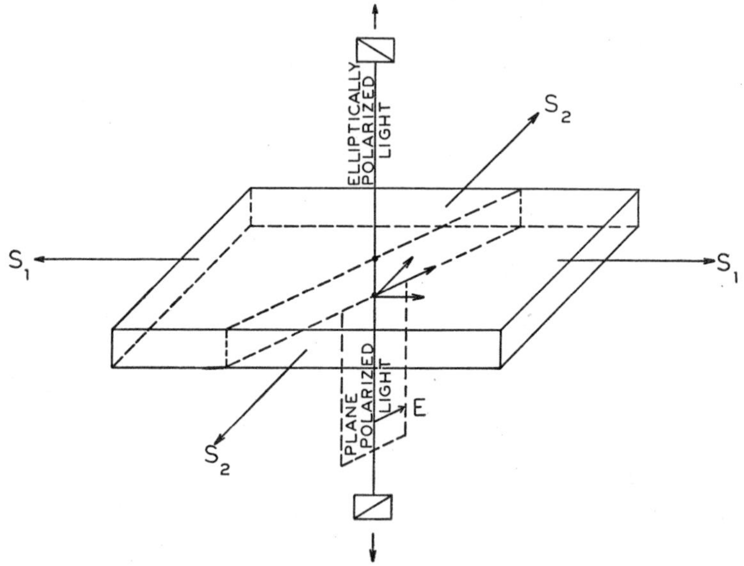

Fig. 84. Schematic illustration of stress birefringence in a transparent amorphous material.

the component polarized in the yz plane to pass through. At the point P, the directions of principal stress, S_1 and S_2, are inclined at the acute angle α from the x and y axes, respectively. When the plane-polarized ray enters the sheet, it is split into two colinear rays, one polarized parallel to each of the two optic axes in the plane of the sheet. These two components suffer different phase retardations while going through the sheet and hence will not, in general, be in phase with each other when they emerge from the sheet. As a result, they recombine to form not a plane-polarized ray, but an elliptically polarized ray which is incompletely blacked out by the analyzing Nicol. The intensity of the light which passes through the polarizing Nicol prism, the stressed sheet, and the analyzing Nicol, depends upon the magnitude of the stress difference $(S_1 - S_2)$ and the orientation of the Nicol prisms relative to the directions of principal stress (α). In a sheet which is nonhomogeneously stressed, the intensity will vary from point to point. At all points where the directions of principal stress are parallel to the directions of polarization defined by the two Nicol prisms (*i.e.*, where $\alpha = 0$), the ray is completely blacked out, just as a doubly refracting crystal appears black under crossed Nicols when oriented with two of its principal directions parallel to the directions of polarization of the Nicols. These points, where $\alpha = 0$, in general define a curve in the specimen, which appears as a black line. Such a locus of points possessing the same directions of principal stress is called an *isoclinic* line.

Furthermore, all points, where the relative phase retardation is either zero or an integral number of wave lengths, also appear completely dark. The locus of points where $\mathrm{r} = n\lambda$ is in general a line, which is of course the locus of points with a common value for the difference of principal stresses ($S_1 - S_2$). The zero-order line, where $\mathrm{r} = 0$, usually degenerates into a point—although in special cases it may appear as a line. Thus a sheet viewed between crossed Nicols, while nonhomogeneously stressed, exhibits dark lines of two kinds: the isoclinics $\alpha = 0$ and the lines along which $\mathrm{r} = \lambda, 2\lambda, 3\lambda$, etc. These two types of dark lines can easily be distinguished. If the Nicol prisms are rotated together to a new orientation, the dark isoclinic naturally moves, whereas the lines of constant difference of principal stresses remain unchanged. If circular polarizers (Nicol prisms plus quarter-wave plates) are used in place of the plane polarizers (Nicol prisms alone), the effect of angular orientation is averaged out and the intensity of transmitted light depends only upon the principal stress at a given point. Viewed between opposite circular polarizers, no dark isoclinic lines appear but the lines of constant ($S_1 - S_2$) which give a relative retardation of $n\lambda$ appear as before.

If polychromatic light is used, each color is individually affected in the manner just described. With crossed Nicol prisms, the isoclinics $\alpha = 0$ appear dark just as in the case of monochromatic light. No point can be completely blacked out because $\mathrm{r} = n\lambda$, however, since, when one color is blacked out, the others will not be. Only the zero-order case, where $\mathrm{r} = 0$, represents simultaneous darkening of all colors; when $(S_1 - S_2) = 0$—in other words, at an isotropic point—complete darkening occurs. A line of constant stress difference other than zero is a line of constant color—hence these lines are called isochromatic lines. Indeed, the *color* of the transmitted light depends only upon the value of ($S_1 - S_2$). Thus in a nonhomogeneously stressed sheet the following pattern is observed through crossed Nicols: along a line of constant stress difference, the *color* is constant—hence the name isochromatic line. Along such an isochromatic line, however, the *intensity* varies according to the *inclination* of the stress axes relative to the Nicol prisms. In particular, where $\alpha = 0$, complete darkening occurs. The dark isoclinic lines where $\alpha = 0$ cut through the isochromatic lines. If there are any isotropic points (or lines) these too appear dark. If the Nicol prisms are rotated, the dark isoclinics shift their positions but the dark isotropic points remain fixed—and the *color* of the light at *any* point remains the same. If circular polarizers are used, the intensity all along an isochromatic line is constant. In particular, the dark isoclinic lines disappear.

From the foregoing it is clear that the photoelastic study of a given stress distribution does not yield the stress distribution directly, but rather yields the *directions* of principal stress at every point and the *difference* between the two principal stresses. Coker and Filon (*1a*) show that if these two quantities, α and $(S_1 - S_2)$, are known for every point and if the actual stress is known at certain points (*e.g.*, boundaries) the stress distribution can be computed.

BIBLIOGRAPHY

BOOKS

(*1*) Campbell, G. A., and Foster, R. M., *Fourier Integrals for Practical Application.* Bell Telephone System Tech. Pub., Monograph B584.

(*1a*) Coker, E. G., and Filon, L., *Treatise on Photo-elasticity.* Cambridge Univ. Press, London, 1931; Macmillan, New York, 1931.

(*2*) *First Report on Viscosity and Plasticity.* Royal Netherlands Academy of Sciences, Noord-Hollandsche, Amsterdam, 1935, 2nd Ed., 1939.

Second Report on Viscosity and Plasticity. Royal Netherlands Academy of Sciences, Noord-Hollandsche, Amsterdam; Interscience, New York, 1938.

(*3*) Glasstone, S., Laidler, K. J., and Eyring, H., *The Theory of Rate Processes.* McGraw-Hill, New York, 1941, Chapter IV.

(*4*) Houwink, R., *Physikalische Eigenschaften und Feinbau von Natur- und Kunstharzen.* Akadem. Verlagsgesellschaft, Leipzig, 1934.

(*5*) Houwink, R., *Elasticity, Plasticity, and the Structure of Matter.* Cambridge Univ. Press, London, 1937.

(*6*) Leaderman, H., *Elastic and Creep Properties of Filamentous Materials and Other High Polymers.* The Textile Foundation, Washington, 1943.

(*7*) Mark, H., *Physical Chemistry of High Polymeric Systems* (High Polymers, Vol. II). Interscience, New York, 1940.

(*7a*) Meyer, K. H., *Natural and Synthetic High Polymers* (High Polymers, Vol. IV). Interscience, New York, 1942.

(*8*) Staudinger, H., *Die hochmolekularen organischen Verbindungen.* Springer, Berlin, 1932.

(*9*) Tammann, G., *Der Glaszustand.* Voss, Leipzig, 1933.

(*10*) Timoshenko, S., *Theory of Elasticity.* McGraw-Hill, New York, 1934.

ARTICLES

(*11*) Aleksandrov, A. P., and Lazurkin, IU. S., "Study of Polymers. I. Highly Elastic Deformation in Polymers," *Acta Physicochim. U.R.S.S.*, **12**, 647–668 (1940).

(*12*) Alfrey, T., "Non-homogeneous Stresses in Visco-elastic Media," *Quart. Applied Math.*, **2**, 113–119 (1944).

(*13*) Alfrey, T., "A Molecular Theory of the Viscoelastic Behavior of an Amorphous Linear Polymer," *J. Chem. Phys.*, **12**, 374–379 (1944).

(*14*) Bekkedahl, N., "Forms of Rubber as Indicated by Temperature-Volume Relationships," *J. Research Natl. Bur. Standards*, **13**, 411 (1934).

(*14a*) Bennewitz, K., and Rötger, H., "Über den plastischen-elastischen Zustand," *Physik. Z.*, **40**, 416–428 (1939).

(*15*) Berger, E., "The Theory of Glass Formation and Glass State," *Kolloid-Beihefte*, **36**, 1–42 (1932).

(*15a*) Boltzmann, L., "Zur Theorie der elastischen Nachwirkung," *Ann. Physik Chem., Erg. Bd.*, **7**, 624 (1876).

(*16*) Boyer, R. F., and Spencer, R. S., "Thermal Expansion and Second-Order Transition Effects in High Polymers. I. Experimental Results," *J. Applied Phys.*, **15**, 398–405 (1944).

(*16a*) Bresler, S. E., and Frenkel, IA. I., "On the Shape and Character of Thermal Motion of Long-Chain Organic Molecules and on the Elasticity of Rubber-like Substances," *Acta Physicochim. U.R.S.S.*, **11**, 485–504 (1939).

(*16b*) Brewster, D., "On the Communication of the Structure of Doubly Refracting Crystals to Glass, Muriate of Soda, Fluor Spar, and Other Substances, by Mechanical Compression and Dilatation," *Trans. Roy. Soc. London*, **106**, 156–178 (1816).

(*17*) Buist, J. M., and Seymour, R. C., "Position of the Rubber-like State on the Plastic-Elastic Scale," *Trans. Inst. Rubber Ind.*, **19**, 64–90 (1943).

(*18*) Carswell, T. S., Hayes, R. F., and Nason, H. K., "Physical Properties of Polystyrene as Influenced by Temperature," *Ind. Eng. Chem.*, **34**, 454 (1942).

(*19*) Clash, R. F., and Berg, R. M., "Vinyl Elastomers," *ibid.*, **34**, 1218 (1942).

(*20*) Davies, J. M., Miller, R. F., and Busse, W. F., "Dielectric Properties of Plasticized Polyvinyl Chloride," *J. Am. Chem. Soc.*, **63**, 361–369 (1941).

(*21*) Dillon, J. H., Prettyman, I. B., and Hall, G. L., "Hysteretic and Elastic Properties of Rubber-like Materials Under Dynamic Shear Stresses," *J. Applied Phys.*, **15**, 309 (1944).

(21*a*) E. I. du Pont de Nemours & Co., "Methacrylate Resins," *Ind. Eng. Chem.*, **28**, 1160–1163 (1936).

(*22*) Eley, D. D., "The Kinetics of Rubber-like Elasticity," *Rubber Chem. Tech.*, **15**, 438 (1942).

(*23*) Ferry, J. D., "Mechanical Properties of Substances of High Molecular Weight. I. Photoelastic Method for Study of Transverse Vibrations in Gels," *Rev. Sci. Instruments*, **12**, 79–82 (1941).

(*24*) Fikentscher, H., and Mark, H., "Ueber ein Spiralmodell des Kautschuks," *Kautschuk*, **6**, 2–6 (1936).

(*25*) Flory, P. J., "Viscosities of Linear Polyesters. An Exact Relationship between Viscosity and Chain Length," *J. Am. Chem. Soc.*, **62**, 1057 (1940).

(*25a*) Flory, P. J., and Rehner, J., "Statistical Theory of Chain Configuration and

Physical Properties of High Polymers. Effects of Hindered Rotation," New York Academy of Sciences Conference on "High Polymers," Jan. 9, 1943.

(*25b*) Frenkel, IA. I., "A Theory of Elasticity, Viscosity and Swelling in Polymeric Rubber-like Substances, *Acta Physicochim. U.R.S.S.*, **9**, 235–250 (1938).

(*26a*) Fuoss, R. M., and Kirkwood, J. G., "Dipole Moments in Polyvinyl Chloride-Biphenyl Solutions," *J. Am. Chem. Soc.*, **63**, 385–394 (1941).

(*27*) Gehman, S. D., "Rubber in Vibration," *J. Applied Phys.*, **13**, 402–413 (1942).

(*28*) Gehman, S. D., Woodford, D. E., and Stambaugh, R. B., "Dynamic Properties of Rubber," *Ind. Eng. Chem.*, **33**, 1032 (1941).

(*29*) Gemant, A., "The Conception of a Complex Viscosity and Its Applications to Dielectrics," *Trans. Faraday Soc.*, **31**, 1582–1590 (1935).

(*29a*) Gemant, A., "Correlation between Elastic Moduli and Viscosity of Liquids and Plastics," *J. Applied Phys.*, **12**, 680–685 (1941).

(*30*) Graves, F. L., and Davis, A. R., "Evaluating Low-Temperature Stiffness and Brittle Point in Elastometers," *India Rubber World*, **109**, 41 (1943).

(*30a*) Guth, E., "The Physics of Rubber. I. Its Observed Elastic and Thermoelastic Behavior," *J. Applied Phys.*, **10**, 201 (1939).

(*31*) Guth, E., and James, H., "Elastic and Thermoelastic Properties of Rubber-like Materials. A Statistical Theory," *Ind. Eng. Chem.*, **33**, 624–629 (1941).

(*31a*) Guth, E., and Mark, H., "Zur innermolekularen Statistik, insbesondere bei Kettermolekülen I," *Monatsh.*, **65**, 93–121 (1934).

(*31b*) Guth, E., and Mark, H., "Die Elastizität des Kautschuks und ihr Zusammenhang mit dem Strukturmodell," *Naturwissenschaften*, **25**, 353–359 (1937).

(*32*) Hahn, S. H., and Gazdik, I., "The Creep of Natural and Synthetic Rubber Compounds in Shear," *India Rubber World*, **103**, No. 5, 51–55 (1941).

(*33*) Hauk, V., and Neumann, W., "Die Temperaturabhängigkeit der Spannung in Kautschuk bei konstanter Dehnung," *Z. physik. Chem.*, **A182**, 285–294 (1938); "The Dependence of the Stress on the Temperature of Rubber Elongated to a Constant Degree," *Rubber Chem. Tech.*, **12**, 520 (1939).

(*34*) Haward, R. N., "The Extension and Rupture of Cellulose Acetate and Celluloid," *Trans. Faraday Soc.*, **38**, 394–403 (1942).

(*35*) Haward, R. N., "The Fast and Slow Extension of Some Plastic Materials," *ibid.*, **39**, 267–280 (1943).

(*35a*) Hetényi, M., "Application of Hardening Resins in Three-Dimensional Studies," *J. Applied Phys.*, **10**, 295–300 (1939); "The Fundamentals of Three-Dimensional Photoelasticity," *Trans. Am. Soc. Mech. Engrs.*, **60**, A149 (1938).

(*36*) Höppler, F., "Rheologic and Elastometric Measurements of Rubber Products," *Rubber Chem. Tech.*, **15**, 115 (1942).

(*37*) Holt, W. L., and McPherson, A. T., "Change of Volume of Rubber on Stretching. Effects of Time, Elongation and Temperature," *J. Research Natl. Bur. Standards*, **17**, 657–678 (1936).

(*38*) Holzmüller, W., and Jenckel, E., "Elastisch-plastische Verformung bei der mechanischen Beanspruchung von Festkörpern," *Z. physik. Chem.*, **A186**, 359–372 (1940).

(*39*) Huggins, M. L., "The Entropy of Long-Chain Compounds in the Gaseous State," *J. Chem. Phys.*, **8**, 181–187 (1940).

(*40*) James, J. M., and Guth, E., "Theoretical Stress-Strain Curve for Rubber-like Materials," *Phys. Rev.*, **59**, 111 (1941).

(*41*) James, H. M., and Guth, E., "Theory of Rubber Elasticity for Development of Synthetic Rubbers," *Ind. Eng. Chem.*, **34**, 1365 (1942).

(*42*) Jenckel, E., and Überreiter, K., "Über Polystyrolgläser verschiedener Kettenlänge," *Z. physik. Chem.*, **A182**, 361–383 (1938).

(*42a*) Kauzmann, W. J., and Eyring, H., "The Viscous Flow of Large Molecules," *J. Am. Chem. Soc.*, **62**, 3113 (1940).

(*43*) Kelsey, R. H., and Dillon, J. H., "Rheological Properties of Natural and Synthetic Rubbers," *J. Applied Phys.*, **15**, 352 (1944).

(*44*) Kemp, A. R., Malm, F. S., and Winspear, G. G., "Brittle Temperature of Rubber under Variable Stress," *Ind. Eng. Chem.*, **35**, 488 (1943).

(*45*) King, G. E., "Bend-Brittle and Shatter Points of Rubber-like Materials," *ibid.*, **35**, 949–951 (1943).

(*45a*) Kirkwood, J. G. and Fuoss, R. M., "Anomalous Dispersion and Dielectric Loss in Polar Polymers," *J. Chem. Phys.*, **9**, 329–340 (1941).

(*46*) Kohlrausch, F., "Experimental-untersuchungen über die elastische Nachwirkung bei der Torsion, Ausdehnung und Biegung," *Ann. Physik*, **158**, 337 (1876); "Über die elastische Nachwirkung bei der Torsion," *Ann. Physik Chem.*, **119**, 337 (1863).

(*47*) Kuhn, W., "Über die Gestalt fadenförimger Moleküle in Lösungen," *Kolloid-Z.*, **68**, 2–15 (1934); "Molekülkonstellation und Kristallitorientierung als Ursachen kautschukähnlicher Elastizität," *ibid.*, **87**, 3–12 (1939).

(*48*) Kuhn, W., "Beziehungen zwischen Viscosität und elastischen Eigenschaften amorpher Stoffe," *Z. physik. Chem.*, **B42**, 1–38 (1939).

(*48a*) Leaderman, H., "Textile Materials and the Time Factor. I. Mechanical Behavior of Textile Fibers and Plastics," *Textile Research*, **11**, 171–193 (1941).

(*48b*) Leaderman, H., "Creep and Creep Recovery in Plasticized Polyvinyl Chloride," *Ind. Eng. Chem.*, **35**, 374 (1943).

(*49*) Liska, J. W., "Effect of Low Temperatures on Young's Modulus of Elastomers," *ibid.*, **36**, 40–46 (1944).

(*50*) Mack, E., Jr., "Molecular Structure and van der Waals Forces," *J. Phys. Chem.*, **41**, 221–231 (1937).

(*51*) Madelung, E., and Flügge, S., "Über Viskosoelastizität," *Ann. Physik*, **22**, 209 (1935).

(*51a*) Mark, H., "Quantitative Ansätze zur Enfassung der Formänderung hochpolymerer Stoffe," *Congr. intern. quím. pura aplicada, 9th Congr., Madrid*, **4**, 197–207 (1934).

(*51b*) Mark, H., "Natural and Synthetic Rubber. The Elasticity of Long-Chain Molecules," *Nature*, **141**, 670–672 (1938).

(*52*) Mark, H., "Phase Transition and Elastic Behavior of High Polymers," *Ind. Eng. Chem.*, **34**, 449 (1942).

(*53*) Mark, H., "Intermolecular Forces and Mechanical Behavior of High Polymers," *ibid.*, **34**, 1343 (1942).

(*53a*) Mark, H., and Valko, E., "Vorgänge bei der mechanischen Verformung von Kautschuk," *Kautschuk*, **6**, 210–215 (1930).

(*54*) Maxwell, C., "On the Dynamical Theory of Gases," *Trans. Roy. Soc. London*, **157**, 49–88 (1867); or *Phil. Mag.*, Ser. 4, **35**, 129–145, 185–217 (1868).

(*55*) Meyer, K. H., and Ferri, C., "Sur l'elasticité du caoutchouc," *Helv. Chim. Acta*, **18**, 570–589 (1935); "The Elasticity of Rubber," *Rubber Chem. Tech.*, **8**, 319–334 (1935).

(*56*) Mikhailov, G., and Kirilina, V., "Study of the Elastic Relaxation by a Resonance Method," *Tech. Phys. U.S.S.R.*, **5**, 842–847 (1938).

(*57*) Mooney, M., "A Theory of Large Elastic Deformation," *J. Applied Phys.*, **11**, 582 (1940).

(*58*) Mooney, M., Wolstenholme, W. E., and Villars, D. S., "Drift and Relaxation of Rubber," *ibid.*, **15**, 324 (1944).

(*59*) Morris, R. E., James, R. R., and Werkenthin, T. A., "Brittle Points of Natural and Synthetic Rubber Stocks," *Ind. Eng. Chem.*, **35**, 864 (1943).

(*60*) Murnaghan, F. D., "Finite Deformations of an Elastic Solid," *Am. J. Math.*, **59**, 235–260 (1937).

(*61*) Ostwald, W., "Zur Theorie des Röntgeneffektes gespannter Gele, im besonderen des Kautschuks," *Kolloid-Z.*, **40**, 58–73 (1926).

(*61a*) Pelzer, H., Zur kinetischen Theorie der Kautschukelastizität," *Monatsh.*, **71**, 444–447 (1938).

(*62*) Peterson, L. E., Anthony, R. L., and Guth, E., "Equation of State of Some Synthetic Rubbers," *Ind. Eng. Chem.*, **34**, 1349 (1942).

(*63*) Philippoff, W., "Dynamische Untersuchungen an kolloiden Systemen. I. Grundlagen und Methode zur Untersuchungen der mechanischen Eigenschaften von Lösungen hochmolekularer organischer Verbindungen. II. Messungen der dynamischen Zähigkeit von Zellitlösungen und Aufstellung einer Dispersionsformel," *Physik Z.*, **35**, 884–900, 900–905 (1934).

(*64*) Powell, R. E., Roseveare, W. E., and Eyring, H., "Diffusion, Thermal Conductivity and Viscous Flow of Liquids," *Ind. Eng. Chem.*, **33**, 430 (1941).

(*65*) Roseveare, W. E., Powell, R. E., and Eyring, H., "The Structure and Dynamics of Liquids," *J. Applied Phys.*, **12**, 669 (1941).

(*66*) Roth, F. L., and Wood, L. A., "Some Relations between Stress, Strain and Temperature in a Pure-Gum Vulcanizate of GR-S Synthetic Rubber," *J. Applied Phys.*, **15**, 749 (1944).

(*67*) Scott, J. R., "The Plastic Behavior of Ebonite," *Rubber Chem. Tech.*, **15**, 826–834 (1942).

(*68*) Sebrell, L. B., and Dinsmore, R. P., "Properties of Some Synthetic Rubbers," *S. A. Journal*, **49**, 368–379 (1941).

(*69*) Selker, M. L., Winspear, G. G., and Kemp, A. R., "Brittle Point of Rubber on Freezing," *Ind. Eng. Chem.*, **34**, 157–160 (1942).

(*70*) Shohat, J., "A New Analytical Method for Solving van der Pol's and Certain Related Types of Non-linear Differential Equations, Homogeneous and Nonhomogeneous," *J. Applied Phys.*, **14**, 40 (1943).

(*71*) Simha, R., "On Relaxation Effects in Amorphous Media," *J. Applied Phys.*, **13**, 201 (1942).

(*72*) Simha R., "Anomalies of Elasticity and Flow and Their Interpretation," *J. Phys. Chem.*, **47**, 348–363 (1943).

(*73*) Smith, H. D., and Eisenschitz, R., "The Flow and Relaxation of Rayon Filaments," *J. Textile Inst.*, 22, 170T (1931).

(*74*) Stambaugh, R. B., "Vibration Properties of Rubber-like Materials," *Ind. Eng. Chem.*, **34**, 1358 (1942).

(*75*) Stambaugh, R. B., "The Retraction of Stretched Rubber," *Phys. Rev.*, **65**, 250 (1944).

(*76*) Stambaugh, R. B., Rohner, M., and Gehman, S. D., "Speed of Retraction of Rubber," *J. Applied Phys.*, **15**, 740 (1944).

(*77*) Tobolsky, A., and Eyring, H., "Mechanical Properties of Polymeric Materials," *J. Chem. Phys.*, **11**, 125 (1943).

(*78*) Tobolsky, A., Powell, R. E., and Eyring, H., "Elastic-Viscous Properties of Matter," in *The Chemistry of Large Molecules* (Frontiers in Chemistry, Vol. I). Interscience, New York, 1943, Chapter V.

(*79*) Treloar, L. R. G., "Elastic Recovery and Plastic Flow in Raw Rubber," *Trans. Faraday Soc.*, **36**, 538 (1940).

(*80*) Treloar, L. R. G., "Stress-Strain Data for Vulcanized Rubber under Various Types of Deformation," *ibid.*, **40**, 59 (1944).

(*81*) Treloar, L. R. G., "The Statistical Length of Rubber Molecules," *ibid.*, **40**, 109 (1944).

(*82*) Tuckett, R. F., "The Kinetics of High Elasticity in Synthetic Polymers," *Trans. Faraday Soc.*, **38**, 310–322 (1942); *Rubber Chem. Tech.*, **15**, 430–437 (1942).

(*83*) Tuckett, R. F., "The Kinetics of High Elasticity in Synthetic Polymers," *Rubber Chem. Tech.*, **16**, 760–766 (1943).

(*84*) Tuckett, R. F., "The Softening of Thermoplastic Polymers. Part I.—Theoretical," *Trans. Faraday Soc.*, **39**, 158–168 (1943).

(*85*) Tuckett, R. F., "The Electrical and Elastic Properties of Amorphous Polar Polymers," *ibid.*, **40**, 448–462 (1944).

(*86*) Überreiter, K., "Über das Einfrieren normaler Flüssigkeiten und Flüssigkeiten mit, 'fixierter' Struktur wie Kautschuk und Kunstharze," *Z. physik. Chem.*, **B45**, 361–373 (1940); "Die Ableitung des Begriffes 'Flüssigkeit mit fixierter Struktur' aus einer Betrachtung über die Zergliederung der thermodynamischen Zustandfunktion bei normalen und hochpolymeren Flüssigkeitein," *ibid.*, **B46**, 157–164 (1940).

(*87*) van der Pol, B., "The Non-linear Theory of Electric Oscillations," *Proc. Inst. Radio Engrs.*, **22**, 1051–1086 (1934).

(*88*) Wall, F. T., "Statistical Thermodynamics of Rubber I," *J. Chem. Phys.*, **10**, 132 (1942); Part II, *ibid.*, **10**, 485 (1942); Part III, *ibid.*, **11**, 527–530 (1943).

(*89*) Weichert, E., "Gesetze der elastischen Nachwirkung für constante Temperatur," *Ann. Physik Chem.*, **50**, 335 (1893).

(*90*) Wiegand, W. B., "Tendencies in Rubber Compounding," *Trans. Inst. Rubber Ind.*, **1**, 141–170 (1926).

(*91*) Wiegand, W. B., and Snyder, J. W., "The Rubber Pendulum, the Joule Effect and the Dynamic Stress-Strain Curve," *ibid.*, **10**, 234–262 (1934).

(*92*) Wildschut, A. J., "The Stress-Strain Relation of Natural and Synthetic Rubbers," *Rubber Chem. Tech.*, **17**, 826 (1944).

(*93*) Wiley, F. E., "Transition Temperature and Cubical Expansion of Plastic Materials," *Ind. Eng. Chem.*, **34**, 1052–1056 (1942).

(*94*) Wood, L. A., Bekkedahl, N., and Roth, F. L., "Density Measurements on Synthetic Rubbers," *ibid.*, **34**, 1291 (1942).

(*95*) Wood, L. A., and Roth, F. L., "Stress-Temperature Relations in a Pure-Gum Vulcanizate of Natural Rubber," *J. Applied Phys.*, **15**, 781 (1944).

(*96*) Zapp, R. L., and Gessler, A. M., "Processing Behavior of High Polymers—Correlation with Elastic-Plastic Properties," *Ind. Eng. Chem.*, **36**, 656 (1944).

C. THREE-DIMENSIONAL CROSS-LINKED POLYMERS

I. INTRODUCTION

While the amorphous linear polymers constitute an important class of materials, the group of three-dimensional cross-linked polymers is perhaps even more important. The former includes the soluble, "fusible" polymers and corresponds roughly to the (noncrystalline) thermoplastic molding materials and unvulcanized rubbers. The latter includes the insoluble polymers and corresponds roughly to the thermosetting resins and vulcanized rubbers. (Textile fibers, in the main, do not fit into either of these classes but usually exhibit very definite crystallinity, as do some thermoplastic molding materials.)

Some of the grosser mechanical effects of cross linking are obvious. For example, it is clear that a highly cross-linked polymer cannot flow, even at a high temperature (unless, of course, primary valence bonds are actually broken). It might appear that a detailed discussion of the viscoelastic properties of a cross-linked polymer would be much more involved than a similar discussion for a linear polymer. This is not necessarily true, however. In certain respects, a cross-linked polymer may even be said to possess simpler viscoelastic properties than a linear polymer. The configurational elastic response of a linear polymer necessarily involves a wide distribution of retardation times, since the kinkiness and orientation of molecular sections of all lengths are concerned. In a cross-linked polymer, the viscoelastic spectrum may well be cut off rather sharply, since the configurational response to stress is predominantly that of the chain sections which connect the mesh points and of subparts of these. Longer chain sections, which actually include branch points, are no longer free to undergo independent micro-Brownian motion. As the temperature is raised, the retarded elastic response of a linear polymer is gradually dominated by flow; the retarded elastic response of a cross-linked polymer simply becomes less retarded, without the appearance of flow.

For this reason, the plastoelastic behavior of a cross-linked polymer should actually be simpler, in certain temperature ranges at least, than that of a linear polymer. This is certainly true in the case of rubber. Slightly vulcanized rubber at room temperature exhibits virtually unretarded configurational elasticity, while flow does not occur. Unvulcanized rubber does not exhibit such a behavior at any temperature. If the temperature is lowered far enough to prevent flow effectively, the configurational elasticity will be markedly retarded. The amplitude of the steady state variation in γ which results from a sinusoidal stress of frequency $\omega/2\pi$ and amplitude unity can be resolved into a component which is in phase with the stress and an out-of-phase component. The in-phase component corresponds to elastic deformation, the out-of-phase to viscous effects. (See chapter B, pages 189–193.) At high frequency (short ⓣ), the response is completely elastic but small. At such high frequencies only the instantaneous elastic response enters. At lower frequencies, the response becomes greater and greater. Finally, at extremely low frequencies, the in-phase, or elastic, response reaches a constant amplitude, while the out-of-phase response increases without limit, due to the occurrence of true flow. With a three-dimensional polymer the situation is different. At the low frequency end, where the in-phase component has reached a constant value, the out-of-phase component becomes zero. This occurs because there is no true flow; any out-of-phase deformation must arise only from the *retardation* to the configurational elasticity. In the range of experimental timescale represented by this region of the curves, the three-dimensional polymer manifestly exhibits a simpler behavior than the linear polymer.

The qualitative truth of the preceding remarks is evident enough. If we wish to discuss in a more quantitative fashion the viscoelastic behavior of three-dimensional polymers, it is necessary to be more specific in our definition of their structures. Such polymers will be divided into six classes, as follows:

(1) Loose regular networks, containing material of low molecular weight.

(2) Loose regular networks, containing linear polymer molecules.

(3) Loose irregular networks, containing material of low molecular weight.

(4) Loose irregular networks, containing linear polymer molecules.

(5) Tight, regular networks.

(6) Tight, irregular networks.

The viscoelastic properties of cross-linked polymers of each of these classes are discussed in section II (see pages 236–268) on the basis of their structures. Thereafter, in section III (see pages 268–304), the *formation* of three-dimensional polymers is discussed. The products formed at different stages of various polymerization, polycondensation, and cross-linking reactions are assigned to one or the other of these six classes of structure. This latter is actually a problem in the chemical kinetics of high polymers. In Chapter B, the chemical structures of high polymers are taken as a starting point, and the general nature of the viscoelastic behavior is deduced therefrom without considering the chemical question of how these structures were formed. This is possible because of the excellent surveys of these reactions which are available. In the field of three-dimensional polymers, there are few discussions of a chemical nature which describe the structures formed, in terms which are easily adaptable to a discussion of the mechanical behavior. Only a few isolated papers, notably those of Flory (*16*) and Stockmayer (*40*) present anything like a quantitative analysis of the structures formed by a given type of reaction. It therefore seems to the author that the inclusion of section III (pages 268–304) is necessary, even though it represents a departure from the subject of mechanical behavior.

II. MECHANICAL BEHAVIOR OF IDEALIZED NETWORK TYPES

1. Loose Regular Networks Containing Material of Low Molecular Weight

A. Equilibrium Behavior

Consider an idealized network of the following type: a series of mesh points are connected by linear chains, as shown in figure 85. Each linear chain contains n chain atoms, and each mesh point is a six-fold junction. This netlike structure is filled with a low molecular weight solvent. Let q represent the fraction of the total volume which is occupied by the solvent. The term "loose" implies that n, the number of chain atoms between two adjacent mesh points, is large.

It is clear that the behavior of such a network depends upon the values of the two parameters n and q. For a given network n is fixed, but q can be varied by forcing more solvent into the structure or drawing solvent out, *i.e.*, by changing the degree of swelling of the polymer. A change in q results in an isotropic expansion or contraction of the net structure. When the polymer is placed in contact with a reservoir containing solvent at an activity a, q assumes a definite equilibrium value.

Let us now consider the equilibrium elastic deformation of such a network under the action of a tensile stress in the x direction. Following the example of Kuhn (*29*) and Wall (*46*), let us assume that during the deformation the mesh points change their relative spacings in the same ratio as the external dimensions are changed. If a tensile strain γ results, two adjacent mesh points which were originally separated by a distance x will be separated by the distance $(1 + \gamma)x$. A separation y or z will be changed to $(1 - \nu\gamma)y$ or $(1 - \nu\gamma)z$, respectively. For a constant volume change, $\nu = 0.5$ and $y' = (1 - \gamma/2)y$, $z' = (1 - \gamma/2)z$. Now the probabilities for a separation x, y, and z, respectively, are given by:

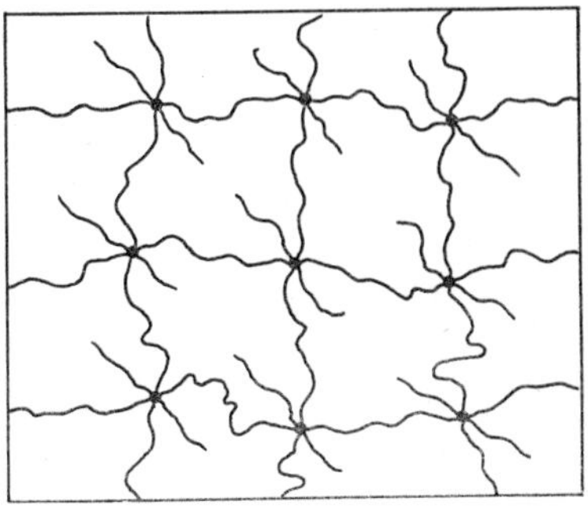

Fig. 85. Schematic representation of an idealized "regular network" polymer.

$$p(x)\,dx = \frac{\beta^2}{\pi^{3/2}}\,e^{-\beta^2 x^2}\,dx \tag{1a}$$

$$p(y)\,dy = \frac{\beta^2}{\pi^{3/2}}\,e^{-\beta^2 y^2}\,dy \tag{1b}$$

$$p(z)\,dz = \frac{\beta^2}{\pi^{3/2}}\,e^{-\beta^2 z^2}\,dz \tag{1c}$$

where

$$\beta^2 = \left(\frac{3}{2\,nl_0^2}\right)\frac{(1 - \cos\theta)}{(1 + \cos\theta)}$$

The probabilities for the new separations x', y', and z' are given by:

$$p(x')\,dx' = \frac{\beta^2}{\pi^{3/2}}\,e^{-\beta^2(1+\gamma)^2x^2}(1 + \gamma)\,dx \tag{2a}$$

$$p(y')\,dy' = \frac{\beta^2}{\pi^{3/2}}\,e^{-\beta^2(1-\gamma/2)^2y^2}\left(1 - \frac{\gamma}{2}\right)dy \tag{2b}$$

$$p(z')\,dz' = \frac{\beta^2}{\pi^{3/2}}\,e^{-\beta^2(1-\gamma/2)^2z^2}\left(1 - \frac{\gamma}{2}\right)dz \tag{2c}$$

Let us now assume that all pairs of adjacent branch points are originally separated by the same distance σ. Thus one-third of the linear chains connect branch points that are separated by $x = \sigma$, one-third points separated by $y = \sigma$, and one-third points separated by $z = \sigma$. It is clear that σ is related to the degree of swelling by the expression:

$$N\sigma^3 = V = Nv_0\left(\frac{1}{1-q}\right) \tag{3}$$

$$\sigma^3 = v_0\left(\frac{1}{1-q}\right) \tag{4}$$

where v_0 represents the actual volume occupied by one linear connecting chain, and N is the number of such chains. The relative probability of the strained configuration, γ, relative to the original unstrained configuration, is given by the expression:

$$\begin{aligned}\ln\frac{P'}{P} = \frac{N}{3}\ln(1+\gamma) + \frac{2\,N}{3}\ln\left(1-\frac{\gamma}{2}\right) - \frac{N\beta^2}{3}(1+\gamma)^2\sigma^2 \\ - 2\beta^2\left(1-\frac{\gamma}{2}\right)\sigma^2\frac{N}{3} + 3\beta^2\sigma^2\frac{N}{3} = \frac{N}{3}\ln(1+\gamma) \\ + \frac{2\,N}{3}\ln\left(1-\frac{\gamma}{2}\right) - \frac{3}{2}\gamma^2\sigma^2\left(\frac{N}{3}\right)\beta^2\end{aligned} \tag{5}$$

Expanding the logarithmic terms as a power series and taking only the first nonzero term, we obtain:

$$\ln\frac{P'}{P} = \frac{N}{3}\gamma^2 - \frac{N}{2}\beta^2\sigma^2\gamma^2 = \gamma^2 N\left[\frac{1}{3} - \frac{\beta^2\sigma^2}{2}\right] \tag{6}$$

The entropy change on extension is hence given by:

$$\mathbf{S}' - \mathbf{S} = k\gamma^2 N\left[\frac{1}{3} - \frac{\beta^2\sigma^2}{2}\right] \tag{7}$$

Finally, the tensile force is given by:

$$F = -\frac{T\,\partial\mathbf{S}}{\partial\gamma} = NkT\left[\beta^2\sigma^2 - \frac{2}{3}\right]\gamma \tag{8}$$

The stress, s_x, is given by F/A, or

$$s_x = N_1kT\left(\beta^2\sigma^2 - \frac{2}{3}\right)\gamma \tag{9}$$

where N_1 is the number of chains per cubic centimeter. If D is the density of the polymer,

$$v_0 = M/N_{av} \cdot 1/D \tag{10}$$

$$s_x = (1 - q)\frac{D}{M}RT\left(\beta^2\sigma^2 - \frac{2}{3}\right)\gamma \tag{11}$$

If $\beta^2\sigma^2 \gg 2/3$, then

$$\sigma^2 = v_0^{2/3}(1 - q)^{-2/3} \tag{12}$$

$$s_x = (1 - q)^{1/3}BT\gamma \tag{13}$$

where B is a constant. This would indicate that, if the degree of swelling, as measured by q, is increased, the Young's modulus of the network will be somewhat decreased. The dilution effect will tend to make the modulus proportional to $(1 - q)$, since in the more highly swollen conditions there are fewer chains per unit area to bear the stress. On the other hand, the increased swelling itself stretches the chains and makes further deformation of a single chain more difficult. This second effect, however, is not sufficient to balance completely the first.

In the above discussion it was assumed that, during the deformation, q (and therefore the volume) remained constant. After the deformation, however, the swollen gel is no longer in osmotic equilibrium with the reservoir of solvent at the activity a. If the ends are constrained so that the x elongation remains fixed, more solvent will enter the network, causing the lateral contractions to disappear. According to the above set of equations [Eqs. (9) through (13)], this secondary lateral expansion will reduce the force necessary to hold the sample in its elongated form to two-thirds of its original value. If γ is small, then the increase in q is small and the secondary dilution effect on the *cross-sectional area* may be neglected. Thus the *stress* as well as the total force is reduced by the additional swelling to two-thirds of the value given by equation (8). If in the beginning we had replaced the assumption of constant degree of swelling by the assumption that the swollen polymer remained in osmotic equilibrium with the solvent reservoir, we would have obtained this result directly. This means that a swollen polymer network, which is initially at equilibrium with a solvent reservoir, can exhibit two distinctly different forms of isothermal stress–strain behavior in tension:

(1) If stretched rapidly, so that osmosis cannot change the degree of swelling, a modulus $(1 - q)BT$ and a Poisson's ratio of 0.5 are observed.

(2) If stretched slowly, so that osmotic equilibrium can be maintained, a modulus of $^2/_3\,(1 - q)BT$ and a Poisson's ratio of 0.5 are observed.

In the same way, it can be shown that a pure shear stress will cause a shear strain, governed in magnitude by a shear modulus equal to $^1/_3\,(1 - q)BT$. After the strain, the network is still in osmotic equilibrium with the solvent reservoir; there is no secondary change in q. In other words, for pure shear the assumption of constant q and the assumption of constant solvent activity lead to the same stress–strain behavior.

The entire treatment presented above is, of course, extremely crude. It is analogous to a treatment of velocity distribution in a gas which assumes that one-third of the molecules are moving parallel to the x axis, one-third parallel to the y axis, and one-third parallel to the z axis—all at the same speed. Fortunately, more refined treatments exist in the case in which $q = 0$, *i.e.*, where only the polymer network itself is present; or where q is a constant.*

Kuhn (*29*) first extended the treatment of Guth and Mark to the case of a three-dimensional network. He implicitly assumed a network structure in which all linear connecting chains were made up of n chain atoms. He further assumed that in the unstrained state the distribution of distances between chain ends was given by the probability distribution function $p(x,y,z)$:

$$\mathrm{D}_0(x,y,z)dx\,dy\,dz = {}^N p(x,y,z)dx\,dy\,dz = \frac{\beta^3 N}{\pi^{3/2}}\,\mathrm{e}^{-\beta^2(x^2+y^2+z^2)}dx\,dy\,dz \quad (14)$$

Kuhn then introduced the concept of the entropy of a single chain, which was a function of x, y, and z, derived from the above probability function:

$$\mathrm{S}(x,y,z) = k \ln p(x,y,z) = \mathrm{C}_1 - k\beta^2(x^2 + y^2 + z^2) \quad (15)$$

The total configurational entropy of the sample in the unstrained state is given by the integral (16).

$$\mathrm{S}_0 = \int_{-\infty}^{\infty}\int_{-\infty}^{\infty}\int_{-\infty}^{\infty} \mathrm{S}(x,y,z)\mathrm{D}_0(x,y,z)dx\,dy\,dz$$

$$= \iiint [\mathrm{C}_1 - k\beta^2(x^2 + y^2 + z^2)]\,\frac{N\beta^3}{\pi^{3/2}}\,\mathrm{e}^{-\beta^2(x^2+y^2+z^2)}dx\,dy\,dz \quad (16)$$

The assumption was now made that in the strained state the separations of chain ends are changed in the same ratio as the macroscopic dimen-

* *Note added in proof:* Flory has since presented a treatment of the elasticity of swollen network polymers which is considerably superior to the above treatment.

sions. Thus for a tensile strain γ, where the volume remains constant:

$$x' = (1 + \gamma)x \tag{17a}$$

$$y' = \left(\frac{1}{1+\gamma}\right)^{1/2} y \tag{17b}$$

$$z' = \left(\frac{1}{1+\gamma}\right)^{1/2} z \tag{17c}$$

Here x', y', and z' are the separations in the strained state of two chain ends which were separated in the unstrained state by x, y, and z. The new distribution of separations, $D'(x,y,z)$ becomes:

$$D'(x,y,z)dx\,dy\,dz = \frac{N\beta^3}{\pi^{3/2}} e^{-\beta^2\left[\frac{x^2}{(1+\gamma)^2}+(1+\gamma)(y^2+z^2)\right]} dx\,dy\,dz \tag{18}$$

The entropy in the strained state is given by:

$$S' = \iiint S(x,y,z)\, D'(x,y,z)dx\,dy\,dz \tag{19}$$

or

$$S' = \iiint [C_1 - k\beta^2(x^2 + y^2 + z^2)] \times e^{-\beta^2\left[\frac{x^2}{(1+\gamma)^2}+(1+\gamma)(y^2+z^2)\right]} dx\,dy\,dz \tag{20}$$

Upon performing the integrations (16) and (20), and introducing an approximation, Kuhn arrived at the relation:

$$S' - S_0 = -\frac{3}{2} Nk\gamma^2 \tag{21}$$

Kuhn did not consider equation (21) to represent the entire entropy change upon extension. He felt that this relation merely took care of the increase in length and that the decrease in lateral dimensions must be considered as well. He therefore derived additional entropy terms associated with the lateral contractions. Treloar (*44*) has shown, however, that equation (21) has already accounted for the entropy changes resulting from the lateral contraction:

"On Kuhn's basis the entropy is reduced on extension because the number of possible configurations is reduced. In stating the probability in terms of x he includes all possible configurations, and therefore all possible values of y and z. The y and z values cannot be considered to have an existence independently of x, and to attribute a separate entropy to them is incorrect."

Using equation (21), rather than Kuhn's reported "total" entropy change ($^7/_2\, Nk\gamma^2$), the Young's modulus becomes 3 NkT.

Wall (*46*) has presented a treatment which starts from the same basic assumptions as those of Kuhn. Instead of introducing the concept of a molecular entropy, he solves the following problem in probabilities. What is the probability P that a system of N chains will possess a separation distribution D(x,y,z) if the probability function for the separations of the ends of a single chain is $p(x,y,z)$? Instead of defining the strain in terms of γ, $(l - l_0/l_0)$, Wall uses the ratio α, equal to (l/l_0). Hence the new distribution function D′(x,y,z) is written as:

$$D'(x,y,z)dx\,dy\,dz = N\frac{\beta^3}{\pi^{3/2}}e^{-\beta^2\left[\frac{x^2}{\alpha^2}+\alpha(y^2+z^2)\right]}dx\,dy\,dz \qquad (22)$$

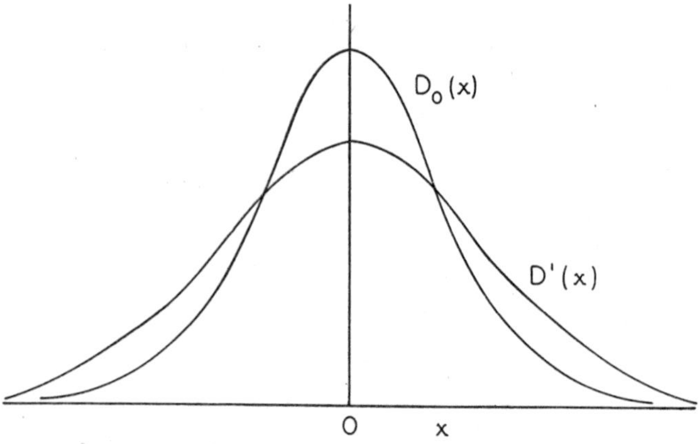

Fig. 86. Equilibrium distribution of mesh-point separations in the unstressed and stressed state.

See figure 86 for a one-dimensional plot of this function. Wall finds that P′, the probability of the distribution (22), is related to P_0, the probability of the most probable distribution, by the expression:

$$\ln\frac{P'}{P_0} = -\frac{N_0}{2}\left(\alpha^2 + \frac{2}{\alpha} - 3\right) \qquad (23)$$

Only now is the concept of entropy introduced:

$$S' - S_0 = k\ln\frac{P}{P_0} = -\frac{1}{2}N_0k\left(\alpha^2 + \frac{2}{\alpha} - 3\right) \qquad (24)$$

This leads to a stress–strain relation of the form:

$$F = NkT\left(\alpha - \frac{1}{\alpha^2}\right) = \rho\frac{RT}{M}\left(\alpha - \frac{1}{\alpha^2}\right) \tag{25}$$

This equation applies to a unidirectional compression as well as an elongation. While equation (25) agrees with Kuhn's result for small deformations, it is apparent that for larger deformations Wall's equation predicts a nonlinear stress–strain relation. Wall carried out a similar treatment for shear strain, and arrived at the conclusion that deformation in *shear* should obey Hooke's law, even though not in extension. Wall derives the value NkT for the shear modulus, and indeed the theory of elasticity demands this value if the Young's modulus is 3 NkT and the polymer is incompressible.

Treloar (*44, 45*) has presented a critical review of the theories of Kuhn and Wall. He points out that an *exact* evaluation of Kuhn's entropy integrals yields an expression for the entropy of elongation which is identical with that of Wall. The difference between the two reported results lies in the fact that Kuhn introduced the approximation:

$$\frac{1}{1+\gamma} = 1 - \gamma + \gamma^2 \tag{26}$$

which is valid for small γ. Treloar also shows that Kuhn's method can be applied to the problem of *shear* deformation, resulting in the same answer obtained by Wall. Treloar concludes:

> The more accurate application of Kuhn's method thus leads to the same stress–strain relations as those derived by Wall. The two methods may be considered to be equivalent mathematically, since they differ only in the particular stage of the argument at which the conception of the entropy is introduced. Wall considered only the entropy to be associated with the whole assembly of molecules; Kuhn, on the other hand, considered that an entropy could be associated with the individual molecule. Wall's treatment must be considered the more satisfactory because it avoids the difficulties encountered in attempting to assign a physical meaning to the entropy of a single molecule.

B. The Tetrahedral Model for the Network Structure of Rubber

Flory and Rehner (*16a*) have developed a very similar theory, which Flory (*15*) has described in simple terms:

> An alternative procedure for statistical treatment of rubber network deformations can be carried out in terms of an average "cell" of the network. Instead of considering the chains as individual elements, the four chains meeting at a junction are considered mutually. The four chains radiating from each junction lead to four "nearest neighbor"

junctions, the average positions of which define a tetrahedron. One such tetrahedron is defined by the points A, B, C, and D in figure 87, considered in three dimensions. If we idealize the network to the extent of making all chains of the same size (same contour length), then the average tetrahedron, or "cell," so defined will be a regular tetrahedron. It should be made clear at the outset that owing to the intertwining of the chains, these tetrahedral cells will overlap extensively, a given element of the volume being

Fig. 87. Schematic diagram of a section of a cross-linked polymer.

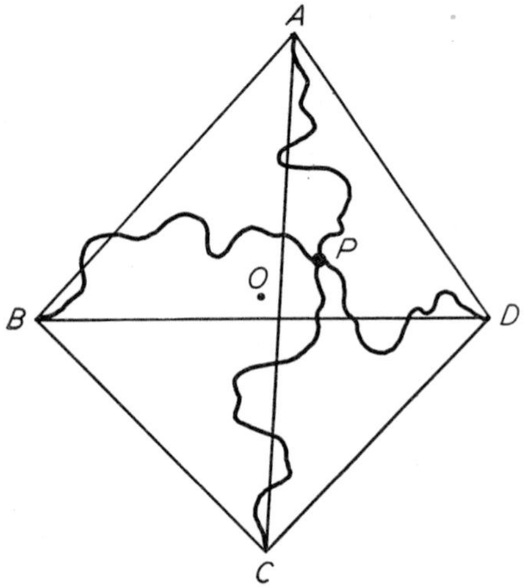

Fig. 88. Tetrahedral model for rubberlike elasticity.

encompassed by many of these elementary tetrahedra. These cells do not adjoin one another with the regularity and volume-filling character of the unit cells of a diamond lattice, for example.

The tetrahedral cell is represented diagrammatically in figure 88. The existence of this cell as a unit of the network structure rests entirely upon the requirement that four chains extending from the corners (A, B, C, and D) shall meet within a volume element $\Delta\tau$ at some point P. The relative number of configurations available to the system of four chains which meet within a particular volume element $\Delta\tau$ is given by the product of four "probabilities" for the individual chains

$$P(\Delta\tau)^4 = \prod_{i=1}^{4} [W(x_i y_i z_i)\Delta\tau_i] \tag{27}$$

where x_i, y_i, z_i, *etc.*, are the coordinates of the same volume element $\Delta\tau$ referred, respectively, to the four corners of the tetrahedron A, B, C, and D. Substituting from equation (1) and integrating over the space in order to obtain the relative number of configurations when the chains meet in the same volume element located any place:

$$P(\Delta\tau)^3 = (\beta^{12}/\pi^6)\left[\int_\tau \exp\,(-\beta^2 \sum_{i=1}^{4} r_i^2)\Delta\tau\right](\Delta\tau)^3 \tag{28}$$

It can be shown from the geometry of the tetrahedron that

$$\sum_{i=1}^{4} r_i^2 = 4a^2 + 4\lambda^2(\alpha^2 + 2/\alpha)/3 \tag{29}$$

where a is the radial distance of P from the center O of the tetrahedron, λ is the distance from O to one of the corners of the undeformed tetrahedron, and α is the relative elongation of the tetrahedron resulting from deformation of the piece of rubber without change in volume. The average tetrahedron is assumed to be deformed in proportion to the changes in macroscopic dimensions. Substituting in equation (28),

$$P = (4\beta^{12}/\pi^5) \int_0^\infty \exp\left[-4\beta^2a^2 - 4\beta^2\lambda^2(\alpha^2 + 2/\alpha)/3\right]a^2\,da \tag{30}$$

The relative configurational probability for the stretched and normal states is obtained by dividing P(α) by P (1). Dividing equation (30) by its value for $\alpha = 1$, the relative configurational probability of the stretched rubber becomes

$$P(\alpha)/P(1) = \exp\left[-4\beta^2\lambda^2\left(\alpha^2 + \frac{2}{\alpha} - 3\right)\Big/ 3\right] \tag{31}$$

The distance λ from the center to a corner of the undeformed tetrahedron may be taken equal to the root mean square chain displacement length (r) which, according to equation (1), is equal to $\sqrt{3/2\beta^2}$. Then, taking the logarithm of equation (31) and multiplying by Boltzmann's constant, the entropy of deformation becomes

$$\Delta S = -2\,k[\alpha^2 + (2/\alpha) - 3] \tag{32}$$

for the tetrahedral cell. Since each cell contains four chains, multiplication by $\nu/4$ should give the entropy change for the network as a whole. The result is identical with Wall's equation (24), from which the elasticity equations (25) and (95′) are derived by standard procedures of thermodynamics . . .

It is significant that the form of the dependence on α (*i.e.*, $\phi(\alpha)$) is unaffected by the degree of cross linking. Stress–strain curves for different degrees of vulcanization, therefore, should be superimposable by altering the stress scale by suitable factors. This prediction finds verification for natural rubber and Butyl rubber vulcanizates differing in degrees of cure. Hence a single quantity, the stress at a given elongation, will suffice to characterize the stress–strain curve as a function of the degree of vulcanization, except at higher elongations where crystallization sets in.

One final remark should be made concerning these theoretical treatments. In a rigorous treatment, the assumption that the microscopic separations of branch points change during strain by the same ratio as the macroscopic dimensions is open to criticism. The proper procedure would seem to be the following: Consider that in the unstrained sample the distribution of separations, $D_0(x,y,z)dx\,dy\,dz$, is given by the probability function $p(x,y,z)dx\,dy\,dz$. When the sample is strained, a new distribution $D'(x,y,z)dx\,dy\,dz$ is established. This new distribution is the most probable distribution which can be formed subject to the constraint that the *mean values* of x, y, and z, respectively, change from the original

M_x, M_y, M_z, to new values M'_x, M'_y, M'_z, defined by the relations:

$$M'_x = M_x(1 + \gamma) \quad (33a)$$
$$M'_y = M_y(1 - \gamma/2) \quad (33b)$$
$$M'_z = M_z(1 - \gamma/2) \quad (33c)$$

Determine this most probable distribution, subject to equation (33), and then assess the relative probability of the distribution $D'(x,y,z)dx\,dy\,dz$, compared with the original $D_0(x,y,z)dx\,dy\,dz$. It seems reasonable that $D'(x,y,z)$ should be similar in nature to Wall's expression:

$$D'(x,y,z) = -\ e^{\beta[\alpha^2x^2+(1/\alpha^2)(y^2+z^2)]} \quad (34)$$

That this should be exactly true is not physically obvious.

The very use of a statistical analysis, with an evaluation of the "entropy change" upon deformation, must be based upon the implicit assumption that each individual connecting chain is free to wander through the descriptive phase space. In other words, even in the unstrained state the separation x,y,z, of the two ends of a given chain is not a fixed vector, but is constantly changing with time. Only the *distribution* of separations remains sharply fixed. Hence it is meaningless to say that upon deformation a fixed separation x,y,z, changes to a fixed separation x',y',z'. It might be preferable to introduce simply the assumption that the *distribution* $D_0(x,y,z)$ changes to the *distribution* $D(x,y,z)$ when the macroscopic deformation α is imposed, rather than to "derive" this basic expression from the assumption as phrased in both Kuhn's and Wall's treatments.

This is not a very serious objection as far as the final results of the treatment are concerned. In fact, the author feels that the present status of this problem is more completely satisfactory than that of any other in the field of the mechanical behavior of high polymers. It can certainly be said that the theories described above succeed admirably in their purpose of providing a rational explanation, on the basis of fundamental physical principles, of the observed equilibrium elastic behavior of loose polymer networks.

C. Theory of Guth and James

The foregoing discussion of the theory of long range elasticity in cross-linked polymers was based on a line of development which began with Guth and Mark, was extended by Kuhn, and most recently has been elaborated by Wall, Treloar, and Flory. A somewhat different treatment of the subject has been furnished in a series of excellent papers by Guth and James, the first of which appeared in 1941 (*18*, *24*, *25*).

In many respects the theory of Guth and James is superior to all previous theories of elasticity in polymer networks:

(1) These authors have extended the theory to cover large deformations, where the polymer chains are stretched nearly to their maximum length.

(2) The mathematical methods introduced to treat the case of large deformations have certain advantages which appear promising for use in further extensions of the theory.

(3) Guth and James have objectified their theoretical conclusions by an intensive comparison with experimental data on a large number of elastomers.

Besides the above, the Guth-James approach has two other possible advantages, the significance of which seem less certain:

(1) These investigators have included the effects of thermal expansion in their equations which relate elongation with stress.

(2) They claim that other treatments of the subject involve fundamental errors of reasoning which are absent in their treatment.

The inclusion of thermal expansion in the stress–strain relation makes this relation somewhat more general, but the writer suspects that the added generality does not justify the loss in simplicity. Guth and James refer the length of a specimen to the unstrained length *at a definite reference temperature.* This means that the quantity L/L_0 is not in general equal to zero even in the absence of a stress. The writer prefers to refer the length of the specimen to the unstressed length at the same temperature, recognizing that this reference length is itself a function of temperature because of thermal expansion. This results in a dissociation of shear effects from volumetric effects. The method of Guth and James does offer some advantages if one considers *adiabatic* changes, however, and there is one problem which presumably can be treated only by the use of their method. This is the extension of the theory of elasticity to the case where temperature gradients exist in the distorted object.

Concerning the second point, Guth and James have specifically objected to the statistical approach of Wall, stating that this approach gives the correct answer for small deformations for reasons which are largely fortuitous. (The results of the small strain theory of Guth and James are of exactly the same form as those of Wall.) It must be admitted that if these objections are correct, the line of development chosen by the writer in this chapter is not the best that could have been chosen. However, the writer feels that, as far as the region of small strains is concerned, the theory of Wall and that of Guth and James are essentially the same. For our purposes, at least, the important advantages of the treatment of Guth and James lie in the fact that it goes beyond previous theories and leads the way to still further extensions, rather than in the theoretical status of the treatment as compared with that of Wall. With this in mind, the writer has chosen the line of development which seemed to him most informative; the theory of Wall has been presented as a prototype of the small strain approximations and the large strain theory of Guth and James is presented as a furthergoing theoretical development. We quote from their paper *(25a)*:

Now it is obvious that the results of [previous sections] can be valid only when the extensions of the chains in the molecular network are not too large compared with their total length, since only in this case can the assumed Gaussian configuration distribution be an adequate approximation. The Gaussian distribution assigns a non-zero probability to any extension of the chain, however great, whereas the actual function for any finite chain must become zero as soon as L exceeds the total length of the chain. As L approaches this limit the true distribution function must fall toward zero faster than the Gaussian function. Then $-\log C(L)$ must increase more rapidly than quadratically, and $Z(L)$ for a single chain must increase more rapidly than linearly, becoming infinite as L approaches L_{max}. This deviation from the linear stress–strain relation will make itself felt when bulk rubber is subjected to large strains; the effect will be the introduction of an upward curvature into the stress–strain curve, the stress increasing indefinitely as the stretched length approaches the finite maximum extension of the network. It is thus evident that with a more careful treatment of the stress–strain relation in molecular chains our model will show an upward curvature in the stress–strain curve similar to that shown in the experimental curve . . . but lacking in the theoretical results of the present section. (The observed upward curvature is not to be explained entirely as due to crystallization effects, as it is evident even for strains insufficient to induce crystallization, or when this is suppressed by swelling.)

We turn, then, to a consideration of the stress–strain relation in a flexible thermally agitated chain when its extension is comparable to its total length.

In applying the equation

$$Z = -kTd[\log C(L,N)]/dL \tag{35}$$

to the computation of the stress–strain relation for a flexible chain under thermal agitation, one is, essentially, considering the chain to have a fixed extension and computing the average force exerted by it. That is, one determines

$$Z = \overline{Z}(L) \tag{36}$$

An alternative approach which offers marked advantages for our problem is that of considering the chain with constant forces exerted on its ends and computing the average extension:

$$L = \bar{L}(Z) \tag{37}$$

For chains of few links, the instantaneous value of L may differ markedly from $\bar{L}$, and the same is true for Z and $\bar{Z}$. Under these circumstances, equations (36) and (37) are by no means converse relations; only in the limit of very long chains will the methods lead to essentially identical results. The advantage of the approach through equation (37) will be made evident by the example at the end of the present section.

We consider first a one-dimensional chain. If a constant force Z be applied to the ends of the chain there will be a potential energy $-ZL$ associated with the extension L. Let the number of configurations available to the chain when its extension is L to within dL be

$$dC = C(L)dL \tag{38}$$

The probability that the chain acted on by the force Z will have the extension L to within dL will then be proportional to

$$dP = e^{+ZL/kT}dC = C(L)e^{+/ZLkT}dL \tag{39}$$

Let

$$f = Z/kT \tag{40}$$

Then

$$\bar{L}(f) = \int LC(L)e^{fL}dL \Big/ \int C(L)e^{fL}dL \tag{41}$$

or

$$\bar{L}(f) = d\left[\log \int C(L)e^{fL}dL\right] \Big/ df \tag{42}$$

If L can take on only discrete values we have, instead,

$$\bar{L} = d[\log \Sigma_L C(L)e^{fL}]/df \tag{43}$$

Let G(x) be the generating function for C(L). That is, for the continuous case

$$G(x) = \int C(L)x^L dL \tag{44}$$

and for the discrete case

$$G(x) = \Sigma_L C(L)x^L \tag{45}$$

Then in either case *

$$\bar{L} = d[\log G(e^f)]/df \tag{46}$$

Often the most convenient method of determining C(L) is by use of the generating function. Equation (46) offers a method of passing from G(x) directly to a relation of the form (37), thus obviating the necessity of determining C(L) and applying (35) to obtain a relation of the form (36).

Another point of view is often useful. We have

$$\langle e^{fL}\rangle_{av} = \int e^{fL}C(L)\,dL \Big/ \int C(L)\,dL \tag{47}$$

Thus

$$\bar{L} = d(\log \langle e^{fL}\rangle_{av})/df \tag{48}$$

As a third approach, we expand the exponential in the integrand, equation (47).

* The discrete case can be formally unified with the continuous case by taking the integrals in the Stieltjes sense.

Then

$$\langle e^{fL}\rangle_{av} = \Sigma_\tau f^\tau/\tau! \int L^\tau C(L)\, dL \Big/ \int C(L)\, dL \tag{49}$$

Let

$$\langle L^\tau\rangle_{av} = \int L^\tau C(L)\, dL \Big/ \int C(L)\, dL \tag{50}$$

the average of L^τ in the force-free case. Using these relations, (48) becomes

$$L = d[\log \Sigma_\tau \langle L^\tau\rangle_{av} f^\tau/\tau!]/df \tag{51}$$

It is instructive to relate the statistical treatments of flexible chains at constant extension, $Z = \bar{Z}(L,T)$, and at constant stress, $L = \bar{L}(Z,T)$, with the corresponding thermodynamic approaches to the problem.

When temperature and extension are chosen as independent variables in the treatment of a thermodynamic system it is natural to introduce the Helmholtz free energy function $\mathbf{F}(L,T)$ and to determine stress from this:

$$Z = (\partial \mathbf{F}/\partial L)_T \tag{52}$$

As we have already noted, the free energy is related to the number of configurations accessible to the system, $C(L)$. ($C(L)$ is the partition function.)

$$\mathbf{F}(L,T) = -KT \log C(L) \tag{53}$$

Thus equation (35) is simply the statistical form of (52).

Now if temperature and stress are chosen as independent variables in treating a thermodynamic system, one introduces the Gibbs function, which, for our system, becomes

$$\mathfrak{G}(Z,T) = U - ZL - TS \tag{54}$$

From this one determines the extension of the system,

$$L = -(\partial \mathfrak{G}/\partial Z)_T \tag{55}$$

Statistically the Gibbs function is related to the sum over all accessible states of the statistical assembly, weighted with the factor $e^{ZL/kT}$. In analogy to (53) we have

$$\mathfrak{G}(Z,T) = -kT \log D(Z) \tag{56}$$

where $D(Z)$ is a generalized partition function

$$D(Z) = \int C(L) e^{ZL/kT} dL \tag{57}$$

which is essentially the Laplace transform of the partition function $C(L)$. Since from (44) we have

$$D(Z) = G(e^{Z/kT}) = G(e^f) \tag{58}$$

it is evident that (46) is the statistical version of the thermodynamic relation (55).

That $Z = Z(\bar{L})$ and $L = \bar{L}(Z)$ are converse relations only in the limit of very long chains becomes, in thermodynamic terms, the statement that only in this limit does there exist an equation of state

$$Z = Z(L,T) \qquad \text{or} \qquad L = L(Z,T)$$

describing the system.

Depending on the circumstances, each of (46), (48), and (51) may serve as useful alternatives to (35).

The extension of these results to the case of a chain in three dimensions involves no difficulty. Let one end of the chain be fixed at the origin. Then the number of configurations of the chain for which its free end will lie in the infinitesimal volume dV will be

$$dC = C(x,y,z)dV \tag{59}$$

If there is no preferred orientation of the system C will be a function of $x^2 + y^2 + z^2$ only.

Let a constant force of components Z_x, Z_y, Z_z be applied to the free end of the chain. Then the probability of finding the end of the chain in volume dV will be proportional to

$$dP = \exp\{(xZ_x + yZ_y + zZ_z)/kT\}C(x,y,z)dV \tag{60}$$

As before, letting

$$\begin{aligned} f_x &= Z_x/kT \\ f_y &= Z_y/kT, \text{ etc.} \end{aligned} \tag{61}$$

one has

$$\bar{x} = \frac{\partial}{\partial f_x} \log \int e^{(xf_x+yf_y+zf_z)}C(x,y,z)dV \tag{62}$$

$$\bar{y} = \frac{\partial}{\partial f_y} \log \int e^{(xf_x+yf_y+zf_z)}C(x,y,z)dV \tag{63}$$

Ordinarily there will be no preferred orientation of the chain in space. Then, if a force is applied in the x direction, one will have $\bar{y} = \bar{z} = 0$. Defining

$$C_x(x) = \int\int C(x,y,z)dy\, dz \tag{64}$$

one finds

$$\bar{x} = \frac{d}{df} \log \int e^{fx}\, C_x(x)\, dx \tag{65}$$

Thus, in this case one can reduce the three-dimensional problem to a one-dimensional problem by projecting the configuration function onto the direction of the applied force. In particular, if the chain consists of independent links, the problem can be reduced to a one-dimensional case at the very start, by projecting the probability distribution for the individual links onto this direction, and employing this projection in the treatment of the chain as a whole. If the links of the chain are not independent—*i.e.*, the probability distribution for each link depends on the orientation of the adjacent links—the projection method can still be applied. One has then to deal with probability distributions for the projections of link extensions onto the force direction, these depending on the values of the projections for adjacent links. Examples of such reductions will be found in succeeding sections.

"As a simple illustration of the application of these methods, we consider a one-dimensional chain of N links, each of which will, in the absence of external forces, contribute to the extension of the chain an amount $+1$ or -1, with equal probability. The relative number of ways in which an extension L of the chain can be obtained is clearly the coefficient of x^L in $(1/2^N)(x + 1/x)^N$. We have, thus,

$$G(x) = (1/2^N)(x + 1/x)^N \tag{66}$$

and

$$C(L,N) = \frac{1}{2^N} \frac{N!}{[(N+L)/2]![(N-L)/2]!} \tag{67}$$

To apply equation (35) one must first use Stirling's approximation, $N! \cong (2\pi N)^{1/2}N^N e^{-N}$, for the factorials. In the case of the factorial $[(N - L)/2]!$ this will not be legitimate for

L arbitrarily close to N, but, by increasing N, this approximation can be made good for values of the fractional extension

$$t = L/L_{max} = L/N \tag{68}$$

arbitrarily close to 1. In terms of the fractional extension one has

$$C(L,N) = \frac{2}{(2\pi N)^{1/2}}(1+t)^{-(N/2)(1+t)}(1-t)^{-(N/2)(1-t)}(1-t^2)^{-1/2} \tag{69}$$

and

$$\bar{Z} = \frac{kT}{2}\log\frac{1+t}{1-t} - \frac{2}{N}\frac{t}{1-t^2} + 0\left(\frac{1}{N^2}\right) \tag{70}$$

To apply (46) we have simply to note that according to (66)

$$G(e^f) = [\cosh f]^N \tag{71}$$

Then

$$\bar{L} = N\frac{d}{df}\log\cosh f = N\tanh f \tag{72}$$

or

$$t = \tanh f \tag{73}$$

exactly. Equation (73) is the inverse of (70) only in the limit of N large, in which all terms on the right, except the first, are to be neglected. Its derivation is almost trivial, there being no terms of order $1/N$ to be separated out and dropped in passing to the limit. This illustrates the essential advantage in computing $\bar{L}(Z)$ instead of $\bar{Z}(L)$; it is the former quantity which varies the more simply with the number of links in the chain. In less simple problems the importance of this advantage is greatly increased, as it becomes much more difficult to construct $C(L,N)$ explicitly. Usually it will be necessary to derive $C(L,N)$ by an inverse Laplace transformation from $G(e^f)$, whereas, by use of (46), the desired stress–strain relation can be derived directly from $G(e^f)$ . . .

The simplest type of flexible chain which one may use to represent a rubber molecule consists of links of fixed length l, each of which will tend to take on all orientations in space with equal probability, whatever may be the orientations of the neighboring links. In this model a link will correspond, not to a single carbon-carbon bond, but to a section of the chain so long that constraints on the relative orientations of the ends are negligible. Just what this length should be is not well defined, and there will be a corresponding uncertainty in the magnitude of the forces computed using this model. In attributing a fixed length to each link we are also making a simplifying assumption which will somewhat affect the form of the stress–strain curve. Nevertheless, this model constitutes so marked an advance over that with Gaussian chains as to deserve consideration. In a later paper we shall compare this model with a more refined, but more intractable, model.

A three-dimensional vector of magnitude l which takes on all orientations with equal probability will have all x components between $-l$ and $+l$ with equal probability. Our three-dimensional chain is thus equivalent to a one-dimensional chain in which the ith link may make any contribution x between $+l$ and $-l$ to the extension, with equal probability when external forces are absent.

To treat this system one may use equation (48). Note that

$$\langle e^{fL}\rangle_{av} = \langle \exp f(x_1 + x_2 + \cdots)\rangle_{av} = \Pi_i\langle \exp fx_i\rangle_{av} \tag{74}$$

since the x's vary independently. Now

$$\langle \exp fx_1\rangle_{av} = \frac{1}{2l}\int_{-l}^{+l}\exp fx_1 dx_1 = \sinh lf/lf \tag{75}$$

Thus for a chain of N links

$$\langle e^{fL}\rangle_{av} = \{\sinh lf/lf\}^N \tag{76}$$

Applying (48), we have at once

$$t = \coth lf - 1/lf = \mathcal{L}(lf) \tag{77}$$

where $\mathcal{L}(x)$ is the Langevin function.

It is not possible to pass rigorously from the stress–strain relation thus derived for a single chain to that for an arbitrary three-dimensional network, since the reduction of the network to an equivalent set of independent chains . . . . is not exact for these non-Gaussian chains. So long, however, as the conditions of stretch of the network are not too extreme we will expect that reduction to lead to a satisfactory approximation. Without further justification of the procedure we pass to the consideration of a model of rubber similar to that previously considered, except that in the unstretched state of the material each independent chain is taken to have an extension equal to κ times its maximum length. The maximum stretch for the model is thus given by a factor of $1/\kappa$, a quantity which will vary with the sample of rubber and will, accordingly, enter our treatment as a variable parameter.

. . . we consider a unit cube of the material, taken, in a first approximation, as incompressible. In the stretched condition $L_xL_yL_z = 1$, as before. If a chain is given an extension L its fractional extension will be $t = L\kappa$. The stress–strain relation for the individual chain may then be expressed as

$$L\kappa = \mathcal{L}(lZ/kT) \tag{78}$$

This defines a relation between the fractional extension of the model in a given direction and the tension of the chains extended in that direction which we express as

$$lZ/kT = \mathcal{L}^{-1}(t) \tag{79}$$

One then finds for the internal pressure in the model stretched only in the z direction, $(L_x = L_y = L_z^{1/2})$,

$$\text{P} = (MkT/lL_yL_z)\mathcal{L}^{-1}(t_y) \tag{80}$$

The stress–strain relation for the model as a whole becomes

$$Z = (MkT/l)[\mathcal{L}^{-1}(t_z) - (L_y/L_z)\mathcal{L}^{-1}(t_y)] \tag{81}$$

or

$$Z = (MkT/l)[\mathcal{L}^{-1}(L_z\kappa) - L_z^{-3/2}\mathcal{L}^{-1}(L_z^{-1/2}\kappa)] \tag{82}$$

This relation involves essentially two parameters: MK/l, which determines the scale of the forces just as in the Gaussian case, and the new maximum stretch parameter κ.

If the argument of the second term in the stress, that due to the internal pressure, is small,

$$\mathcal{L}^{-1}(t) \cong 3\,t \tag{83}$$

$$Z \cong (MkT/l)[\mathcal{L}^{-1}(L_z\kappa) - 3\,\kappa/L_z^2] \tag{84}$$

When this approximation can be applied to both terms—all extensions small compared to the maximum—one has simply

$$Z \cong (3\,M\kappa kT/l)[L_z - 1/L_z^2] \tag{85}$$

as for a Gaussian model. Putting $\kappa = 1/Nl$ relation (85) reduces exactly to:

$$Z = M[kT/<L^2>_{av}][L_z - 1/L_z^2]^* \tag{86}$$

remembering that $\langle L^2\rangle_{av} = \frac{1}{3} Nl^2$.

It should be noted that predictions of the theory for shear, stretch in two directions, swelling, and so on, ... for Gaussian chains will also be modified for higher extensions. Since these modifications are not formally interesting, and are quite insignificant so long as one does not deal with extreme distortions of the material, we shall not discuss them at this point . . .

The appearance of the Langevin function in these results is most easily understood by consideration of a method of treating stress–strain relations which is applicable only to chains of independent links. In cases in which the contribution of each link to the extension is independent of that of every other link, the reduction of the total problem to a one-dimensional equivalent may be accomplished by making a corresponding reduction for each individual link. We consider than a chain of N identical independent links, each of which will, in the force-free case, contribute to the x component of the extension of the chain according to the probability distribution c(x). Then

$$\langle e^{fL_x}\rangle_{av} = [\langle e^{fx}\rangle_{av}]^N \tag{87}$$

the average on the right being computed for an individual link. Consequently,

$$L_x = N\, d(\log \langle e^{fx}\rangle_{av})/df \tag{88}$$

or

$$\bar{x} = \int x \exp (xZ_x/KT)c(x)\, dx \Big/ \int \exp (xZ_x/kT)c(x)\, dx \tag{89}$$

Here we do not deal with t, as before, since the maximum extension might be infinite, but rather with $\bar{x}$, the average contribution of each link to the extension.

Equation (89) states that the contribution of each independent link in a flexible chain can be computed as if it were the only link present and the external forces were applied directly to its ends. This is true whether or not all links in the chain are described by the same distribution function c(x).

The situation of an independent link in an extended flexible chain is thus completely analogous to that of a polar molecule in an electric or a magnetic field. The thermal agitation of the chain tends to disorient the links, to make the average contribution to the extension vanish, while the tension of the chain, in effect, is equivalent to a uniform field of force tending to align the links. The computations of the average contribution of a link to the extension and of the average contribution of a polar molecule to, say, the magnetic moment of a material are thus formally identical. If the link has a fixed length, the molecule a fixed moment, the computations are identical in detail; the Langevin function appears in each result.

In the same way the function tanh f which appears in equation (73) for the extension of a chain of links for which only two configurations are possible is the function which appears in Ehrenfest's classical theory of magnetism, which assumed the existence in crystals of polar atoms having two orientations of equal potential energy in the absence of a magnetic field. A chain model in which each link could take on a discrete

* Equation(86) is of the same form as Wall's equation (25), page 243.—AUTHOR'S NOTE

set of orientations would similarly lead to the Brillouin function, of which Ehrenfest's tanh x is the simplest special case.*

We conclude this section with a more explicit statement of the role of the Gaussian distribution as an approximation in the case of chains of independent links. We assume that $C(x)$ is an even function of x, as it must be if there is no preferred direction in space. Then, expanding the exponentials of equation (89) one has

$$t = \int \left\{ fx^2 + \frac{1}{3!}f^3x^4 + \frac{1}{5!}f^5x^6 + \cdots \right\} c(x)dx \Big/ \int \left\{ 1 + \frac{1}{2!}f^2x^2 + \cdots \right\} c(x)\,dx \quad (90)$$

or

$$t = f\langle x^2\rangle_{av} + f^3\{\tfrac{1}{6}\langle x^4\rangle_{av} - \tfrac{1}{2}(\langle x^2\rangle_{av})^2\} + \cdots \quad (91)$$

For very small f and t, the relation between these quantities is determined by the value of $\langle x^2\rangle_{av}$, and is otherwise independent of the form of the distribution function. For larger extensions there will be deviations from the linear relation between t and f which will be determined by the relative values of $\langle x^2\rangle_{av}$, $\langle x^4\rangle_{av}$, $\cdots$, for a single link. If these are all in the same ratio as for a Gaussian chain, the higher terms in (91) all vanish, and $t = \langle x^2\rangle_{av}f$ always. Otherwise, there is a deviation from the linear relation of f and t which is quite unaffected by any increase in the number of links in the chain. That is, as the number of links in the chain increases, the linear relation of Z and L holds to greater and greater values of L, but not of L/N; deviations from the linear relation of L and Z depend only on the fractional extension. Correspondingly, an increase in the number of links will make $C(L)$ approach the Gaussian form for any given range of L, but, in general, only for L small as compared with the maximum extension of the chain. Similarly, by making the chain long enough, one can make the $\langle L^\tau\rangle_{av}$ of (50) approach the values for a Gaussian chain, for any given range of τ. There will, however, always be deviations of these quantities from the Gaussian values at larger τ, and these deviations will be important if the fractional extension of the chain becomes large. In short, the Gaussian approximation for the distribution function is dependable only if the fractional extension of the chain is sufficiently small—smaller, as our results show, than extensions actually encountered in bulk rubber.

The nature of the Gaussian form as an approximation to the more exact form of the configuration function may be illustrated more explicitly by reference to the one-dimensional problem treated . . . Neglecting a slowly varying factor $(1 - t^2)^{-1/2}$ in equation (69), we have

$$C(L,N) \cong \frac{2}{(2\pi N)^{1/2}} (1 + t)^{-(N/2)(1+t)} (1 - t)^{-(N/2)(1-t)} \quad (91a)$$

This can be written without further approximation as

$$C(L,N) \cong \frac{2}{(2\pi N)^{1/2}} \exp\left\{ -\frac{N}{2} \int \log\frac{1+t}{1-t}\,dt \right\} \quad (92)$$

Since

$$\log\,[(1 + t)/(1 - t)] = 2(t + t^3/3 + t^5/5 + \cdots) \quad (93)$$

* P. Ehrenfest, *Proc. Acad. Sci. Amsterdam* (Dec. 18, 1920) or *Leiden Communications*, Suppl. 44b; see also P. Debye in Marx, *Handbuch der Radiologie*, Vol. VI, p. 712. For the Brillouin function, L. Brillouin, *J. phys., radium*, 8, 74 (1927); also P. Debye, *loc. cit.*, p. 713. More recent accounts are given by: J. H. van Vleck, *The Theory of Electric and Magnetic Susceptibilities*, Oxford Univ. Press, London, 1932, pp. 257 and 289; and R. H. Fowler and E. A. Guggenheim, *Statistical Thermodynamics*, Cambridge Univ. Press, London, 1939, and Macmillan, New York, 1940, pp. 629–630.

it is evident that, for small enough t, where all terms but the first are negligible, we have essentially the Gaussian distribution. Deviations from the Gaussian law set in when

$$(N/2)\int \frac{2}{3}t^3\,dt = Nt^4/4 \qquad (94)$$

becomes appreciably different from zero—for greater absolute extensions Nt and smaller relative extensions t as N is increased—and are very great when t is comparable to 1.

Returning for the moment to the case of the three-dimensional polymer swollen with a low molecular weight solvent, it is clear that such a swollen network can be treated by the refined methods of Kuhn, Wall, and Guth and James if in the unstrained state the distribution of chain end separations, $D_0(x,y,z)$, is given by the probability function, $p(x,y,z)$. For a given network, this can only be true for some one value of q. Presumably the refined approach could be applied for other values of q by making the assumption: When a network is dilated isotropically (q is increased), the separations of individual mesh points increase in the same ratio as the macroscopic dimensions of the sample. Or, more correctly, the (unstrained) distribution, $p(x,y,z)$ is changed by dilation to the distribution $p[(1 - \delta)x, (1 - \delta)y, (1 - \delta)z$, where δ is the fractional linear dilation factor for the macroscopic sample. This has not as yet been done.

While Guth and James have extended the kinetic theory to the domain of large elongations, it would seem that Flory and Rehner have made the most detailed study of the correlation between *network structure* and elastic behavior. A few words to explain exactly what we mean by this statement may not be amiss. Let us tentatively say that the stress–strain curve of a cross-linked elastomer can be written as:

$$S = AB(\gamma) \qquad (95)$$

where A is a constant reflecting the tightness of the network structure and $B(\gamma)$ is a function of strain only. If this is true, it would be quite possible for one investigator to emphasize the nature of the function $B(\gamma)$, refining it so as to apply to large strains, and for another investigator to emphasize the dependence of A upon structure, while considering only small or moderate strains. Something of the sort seems to be the case.

Equation (95) corresponds to (95′) used by Flory (*15*).

$$S = (RT(\nu/V)\varphi(\alpha) \qquad (95')$$

or

$$S = (RT\rho/M_c)\varphi(\alpha) \qquad (95'')$$

Regarding the (small strain) theory of Guth and James, Flory (*15*) comments as follows:

. . . The dependence of f on α [*i.e.*, S on γ] is precisely that found by other methods which treat the statistical mechanics of the actual rubber network. However, the coefficient m, expressing the number of chains *per unit area* of the hypothetical "parallel chain" model, is a fiction in terms of the actual network of irregular chains. The real chains occupy volume, not an area . . .

In conclusion, this procedure yields a satisfactory form for the dependence of stress on strain (α), but it fails to connect elastic properties with network structure. Thus, the important relationship obtained by other methods between the elastic force of retraction and the number of chains per unit volume, or the directly related concentration of cross linkages, is obliterated by the replacement of the network by sets of parallel chains.

And later:

The connection between elastic properties and vulcanizate structure is of more far-reaching importance than the exact form of the stress–strain curve. Wall's equation, which is substantiated by Treloar's modification of Kuhn's treatment, and by the method of Flory and Rehner, furnishes an explicit expression for the constant of proportionality between $\varphi(\alpha)$ and the absolute tension. This proportionality constant contains the number of chains, ν, which for an ideal network formed from indefinitely long primary molecules must equal twice the number of cross linkages. Thus, the tension of any given elongation is predicted to be proportional to the degree of cross linking of the molecules.

D. Network Defects. Influence of Molecular Weight of Original Linear Polymer on Elastic Properties of a Network

In the paper quoted above (*15*), Flory proceeds to discuss the detailed correspondence between network structure and elastic properties. He includes the effects of network "defects," such as entanglements, intramolecular cross links, and terminal chains or tails.

The various derivations of the basic equations . . . stem from the same physical concepts of network structure. In attempting refinements which will remove the discrepancies between theory and experiment . . . it will be necessary therefore to reconsider this structure in greater detail.

Network Entanglements.—The fact that the elastic force of retraction in Butyl rubber vulcanizates exceeds the value calculated from equation (95′), in which $\nu/2$ is identified as the number of chemical cross linkages, suggests that types of chain interactions other than primary valence attachments between chains are to be reckoned with. Several possibilities require consideration.

Attachments between chains due to van der Waals forces have been postulated as a source of cross linkages in rubberlike materials. There is no doubt as to the existence of such forces between polymer molecules. The question of concern here is the permanence with which these forces may unite neighboring chains. In order for such an attachment to function as a network cross linkage, obviously it must endure at least over the interval of the elasticity measurement. On the other hand, the existence of the rubbery state in any high polymer predicates a high degree of internal mobility which will allow elements of the chains to slip past one another during deformation. van der Waals attractions between chains must be small in order for the material to be rubberlike.

In harmony with this deduction rubberlike materials usually possess nonpolar (hydrocarbon) chains or, if they contain strong polar groups, rubberlike character is exhibited only at elevated temperatures or in the presence of a solvent or plasticizing substance capable of satisfying the forces of the polar groups. The probable existence of occasional strong polar, or possibly ionic, interchain bonds in certain rubbery materials cannot be denied, *e.g.*, in aqueous protein gels and possibly to a very limited extent in raw, unmasticated natural rubber containing traces of polar substituents. The occurrence of a significant number of such bonds in vulcanized natural rubber or in hydrocarbon synthetic rubbers is exceedingly unlikely in view of their nonpolar nature and the consequent weak van der Waals forces between chains. If such bonds contributed to the elastic properties, their number should decrease with temperature and the elastic retractive force should show a corresponding diminution, which is contrary to observation. Furthermore, the correlation of swelling behavior of Butyl vulcanizates with elastic properties demonstrates that about as many cross linkages are operative in the presence of solvent as in its absence. van der Waals bonds would be expected to be eliminated, or at least diminished in number, in the presence of a solvent.

It has been suggested that long chains, merely owing to their irregular configurations, become entangled with one another to the extent that a molecule is unable to extricate itself from its neighbors. Two arguments, one theoretical and the other based on direct experiments, can be leveled against the view that these entanglements of linear (non-network) molecules are equivalent in their contribution to elasticity to permanent, or primary valence, cross linkages. Investigations of electrical and viscous properties of polymers in the rubberlike or liquid state reveal that within each chain small elements, or segments, composed of perhaps ten or twenty chain atoms are constantly rearranging their positions at a rapid rate under the influence of thermal agitation. Successive random rearrangements of these segments lead to diffusion not only of the segments, but of the molecule as a whole from one configuration and position to another. Hence, a molecule does not maintain fixed relationships with respect to its neighbors. Although entanglement of linear molecules is a factor contributing to resistance to flow (high viscosity) and to a low *rate* of solution, it should not be expected to eliminate plastic flow or to affect *equilibrium* solubility. These contentions are confirmed by experimental results: All linear polymers regardless of molecular weight display the properties of unvulcanized rubber above their brittle point temperatures, *i.e.*, they are soluble in suitable solvents, and under stress they undergo plastic flow at a nondiminishing rate.

The situation is otherwise if there exists a primary valence network structure. Here entanglements of chains may lead to restraints which are equivalent to additional chemical cross bonds in their contribution to network properties. Consider, for example, two chains, one looped about the other, such as are shown in figure 89. While the chains *AB* and *CD* are not bound together at fixed points as in a chemical cross linkage, they nevertheless are permanently prevented from crossing each other. The configurations available to each chain are limited by interference with the other. This type of restraint, which will be called a network entanglement, is of a permanent nature; it cannot be circumvented without disrupting a portion of the primary valence network. One of these entanglements may not be quantitatively equivalent to a chemical cross bond in its contribution to elastic properties. However, a number of them along each chain may raise the effective number of cross linkages appreciably above the actual number.

It should be re-emphasized that these network entanglements would offer no permanent barriers to chain configuration were it not for the chemical cross bonds which are responsible for the primary valence network structure. Their existence as permanent features of the structure is dependent upon the presence of a primary valence cross linkage.

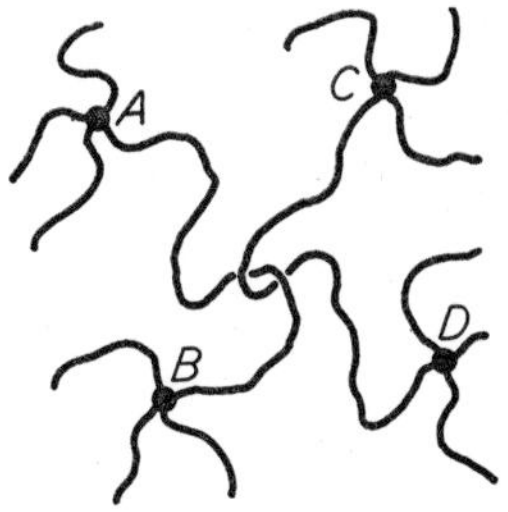

Fig. 89. Chain entanglement.

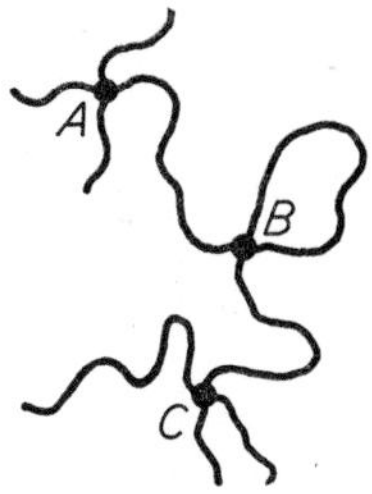

Fig. 90. Wasted (intramolecular) cross link.

Intramolecular Cross Linkages.—Occasionally two parts of the same molecule may become cross-linked, thus forming a loop as shown in figure 90. If there are no other intervening cross linkages with other chains along the loop, then configurations of the loop will be unaffected by deformations. This portion of the structure can contribute no reaction to deformation. The entire portion between the cross linkages A and C will act as a single chain, and the cross linkage B is wasted. Cross linkages of this type should be deducted from the total number in obtaining the number of effective cross linkages. Estimates of the number of such intramolecular cross linkages for flexible chains of random configuration indicate that they constitute only a few percent of the total. Their further consideration is scarcely warranted at the present time.

Terminal Chains: the Effect of Initial Molecular Weight.—Previous treatments of rubber elasticity have disregarded the influence on network structure and properties of the molecular weight of the initial rubber molecules from which the network is formed by vulcanization. In other words, the molecules were assumed to be infinitely long. Experiments already have been quoted which emphasize the marked dependence of elastic properties on initial molecular weight of the raw rubber. These are supported by widespread experience in rubber technology. The reason for this dependence is found in the fact that each end of an initial molecule contributes a flaw to the final network structure. The portion of a molecule from one end to its first cross linkage along its length, as depicted in figure 91, contributes nothing to the response of the network to deformation. The chain AB is always free to assume any configuration whatever, owing to the freedom of the end A. Similarly, attachment of the network at the point B in figure 91, to a molecule such as DE which is bound to the network at no other point produces no increase in the effective number of chains. Not only are the two chains DB and BE of molecule DE inactive, but the cross linkage at B is not a point of constraint on the chain AC. Hence, the portion of the network from A to C is to be considered as a single chain as if the cross linkage at B were not present.

The discussion of imperfections in networks of finite chains might be extended to more complex situations. However, the above should be sufficient to demonstrate qualitatively the manner in which finite molecule length will affect the network structure. Quantitative derivation of the effect of molecule length on network properties can best be accomplished by assuming a different approach.

We consider the process of network formation by successive cross linking of molecules. Let it be supposed that cross linking is allowed to occur only between molecules, or cross-linked combinations of molecules, which have not been connected directly or indirectly by previously introduced cross linkages. When there are a total of $N - 1$ cross linkages connecting N primary molecules "intermolecularly," all molecules will be bound to a single ramified structure. Before allowing the cross-linking process to continue further, let us consider the properties of the macrostructure developed at this stage.

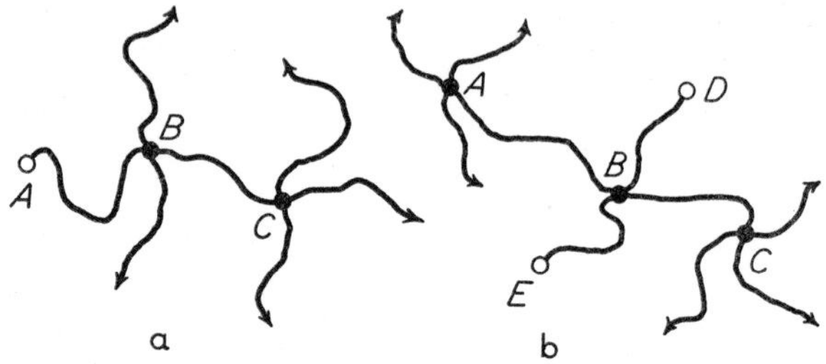

Fig. 91. Linear tails attached to network.

It would be incorrect to call it a network, inasmuch as it contains no netlike structure, *i.e.*, it possesses no circuitous connections within its structure. Because of this fact one portion of the structure can be shifted to a new position or configuration without affecting permanently the configurations of other parts. So far as their average configurations (as apart from their positions in space) are concerned, the various elements of the structure are independent of one another. Likewise, macroscopic deformation does not impose permanent restraints on the configurations of component portions of the structure. This somewhat hypothetical structure should be expected to display a static modulus of elasticity equal to zero.

Additional cross linking necessarily will be "intramolecular." Closed circuits of interconnected molecules will be produced, and the structure can then properly be referred to as a network. It becomes apparent that it is these circuitous paths in the network which are effective in transmitting the effects of changes of configuration of one part of the structure to another part. Macroscopic deformation can no longer occur without a change in internal configuration which cannot be dissipated through chain rearrangements, barring primary valence rupture. A little consideration will show that for each additional network cross linkage one new closed circuit, and two active network chains, are formed. (It will be recalled that the number of chains in an ideal network formed from "infinitely" long molecules is twice the number of cross linkages.)

In the course of the actual formation of the network, inter- and intramolecular cross linking are not sharply differentiated. Nevertheless, the number of circuitous paths in the network, exclusive of non-network, or sol constituents, necessarily will be equal at any stage of the process to the total number of cross linkages, $\nu_0/2$, in the network minus the number, $N - 1$, of cross linkages required to combine the primary molecules into a single continuous structure without intraconnecting two parts of the structure to form closed circuits. Hence, the total number of circuitous paths in the network, or, alternatively, the total number of "intrastructural" cross linkages, will be

$$\nu/2 = (\nu_0/2) - N \qquad (96)$$

where $N - 1$ is replaced by N. The effective number of chains will be given by twice this quantity, or

$$\nu = \nu_0[1 - (2\,N/\nu_0)] = \nu_0[1 - (2\,M_c/M)] \qquad (97)$$

By introducing this expression into equation (95′) . . . a revised relationship between elastic retractive force and network properties is obtained which takes into account the effects of finite length of the initial molecules. This equation may be written

$$\tau = [RT\nu_0/v][1 - (2\,M_c/M)]\varphi(\alpha) \qquad (98)$$

Before discussing this equation further, two aspects of its application should be clarified. In the first place the manner in which the occurrence of network entanglements such as have been discussed above will require modification of equation (98) must be considered. Inasmuch as entanglements affect only the active chains of the network, and not the terminal inactive chains such as AB in figure 91a, their effect to a first approximation should be proportional to the number ν of active chains and not to ν_0. It will be necessary, therefore, to increase ν in equation (97) by a factor g. This factor probably will depend on M_c, and perhaps on the character of the vulcanization. The modified equation for the tension becomes

$$\tau = [RTg\nu_0/v][1 - (2\,M_c/M)]\varphi(\alpha) \qquad (99)$$

It is important to note that the factor which introduces the correction for the molecular weight M of the primary rubber molecules is unaffected; M_c refers to the average molecular weight between primary valence cross linkages, unmodified by entanglements.

Secondly, the above method for computing the number of closed circuits in the network requires revision when the average number of cross linkages attached to each molecule is small. Here an appreciable proportion of the material consists of a sol fraction which is unattached to the network structure. The proportion of sol is determined by the "cross-linking index" γ, which for primary molecules of uniform length is equal to ν_0/N, *i.e.*, to twice the ratio of cross linkages to primary molecules. Incipient network formation occurs at $\gamma = 1$. As the number of cross linkages is increased, the proportion of gel (network) increases rapidly toward an asymptotic 100 per cent. It is only the gel fraction which is responsible for elasticity. Hence, in employing equation (97), ν_0 and N should refer exclusively to the gel fraction. Equations have been derived previously for obtaining the cross-linking index, γ'', for the gel and the percentage of gel from the cross-linking index, γ, of the material as a whole. ν_0 and N for the gel alone can then be computed and the revised expression for ν introduced in place of equation (97). Trial calculations of this sort show that above $\gamma \sim 3$, where the percentage of sol is small, no appreciable error results if ν_0 and N are allowed to refer to the total material without distinguishing sol from gel. Hence, so long as M is at least three times M_c, the second factor in equations (98) and (99) requires no correction for the existence of a small fraction of inactive sol.

E. Nonequilibrium Behavior

The most striking applications of the above equilibrium theories lie of course in the field of the cross-linked elastomers at moderately high temperatures, where the equilibrium aspects of the deformation are not obscured by the retardation effects present at lower temperatures. Very little has been done toward providing a complete theory, embracing both equilibrium and rate of approach to equilibrium. In this section a few qualitative deductions are made by applying the theory of section 1 (pages 236 *et seq.*) to a regular three-dimensional network.

The aim of such a theory is to deduce, from the structure of the polymer, the whole distribution of elastic retardation times $J(\tau)$. The theory outlined in section 1 permits such a function to be derived for a linear polymer, but unfortunately contains specific assumptions of very doubtful validity (*e.g.*, the unqualified use of the $\sqrt{Z}$ relationship). Also, no detailed distribution of retardation times has as yet been experimentally worked out for any (amorphous linear) polymer. Thus it is not possible to state with any assurance the form of the typical viscoelastic spectrum for a linear amorphous polymer; but we should be able to predict roughly the *effects of changes* in structure upon the spectrum. An attempt has already been made to predict the effect of molecular weight heterogeneity on the mechanical spectrum of a *linear* polymer. In section 1 a simple reference form was assumed for the function $D(\tau)$ for a monodisperse polymer, and the general nature of the function for *mixtures* of more than one molecular weight was estimated. A similar qualitative discussion is made here. It too must be recognized as completely hypothetical, with no quantitative validity on the theoretical side and no quantitative confirmation on the experimental side. A three-dimensional polymer made up of chains of n atoms is compared with a monodisperse linear polymer whose *molecules* contain n units.

The very short chain sections of a loose polymer network must respond to stress in much the same fashion as similar sections in a linear polymer of the same chemical chain structure. Such a short section "has no way of knowing" whether it is part of a linear molecule or of a chain connection two mesh-points of a network. Thus the low τ region of the distributing curve $D(\tau)$ must be similar in the two cases. As we proceed to chain sections which are comparable in size with the number n, it would seem very likely that the sections of the three-dimensional polymer are somewhat more constrained than those of the linear polymer. Hence the amount of elastic deformation possessing the corresponding range of retardation time is presumably somewhat smaller. On the other hand, sections containing more than n chain atoms do not exist in the linear polymer. Hence the viscoelastic spectrum is cut off sharply at the corresponding retardation time. In the three-dimensional polymer larger sections do exist, although they are not free to undergo completely independent micro-Brownian motion. Hence we might expect a small amount of elastic deformation of longer retardation time. The most striking difference, of course, is in the true viscosity. For the linear polymer, this is a definite finite value; for the three-dimensional polymer, it is essentially infinite. These effects are indicated schematically in figure 92. The important thing about this viscoelastic spectrum is that in an experiment whose timescale is much greater than τ, the response of

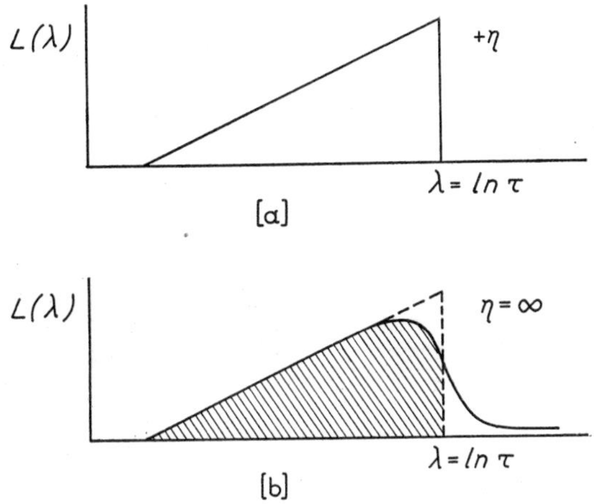

Fig. 92. Hypothetical distribution of elastic retardation times for a linear polymer [a] and for an idealized regular network polymer [b].

the network is essentially an equilibrium elastic response. There may be a slight additional "creep," due to the tail of the distribution curve, but this is small in comparison with the principal elastic deformation of $\tau < \tau_1$. The equilibrium theories described in the preceding section furnish a theoretical value of the *total* elastic deformation contributed by chain segments up to the length n. This is indicated by the shaded area of figure 92b. (Actually, since these theories in their present state do not take complete account of the *constraints* at the ends of the connecting chains, they may tend to overestimate the value of this integral quantity.) Kirkwood (*26a*) has recently developed a molecular theory of the non-equilibrium viscoelastic behavior of cross-linked polymers.

2. Loose Regular Networks Containing Linear Polymer Molecules

Consider a regular polymeric network, made up of linear connecting chains of n_1 chain atoms, with a certain amount of linear polymeric material, of chain length n_2, intermixed in the interstices. Let q represent the volume fraction of linear polymer in the system. It is clear that the viscoelastic spectrum of such a system depends upon the values of n_1, n_2, and q. For any given n_1 and n_2 there is some one value of q for which the mesh points of the network, in the unstrained configuration, follow

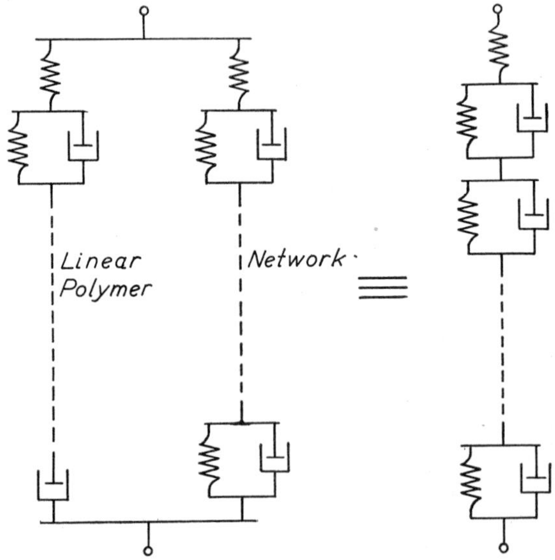

Fig. 93. Hypothetical models for viscoelastic properties of network polymer.

the probability distribution (Eqs. 1). If more linear polymer is forced into the system, the network is dilated, and the probability distribution is changed from $D_0(x,y,z)$ to something very similar to $D_0[(1 - \delta)x, (1 - \delta)y, (1 - \delta)z]$. Here, only the case where q has the value which makes $D_0(x,y,z) = p(x,y,z)$, is considered.

In this case, the *equilibrium* properties of the system of network plus linear polymer are very similar to those of the same network swollen to the same extent, q, by a low molecular weight solvent. Indeed, to the extent that these theories are correct, the two cases are identical. In each case, the stress must finally be supported by the network alone.

The interstitial material, be it linear polymer or low molecular weight solvent, cannot assist in supporting the stress after equilibrium has been attained.

The linear polymer, however, affects profoundly the *rate* at which the equilibrium state of strain is attained. The viscoelastic spectrum of the system can be expected to be similar to figure 93 (page 264). (As was pointed out before, there is no available evidence which proves that such a parallel coupling exactly gives the proper spectrum for a multicomponent material, but it is certainly a good approximation.) If this is converted to a single equivalent one-dimensional model, there will be obtained a new distribution of retardation times, $J(\tau)$, which is the overall spectrum for the system: network plus linear polymer. Since the network itself undergoes no true flow response, the combined system can undergo no true flow. The detailed form of the dependence of $J(\tau)$ upon the values of n_1 and n_2 is completely a matter of conjecture, since absolutely no experiments have been made with the aim of determining this. However, as before, a guess can be made on the basis of our general theory. In figure 94 at the right, the results of such a guess are indicated: (*a*) the case in which $n_1 < n_2$; (*b*) the case in which $n_1 = n_2$; (*c*) the case in which $n_1 > n_2$.

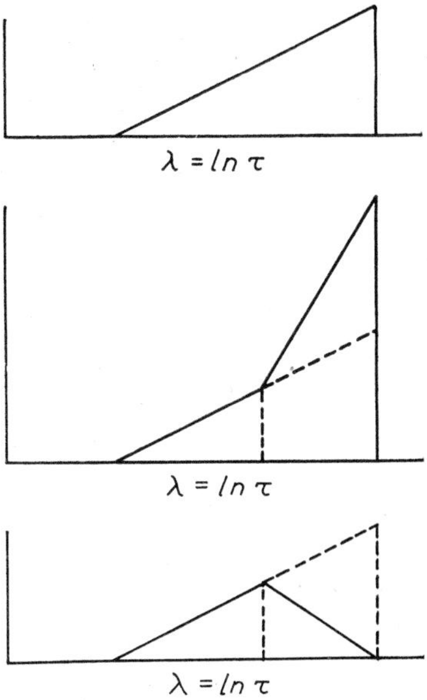

Fig. 94. Hypothetical distributions of elastic retardation times for an idealized polymer network and for polymer networks containing interstitial linear polymer.

As before, we can expect that the low τ part of the spectrum is determined almost entirely by the chemical structure of the chains, since the local kinks are affected by stress in much the same way whether they are parts of linear molecules or of linear chains connecting the mesh points of a network. It is in the high τ region that differences appear, as indicated in figure 94.

There is one important distinction between the behavior of a network filled with low molecular weight solvent and one filled with linear polymer molecules. We have seen that the former assumes a degree of swelling, q, which depends upon the activity of the solvent in the surrounding environment, and that in general a deformation results in a change in the equilibrium value of q for a given activity. This is not true when the interstitial material is linear polymer. Even in a high vacuum, which should (thermodynamically speaking) cause all the interstitial material to evaporate out of the network, q remains practically unchanged, because of the infinitesimal *rate* of evaporation of the linear high polymer. Hence such a structure need not be held in equilibrium with a reservoir of linear polymer in the first place. Furthermore, if the activity of the linear interstitial material is changed by a deformation of the structure, no change in q follows.

3. Loose Irregular Networks

In view of the vagueness of our understanding even of regular networks, little can be said with any degree of certainty about irregular networks. About all that can be done is to formulate the problem in

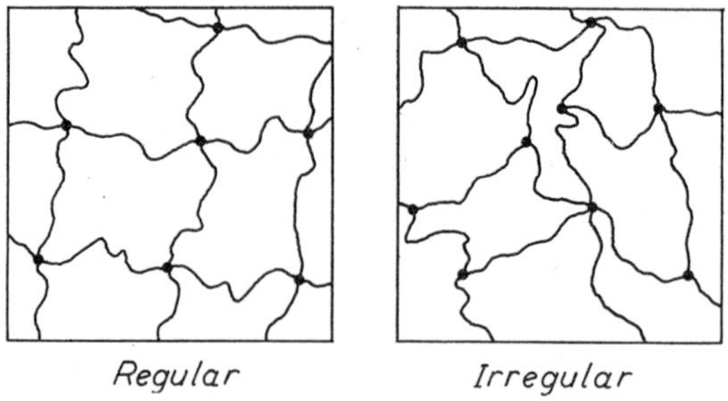

Fig. 95. Schematic representation of regular and irregular network structures.

proper terms. Instead of a network composed of linking chains of the uniform length n, we must consider a network composed of linking chains of all lengths. This contrast between a regular and an irregular network is indicated in figure 95. Such a network would be fairly well described by the number distribution curve for the lengths of the connecting linear chains—$N(n)$. If the network contained interstitial linear polymer, it would be necessary to specify both $N(n_1)$, the distribution of connecting chains, and $N(n_2)$, the distribution curve of the interstitial material. The question which we would like to answer is an involved one: For a given type of polymer, what are the effects of q, $N(n_1)$, and $N(n_2)$, upon the viscoelastic spectrum, $J(\tau)$?

Guth and James (*24, 25*) have suggested that the detailed form of $N(n_1)$ is not important in determining the *equilibrium* elastic behavior of such a network. They prove that in the case of a Gaussian distribution function an irregular network behaves exactly like a regular network. It does not follow, however, that the transient viscoelastic response of an irregular network is identical with that of a regular network.

The problem involved here is not one which is likely to be satisfactorily answered for some time. There is no obvious means for experimentally determining $N(n_1)$. A linear polymer may be fractionated, to obtain a set of essentially monodisperse fractions. These fractions can be combined to yield a polydisperse material of any chosen distribution curve. Mechanical studies can be made on the original sample, the fractions, and the mixtures possessing synthetic distribution curves. No such simple procedure suggests itself in the case of the three-dimensional network. The only method of determining $N(n)$ is by means of a *statistical analysis of the chemical reaction in which the network was formed*, rather than by a direct physical study of the structure itself. It is for this reason that the discussions of section III (see pages 268–304) are included.

4. Tight Networks

An extremely *tight* network represents the opposite extreme from the loose networks which have already been discussed. The diamond structure might be chosen as the typical regular tight network. In diamond, each atom represents a mesh point, and hence the connections between mesh points are single valence bonds. Such short connecting "chains" possess no flexibility of the type characteristic of a loose network. When diamond is deformed, valence bonds must be stretched and valence angles deformed. Hence the free energy increase is predominantly an energy increase, rather than an entropy decrease. The elastic constants of diamond can be computed from the known properties of the C—C bond by obvious methods. From the theoretical point of view, the most difficult structures to analyze are those of intermediate tightness. As a "loose" network is "tightened" by the successive introduction of more cross links, a point is reached beyond which the theoretical considerations of the previous sections cannot be expected to be quantitatively correct. These theories are all based upon equation (1), which gives the probability distribution for various separations of the ends of a chain of n units. But equation (1) is only valid for a *long* chain, where n is large. In order to treat the case of a network made up of fairly short chains, it would be necessary first of all to derive a probability function valid for short chains, to replace equation (1). With a still tighter network (still smaller n), not only the specific form, but even the general point of view, of these theories must be abandoned. This is because the flexibility of the connecting chains is lost—as best exemplified in diamond. Extremely tight networks, where $n = 1$, 2, or 3, could be treated in a manner similar to diamond by considering only the deformation of valence bonds and angles. In intermediate cases, a macroscopic strain means a new microscopic distribution among chain configurations and also, simultaneously, a state of bond deformation. A theory adequate to handle such intermediate cases would presumably cover the entire range of tightness from diamond to slightly vulcanized rubber. For very small n, the entropy contribution would drop out and the theory would reduce to the valence bond and angle approach which must be used for diamond. For very large n the energy contribution would disappear and the theory would reduce to the loose network approach of section 1 (pages 236–267). No such general theory has yet been offered and, therefore, polymeric networks of intermediate tightness must be recognized as outside the scope of present theoretical methods.

III. THE FORMATION OF THREE-DIMENSIONAL POLYMERS

It was pointed out in a previous section (I, page 235) that, at present, a principal method of determining in detail the structure of a three-dimensional polymer consists in the statistical analysis of the chemical processes by which the network was formed. Three general methods of formation of polymer networks are discussed here:

(1) Polycondensation reactions involving molecules of functionality greater than two.

(2) Cross linking of linear polymer molecules (vulcanization type reaction).

(3) Polymerization reactions involving divinyl monomers.

1. Polycondensation Reactions

Carothers (*1*) repeatedly pointed out that while the polycondensation of bifunctional molecules (*e.g.*, dibasic acids with dialcohols) would give rise to linear polymer molecules, the polycondensation of tri- or tetrafunctional molecules would give rise to three-dimensional network structures. This qualitative idea has been thoroughly and quantitatively elaborated by Flory (*16*) in a series of papers. Recently, Stockmayer (*40*) has discussed the problem from a somewhat different point of view, arriving at conclusions similar to those of Flory. It would be difficult to improve upon the discussion presented by Flory in his original papers on the subject. Most of the following discussion is therefore quoted verbatim from these papers.

One of the most important results of Flory's treatment is the quantitative interpretation of the gelation process, by which polymer molecules of essentially infinite extent are formed. It is often observed that the gelation of a condensation polymer occurs very sharply at a critical extent of reaction, which is independent of temperature, catalyst concentration, etc. Furthermore, "common experience shows that gelation occurs long before all of the material is bound together in one molecule. Usually it is possible to extract soluble material, the molecular weight of which is not extremely large, from the gelled polymer."

First, we consider systems which contain trifunctional units; in addition to these there also may be present units which are bifunctional (and monofunctional units also, for that matter). As an example, consider a glycerol–ethylene glycol–succinic acid mixture in which the formation of a typical polymer molecule is indicated by:

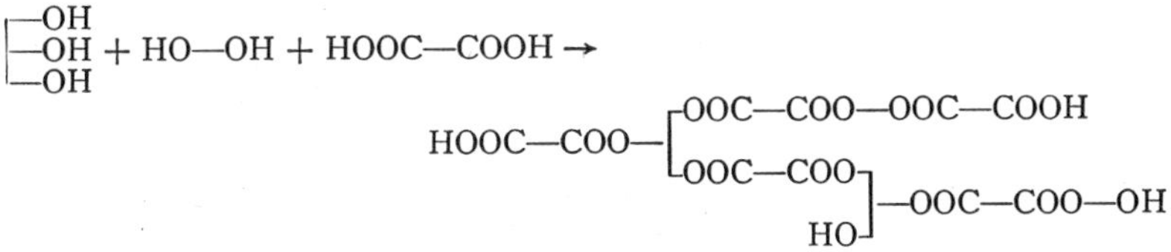

The polymeric structures which are formed may be represented schematically as in figure 96. The portion of the molecule between two "branch" units, *i.e.*, trifunctional units (glycerol), or between a branch unit and a "terminal group" (unreacted OH or COOH), is represented by a straight line. Such a portion of a molecule will be called a "chain." The length of the chains will vary, but this is not important here. Even an unreacted functional group of a branch unit (*e.g.*, an unreacted OH of a glycerol unit) is to be considered as an end of a chain which extends from a branch to a terminal group (except in case 3, *cf. seq.*). For the present it is assumed that the functional groups of the branch unit are all equivalent. The network, or molecule, containing n branches possesses $2n + 1$ chains.

Suppose the chain within the first circle in figure 96 has been selected at random from the polymer mixture. We wish to know the probability that this chain is a part of an infinite network. In the present paper we wish in particular to determine under what conditions this probability will be greater than zero. Our first concern is the fate of the ends of the particular chain selected at random. In figure 96 this chain gives rise to two branches, one at each end. The four new chains extending from these branches lead to three branches (on circle 2) and one terminal group. The resulting six chains lead to two branches on circle 3, etc. The network built about the chain selected at random in figure 96 could be designated 2, 3, 2, 2, 1, 0, where the figures indicate the numbers of branches found on successive circles.

Let it be assumed for the present that there exists a certain probability α that any given one of the functional groups of a branch unit leads, via a sequence of bifunctional units, to another branch rather than to a terminal group. That is, α is taken to be the probability that any given chain extending outward from one of the circles in figure 96 ends in a branch on the next circle. It is obvious that α will depend on the ratios of the various ingredients and on the extent of reaction of the functional groups. Details of the methods for calculating α's will be postponed until their critical values have been discussed.

If on the i-th circle there are Y_i branches, then the *expected number* of branches (arising from the 2 Y_i new chains) on the $i + 1$ circle will be $2\alpha Y_i$. The actual number of branches on the $i + 1$ circle probably will differ from the expected number, but by

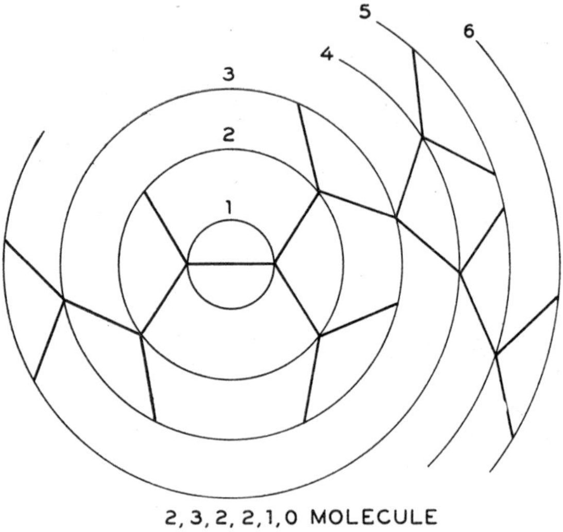

Fig. 96. Schematic representation of a trifunctionally branched three-dimensional polymer molecule.

making Y_i sufficiently large the ratio of Y_{i+1} (*actual*) to Y_{i+1} (*expected*) can be made as near unity as we please.* Thus, if Y_i is sufficiently large, Y_{i+1}/Y_i will differ negligibly from 2α. Even though the network reaches circle i with a large value of Y_i, if $\alpha < 1/2$ subsequent values Y_{i+1}, Y_{i+2} . . . Y_r will be less than Y_i. It becomes intuitively evident that eventually Y_r for some value of $r > i$ must reach zero, whereupon further propagation of the network ceases. Thus, when $\alpha < 1/2$, infinite networks are impossible.

When $\alpha > 1/2$, the expected value of Y_{i+1} exceeds Y_i. By analogous reasoning the conclusion is reached that the network may continue indefinitely, *i.e.*, infinite networks are possible. When $\alpha = 1/2$ it can be shown by more elaborate methods that the probability of an infinite network is zero. Therefore, when trifunctional branch units are involved, infinite networks are possible only when $\alpha > 1/2$.

* This statement is based on Bernoulli's theorem. See J. V. Uspensky, *Introduction to Mathematical Probability*, McGraw-Hill, New York, 1937, Chapter VI.

If the branch units are tetrafunctional, then each chain that ends in a branch gives rise to three new chains. The expected value of Y_{i+1} is $3\alpha Y_i$. Proceeding along the lines of the arguments used above, α must exceed $1/3$ if infinite networks are to be possible.

Considering polymers containing branching units of functionality f, the critical value of α can be expressed by the general relationship

$$\alpha_c = 1/(f - 1) \qquad (100)$$

Regardless of the nature and variety of branching units, the existence of infinite networks requires that the expected value of Y_{i+1} must be greater than Y_i. This is the most general statement of the critical condition. Its analogy to the critical condition for explosion in certain gas phase chain reactions is obvious.*

Flory then considers the relation between the factor α and the extent of reaction, p, as follows:

1. Consider first systems in which there is only one variety of functional group, *e.g.*, a mixture of glyceryl tri-ester and a glycol di-ester of a drying oil acid capable of undergoing dimerization. If the branch unit is trifunctional, the polymerization may be represented by

$$\text{A—A} + \text{A}\!\!\!-\!\!\!\left\langle\begin{array}{c}\text{A}\\ \text{A}\end{array}\right. \rightarrow \left.\right\rangle\!\!-\!\!\text{A(A—A)}_n\text{A}\!\!-\!\!\!\left\langle\right.$$

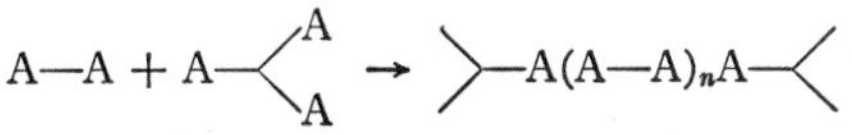

It is assumed that all A's are equally reactive, and that reaction of one functional group of a unit does not modify the reactivities of other unreacted groups of the same unit. The probability, p, that any particular A group has undergone reaction is equal to the ratio of reacted A's to all A groups. This can be determined by analysis.

The probability that an A group of a branch is connected to an A—A unit is given by the product of the probability p that it has reacted multiplied by the probability $(1 - \rho)$ that the unit to which it is joined is not a branch unit. Here ρ is the ratio of A's belonging to branch units to the total number of A's. The probability that the particular A group of the branch unit is connected to a sequence of n bifunctional units followed by a branch unit is: $p^n(1 - \rho)^n p\rho$.

The probability α that such a chain ends in a branch regardless of the number n of bifunctional units is given by the sum of such expressions having $n = 0, 1, \ldots$ etc., respectively. That is

$$\alpha = \sum_{n=0}^{\infty} p^n(1 - \rho)^n p\rho \qquad (101)$$

Upon evaluating the summation

$$\alpha = p\rho/[1 - (1 - \rho)p] \qquad (102)$$

If $\rho = 1$, *i.e.*, if all units are branch units (of the same functionality $f > 2$), then $\alpha = p$.

2. If there are two types of functional group A and B (*e.g.*, OH and COOH in polyesterification), then the formation of chains may be represented similarly by

$$\text{A—A} + \text{A}\!\!\!-\!\!\!\left\langle\begin{array}{c}\text{A}\\ \text{A}\end{array}\right. + \text{B—B} \rightarrow \left.\right\rangle\!\!-\!\!\text{A[B—BA—A]}_n\text{B—BA}\!\!-\!\!\!\left\langle\right.$$

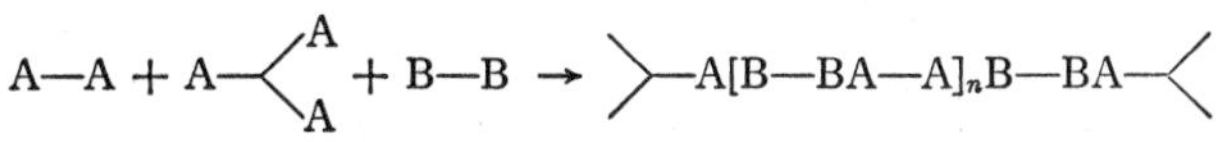

* See N. Semenoff, *Chemical Kinetics and Chain Reactions*. Oxford Univ. Press, London, 1935, p. 45.

If all groups (of the same kind) are equally reactive, regardless of the status of other groups belonging to the same unit, the probability p_A that any particular A group has undergone reaction equals the fraction of the A's which have reacted; similarly, p_B equals the fraction of B's which have reacted. If r is the ratio of all A to all B groups, then $p_B = rp_A$, since the number of reacted A groups equals the number of reacted B groups.

The probability that a given functional group (A) of a branch unit is connected to a sequence of $2n + 1$ bifunctional units followed by a branch unit is

$$[p_A p_B(1 - \rho)]^n p_A p_B \rho \tag{103}$$

where ρ is the ratio of A's belonging to branch units to the total number of A's. Then

$$\alpha = \sum_{n=0}^{\infty} [p_A p_B(1 - \rho)]^n p_A p_B \rho \tag{104a}$$

$$= p_A p_B \rho/[1 - p_A p_B(1 - \rho)] \tag{104b}$$

$$= rp_A^2 \rho/[1 - rp_A^2(1 - \rho)] \tag{104c}$$

$$= p_B^2 \rho/[r - p_B^2(1 - \rho)] \tag{104d}$$

Which of the equations (104c) or (104d) is the more convenient to use will depend upon which of the unreacted groups, A or B, is the one determined analytically.

When $\rho = 1$, *i.e.*, when there are no A—A units

$$\alpha = rp_A^2 = p_B^2/r \tag{105}$$

When $r = 1$, *i.e.*, when A and B groups are present in equivalent quantities $p_A = p_B = p$, and

$$\alpha = p^2\rho/[1 - p^2(1 - \rho)] \tag{106}$$

If the branch unit is trifunctional, the extent of reaction which yields the critical value $\alpha = 1/2$ is reached according to equation (104b) when

$$p_A p_B = 1/(1 + \rho) \tag{107}$$

If A groups are present in excess ($r > 1$), $p_B = 1$ and $p_A = 1/r$ when the reaction is complete. If B groups are in excess ($r < 1$), $p_B = r$ and $p_A = 1$ at completion of the reaction. Hence, the critical value of α can be reached only when r lies within the range

$$(1 + \rho) > r > 1/(1 + \rho) \tag{108}$$

which defines the quantities of excess of one functional group or the other which may be tolerated without rendering the critical value of α inaccessible.

Similarly, if the branch units are tetrafunctional the critical value $\alpha = 1/3$ is reached when

$$p_A p_B = 1/(1 + 2\rho) \tag{109}$$

3. So far it has been assumed that all functional groups of the same kind (A or B) are equally reactive. In one very important case, namely, the glycerol–dibasic acid reaction, the secondary hydroxyl group of the glycerol probably is somewhat less reactive than either primary hydroxyl. If we select one of the functional groups of a glycerol unit at random, without knowing whether it is a primary or a secondary group or whether or not other groups of the same unit have reacted, there is, of course, a definite probability p that it has reacted. However, in the evaluation of α it is known beforehand

that at least one of the hydroxyls of the glycerol must have reacted in order to terminate the chain from the preceding circle (see Fig. 96). If the primary hydroxyl groups are more reactive than the secondary one, there is less than one chance in three that the hydroxyl which is known to be esterified is the secondary one. Hence, with regard to the two remaining hydroxyl groups, the chance that one of them selected at random has reacted is some quantity π less than p. Furthermore, the probability that both remaining groups have reacted is less than π^2. From these considerations it follows that the probability α that one of the two remaining functional groups of the branch unit leads to another branch is not independent of the fate of the other functional group of the branch. In other words α is not an independent probability, and the method presented in the preceding section fails here.

The problem can be solved by the following modification of previous procedure, provided that the relative reactivities of the primary and secondary groups are known. Only those glycerol units all three hydroxyls of which have reacted will be considered as branch units; if only two have reacted the glycerol unit will be considered to continue the chain, and if but one has reacted it will end the chain.

The particular example under consideration here is the reaction of two moles of glycerol with three of a dibasic acid. Let

$$p' = \frac{[\text{primary hydroxyls reacted}]}{[\text{primary hydroxyls present initially}]} \tag{110}$$

$$p'' = \frac{[\text{secondary hydroxyls reacted}]}{[\text{secondary hydroxyls present initially}]} \tag{111}$$

$$p = \frac{[\text{carboxyls reacted}]}{[\text{carboxyls present initially}]} \tag{112}$$

$$p = 2/3\, p' + 1/3\, p'' \tag{113}$$

Presumably, p may be directly determined experimentally. If the relative reactivity of primary and secondary groups is known, p′ and p″ can be calculated from p.*

The probability that any particular carboxyl group is esterified by a primary hydroxyl group is $2\,pp'/(2\,p' + p'')$; the probability that it is esterified by a secondary hydroxyl is $pp''/(2\,p' + p'')$. The probability that any particular carboxyl group is connected to a glycerol unit any two hydroxyl groups of which have reacted, while the third remains unreacted is

$$\theta_2 = \frac{2\,pp'^2(1 - p'') + 2\,pp'p''(1 - p') + 2\,pp'p''(1 - p')}{(2\,p' + p'')} \tag{114}$$

$$= \frac{2\,pp'(p' + 2\,p'' - 3\,p'p'')}{2\,p' + p''} \tag{115}$$

* If the relative rates of reaction determine the relative proportions of primary and secondary groups esterified, it can be shown that $(1 - p') = (1 - p'')^{k'/k''}$, where k′ and k″ are the rate constants for reaction of primary and secondary groups, respectively. In view of the rapidity with which ester interchange occurs in polyesters, the position of the equilibrium

$$R{-}COO{-}CH\langle \; + HO{-}CH_2{-} \rightleftharpoons R{-}COO{-}CH_2{-} + HO{-}CH\langle$$

is probably the factor which determines p′ and p″. If this is the case, then $(1 - p'')/p'' = K(1 - p')/p'$ where K is the constant for the above equilibrium.

Similarly, the probability that the carboxyl group is connected to a completely esterified glycerol is

$$\theta_3 = 3\,pp'^2p''/(2\,p' + p'') \tag{116}$$

According to the above modification of the general procedure, the probability of chain continuation is θ_2; the probability of chain termination with a branch unit is θ_3. By the preceding method

$$\alpha = \sum_{n=0}^{\infty} \theta_2^n\theta_3$$
$$= \theta_3/(1 - \theta_2) \tag{117}$$

Thus, α's can be calculated when reactivities of the functional groups differ, provided that the necessary data are available for distinguishing p′ and p″.

When $p' = p'' = p$, the case under consideration here becomes equivalent to that previously discussed under 2 when $\rho = 1$ and $r = 1$. In this situation (117) reduces to

$$\alpha = p^3/[1 - 2\,p^2(1 - p)] \tag{118}$$

but equation (102) for the preceding case gives

$$\alpha = p^2 \tag{119}$$

The non-identity of these expressions is a consequence of the difference between the patterns, corresponding to figure 96, for describing the configuration of a given molecule according to which definition is used for a branching unit. However, both (119) and (118) lead to the same critical value of $p = 1/\sqrt{2}$ when $\alpha = 1/2$.

In the same paper Flory discusses the experimental verification of the above equations:

For the purpose of comparing observed gel points with the critical points at which infinite networks become possible, experiments have been carried out with three-dimensional polyesterifications in which either tricarballylic acid or pentaerythritol was the branch unit. In the latter the four hydroxyls are exactly equivalent. In the former, one of the carboxyl groups is attached to a secondary carbon atom and the other two to primary carbons. The difference in their reactivities probably is negligible in view of the results obtained by Menschutkin on rates and equilibria in the esterification of primary and secondary carboxylic acids.

In the theory given above it has been assumed that the reactivity of a functional group is unaffected by condensation of other groups of the unit. As is well known, such a condition is generally fulfilled satisfactorily if the functional groups are sufficiently far apart in the molecule. The carboxyl groups in tricarballylic acid are separated by two atoms, as in succinic acid. In the latter it is known that the rate of esterification of one carboxyl group is not changed appreciably if the other has reacted. In pentaerythritol the hydroxyl groups are separated by three carbon atoms, which probably is sufficient.

Finally, if A—A units are present in addition to the branch unit A—<(A)(A), it is necessary that the A groups of both units be equally reactive. Results which follow indicate that this source of error is not important with the combinations which have been used . . .

The results from one of the experiments with tricarballylic acid, succinic acid and diethylene glycol are shown in figure 97. Values of p calculated . . . from the titers of samples removed at intervals are plotted against time.* The values of α and DP_n shown in figure 97 were calculated from p, ρ and r (in this case $r = 1$). Also included in figure 97 is the experimentally measured viscosity† which increases slowly at first, but very rapidly when the gel point is approached. This behavior is a well recognized characteristic of three-dimensional polymerizations.

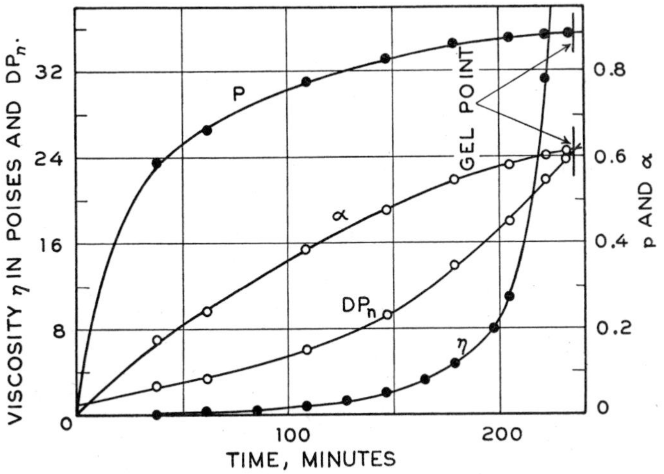

Fig. 97. Results for the third experiment reported in Table IX (109° C.; 0.20 equivalent percent of *p*-toluenesulfonic acid catalyst).

There is no difficulty in locating the gel point. Within an interval of about two minutes, in a reaction such as the one portrayed by figure 97, the polymer loses completely its ability to flow in the viscometer and it becomes elastic. Samples removed just prior to gelation are completely soluble in chloroform or chloroform–dioxane mixture. Samples removed two or three minutes after gelation do not dissolve completely in such solvents, a small amount of very gelatinous precipitate remaining suspended in the solution. The rate of increase in α near the gel point is so small that a negligible error is introduced by the brief extrapolation to the gel point from the data for the last sample titrated.

Data concerning gel points obtained in this way are presented in Table IX. Observed critical values of α in the last column have been obtained from r, ρ and p (obs.) using equation (104c). The calculated critical values of p have been obtained from r, ρ and $\alpha = 1/2$ using (104c), which is based on the hypothesis that gelation is caused by formation of infinite networks, and on the assumption that no intramolecular reaction occurs.

* These results are not believed to be appropriate for kinetic interpretation. The water formed in the reaction may not have been removed fast enough, especially when the material became quite viscous, to prevent appreciable simultaneous hydrolysis.

† As the polymers begin to show elastic properties before the gel point is reached, it is probable that near the gel point rate of shear is not proportional to shear stress, and the viscosity is not a characteristic constant independent of the method of measurement.

Observed values of p and α show that the reaction proceeds appreciably beyond the calculated critical point before gelation occurs. In the last experiment in the table possible differences in reactivities of various carboxyl groups could not vitiate the results, inasmuch as values of r and ρ were such that nearly all of the carboxyl groups had reacted before gelation occurred. Yet, the observed value of α does not differ notably from those in other experiments. In another experiment in which $r = 0.800$ and $\rho = 0.250$ and p (calcd.) = 1.000 for $\alpha = 1/2$, gelation did not occur even when the reaction was practically complete. The ultimate viscosity indicated that the polymer was not very near gelation. Thus, values of α in excess of one-half prior to gelation are not due to unequal reactivities of the functional groups.

TABLE IX

GEL POINTS FOR POLYMERS CONTAINING TRICARBALLYLIC ACID

Additional ingredients, diethylene glycol and	r = [COOH]/[OH]	ρ[a]	p at gel point obsd.	p at gel point calcd.[b]	α observed at gel point
Adipic acid	1.000	0.293	0.911	0.879	0.59
Succinic acid	1.000	0.194	0.939	0.916	0.59
Succinic acid	1.002	0.404	0.894	0.843	0.62
Adipic acid	0.800	0.375	0.9907	0.955	0.58

[a] $\rho = 3 \times$ (tricarballylic acid)/(total carboxyl groups).
[b] Calcd. from [a modification of] equation (102) when $\alpha = 1/2$.

In the polymerization of pentaerythritol with an equivalent quantity of adipic acid ($r = 1$, $\rho = 1$), gelation occurred at p = 0.606 which corresponds to $\alpha = p^2 = 0.366$, compared with α (theor.) = 0.333 for tetrafunctional branch units.

Although the discrepancies between theory and experiment are well beyond the experimental error, there is sufficient correlation to lend support to the hypothesis that gelation is due to infinite networks. The discrepancies probably are no greater than may be attributed to the occurrence of some intramolecular reaction, which in the theoretical treatment has been neglected. Comparing observed and calculated values of p, it appears that if from 2 to 6 percent (depending on the ingredients and their ratios) of the interunit linkages are intramolecular, perfect agreement with theory is possible. In view of the results of Kienle and co-workers and of Bradley this is not unreasonable.

In a later paper (*16*) Flory went even further, and predicted upon the same basis the way in which the weight average and number average molecular weights of the polymer before gelation, and of the sol fraction after gelation, as well as the weight of the gel fraction, change during the reaction:

The statistical treatment evolves from the scheme for representing the "plan" of a three dimensional polymer molecule depicted in figure 96 of the preceding paper. The first task is to find the probability W_n that a chain selected at random from the polymeric mass is a part of a network composed of z chains combined by n trifunctional branch units, where $z = 2n + 1$. The probability that both ends of the chain selected a t random lead to branch units is α^2. The probability that there is a branch at one end (not at either of the ends) and an unreacted terminal group at the other end is $\alpha(1-\alpha)$. A branch unit at an end of the chain gives rise to two new chains, each of which furnishes an additional chain end. The probability that these two additional chain ends lead to networks containing a total of n' additional branch units is $W_{n'}$. It follows that

$$W_n = \alpha(1-\alpha)W_{n-1} + \alpha^2 W_{n-2}W_0 + \alpha^2 W_{n-3}W_1 + \cdots + \alpha^2 W_0 W_{n-2} + \alpha(1-\alpha)W_{n-1} \quad (120)$$

or, letting $W_{-1} = (1-\alpha)/\alpha$

$$W_n = \alpha^2 \sum_{i=0}^{n} W_{n-i-1}W_{i-1} \quad (121)$$

This is the recurrence relationship upon which all subsequent deductions depend.*

A. Solution of the Recurrence Relationship

Let a function $\varphi(\xi)$ be defined by

$$\varphi(\xi) = \sum_{n=0}^{\infty} W_{n-1}\xi^n \quad (122)$$

Then

$$[\varphi(\xi)]^2 = \sum_{n=0}^{\infty} \xi^n \sum_{i=0}^{n} W_{n-1-i}W_{i-1}$$

$$= 1/\alpha^2 \sum_{n=0}^{\infty} W_n \xi^n \quad (123)$$

$$= \varphi(\xi)/\alpha^2\xi - W_{-1}/\alpha^2\xi$$

The solution of (123) is

$$\varphi(\xi) = \frac{1 \pm \sqrt{1 - 4\alpha^2\xi W_{-1}}}{2\alpha^2\xi} \quad (124)$$

Substituting $W_{-1} = (1-\alpha)/\alpha$ and letting $\alpha(1-\alpha) = \beta$

$$\varphi(\xi) = \frac{1 \pm \sqrt{1 - 4\beta\xi}}{2\alpha^2\xi} \quad (125)$$

Binomial expansion of $(1 - 4\beta\xi)^{1/2}$ gives

$$1 + \sum_{n=1}^{\infty} \frac{(-1)\cdot 1\cdot 3\cdot 5 \cdots (2n-3)(2\beta\xi)^n}{n!} = 1 - 2\sum_{n=0}^{\infty} \frac{(2n)!(\beta\xi)^{n+1}}{n!(n+1)!} \quad (126)$$

Substituting this expression in (125), where we reject the alternate positive sign as it leads to probabilities which are negative

$$\varphi(\xi) = 1/\alpha^2 \sum_{n=0}^{\infty} \frac{(2n)!\beta^{n+1}\xi^n}{n!(n+1)!} \quad (127)$$

Comparing (127) with (122) we obtain the distribution function

$$W_n = (1-\alpha)^2 \frac{(2n+2)!\beta^n}{(n+1)!(n+2)!} \quad (128)$$

* For situations in which it is not permissible to consider that α is an independent probability (independent of the fate of the other end of the chain . . . it will be necessary merely to modify W_{-1} appropriately.

Equation (128) expresses the probability that a chain selected at random is a part of a network containing n branch units. Since, according to the assumptions, the length of an individual chain is totally independent of the size of the network of which it is a part, W_n is also the weight fraction of networks possessing n branch units. The weight fraction W_z of networks composed of z chains ($z = 2n + 1$) is

$$W_z = \frac{(1-\alpha)^2(z+1)!\beta^{(z-1)/2}}{[(z+1)/2]![(z+3)/2]!} \qquad (129)$$

where z, of course, is restricted to odd integral values. The quantity z will be referred to as the *molecular complexity*.

Some of the properties of the functions for W_n, or W_z, are grasped more readily when they are replaced by the approximate expressions obtained by introducing Stirling's formula, $n! \cong \sqrt{2\pi n}(n/e)^n$, together with other approximations appropriate when n is large. Then

$$W_n \cong \frac{1-\alpha}{\alpha\sqrt{\pi}} \frac{(4\beta)^{n+1}}{(n+1)^{3/2}} \qquad (130)$$

B. Distribution of Species with Respect to Complexity (z)

Three features of the function W_n are particularly important to the subsequent discussion. First, W_n approaches zero as $n \to \infty$ for all values of β in the physically significant range 0 to 1/4. Second, the series $\sum_{n=0}^{\infty} W_n$ converges for all values of β in the same range (including $\beta = 1/4$), in compliance with physical necessity. Finally, W_n may be expressed in the form

$$W_n = (1-\alpha)^2 F(\beta, n) \qquad (131)$$

As α increases starting from zero, β increases from zero to a maximum of 1/4 when $\alpha = 1/2$, and then returns to zero as α proceeds to unity. The point $\alpha = 1/2$ (*i.e.*, $\beta = 1/4$) represents the gel point as deduced in the preceding paper.

It is obvious from (131) that for every value of β($\beta = 1/4$ excepted), there will be two values of W_n, one for $\alpha < 1/2$ and one for $\alpha' = (1-\alpha) > 1/2$. The distribution of finite species in the polymeric mixture after gelation has occurred ($\alpha > 1/2$) is identical with that for the same value of β before gelation ($\alpha < 1/2$), except for the constant factor $(1-\alpha)^2$ in (128) and (129). That is, the ratio of the weight fractions of each finite species in the two distributions is given by $(1-\alpha)^2/\alpha^2$. In figure 98, W_z calculated from (129) is plotted against z for several values of α in the region up to the gel point. Although only odd integral values of z are significant, continuous curves have been drawn. By appropriately altering the ordinate scale, the same curves may be applied to the sol fractions (*cf. seq.*) in gelled polymers. The curve for $\alpha = 0.25$ represents the complexity distribution for the sol fraction when $\alpha = 0.75$, provided that ordinate values are multiplied by one-ninth. The curve for $\alpha = 0.15$ represents $\alpha = 0.85$ when ordinates are multiplied by 0.0311. In every case the weight fraction decreases continuously toward zero as the complexity increases, the rate of decrease becoming less as α approaches 1/2. For all values of α a considerable fraction of the material is present as single chains ($z = 1$). For $\alpha = 0.15$, 0.25, and 0.50 the weight fractions for $z = 1$ are 0.72, 0.56, and 0.25, respectively. Never is any large fraction of the material found in finite species of great complexity.

C. The Sol–Gel Ratio

The sum of the weight fractions of all finite species is given by

$$W_s = \sum_{n=0}^{\infty} W_n = \varphi(1) - W_{-1} \tag{132}$$

Substituting (125) for $\varphi(1)$

$$W_s = \frac{1 - \sqrt{1 - 4\beta} - 2\beta}{2\alpha^2} \tag{133}$$

where the minus sign has been chosen for the reason previously mentioned. When $\alpha < 1/2$

$$\sqrt{1 - 4\beta} = 1 - 2\alpha \tag{134a}$$

When $\alpha > 1/2$

$$\sqrt{1 - 4\beta} = 2\alpha - 1 \tag{134b}$$

Hence

$$W_s = 1 \qquad \alpha \leqq 1/2 \tag{135a}$$

$$W_s = (1 - \alpha)^2/\alpha^2 \qquad \alpha > 1/2 \tag{135b}$$

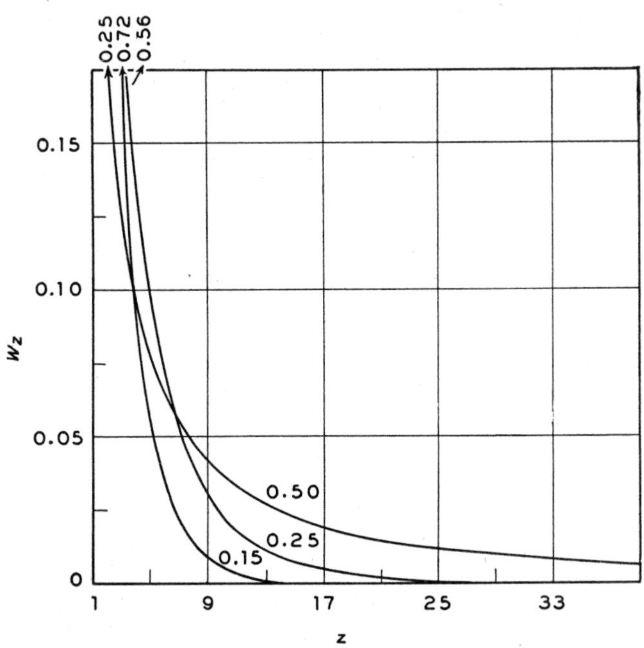

Fig. 98. Weight fractions of species of various complexities z for the values of α indicated.

All of the polymeric material is accounted for by summing all weight fractions W_n given by equation (128) when α does not exceed 1/2. Beyond the gel point, where α exceeds 1/2, some of the material is not included in the sum of all W_n's.

It should be recalled in this connection that in the derivation of the recurrence relationship (121) only molecular species containing n branch units and $n + 2$ unreacted terminal groups are reckoned with. Infinite networks which continue to branch out indefinitely through the polymeric mixture are excluded from consideration by the nature of the procedure employed. A value of ΣW_n less than unity means, therefore, that some of the material is not present in finite networks. The weight fraction W_g of infinite networks may be found by difference. That is

$$W_g = 1 - W_s = (2\alpha - 1)/\alpha^2 \quad (136)$$

Equations (136) and (135) give the weight fractions of sol (finite molecular weight) and gel (infinite molecular weight) in the polymer beyond the gel point. The sol–gel ratio is given by the ratio of W_s to W_g.

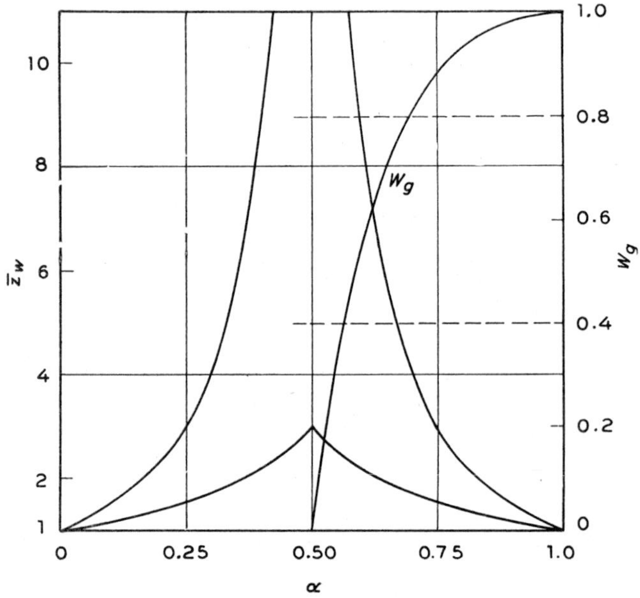

Fig. 99. Weight fractions of gel (W_g), and number average and weight average complexities ($\bar{z}_n$ and $\bar{z}_W$, respectively) as a function of α. The $\bar{z}_n$ and $\bar{z}_W$ curves beyond $\alpha = 0.5$ refer to the sol fraction only.

In figure 99 the weight fraction of gel is plotted against α. The gel fraction makes its appearance abruptly when α exceeds 1/2, increases rapidly with α at first, and then gradually approaches unity as α goes to unity. According to the results of the preceding section, as α increases beyond the critical value, the complexity of the sol fraction decreases. This is the result of preferential conversion of complex species to infinite networks as α continues to increase.

D. Number Average and Weight Average Complexities

Since high polymers are almost invariably composed of mixtures of molecules of various sizes, it is necessary to employ average molecular weights in the interpretation of their properties. However, it is always important to select the appropriate average. For colligative properties one must use the ordinary number average molecular weight $\bar{M}_n$, which is the ratio of total weight of material to total number of molecules. For the interpretation of viscous behavior of polymers and their solutions the weight average molecular weight $\bar{M}_W = \Sigma W_x M_x$ must be used,* where W_x is the weight fraction of species having molecular weight M_x.

If N_0 is the number of chains and Y is the number of branches, and it is assumed that no intramolecular reaction occurs, then the total number of networks, or molecules, equals $N_0 - 2$ Y or $N_0[1 - (4\alpha/2)]$. The number average number of chains per molecule, or the number average complexity, is

$$\bar{z}_n = 1/[1 - (4\alpha/2)] \tag{137}$$

The weight average number of chains per molecule, or weight average complexity, is given by

$$\bar{z}_W = \sum_{n=0}^{\infty} (2\,n + 1)W_n \tag{138}$$

For large n, introducing equation (130)

$$\bar{z}_W \cong \frac{2(1 - \alpha)}{\alpha\sqrt{\pi}} \sum_{n=0}^{\infty} \frac{(4\beta)^{n+1}}{\sqrt{n + 1}} \tag{139}$$

The series in (139) is convergent for all values of β up to the critical point $\beta = 1/4$. At the critical point $\bar{z}_W$ reaches infinity, although, according to the preceding discussion, no infinite networks are present until β exceeds 1/4. Beyond the gel point, $\bar{z}_n$ and $\bar{z}_W$ for the sol fraction are given by the above expressions with $\alpha(> 1/2)$ replaced by $(1 - \alpha)$.

In figure 99, $\bar{z}_n$ and $\bar{z}_W$ are plotted against α: beyond $\alpha = 1/2$, the values refer to the sol fraction. The curve for $\bar{z}_W$ has been calculated by carrying out numerical evaluation of the lower terms in (138), supplemented, for higher values of n, with an evaluation of the integral corresponding to the series in (139).†

During a polymerization process in which bi- and trifunctional units are joined together at random, as in a condensation polymerization, not only does the degree of branching α increase as the reaction progresses, but the chains increase in length as well. Equations (137) and (138) do not reflect, therefore, the true course of the corresponding average molecular weights; as the polymerization proceeds, the average molecular weights will increase more rapidly than the corresponding complexities z. However, it can be shown that the ratio of the two average molecular weights vary approximately as $\bar{z}_W/\bar{z}_n$. This ratio increases with $\alpha(\alpha < 1/2)$ and becomes infinite at the gel point.

From another point of view, it can be shown that at the gel point the number average molecular weight $\bar{M}_n$ is only three-halves what it would have been at the same

* E. O. Kraemer, and W. D. Lansing, *J. Phys. Chem.*, **39**, 153–68 (1935). P. J. Flory, *J. Am. Chem. Soc.*, **62**, 1057 (1940).

† This integral is $\int_{n+1}^{\infty} \frac{(4\beta)^{n+1}}{(n + 1)^{1/2}}\,dn$, where the n-th term is the last included in the numerical summation according to (138). A change of variable to $y = [-2(n + 1) \ln (4\beta)]^{1/2}$ yields the error function $\int_{y}^{\infty} e^{-y^2/2}\,dy$ which can be evaluated from tables.

extent of reaction had the trifunctional units been replaced stoichiometrically with bifunctional units. Although the branch units impart no great increase in $\bar{M}_n$, they may produce a very marked increase in $\bar{M}_W$, particularly if α is near the critical value 1/2. The exceptional condition of infinite disparity between weight and number average is encountered when $\alpha = 1/2$.

It has been shown recently that viscosities of certain molten linear polymers are related to their weight average molecular weights $\bar{M}_W$ by the simple formula

$$\log \eta = A + C(\bar{M}_W)^{1/2} \tag{140}$$

Although this relationship without modification cannot be expected to hold for three-dimensional polymers, the viscosities of the latter probably depend upon the weight average in such a way that the viscosity will increase without limit as $\bar{M}_W$ increases. The course of the viscosity increase* during three-dimensional polymerization finds immediate explanation if viscosity is assumed to depend on $\bar{M}_W$ in this way. The viscosity increases very slowly at first, but as the gel point is approached the rate of viscosity rise becomes increasingly rapid. Since $\bar{M}_W$ becomes infinite at the critical point, the viscosity should become infinite also.

E. Distribution of Species with Respect to Size

Figure 98 offers a rough idea of the distribution of polymer among species of various sizes, provided that it is understood that the weight fraction of species of each complexity z should be replaced by a distribution of molecules ranging in size from very much less to very much more than z times the average molecular weight per chain. The greater the value z, the sharper is this distribution and the more nearly the size distribution curve resembles the complexity curve shown in figure 98. The following quantitative derivation of the actual size distribution affords a more accurate representation of the composition of a three dimensional polymer formed by random linking together of bi- and trifunctional units.

Let q represent the probability of continuation of a chain; that is, q is the mean probability that a given functional group has condensed with a functional group of a bifunctional unit. Then

$$q = p\,\frac{(G - 3\,Y)}{G} \tag{141}$$

where G is the total number of functional groups, Y is the number of trifunctional branch units and p is the extent of reaction, or the fraction of the G groups which have condensed. The probability that a chain selected at random contains y units is given† by $(1 - q)q^{y-1}$. The probability that there are x units in a network of z chains selected at random is

$$Q_{xz} = \Sigma\,[(1 - q)q^{y_1-1}(1 - q)q^{y_2-1} \cdots (1 - q)q^{y_z-1}] \tag{142}$$

where the summation is over all values of the y's consistent with

$$y_1 + y_2 \cdots y_z = x$$

Then

$$Q_{xz} = q^{x-z}(1 - q)^z \frac{(x - 1)!}{(z - 1)!(x - z)!} \tag{143}$$

* See figure 97.

† P. J. Flory, *J. Am. Chem. Soc.*, **58**, 1877 (1936).

Since the average number of units per chain is $1/(1-q)$, the average number of units in a z chain network is $z/(1-q)$. Of the total quantity of z-chain species, the weight fraction composed of x units is

$$xQ_{xz}(1-q)/z \qquad (144)$$

Of the total polymer, the weight fraction composed of x-unit, z-chain species is given by

$$w_{xz} = xw_zQ_{xz}(1-q)/z \qquad (145)$$

The weight fraction of x-unit species, regardless of the number of chains is

$$w_x = \sum_{z=1,3,5\ldots}^{\infty} xw_zQ_{xz}(1-q)/z \qquad (146)$$

Replacing z with $(2n+1)$, and substituting (128) for W_n and (143) for Q_{xz}

$$w_x = 2(1-\alpha)^2(1-q)^2q^{x-1} \sum_{n=0}^{\infty} \frac{h^n x(x-1)\cdots(x-2n)}{(n+2)!n!} \qquad (147a)$$

where

$$h = \beta(1-q)^2/q^2 \qquad (147b)$$

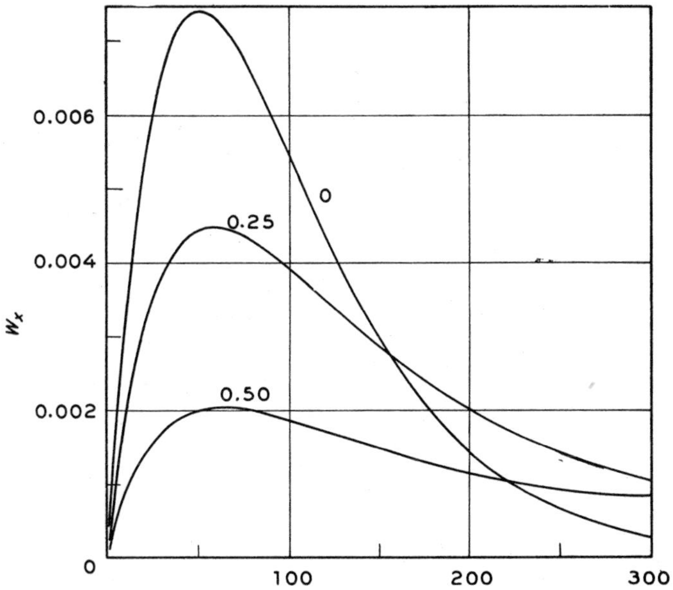

Fig. 100. Weight fraction distributions according to size for q = 0.98 (average chain length = 50) and α = 0, 0.25, and 0.50, respectively. The integrated area under each curve extrapolated to infinity is unity. The abscissa is x.

Since the summation in equation (147) converges rapidly, except when x is very large, it has been possible to carry out the necessary numerical calculations for the construction of the curves for w_x plotted against x, as in figure 100. Here q has been taken equal to 0.98; hence, the average chain length is 50 units. Curves for $\alpha = 0, 0.25$, and 0.50 (critical point) are shown for a comparison of the dependence of the nature of the distribution on branching. The area under each curve extended to infinity is the same. The position of the maximum is shifted comparatively little by an increase in α, although the height of the maximum decreases rapidly as α increases. The quantity of high molecular weight material increases at the expense of the low molecular weight species in such a way that the distribution curve is flattened as α increases. The curve for $\alpha = 0.25$ in figure 100 is also applicable to the sol fractions in gelled polymers when $\alpha = 0.75$.

These curves do not represent the quantities of various species at successive stages of the polymerization, inasmuch as both q and α increase as the reaction progresses (see Eq. 141). They are merely intended to show the dependence of the shape of the distribution curve on the degree of branching α.

2. Cross Linking of a Linear Polymer

Consider a linear polymer, possessing a molecular weight distribution curve (weight distribution) $D(M)$. If this linear polymer is now cross-linked by some chemical reaction, what can be said concerning the molecular structure after a given amount of cross linking has taken place? A typical example of such a reaction is the vulcanization of rubber.

A. Special Case: Monodisperse Polymer

Flory (*16*) has treated this problem in the special case of a linear polymer which, to begin with, is monodisperse. A résumé of his treatment follows.

Flory defines a quantity ρ as the probability that any unit selected at random is cross-linked. Thus for a vulcanized rubber, ρ is twice the ratio of sulfur cross linkages to the total number of isoprene units.

The probability that a chain selected at random possesses i cross linkages, the i neighboring chains possess j additional cross linkages, the next tier of j chains possess k additional cross linkages, etc., and finally zero cross linkages in the s-th tier is

$$R_{i,j\cdots r,0} = P_i P_{ij} P_{jk} \ldots P_{r,0} \tag{148}$$

$$R_{i,j\cdots r,0} = \frac{[(\nu+1)!(i\nu)!(j\nu)!\cdots(r\nu)!]\rho^{z-1}(1-\rho)^{z(\nu-1)+2}}{[(\nu+1-i)!(i\nu-j)!(j\nu-k)!\cdots(r\nu)!][i!j!\cdots r!]} \tag{149}$$

where the total number of chains in the molecule is given by $z = 1 + i + j \cdots r$. Since ν is large, it is permissible to let

$$(m\nu)!/(m\nu - n)! = (m\mu)^n$$

where $(\nu - 1) < \mu < \nu$. Then*

$$R_{i,j\cdots r,0} = \left[\frac{i^i j^k \cdots r^0}{i!j!\cdots r!}\right](\mu\rho)^{z-1}(1-\rho)^{z(\nu-1)+2} \tag{150}$$

* It is evident from the nature of the approximations involved that the best value which can be chosen for μ must lie between ν and $(\nu - 1)$. It will be assumed . . . that $\mu = \nu - 1/2$.

The probability that the chain selected at random is connected to (z − 1) other chains by any possible configuration is

$$W_z = (\mu\rho)^{z-1}(1-\rho)^{z(\nu-1)+2} \sum \frac{i^i j^k \cdots r^0}{i!j! \cdots r!} \tag{151}$$

where the summation is over all combinations of i, j, k, etc., consistent with the conditions $i + j + k \cdots + r = z - 1$ [and] $i > 0$, [and] $j > 0$, etc. The additional requirements that $i < (\nu + 1)$, $j < \nu$, and $k < \nu$, etc., can be overlooked since ν is large and in all situations of interest here the probability of an i, j or k, etc., greater than ν would be negligibly small.

The author has found by numerical evaluations that the summation in (151) is exactly equal to $z^{z-1}/z!$ for values of z from 0 to 9. Salkover has shown that the validity of this simple expression for all values of z can be established by induction. Substitution in (151) gives for the weight fraction of the species composed of z chains the comparatively simple expression

$$W_z = \frac{(1-\rho)^2}{\mu\rho} \frac{z^{z-1}}{z!} \left(\frac{\beta}{e}\right)^z \tag{152}$$

where

$$\beta/e = \mu\rho(1-\rho)^{\nu-1} \tag{152a}$$

The distribution function (152) is subject to the approximations introduced in the preceding paragraphs. It will be shown below that certain further approximations, appropriate when ν is large, are necessary in order to give (152) the proper limiting characteristics. Substituting

$$(1-\rho)^\nu = e^{-\nu\rho}[1 - (\nu\rho^2/2) + (\nu\rho/4 - 2/3)\,\nu\rho^3/3! + \cdots] \tag{153}$$

in (152a) and letting $\mu = \nu - 1/2$

$$\beta/e \cong e^{-\nu\rho}[1 - (\nu\rho^2/2) + \cdots](\nu - 1/2)\rho/(1-\rho) \tag{154}$$

or

$$\beta/e \cong \gamma e^{-\gamma}[1 - (1-\gamma)^2/2\,\nu + \cdots] \tag{155}$$

where $\gamma = \nu\rho$. When the number $(\nu + 1)$ of units per chain is large, the cross-linking index γ is approximately equal to the number of cross-linked units per chain, or twice the number of cross linkages per chain. Situations of most interest are those for which γ is of the order of unity, where higher terms of the series in (155) are negligible. In any case the magnitude of the error introduced by setting $\mu = \nu - 1/2$ probably justifies omission of all terms above the first, giving

$$\beta \cong \gamma e^{1-\gamma} \tag{156}$$

Regardless of whether equation (155) or (156) is used, β reaches a maximum value of unity when $\gamma = 1$, and decreases for higher values of γ. The function $\beta(\gamma)$ is analogous to $\beta(\alpha)$ of the preceding paper. For every value of β (except $\beta = 1$) there are two solutions γ of (156), one of them less then unity and the other greater than unity (see Fig. 101).

Substituting (156) in (151) and replacing $(1-\rho)^2/\mu\rho$ with $1/\gamma$, an approximation which is of the same order as that introduced in the derivation of equation (151)

$$W_z = \frac{z^{z-1}}{\gamma z!}(\gamma e^{-\gamma})^z = \frac{z^{z-1}}{\gamma z!}\left(\frac{\beta}{e}\right)^z \tag{157}$$

Introducing Stirling's approximation $z! \cong \sqrt{2\pi z} - (z/e)^z$

$$W_z \cong (1/\gamma\sqrt{2\pi})\beta^z/z^{3/2} \tag{158}$$

These distribution functions are similar to those of the preceding paper. Throughout the physically accessible range $\beta = 0$ to 1, W_z is finite for all values of z and $\sum_{z=1}^{\infty} W_z$ is convergent.

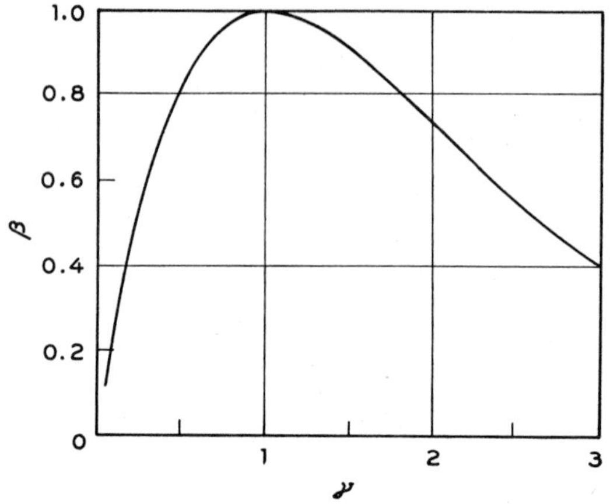

Fig. 101. β *vs.* the cross-linking index γ.

The Sol–Gel Ratio.—It has been found that

$$\sum_{z=1}^{\infty} (z^{z-1}/z!)(\beta/e)^z = \gamma' \tag{159}$$

where γ' is the lower of the two roots of (156) for the particular value of β (see Fig. 101). Hence, when $\gamma \leqq 1$

$$\sum_{z=1}^{\infty} W_z = 1 \tag{160a}$$

and when $\gamma > 1$

$$\sum_{z=1}^{\infty} W_z = \gamma'/\gamma \tag{160b}$$

where γ' is the lower root of (156) for the value of β corresponding to γ.

In complete analogy with the results for trifunctionally branched polymers, the summation of the weight fractions of all finite species is unity until the critical value of the cross-linking index γ is exceeded. Thereafter, the summation decreases continuously as γ increases. This decrease in ΣW_z below unity is attributed to the formation of infinite networks, which are not accounted for in the distribution function. Hence, $\gamma = 1$ represents the critical value for incipient gelation, and, when γ is greater than unity, weight fractions of sol and gel are, respectively,

$$W_s = \gamma'/\gamma \tag{161}$$

and

$$W_g = 1 - (\gamma'/\gamma) \tag{162}$$

where γ and γ' are roots of (156) for the same value of β . . .

Number Average and Weight Average Molecular Weights.—By a procedure analogous to that presented in the preceding paper, the number average number of chains per molecule can be shown to be

$$\bar{z}_n = 1/(1 - \gamma/2) \tag{163}$$

assuming that no intramolecular cross linking occurs. The weight average number of chains is

$$\bar{z}_W = \sum_{z=1}^{\infty} \frac{(\beta z/e)^z}{\gamma z!} \tag{164}$$

$$\backsimeq (1/\gamma\sqrt{2\pi}) \sum \beta^z/z^{1/2} \tag{165}$$

The number and weight average molecular weights are proportional to $\bar{z}_n$ and $\bar{z}_W$, respectively, since the chains are assumed to be of uniform length. As was found in the preceding paper, $\bar{z}_W$ reaches infinity at the critical point, $\beta = 1$, $\gamma = 1$. On the other hand, $\bar{z}_n$ is only equal to 2 at the critical point.

Although the information contained in figure 101 applies only to the special case of a monodisperse starting material, we shall see that *the position of the critical gelation point at* $\gamma = 1$ is independent of the molecular weight distribution curve. That is, if ν, the polymerization degree of the monodisperse polymer of Flory's treatment, is replaced by $\bar{\nu}_W$, the weight average polymerization degree of a polydisperse starting material, Flory's equation ($\nu\rho = 1$) still fixes the critical gelation point.

B. General Case: Arbitrary Initial Distribution Curve

In order to treat the general case we must introduce and define some new terms:

n = the number of monomeric segments in a given linear molecule or linear chain which is part of a cross-linked molecule.

$D(n)$ = the weight distribution curve of the *initial linear* polymer, in terms of n rather than of molecular weight. The symbol D will invariably refer to this same function.

N = the number of monomeric segments in a given cross-linked molecule.

m = the number of linear chains in a cross-linked molecule.

Hence $N = n_1 + n_2 + n_3 + \cdots + n_m$.

$W_m(n_1, n_2, n_3 \cdots n_m)$ = weight distribution function giving amount of material of complexity m, made up of the specific linear chains $n_1, n_2, n_3 \cdots n_m$.

$W_m(N)$ = Weight distribution function governing the amount of cross-linked polymer of complexity m, with a total of N monomeric segments per molecule, regardless of the sizes of the individual linear chains.

$W(N)$ = Weight distribution function governing the amount of cross-linked polymer, of *any* complexity, which has a total number of monomeric segments equal to N.

W_m = Weight distribution function giving the amount of polymer of complexity m, regardless of molecular weight.

X = Fraction of all monomeric segments in the sample which are cross-linked to other chains.

Before presenting the general formula for $W_m(N)$, let us consider the terms $W_1(N)$, $W_2(N)$, and $W_3(N)$. It is clear that $W_1(N)$ must be given by:

$$W_1(N) = (1 - X)^N D(N) \tag{166}$$

Molecules of complexity 2 have a double variability. We must first determine $W_2(n_1, n_2)$ and then $W_2(N)$. If the convention is adopted of labeling the *smaller* of the two linear chains n_1 and the larger n_2, then $W_2(n_1, n_2)$ gives the total weight distribution of molecules composed of two linear chains of size n_1 and n_2:

$$W_2(n_1,n_2) = X(1 - X)^{n_1+n_2-2}(n_1 + n_2)D(n_1)D(n_2) \tag{167}$$

It follows that $W_2(N)$ is given by:

$$W_2(N) = \int_0^{N/2} X(1 - X)^{N-2}\, ND(n_1)\, D(N - n_1)\, dn_1 \tag{168}$$

This can, however, be rewritten by removing the restriction that n_1 is the smaller chain:

$$W_2(N) = \int_0^{N} X(1 - X)^{N-2} n_1\, D(n_1)\, D(N - n_1)\, dn_1 \tag{169}$$

For molecules of complexity 3, let us first introduce the convention that $n_1 < n_2 < n_3$:

$$\begin{aligned} W_3(n_1,n_2,n_3) = X^2(1 - X)^{n_1+n_2+n_3-4}[&n_1(n_1 + n_2 - 2) \\ &+ n_1(n_1 + n_3 - 2) + n_2(n_2 + n_1 - 2) + n_2(n_2 + n_3 - 2) \\ &+ n_3(n_3 + n_2 - 2) + n_3(n_3 + n_1 - 2)]D(n_1)\, D(n_2)\, D(n_3) \end{aligned} \tag{170}$$

To simplify this equation, let us introduce the approximation of neglecting 2 next to $(n_1 + n_2)$, etc. This is permissible if $2 \ll (n_1 + n_2)$, $2 \ll (n_2 + n_3)$, etc.

$$\begin{aligned} W_3(n_1,n_2,n_3) &= X^2(1 - X)^{n_1+n_2+n_3-4} \\ &\times 2(n_1^2 + n_2^2 + n_3^2 + n_1n_2 + n_1n_3 + n_2n_3)D(n_1)\, D(n_2)\, D(n_3) \end{aligned} \tag{171}$$

It is clear that $W_3(N)$ is given by:

$$W_3(N) = \int_0^{N/3} \int_0^{\frac{N-n_1}{2}} W_3(n_1,n_2,N - n_1 - n_2)dn_1\, dn_2 \quad (172)$$

As before, this can be rewritten by removing the restriction $n_1 < n_2 < n_3$. This makes n_1 and n_2 independent variables.

$$W_3(N) = \int_0^{N} \int_0^{N-n_1} X^2(1 - X)^{N-4} n_1(n_1 + n_2) \times D(n_1)\, D(n_2)\, D(N - n_1 - n_2)dn_1\, dn_2 \quad (173)$$

Proceeding in the same manner, there is obtained for $W_4(N)$ the expression:

$$W_4(N) = \int_0^{N} \int_0^{N-n_1} \int_0^{N-n_1-n_2} X^3(1 - X)^{N-6} \times (n_1)(n_1 + n_2)(n_1 + n_2 + n_3)\, D(n_1)\, D(n_2)\, D(n_3) \times D(N - n_1 - n_2 - n_3)\, dn_1\, dn_2\, dn_3 \quad (174)$$

Finally, the general expression for $W_m(N)$ is:

$$W_m(N) = \int_0^{N} \int_0^{N-n_1} \int_0^{N-n_2} \cdots \int_0^{N-n_1-n_2\cdots-n_{n-1}} X^{(m-1)} \times (1 - X)^{N-2m+2}(n_1)(n_1 + n_2)(n_1 + n_2 + n_3) \cdots \times (n_1 + n_2 + n_3 + \cdots + n_{m-1})\, D(n_1)\, D(n_2) \cdots \times D(n_{m-1})\, D(N - n_1 - n_2 \cdots - n_{m-1}) \times dn_1\, dn_2\, dn_3 \cdots dn_{m-1} \quad (175)$$

This can be condensed into the form:

$$W_m(N) = \int_0^{N} \int_0^{N-n_1} \int_0^{N-\sum_i^{m-1} n_i} X^{(m-1)}(1 - X)^{N-2m+2} \times [\prod_i^{m-1} (\sum_j^{i} n_j)][\prod_i^{m-1} D(n_i)]\, D(N - \sum_i^{m-1} n_i) \prod_i^{m-1} dn_i \quad (176)$$

This expression is based on a series of approximations such as equation (171), in which 2 is neglected compared with the values n_1, n_2, etc. If this approximation is removed, the term $\prod_i^{m-1} \sum_{j=1}^{i} n_j$ must be replaced by a slightly more complicated term:

$$\prod_{i=1}^{m-1} [(\sum_{j=1}^{i} n_j) - 2i + 2] \qquad (177)$$

for small values of X, however, equation (176) provides a good approximation to $W_m(N)$. $W(N)$ and W_m can now be written by inspection:

$$W(N) = \sum_{m=1}^{\infty} W_m(N) \qquad (178)$$

$$W_m = \int_0^{\infty} W_m(N)dN \qquad (179)$$

For values of X well below that which causes structural gelation, small values of m predominate. Hence, $W(N)$ is closely approximated by the first few terms of the sum of equation (178). On the other hand, after gelation this expression ceases to be useful as far as the whole sample is concerned. It can still be applied to the sol fraction, however. When X is well above the critical gelation value, the sol fraction is predominantly composed of material of fairly low complexity. Thus the first few terms of equation (178) give $W(N)$ for the sol portion. In the neighborhood of the gelation point, equations such as (178) are of little value, since in this region a large number of terms would have to be evaluated.

The gel fraction can also be described in quantitative terms. The total weight fraction of gel is given simply by difference:

$$W_{(gel)} = 1 - W_{(sol)} \qquad (180)$$

The number of monomeric segments lying between two mesh points of the network, n_g, will follow the (number) distribution law:

$$N(n_g) = (1 - X)^{n_g}X \qquad (181)$$

Furthermore, the gel fraction contains, in addition to the network proper, a number of linear "tails," equal in number to twice the number of linear molecules in the network. If we let n_t represent the number of monomeric segments in a given "tail," the tails follow the (number) distribution function:

$$N(n_t) = (1 - X)^{n_t}X \qquad (182)$$

We now have at our disposal a set of equations which allow us to predict in some detail how the structure of a linear polymer, with initial distribution curve $D(n)$, will change as a cross-linking reaction proceeds.

First of all, while X is small, the initial molecular weight distribution curve $D(n)$ is shifted toward higher molecular weights. The distribution curve $W(N)$ after a very small amount of cross linking, dX, is given by:

$$W(N) = D(N) - N\,D(N)\,dx + dx\int_0^N n_1\,D(n_1)\,D(N - n_1)\,dn_1 \qquad (183)$$

This indicates that the lower part of the initial distribution curve remains essentially unchanged, the middle part is decreased in importance, and the high N portion increased in importance. This is indicated in figure 102. As the reaction proceeds, the high molecular weight "tail" of the distribution curve shoots out to higher and higher molecular weights.

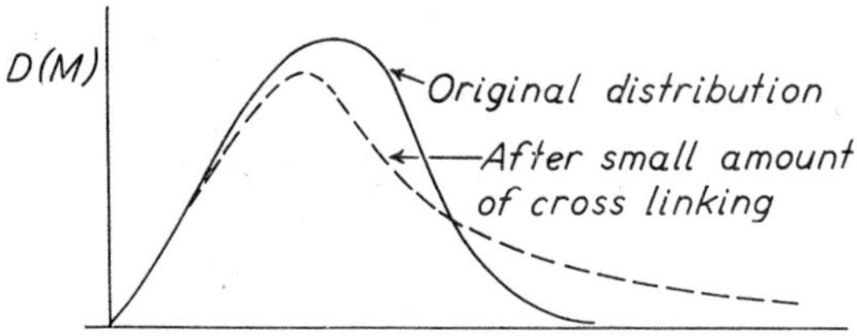

Fig. 102. Effect of cross linking on molecular weight distribution curve of a linear polymer.

This process is governed by equation (183). Eventually structural gelation occurs, according to $X\bar{n}_w = 1$. Beyond the point of gelation, the polymer consists of a three-dimensional network structure, or "gel fraction," and a quantity of interstitial material of finite molecular weight, the "sol fraction." The molecular weight distribution and the complexity distribution of the sol fraction are governed by equations (176), (178), and (179). As in the case of an initially monodisperse polymer, the average complexity and molecular weight of the sol fraction *decreases* with increase of X after the gel point is passed, and it is obvious that the total quantity of sol also decreases. Meanwhile, increase of X results in both an increase in the amount of material in the gel fraction and an increase in the *tightness* of the network, according to equation (181).

It may even be said that *any* structural information concerning such a cross-linked polymer, which may be demanded by a molecular theory of viscoelastic response, can be calculated by extensions of these equations. In this section, of course, certain implicit assumptions were made which may not be valid in particular cross-linking reactions. For example, it was assumed that every segment of the initial linear polymer is just as reactive as any other segment. In the light of present knowledge, this is certainly the most reasonable starting assumption for a mathematical treatment, but it may not hold in all cases. There is some evidence that in a rubber molecule the ethylenic group at the end of the chain is much more reactive than the others. If this is true, the treatment above must be modified in order to apply quantitatively to the vulcanization of rubber.

3. Polymerization Reactions Involving Divinyl Compounds

The third general method of producing three-dimensional network structures is by polymerization reactions involving divinyl monomers. The statistical problem here is identical with that of case 2 (pages 284–292), and should not be confused with a polycondensation reaction involving tetrafunctional molecules. The statistical considerations of case 2 are repeated here, but the results of that section are used without comment. In order to discuss the problem, however, it is first necessary to formulate the basic rules governing the *copolymerization* of two or more vinyl monomers.

The accepted theories of vinyl polymerization agree that polymerization is a chain reaction, consisting of at least three steps: (*1*) chain initiation or activation; (*2*) propagation, or growth; and (*3*) chain termination. Mark, Price, and others have pointed out that there are a large number of different ways in which activation and termination can take place, and that even in a single polymerization more than one type of activation may occur. Some authors have found it necessary to postulate the existence of additional processes such as chain transfer, branching, etc. The complete kinetic analysis of a vinyl polymerization is thus a very complicated problem. If more than one vinyl monomer is present, the problem obviously becomes still more difficult.

In principle, a complete kinetic analysis of a vinyl polymerization would permit the prediction of every detail of the reaction—per cent of polymerization as a function of time, molecular weight distribution curve at each stage of the polymerization, etc. In practice, the number of unknown rate constants which must be determined is large. Practically all of the information which can be deduced from the kinetic model, once it is established, must be determined experimentally in order to fix the values of the various rate constants. In fact, the number of unknown rate constants is often greater than the number of experimental quantities which can be determined with reasonable effort. Vinyl polymerization is in this sense much more complicated than the simplest cases of polycondensation.

This discussion therefore treats vinyl copolymerization and cross linking in terms only of the propagation reaction. Since the initiation and termination steps are not considered, the theoretical deductions obtained are limited in scope. No information at all can be obtained concerning the effect of temperature, monomer concentration, catalyst concentration, etc., on over-all rate, on molecular weight, or on amount of branching due to chain transfer. On the other hand, concentration on the propagation step means that those conclusions which can be drawn are, although few in number, much more certain than the conclusions of a more general approach. In this discussion, certain conclusions are reached which depend only upon the correctness of the general picture of polymerization now commonly held. These conclusions, which are indicated by an asterisk (*) at the end of the conclusion, do not depend upon the correctness of any of the special hypotheses which have been presented by various authors in the past. Regardless of whether the initiation process is first or second order, catalyzed or uncatalyzed, and regardless of whether termination is caused by active chains colliding or by solvent deactivation, these asterisked conclusions are unaffected. The only special assumption is that branching and chain transfer, if they occur at all, are infrequent as compared to ordinary propagation. The penalty for this secure position, as pointed out above, is that no predictions at all can be made concerning over-all rates, molecular weight, etc.

While such a limited treatment yields nothing of interest in the case of an ordinary vinyl polymerization, it would seem to be worthwhile in the case of copolymerization reactions. In a copolymerization, the first question which must be answered is a statistical-chemical question—the distribution of the two monomeric constituents along the polymer chain. Such questions as molecular weight, molecular weight distribution curve, etc., become of interest only after the chemical problem of producing a true copolymer (or at least of evaluating the extent of copolymerization).

The discussion is divided into the following parts:

(A) Copolymerization of vinyl compounds.
(B) Definition of "symmetry" and "independence."
(C) Polymerization of a symmetrical divinyl compound.
(D) Polymerization of an unsymmetrical divinyl compound.
(E) Copolymerization of a vinyl monomer with a symmetrical divinyl monomer.
(F) Copolymerization of a vinyl monomer with an unsymmetrical divinyl monomer.

A. Copolymerization of Vinyl Compounds

Consider the two vinyl monomers A and B. Four propagation rate constants govern the growth of active polymer chains.

$$\begin{array}{llll} \cdots A^* + A & \text{governed by} & k_{AA} \\ \cdots A^* + B & \text{"} \quad \text{"} & k_{AB} \\ \cdots B^* + A & \text{"} \quad \text{"} & k_{BA} \\ \cdots B^* + B & \text{"} \quad \text{"} & k_{BB} \end{array}$$

However, we are not concerned here with the absolute values of the four rate constants, but rather with the two relative values, α and β, below:

$$\alpha = \frac{k_{AB}}{k_{AA}} \qquad \beta = \frac{k_{BB}}{k_{BA}} \tag{184}$$

These two ratios completely define the chemical nature of the resulting polymer, if the propagation reaction is bimolecular.

The first question is: If we start with a mixture or solution of the two monomers, which are present in the molar concentrations (or activities) A and B, respectively, what is the composition of the initial copolymer which forms?

$$\left(\frac{B}{A}\right)_{\text{in initial polymer}} = \frac{B}{A}\frac{k_{AB}}{k_{BA}}\frac{(k_{BB}B + k_{BA}A)}{(k_{AB}B + k_{AA}A)} \tag{185}$$

$$= \frac{B}{A}\alpha\frac{(\beta B + A)}{(\alpha B + A)} \tag{186}$$

In the special case of an equimolecular mixture of monomers, where A = B, the initial polymer has the composition:

$$\left(\frac{B}{A}\right)_{\text{initial polymer}} = \frac{k_{AB}}{k_{BA}}\frac{(k_{BB} + k_{BA})}{(k_{AB} + k_{AA})} = \frac{\alpha(\beta + 1)}{(\alpha + 1)} \tag{187}$$

Thus the initial polymer does not, in general, possess the same composition as the starting monomer mixture. This desirable condition occurs only in the special case where α and β are related by equation (188):

$$\beta = \frac{\alpha(B - A) + A}{\alpha B} \tag{188}$$

Only when $\alpha = \beta = 1$ does the initial polymer possess the same composition as the starting monomer mixture for *all* starting compositions.

When equation (188) is not obeyed, the initial polymer is relatively richer in one component than in the other. The more reactive monomer is thus used up more rapidly, leaving the monomer mixture relatively poorer in this component. It necessarily follows that the last polymer to be formed is relatively richer in the less reactive constituent. The over-all polymerization product is thus a mixture of copolymer molecules of different chemical constitution. The variation of copolymer composition with extent of polymerization is a soluble mathematical problem, but the result is complicated, and probably the explicit expression would be of no value. A more pertinent problem is the *prevention* of this variation in composition, as discussed in the next paragraphs.(*)

If α and β are known for a given pair of vinyl monomers, it should be possible to prepare a copolymer (initial) of desired composition X, by starting with a monomer mixture in which the two components have the relative activity y, where y is determined by X, α, and β; as follows:

$$\left(\frac{B}{A}\right)_{\text{initial polymer}} = X \qquad \left(\frac{B}{A}\right)_{\text{starting monomer mixture}} = y$$

$$y = \frac{(X - 1) + \sqrt{(X - 1)^2 + 4\frac{\beta}{\alpha}X}}{2\beta} \tag{189}$$

This choice of initial monomer concentrations gives an *initial* copolymer of the desired composition, but as the polymerization proceeds, the polymer formed becomes richer and richer in the less reactive component. If it is desired to produce a uniform polymer, all of the composition X, then not only must the starting monomers be present in the ratio y, but this monomer ratio must be maintained throughout the course of the polymerization. This can be done by continuously added additional quantities of the more reactive monomer.(*)

If satisfactory analytical methods are available, it should not be difficult to evaluate the two determining ratios of rate constants, α and β. This can be done by polymerizing two monomer mixtures, in one of which A is present in large excess, in the other of which B is in large excess, isolating and analyzing the initial polymer formed in each case. When A is present in large excess,

$$\left(\frac{B}{A}\right)_{\text{initial polymer}} = \frac{B}{A}\alpha \tag{190}$$

When B is present in large excess,

$$\left(\frac{B}{A}\right)_{\text{initial polymer}} = \frac{B}{A}\beta \tag{191}$$

What constitutes a "large excess" depends upon the relative reactivity of the two monomers. Hence in doubtful cases, equation (185) should be employed, rather than (190) and (191). Two widely separated initial concentrations should serve to define α and β.

It may be important to know how the monomers are arranged in the polymer molecule, as well as the relative amounts. Thus if k_{AA} and k_{BB} are much larger than k_{AB} and k_{BA}, the copolymer molecule mainly consists of long strings of B's and long strings of A's:(*)

—B—B—A—A—A—A—A—A—B—B—B—B—B—A—A—A—A—B—B—B—B—

On the other hand, if k_{AB} and k_{BA} are larger than k_{AA} and k_{BB}, the tendency is to form a regular alternating structure:

—A—B—A—B—A—B—A—B—A—B—

If we pick at random two neighboring monomer segments in an initial copolymer molecule, they may be a pair of A's, a pair of B's, or a mixed pair. The probability of an A being followed by another A is given by P_{AA}, of an A being followed by a B by P_{AB}, etc.:

$$P_{AA} = \frac{A}{A + \alpha B} \tag{192a}$$

$$P_{AB} = \frac{\alpha B}{A + \alpha B} \tag{192b}$$

$$P_{BA} = \frac{A}{A + \beta B} \tag{192c}$$

$$P_{BB} = \frac{\beta B}{A + \beta B} \tag{192d}$$

Such frequencies of neighbor pairs of different kinds may be important in chemical reactions involving simultaneous reaction of pairs of substituents, (*e.g.*, dechlorination of polyvinyl chlorides with zinc, or reaction of polyvinyl alcohols with aldehydes). Such distribution functions are also without doubt important factors in determining the mechanical behavior of a copolymer.(*)

Nonmathematical Predictions Concerning Copolymerization.—In addition to the preceding mathematical expressions, it is possible to deduce a number of qualitative generalizations from the limited theoretical treatment which we have adopted. Some of these nonmathematical deductions follow:

(1) The relative values of the over-all polymerization rates of two vinyl monomers (separate ordinary polymerization) do *not* furnish a good criterion of the extent to which the two monomers will copolymerize. The over-all rate of polymerization is determined by the activation and termination rate constants, as well as the propagation rate constant. Even if two vinyl monomers have the same propagation constant, moreover, they will not necessarily copolymerize. $k_{AA} = k_{BB}$, but the extent of copolymerization is governed by the ratios (k_{AB}/k_{AA}) and (k_{BA}/k_{BB}). Copolymerization involves a specific interaction between two monomers and cannot be predicted from the separate behaviors of the two individual monomers. This does not mean that such methods of prediction cannot be developed but merely that they do not follow from our present theoretical treatment. As far as the writer knows, no satisfactory method of prediction has yet been developed).(*)

(2) Variables which affect only the activation and termination processes should not affect the extent of copolymerization. Thus catalyst concentration and inhibitor concentration should not appreciably influence the chemical nature of the polymer, although these variables markedly influence molecular weight.(*)

(3) A change in temperature results in a change in the value of α and β and thus in the chemical constitution of the polymer, if the activation energies for the four propagation processes are different. However, since these activation energies are small in magnitude, differences among such must be small. One would therefore expect α and β to be only moderately temperature dependent.(*)

(4) The absolute values of the monomer concentrations A and B may be important, as well as the ratio (A/B). If the solution is nonideal, the *activities* of A and B are not simply equal to their concentrations.(*)

The propagation step when 3 monomers are present is governed by 9 rate constants—k_{AA}, k_{AB}, k_{AC}, k_{BA}, k_{BB}, $\cdots$ etc. These reduce to 6 governing ratios

$$\alpha_1 = \frac{k_{AB}}{k_{AA}}, \quad \alpha_2 = \frac{k_{AC}}{k_{AA}}, \quad \alpha_3 = \frac{k_{BA}}{k_{BB}}, \quad \alpha_4 = \frac{k_{BC}}{k_{BB}}, \quad \alpha_5 = \frac{k_{CA}}{k_{CC}}, \quad \alpha_6 = \frac{k_{CB}}{k_{CC}} \tag{193}$$

These 6 ratios can be obtained by experiments on the three possible pairs of monomers. It would be premature to write down the complicated expressions giving the composition of initial copolymer, etc., in a tripolymerization, but these expressions are obvious extensions of (185), (190), etc. The computation of the necessary monomer mixture for the production of a desired tripolymer composition would probably be too complicated to be of practical value.

The following nonmathematical generalizations can be made:

(1) Although it is not possible to predict the course of a copolymerization reaction from the nature of the two individual polymerizations, it should be possible to predict the course of a tripolymerization from the nature of the three separate dipolymerizations. The governing equations are not given here merely because they are algebraically complicated.(*)

(2) Two vinyl monomers which do not normally copolymerize may be caused to do so by the introduction of a third polymerizable component which copolymerizes readily with both of the original monomers.(*)

(3) In order to effect a marked copolymerization of two monomers which do not ordinarily copolymerize, it would seem necessary to add appreciable quantities of the third component. Small traces would not be sufficient.(*)

(4) Only in very special cases should it be possible to tripolymerize a mixture to yield a homogeneous tripolymer.(*)

(5) Considerations (2), (3) and (4) on page 297 apply here as well.(*)

B. Definition of Symmetry and Independence

Let us define a "symmetrical" divinyl compound as one in which the two vinyl groups are identical, and an unsymmetrical divinyl compound as one in which the two vinyl groups are not identical. Thus, divinylbenzene, divinyl ether, divinyl maleate, etc., are symmetrical, whereas vinyl acrylate, vinyl chlorovinyl ether, etc., are unsymmetrical.

Let us define a divinyl compound with "independent" vinyl groups as one which possesses the following characteristic: When one of the vinyl groups is incorporated into a polymer chain, the reactivity of the second, unreacted, vinyl group is not changed. We should expect that a compound in which the vinyl groups are separated by a long, unconjugated chain would fit this definition. There are two different ways in which polymerization of one vinyl group can change the reactivity of the second group:

(1) A change in the electronic structure of the second double bond. If a butadiene type molecule should undergo vinyl type polymerization, through one double bond, the second double bond is very much affected. Originally it is part of a conjugated system; afterwards, a simple vinyl group. The same should be true, to a smaller extent, of divinyl benzene, since there is indirect electronic interaction between the two vinyl groups

of this molecule. Such an effect should change reactivity of the second vinyl group by means of changes in activation energy.

(2) A steric hindrance. If the two vinyl groups are close together, the incorporation of one group into a polymer chain may cause a geometric hindrance to the reactivity of the second. One would expect offhand that *o*-divinyl benzene would be subject to more such steric hindrance than *p*-divinylbenzene, etc. However, it is impossible to predict these effects quantitatively; and in most cases they are probably small. Steric hindrances should affect the rate constant through the A factor.

Unless "interdependent" vinyl groups are explicitly specified, all the following remarks refer to compounds in which the vinyl groups are independent.

C. Polymerization of a Symmetrical Divinyl Compound

A symmetrical divinyl compound, with independent vinyl groups, must by definition (Sec. III. 3A., pages 294–298) polymerize according to the kinetics of a simple vinyl polymerization. As far as the kinetics of polymerization are concerned, the two vinyl groups act as two separate vinyl monomers. The physical properties of the resulting polymer, however, are markedly different from those of a simple vinyl polymer. Every monomer both of whose vinyl groups have entered into polymeric chains acts as a cross link between these two linear chains. When enough of such cross links are present, the polymer exhibits a three-dimensional cross-linked structure and is insoluble and infusible. We know from section III. 1 (pages 269 *et seq.*) that gelation occurs when the number of cross links is equal to 1/2 the number of linear chains. To avoid any misunderstanding, it should be explicitly stated that a "linear chain" in this section may be either a linear polymer molecule or a linear polyvinyl chain which is part of a larger, cross-linked, molecule.

Thus gelation occurs when X, the fraction of all vinyl groups which have polymerized, is equal to $(1/[P - 1])$ where P is the weight average degree of polymerization of the linear polyvinyl chains. This would mean, for example, that if $P = 100$, gelation will occur after about 1% of the vinyl groups are polymerized. At this point about 98% of the monomer molecules are still unpolymerized. Even if the two vinyl groups are somewhat interdependent, the gelation point is probably related to P (roughly at least) by the following expression (neglecting 1 beside P):(*)

$$X_{\text{gelation}} = a/P \tag{194}$$

If the polymerization of the first vinyl group reduces the reactivity of the second group, a is a constant which is greater than 1.

It is clear that any expedient which reduces P allows more monomer to be used up before gelation. Increase in temperatures or catalyst concentration, or reduction in monomer concentration in solution polymerization, accomplish these objectives.(*)

By introducing hypotheses concerning the nature of the activation and termination steps, it would be possible to derive relations between monomer concentration, catalyst concentration, etc., and the location of the gel point.

Alternatively, empirical relationships between concentration and polymerization degree for vinyl polymers could easily be extended to cover the gelation of divinyl polymers. Thus, if, as sometimes seems to be true, the average chain length is directly proportional to the square root of monomer concentration and inversely proportional to the square root of catalyst concentration, then the gel point as a function of these variables is the following:

$$X = a\sqrt{\frac{C_{cat}}{C_{mon}}} \qquad (195)$$

where a is a constant.

One important structural feature of a polymerized symmetrical divinyl compound is the *random distribution of the cross links.* Since each vinyl group is equally reactive, the positions of the doubly reacted monomer groups is completely random. Hence the distribution curves for the chains connecting mesh points and for the loose linear tails is identical with those already defined for the case where a linear polymer is cross-linked by a vulcanization type reaction. These equations are not repeated here. Furthermore, the number of cross links increases in a regular fashion as the polymerization proceeds. The probability that any monomeric group is doubly reacted (*i.e.*, acts as a cross link) is equal to the square of X, the fraction of all vinyl groups which have reacted.

D. Polymerization of an Unsymmetrical Divinyl Compound

The polymerization of an unsymmetrical divinyl compound A ··· B possesses all the kinetic complications of an ordinary copolymerization (Sec. III. 3A, pages 294–298) with the additional complications of cross linking. Since we are dealing with the case where one vinyl group is more reactive than the other, gelation does not occur so early as in the case of III. 3C (pages 299–300). The initial polymer formed mainly consists of linear chains of the more active vinyl group, with dangling side groups containing the less reactive vinyl groups. At a high extent of reaction, even these groups do of course polymerize, eventually giving a three-dimensional cross-linked structure. The onset of gelation should occur at a point X (fraction of vinyl groups polymerized) defined as follows:

$$X = \frac{1}{4\,P}\frac{(\alpha\beta + 2\alpha + 1)^2}{\alpha(\alpha + 1)(\beta + 1)} \qquad (196)$$

In the above equation α and β are the governing ratios of propagation rate constants, as defined in section III. 3A (pages 294–298). If vinyl group B is *much* more reactive than group A, in the presence of either variety of active chain end, then both α and β are much greater than unity, and equation (196) reduces to (197):

$$X = \frac{\beta}{4\,P} \qquad (197)$$

If vinyl group A is much more reactive than group B, in the presence of either variety of active chain end, then both α and β are much less than unity, and equation (196) reduces to (198):

$$X = \frac{1}{4\,P\alpha} \qquad (198)$$

Thus the greater the difference in reactivity between the two vinyl groups, the further polymerization proceeds before gelation.(*) The considerations of section IIB concerning the effect of polymerization degree on the gelation point apply here as well. However, it should be noted that a rather large difference in reactivity is necessary in order to shift the gelation point appreciably.(*) If $\alpha = \beta = 10$, for example (B is 10 times as reactive as A), then the gelation point occurs at a value of X which is only about three times the value which would apply if $\alpha = \beta = 1$, corresponding to equal reactivity. Only at very high values of α and β does the simple proportionality (197) apply, and only at very low values of α and β does the simple proportionality (198) apply.

It should also be remembered that neither equation (196), (197), nor (198) can be applied for large values of X. As the more reactive groups are used up, the introduction of the other vinyl groups into polymer chains are favored by their relatively high concentration. Hence the relative amount of cross linking is greater than that calculated on the basis of the initial polymer composition. The gelation point comes earlier in the polymerization than the point predicted by equation (196). This error is negligible when the gel point comes at a small value of X.

We have seen that the cross links in a symmetrical divinyl polymer are randomly arranged. The same is true in the case of a polymerized unsymmetrical divinyl monomer. The number of cross links is no longer a simple function of the extent of reaction, however. At the beginning of the polymerization there are very few cross links formed. In fact, at any stage in the reaction, the probability that a given unit serves as a cross link is less than the square of X.

E. Copolymerization of a Vinyl Monomer with a Symmetrical Divinyl Monomer

Consider the vinyl monomer A and the divinyl monomer B $\cdots$ B. Let A be the molar concentration of A, and B the molar concentration of B vinyl groups. (Thus B is *twice* the molar concentration of B—B molecules). Gelation occurs when the fraction X of all vinyl groups have entered polymer chains:

$$X = \frac{1}{P}\frac{B}{A+B}\frac{(A^2 + 2\alpha AB + \alpha\beta B^2)^2}{(\alpha\beta B^2 + \alpha AB)^2} \quad (198a)$$

If the component A is present in large excess, equation (198a) reduces to (199):

$$X = \frac{1}{P\alpha^2}\left(\frac{A}{B}\right) \quad (199)$$

The following qualitative remarks would seem to be justified in this second case, where the cross-linking agent is present in much lower concentration than the principal monomer:

(1) The usual inverse dependence of gelation point on average length of linear chains applies here. Any condition which reduces P tends to delay the gelation.(*)

(2) The greater the preponderance of A over B, the further reaction proceeds before gelation occurs.(*)

(3) The position of the gelation point is very strongly dependent upon the ratio α. If α is doubled, the gelation occurs about four times as early in the polymerization.(*)

(4) If P is proportional to the square root of the ratio of the concentration of A to the catalyst concentration, then the gelation point depends on these variables as follows:

$$X = \frac{a\sqrt{A}\sqrt{\text{Catalyst}}}{\alpha^2 B} \quad (200)$$

(5) Considerations (3) and (4) of section III. 3A (pages 294–298) apply here.(*)

(6) Equations (198), (199), (200) apply strictly only for small values of X. If $\alpha > 1$, then B groups are used up faster than A groups, leaving the unreacted monomeric material poorer in B. Hence if gelation is predicted to occur at a high value of X, it is delayed still more by the depletion of B. On the other hand, if $\alpha < 1$, then A is used up faster than B, and gelation occurs somewhat earlier than predicted by equation (198).(*)

(7) If it is desired to produce a thermoplastic polymer which has vinyl side groups available for subsequent cross linking, special methods must be employed (*e.g.*, stopping polymerization before the gel point). This involves difficulties. If the final material is to be highly cross-linked, a large amount of divinyl monomer must be used. The greater the relative amount of divinyl monomer, the earlier gelation occurs.(*)

(8) If $\alpha \neq 1$, the resulting polymer is not homogeneous in its distribution of monomer groups. If $\alpha < 1$, for example, the first polymer molecules formed have relatively few vinyl side chains which serve for cross linking. Later polymer molecules have a large number of such side chains. Thus finally when X approaches unity, the cross-linked polymer is not *uniformly* cross-linked. Along some chains, cross links appear only at rare intervals, or not at all. Along others, cross links are very frequent. The greater the difference between k_{AA} and k_{AB}, the further polymerization proceeds before gelation, but the more nonuniform is the resultant cross-linked polymer.(*)

(9) To summarize, in such a copolymerization we have many controllable variables at our disposal, as (*a*) temperature, (*b*) relative and absolute concentration of monomers, (*c*) catalyst concentration, (*d*) value of α (through choice of cross-linking agent), (*e*) inhibitor concentration, etc. On the other hand, there are many features of the polymer which must be fixed by the proper choice of these variables, as (*a*) gelation point, (*b*) degree of cross linking of final polymer, (*c*) uniformity of final polymer, (*d*) mean chain length at the gelation point, and (*e*) other desired structural features.

High temperature and high catalyst concentration shift the gel point to higher amounts of reaction, but reduce the mean chain length of the thermoplastic material which is formed prior to the gel point. A low concentration of cross-linking agent also moves the gel point to a higher percentage of reaction, at the expense of the degree of cross linking of the final polymer. A low value of α allows more polymerization to take place before gelation at the expense of uniformity of cross-link spacing in the final polymer.

We have seen that the polymer formed from a symmetrical or unsymmetrical divinyl monomer contains cross links which are arranged at random, giving rise to distribution curves for connecting chains and free tails which are identical with equation (181). This is not true of a copolymer formed from a vinyl monomer and a divinyl monomer. Such a copolymer has its cross links distributed in a pattern which is more irregular than a random distribution. That is, the distribution curve for the connecting chains between mesh points is broader than the random distribution curve. Indeed, if the relative reactivities of the vinyl monomer and the divinyl monomer are widely different, there are many very long connecting chains and also many very short connecting chains. This heterogeneity of network structure undoubtedly has a marked effect on the mechanical behavior of the polymer.

F. Copolymerization of a Vinyl Monomer with an Unsymmetrical Divinyl Monomer

The copolymerization of a vinyl monomer A with a divinyl monomer B $\cdots$ C entails all the kinetic complications of a tripolymerization (Sec. III. 3A, pages 294–298) and, as well, the complications of cross linking. No attempt will be made to write down the general equations governing such a polymerization.

IV. STRUCTURES AND MECHANICAL PROPERTIES OF ACTUAL THREE-DIMENSIONAL POLYMERS

The emphasis in sections II and III of this chapter has been almost entirely upon the theoretical aspects of the problem. Section II dealt with the mechanical behavior to be expected from various idealized types of cross-linked structures, and section III dealt with the nature of the structures which are formed in various idealized types of chemical reaction. It is now necessary to consider actual cases of three-dimensional polymers and see to what extent they fit the idealized patterns of these earlier sections.

1. Vulcanized Rubber

In this book the primary effects of rubber vulcanization are interpreted upon the basis of *covalent cross linking* of linear rubber molecules. Vulcanized rubber is thus pictured as possessing a three-dimensional net molecular structure. It must be admitted that the purely chemical evidence for such cross linking is not conclusive. Indeed, some authorities express doubt, in varying degrees, that vulcanization entails primary valence cross linking at all. Midgley (*32*), for example, very strongly espouses the point of view that the effects of vulcanization are due to increased *intermolecular* associative forces, rather than primary valence links, between polyisoprene chains. The author feels, however, that the evidence supporting the presence of primary cross links in vulcanized rubber, although indirect, is conclusive enough to warrant the confident use of the hypothesis.

On the other hand, there can be no doubt that increased associative forces also play an important role in determining the mechanical properties of vulcanized rubber. The behavior of ebonite may allow us more or less to isolate these two effects and evaluate them individually. Ebonite at room temperature is hard and inflexible. Upon heating, it softens in a narrow temperature range to a "rubbery" material of low modulus, with long range reversible elasticity. In the critical temperature range it exhibits the retarded effects characteristic of the brittle point. The high-temperature modulus, although low, is nevertheless higher than that of slightly vulcanized rubber. Two outstanding differences between ebonite and slightly vulcanized rubber are thus: (*1*) the higher brittle point; and (*2*) the higher high-temperature modulus of the former. The first effect is presumably due to the intermolecular associative forces caused by the interaction of sulfur atoms, while the latter is the result of the primary valence network. If α represents the fraction of the combined sulfur which is present in the form of covalent interchain cross links, then $(1 - \alpha)$ represents the fraction which is simply added to single polyisoprene chains. Presumably the fraction α plays the important role in the primary changes accompanying vulcanization (insolubility, reduction of flow, reduction of extension, etc.). On the other hand, both the fraction α and the fraction $(1 - \alpha)$ presumably are important in raising the brittle point. If bound sulfur atoms are able to exert strong forces upon polyisoprene hydrocarbon, then the "associative" effects of combined sulfur should be proportional to concentration (at low concentration). If, however, significant associative forces act only between sulfur and sulfur, then the magnitude of such effects should increase with the *square* of the sulfur concentration at low concentration.

Hauser and Cze (*21*) have investigated this problem from a chemical standpoint and have come to the conclusion that during the vulcanization of rubber sulfur is added both intermolecularly, to form cross links, and intramolecularly, with the end groups of the rubber molecules being particularly susceptible to cross-link formation:

The formation of soft vulcanized rubber has been accounted for by sulfur cross linkages between rubber molecules. On the other hand, the formation of hard rubber is believed to be due to intramolecular addition of sulfur, since ebonite is still noticeably thermoplastic. Soft rubber formation always precedes hard rubber formation. From the insolubility and infusibility of soft rubber and the thermoplasticity of hard rubber, it becomes apparent that cross linkages are mostly formed in the early part of vulcanization. After a certain number of cross linkages have been formed, further combination of sulfur does not seem to produce more. This is an assumption that has to be accounted for. According to Boggs and Blake, the terminal unsaturated groups are more reactive than those in the middle of the molecular chains. Thus, reaction will occur there first. Therefore it can be assumed that cross linking at the terminal double bonds is primarily responsible for the formation of soft rubber. Of all possibilities it is most probable that such cross linking will involve only one terminal double bond and any other double bond which happens to be in the nearest neighborhood. For a single rubber molecule, cross linking will therefore precede intramolecular addition, owing to the higher reactivity of the terminal double bonds. In a mass of rubber molecules both reactions will occur simultaneously, since not all of the molecules will react at the same time. Over a longer period of vulcanization, intramolecular addition of sulfur will become increasingly predominant, while cross linking will cease.

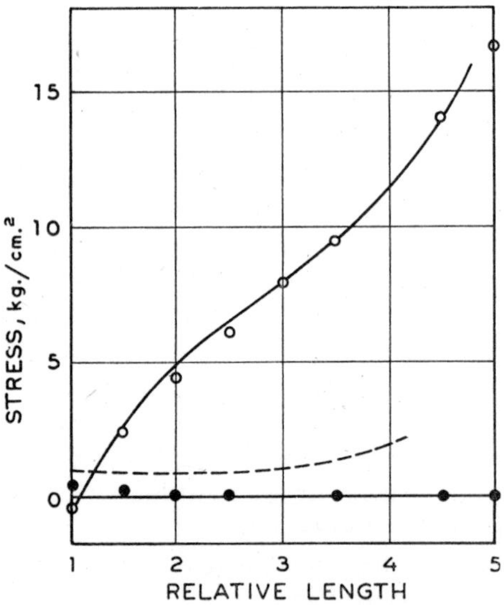

Fig. 103. Comparison between theoretical and experimental stress–strain curves for a Hevea gum sample cured without accelerator. The solid line is entropy contribution (experimental), the circles representing theoretical values of entropy contribution; the broken line is internal energy contribution (experimental), the solid circles representing theoretical values for internal energy contribution.

Guth and James have gone most thoroughly into the question of how the form of the equilibrium stress–strain curve of vulcanized rubber and other elastomers compares with the theoretical predictions of section II (pages 236 *et seq.*). In order to answer this question completely, the observed stress-strain curve must be analyzed into an entropy part and an internal energy part, and each of these must be compared with theoretical predictions. Guth and James have done this for an unaccelerated natural

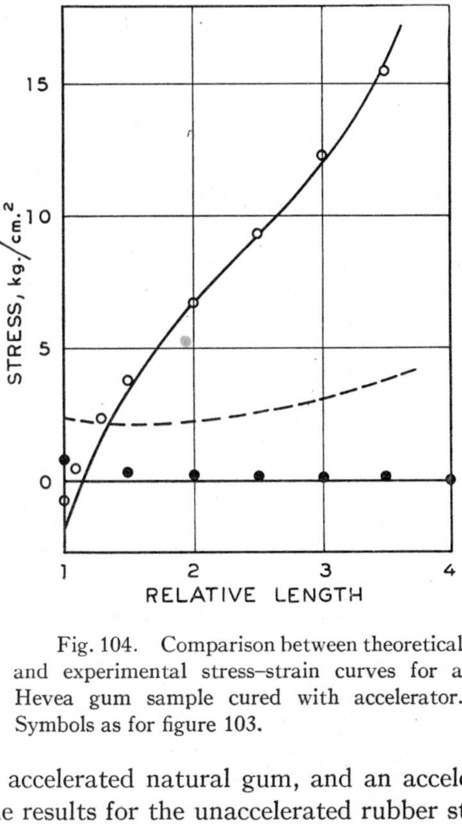

Fig. 104. Comparison between theoretical and experimental stress–strain curves for a Hevea gum sample cured with accelerator. Symbols as for figure 103.

gum rubber, an accelerated natural gum, and an accelerated pure gum Hycar OR. The results for the unaccelerated rubber stock are given in figure 103. (These authors refer the length of the sample to the unstressed length at a certain reference temperature. At any other temperature, therefore, the unstressed relative length is not unity, and the stress–strain curve does not start exactly at the origin.) It can be seen that the stress arising from entropy changes fits the theoretical curve quite well. In particular, there is a slight S shape to this curve, just as predicted by the extended theoretical treatment of Guth and James. Our general theoretical position in the case of amorphous polymers has been to assume that no changes in internal energy accompany deformation. Guth and James, however, include thermal expansion effects and hence predict theoretically a small amount of stress which is connected with internal energy changes. Experimentally it turns out that the energy effect is considerably larger than that predicted theoretically. It is, however, still small compared with the entropy effect.

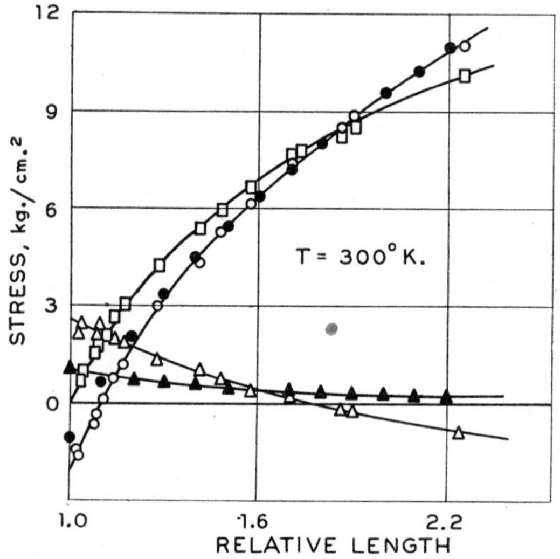

Fig. 105. Comparison of theoretical and experimental stress–strain curves for an accelerated pure Hycar OR gum stock. Open squares represent total force; open circles represent experimental values for entropy contribution; solid circles represent theoretical values for entropy contribution; open triangles represent experimental values of internal energy contribution; solid triangles represent theoretical values for internal energy contribution.

Similar comparison between experiment and theory, for accelerated rubber and Hycar, are given in figures 104 and 105. Again the entropy effect follows the theoretical curve, while the energy effect is somewhat in error.

The following general conclusions from these three cases would seem to be indicated:

(a) The resistance to deformation is predominantly, but not entirely, an entropy effect. Our idealized "amorphous" polymer, therefore, does not exactly correspond to a real elastomer, although it seems to be a good first approximation thereof.

(b) As far as the entropy effect alone is concerned, theory and experiment are in satisfactory agreement.

In the theoretical discussion it was pointed out that elaborations of the simplest network theories went in two different directions:

(1) Consideration of larger degrees of extension,

(2) More detailed consideration of the effects of network structure on the behavior in the region of small strains.

We have just seen that the theoretical predictions of Guth and James, concerning large deformations, are in good agreement with experiment. We shall now consider the experimental confirmation of the predictions of Flory and Rehner concerning the effects of network structure on the multiplicative constant which appears in the various theoretical stress–strain expressions. Flory (*15*) reports as follows:

> The degree of cross linking in a vulcanizate is not easily determined directly. Prior to a recent investigation of the physical properties and structure of Butyl rubber, no comparison between the tension at a given elongation and the independently estimated degree of cross linking in a vulcanized rubber were available. Butyl rubber, a copolymer of isobutylene with a small percentage of diolefin, provides an ideal case for such a test, inasmuch as the cross-linking capacity can be controlled through the diolefin content of the polymer. The concentration of cross linkages formed in the vulcanization (fixed recipe) of Butyl polymers of a given diolefin content was determined as follows: Raw polymers were separated by fractionation into a series of samples of comparatively narrow molecular weight range, each of which possessed the same percentage of unsaturated (diolefin) units and, hence, the same cross-linking capacity. Each of these was compounded and cured under standardized conditions; thus were produced in each sample the same number of cross linkages per unit amount of polymer. The vulcanizates were extracted with cyclohexane at room temperature to remove soluble constituents. These are negligible for fractions of high molecular weight where each molecule on the average enters into a number of cross linkages. As the molecular weight is decreased the percentage of "sol" eventually increases rapidly, reaching 100% at the "gel point" or critical molecular weight M' for incipient insolubility. This critical molecular weight was estimated by an extrapolation of the percentage of sol plotted against molecular weight of the fraction.
>
> From the theory of random cross linking it is known that for molecules of uniform length incipient gelation occurs when the number of cross linkages equals half the number of initial molecules. Hence, the concentration of cross linkages in moles per gram is equal to $1/2\,M'$ throughout the entire series of vulcanizates from polymers of the same cross-linking capacity. Recalling that in a network formed from indefinitely long molecules the number of chains is twice the number of cross linkage, it is evident that M_c equals M', the critical molecular weight for incipient gelation at fixed cross-linking capacity.

Several stress–strain curves for Butyl rubber vulcanizates prepared from fractionated samples differing in molecular weight and in unsaturation are shown in figure 106. The values for M_c, estimated as outlined above, are 35,000 and 20,000, respectively, for the vulcanizates from the low and high unsaturation samples. The tensions at 300% elongation for the high molecular weight rubbers, 108 and 134 p.s.i., respectively, are greater than the values, 38 and 66 p.s.i., calculated from the M_c values using equation (95″). In addition to the discrepancy in magnitudes, the change in "modulus" with the degree of cross linking is less than a direct proportionality predicted by theory. Furthermore, the dependence on molecular weight is rather large.

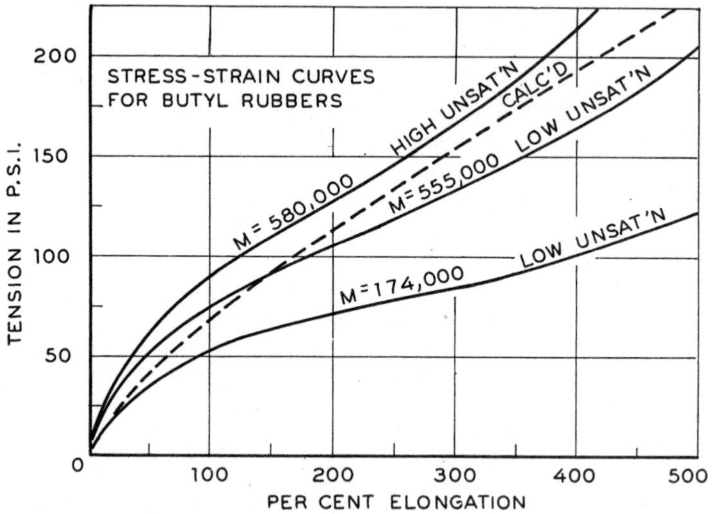

Fig. 106. Stress–strain curves for several pure gum vulcanizates from fractionated Butyl rubber polymers.

Correlation between the [elementary] theory [*i.e.*, page 245] and experimental results on the stress–strain properties of rubber and rubberlike materials may be summarized as follows. The statistical theory of rubber elasticity predicts a form for the stress–strain curve which is in good agreement with experiment. The effect of change in heat content with elongation is small. On the other hand, the magnitude of the observed tension at a given elongation is somewhat larger than the above theory predicts, at least in the case of Butyl rubber. The tension varies less rapidly with the concentration of cross linkages than the predicted direct proportionality. The large observed dependence on the initial molecular weight of the unvulcanized polymer is nowhere taken into account in the elementary theory. Further refinements of the theory discussed . . . provide explanations for these deviations.

These further theoretical refinements are the effects of "network defects," discussed on pages 257–261. Flory proceeds to correlate the experimental data with the predictions of the refined theory:

In figure 107 the force of retraction at 300% elongation ($\alpha = 4$) for a series of pure gum Butyl rubbers vulcanized to the same degree of cross linking (constant M_c) is plotted against the reciprocal of the molecular weight prior to vulcanization. Fractionated polymers of relatively homogeneous molecular weight were used. The plot is observed to be linear in agreement with equations 98 and 99 over the range $M = 114{,}000$ to 730,000. The equation of the straight line in p.s.i. is

$$300\% = 127\,[1 - (77{,}000/M)] \tag{201}$$

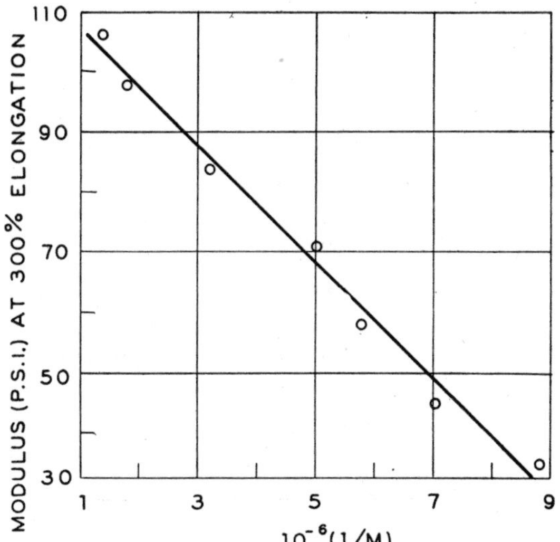

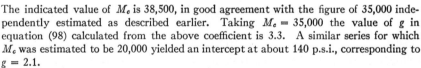

Fig. 107. Relationship between modulus and swelling for a series of Butyl vulcanizates.

The indicated value of M_c is 38,500, in good agreement with the figure of 35,000 independently estimated as described earlier. Taking $M_c = 35{,}000$ the value of g in equation (98) calculated from the above coefficient is 3.3. A similar series for which M_c was estimated to be 20,000 yielded an intercept at about 140 p.s.i., corresponding to $g = 2.1$.

The results shown in figure 107 furnish excellent confirmation for the second factor in equations (98) and (99) and for the explanation which has been given for the influence of molecular weight prior to vulcanization on elastic properties of the vulcanizate. The effects of entanglements in augmenting the elastic tension appear to be rather large. As the degree of cross linking is increased, and M_c decreases correspondingly, the entanglement coefficient g decreases, presumably due to the diminished number of entanglements per chain as the average length of the chains is reduced.

These rather large g factors may in part be due to a peculiarity of Butyl vulcanizates. In the vulcanization of this rubber there are only a limited number of points at which cross linking may occur, namely at the diolefin units which are present only in relatively very small number. Furthermore, the process probably is exhaustive; all diolefin units either enter into cross linkages, or are permanently lost for this purpose due to side reactions in the sulfur vulcanization process. In order for the rarely occurring unsaturated units to meet in juxtaposition, some extreme configurations probably are required. In these the degree of entanglement may be much greater than would occur in a more highly unsaturated rubber in which vulcanization is possible at almost any point were two chains meet.

Nonequilibrium Behavior

The next question is the nonequilibrium viscoelastic behavior of vulcanized rubber. In figure 108 is shown a series of deformation–time curves for hard rubber at different temperatures. It is seen that the

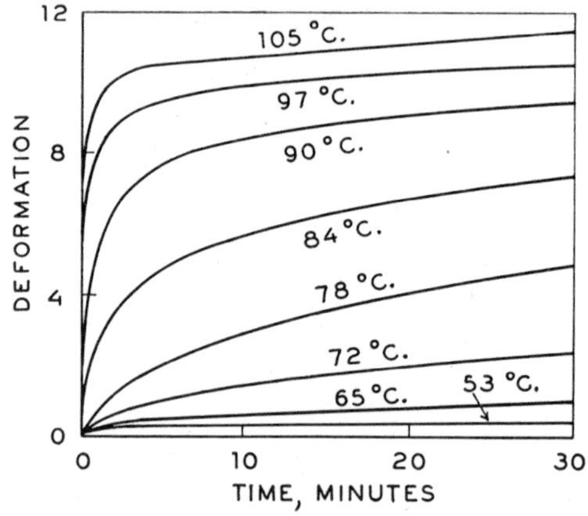

Fig. 108. Deformation–time curves for hard rubber at different temperatures (after Scott).

final equilibrium deformation is nearly independent of temperature, and that the principal effect of temperature is in the rate of attainment of elastic equilibrium. In figure 109 is shown a series of recovery curves following long-duration creep tests at various temperatures. A logarithmic time coordinate is used here. The curves are seen to exhibit the typical sigmoidal shape which is predicted theoretically. Furthermore, the effect of temperature is to shift the curves along the time axis with very little change in shape. The amount of such shift as a function of temperature, however, seems rather erratic. The very large shift between 81° and 82° C. could perhaps be explained by assuming that the "long-duration" test which preceded this recovery test was not of sufficient duration to allow complete elastic equilibrium to be established. Indeed, if the creep test were of the same duration as the following recovery test, one expects just such an effect. Even so, the position of the 88° curve relative to the 82° curve and the 92.5° curve is not in agreement with our theoretical expectations.

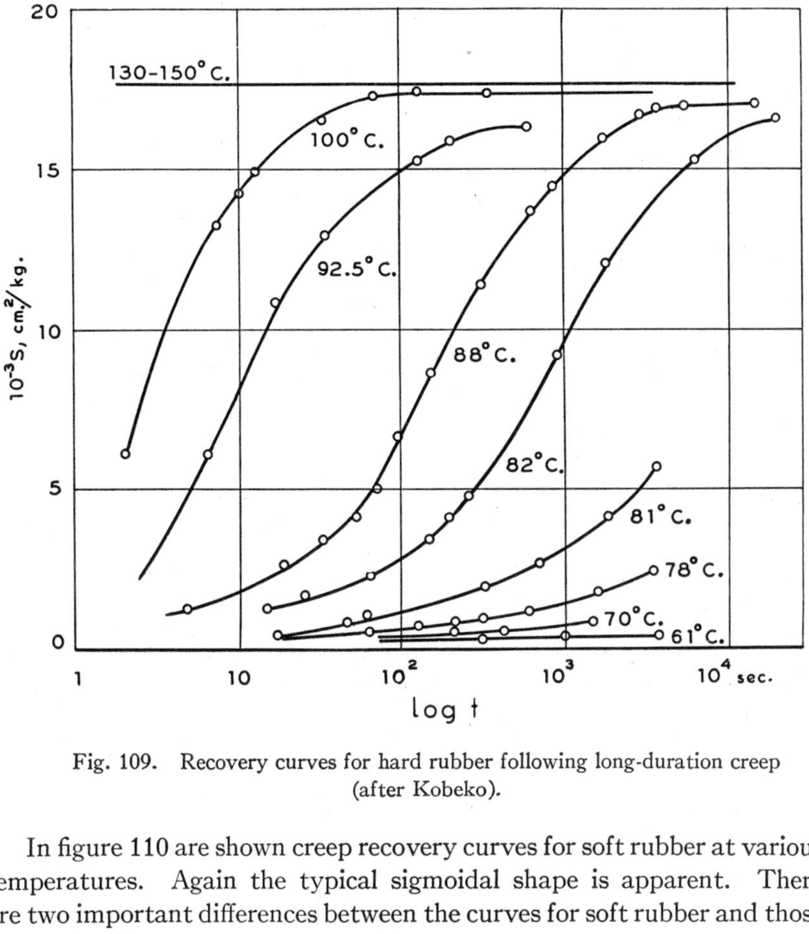

Fig. 109. Recovery curves for hard rubber following long-duration creep (after Kobeko).

In figure 110 are shown creep recovery curves for soft rubber at various temperatures. Again the typical sigmoidal shape is apparent. There are two important differences between the curves for soft rubber and those for hard rubber:

(1) The position of the temperature range in which the creep occurs at a moderate rate. (This can be looked at alternatively as a horizontal displacement of the creep curves at any given temperature.) This simply reflects the fact that the brittle temperature of hard rubber is higher than that of soft rubber.

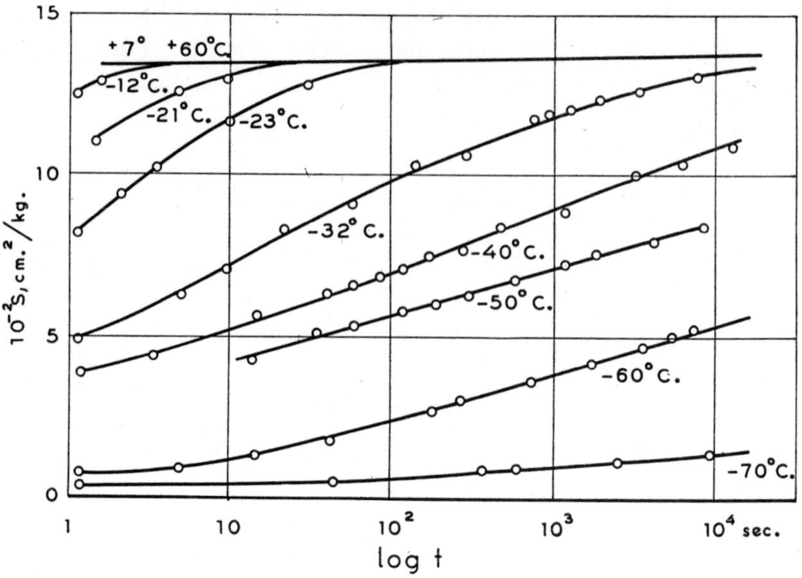

Fig. 110. Creep recovery curves for soft rubber following long-duration creep (after Kobeko).

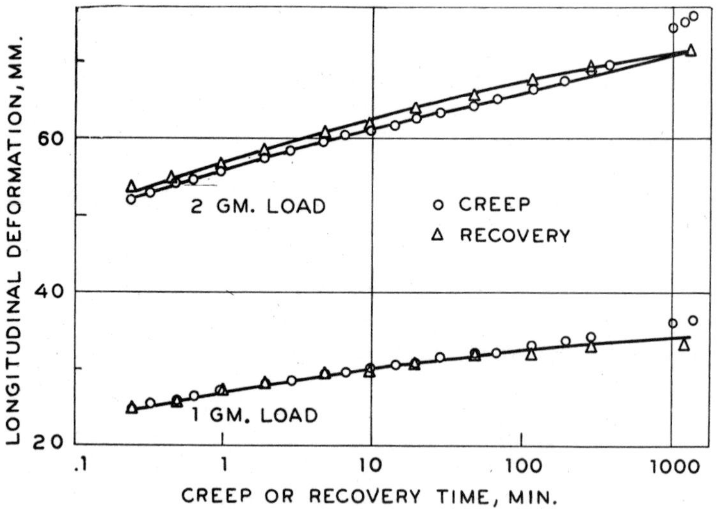

Fig. 111. Creep and creep recovery of a soft vulcanized rubber thread in tension.

(2) The creep curves of soft rubber are much more flat than those of hard rubber. This indicates that the distribution of elastic retardation times for hard rubber is more sharply concentrated about the maximum value than in the case of soft rubber.

As the temperature is increased, the creep curve for soft rubber is shifted to lower timescales. There seem also to be some changes in the shapes of these curves, which is not in harmony with our approximate theoretical predictions. Furthermore, the amount of the horizontal shift seems to be somewhat erratic, just as in the case of hard rubber. This is unexplained by the theory.

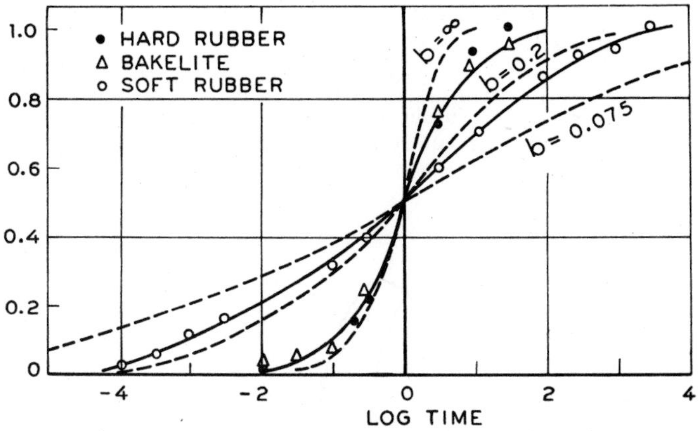

Fig. 112. Normalized creep functions for rubber, hard rubber, and Bakelite. Weichert's computed normalized relaxation functions are also shown.

The creep and creep recovery at different constant loads was studied by Kohlrausch (*28*). Some results are shown in figure 111. It is seen that the recovery curve is nearly identical with the creep curve, as demanded by the superposition principle. Furthermore, the curve for a load of two grams is fairly close to twice that for a load of one gram. This indicates that in this range of conditions soft rubber behaves essentially as a linear viscoelastic material. (The term "linear" here refers to the fact that the material can be represented by a model consisting of ideal springs and dashpots; it does not mean that the *structure* of the polymer molecule is devoid of cross links.)

Leaderman (*5*) has converted some of the preceding results into "normalized creep functions." The actual creep curves are adjusted so that unit time corresponds to the attainment of half the total delayed

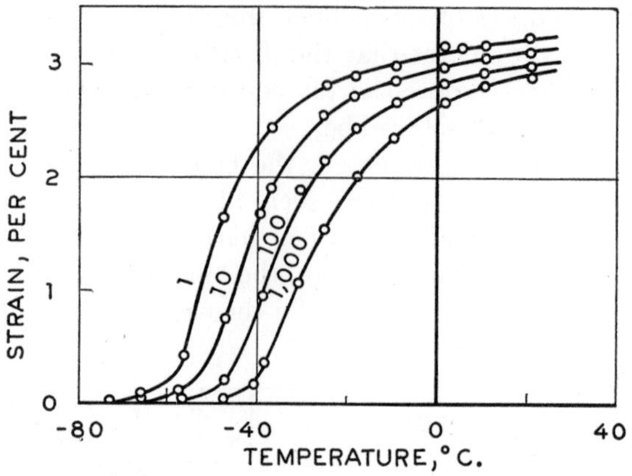

Fig. 113. Strain amplitude of plasticized polymethyl methacrylate at various frequencies of stressing, as a function of the temperature (after Alexandrov and Lazurkin).

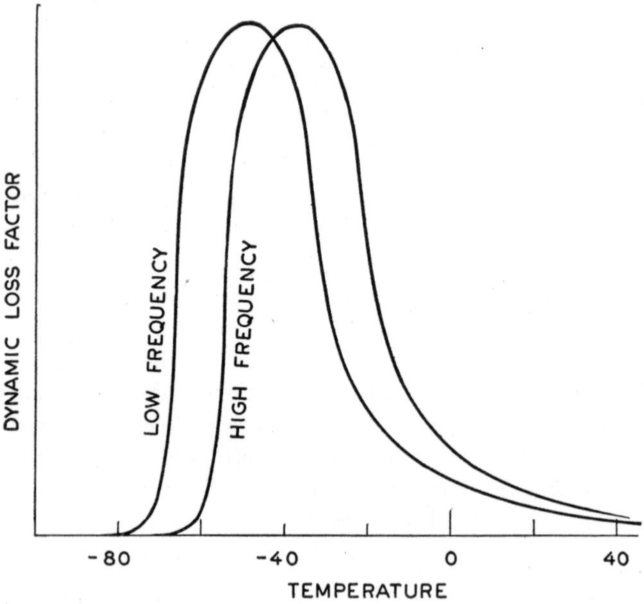

Fig. 114. Dynamic loss factor *vs.* temperature for vulcanized rubber at high and low frequencies.

deformation, by shifting the curves along the log t axis. Furthermore, the total delayed deformation is set equal to unity. Thus all creep curves, plotted in this fashion, pass through the point 0, 1/2 and approach 0 and 1 as asymptotes at the left and right respectively (Fig. 112). On the same diagram with the normalized creep functions for hard and soft rubber Leaderman presents theoretical curves deduced from the assumed distribution of retardation times:

$$J(\tau)\, d\tau = \mathrm{A}\, e^{-b(\ln \tau/\tau_0)^2}\, d \ln \tau \qquad (202)$$

where b is a parameter which determines the breadth of the distribution. It can be seen that the creep curve for hard rubber corresponds to a fairly high value of b—*i.e.*, a sharp distribution of retardation times. The curve for soft rubber corresponds to a smaller value of b—*i.e.*, to a broad distribution in retardation times. This is certainly in qualitative agreement with our theoretical predictions. Whether the agreement is at all satisfactory from a quantitative standpoint could only be decided on the basis of more information concerning the structures of these polymers than is at our disposal.

Another experimental approach to the nonequilibrium viscoelastic behavior of vulcanized rubbers is the study of the amplitude and phase of the strain response to sinusoidal stresses (Fig. 113). This can be expressed in terms of a dynamic modulus and a mechanical loss factor, the significance of which have already been discussed. In figure 114 are shown schematic loss factor–temperature curves for typical rubber stocks.

2. Phenol-Formaldehyde and Related Resins

At an opposite extreme from the elastomers, from the standpoint of mechanical behavior, are phenolic and related resins. Whereas an elastomer, by definition, has its "softening point" well below room temperature, a thermoset phenolic resin is hard and inflexible at and well above room temperature. Such resins would appear to offer many interesting possibilities for study of the relation between molecular structure and viscoelastic behavior. By replacing varying amounts of phenol by a bifunctional molecule such as *o*- or *p*-cresol, it is possible to vary the degree of cross linking over very wide ranges, producing on the one hand completely nonhardening resins, and on the other hand the most tightly cross-linked networks. Unfortunately, however, no such exhaustive study has been made. There is little quantitative information available concerning the viscoelastic behavior of phenolic resins, much less the connection between this behavior and the molecular structure.

One reason for this is the fact that in the case of phenolic resins, more completely than in the case of elastomers, emphasis has been placed upon ultimate strength properties—tensile strength, impact strength, etc. In the working range of temperatures, the viscoelastic spectrum of response is frozen in completely enough that it is not a primary practical problem.

Most commercial phenolic resins are incorporated with fillers such as wood flour or tire cord. As a result, investigation of physical properties is likely to be made upon a complex system of resin plus filler rather than upon pure resin.

Further, the molecular structures of phenolic resins are not simple and can hardly be considered to be nearly as well known as, for example, the structures of the rubbers with which Flory worked. Hence correlation of *any* physical properties with network structure is much more difficult in the case of phenolic resins. Finally, under the conditions where most of the interesting viscoelastic phenomena would occur, a phenolic resin is likely to undergo chemical reaction, changing its network structure simultaneously with the deformation process which is being studied.

As a result of all these difficulties, it is not possible to present nearly so satisfactory a review of the viscoelastic properties of phenolic resins as of rubber and synthetic rubbers. The following remarks are little more than qualitative statements of behaviors which are already commonly known.

An *o*- or *p*-substituted phenol such as cresol when condensed with formaldehyde acts as a difunctional molecule. Hence, the resulting polymer consists largely of linear chain molecules. (Closed rings may also be formed to some extent.) Cross linking is absent, unless occasional cresol molecules act as trifunctional units. The resin so obtained is thus essentially a linear polymer, and fits into the pattern of Chapter B. At sufficiently high temperatures it exhibits a retarded elastic response to stress, and undergoes true flow. Because of the internal rigidity of the chain (benzene rings are actually in the chain) and because of the strong intermolecular forces present, the softening point of such a resin may be well above room temperature. The absence of cross links, however, demands that even if the degree of condensation is high, the resin can be made to soften (show high elasticity) and "melt" (show true flow) if the temperature is raised far enough. For these reasons, such a polymer is often designated as a "nonhardening" resin, even though it is solid at room temperature.

When phenol reacts with formaldehyde, condensation can occur at three places on the molecule. Phenol is thus trifunctional, and the resulting polymer is cross linked. At the beginning of such a condensation reaction, only small polymer molecules are present, and the condensation product is a viscous liquid whose viscosity increases as the reaction continues. Eventually the viscosity increases to the point where the resin appears to be a solid at room temperature, while still "fusible" at higher temperatures, and still soluble. At this stage, therefore, the degree of cross linking is too small to form a single tight-knit three-dimensional

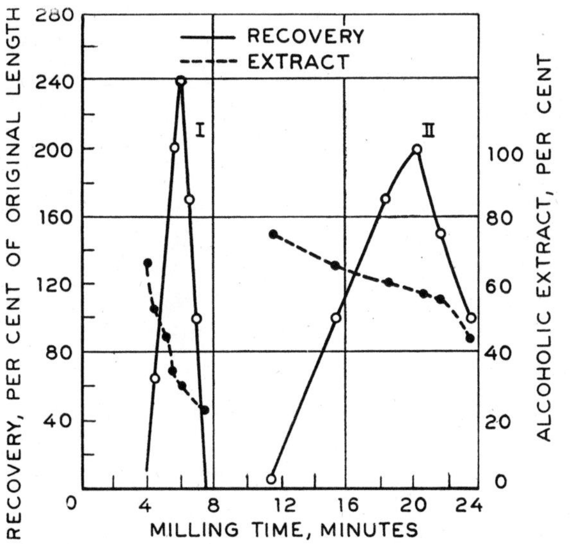

Fig. 115. Elastic recovery and percentage of solubles of phenolic resin as a function of milling time.

structure, although there may be present small clumps of monomeric units which are linked together in cross-linked polymeric structures. As the condensation proceeds further, the sample forms a three-dimensional network structure. Flow is eliminated, only the interstitial material is soluble, etc. This structure then becomes tighter and tighter. In the early stages of such a polycondensation reaction high elasticity is not observed because it is overshadowed by viscous flow. In the middle stages high elasticity is observed. Finally, in the last stages, the close knit three-dimensional network is too tight to allow much configurational elasticity.

An intermediate case between *o*- and *p*-cresol and phenol is a mixture of these—or a mixture of *o*-, *m*-, and *p*-cresols. Houwink (*4*) has made a crude study of the changes of high elasticity with milling time for two such resins. In one case a cresol mixture containing 40 to 45% *m*-cresol was used, in the other 58 to 60% *m*-cresol. In both cases, the measured "high elasticity" rose from a low value (because of the predominance of viscous flow), went through a maximum, and finally dropped off as the tightness of cross linking increased. This change in mechanical properties was accompanied by a reduction in the soluble fraction of the resin. In one respect, these experiments do not agree with what we might expect from previous theoretical considerations. Resin I contains less trifunctional material (*m*-cresol) than does resin II. We would therefore expect that, other conditions being the same, resin I could be carried to a lower alcohol solubility than resin II, before the degree of cross linking became so great as to reduce strongly the amount of configurational elasticity. Figure 115 indicates the reverse is true. Whether this disagreement is due to inadequacy of the theory, to nonidentical conditions of reaction, or to the crude method of estimating high elasticity, it is difficult to say.

Houwink (*4*) reports that as the polycondensation of a phenolic resin proceeds, the flow becomes extremely non-Newtonian in the range where high elasticity is observable. He represents the flow response by the empirical equation:

$$D = \frac{1}{\eta^*} S^n \tag{203}$$

In table X (*4*), the variation of the exponent n as a result of polymerization is shown.

TABLE X

RELATION BETWEEN DEGREE OF QUASI-FLOW (INDICATED BY n) AND THERMORECOVERY

Substance	Polymerization	Exponent n of the relation: $D = \frac{1}{\eta^*} S^n$	Thermorecovery in per cent of total deformation
m-Cresol-formaldehyde resin	Original	1	2
	5 hours at 70° C.	5	27
	10 hours at 70° C.	12	100
Phenol-formaldehyde resin	Original	1	0
	1 hour at 100° C.	1	7
	2 hours at 100° C.	3	35

Finally, the set of creep curves shown in figure 116 indicates that under the proper conditions a phenolic resin can exhibit viscoelastic properties which are quite similar to those of a highly vulcanized rubber.

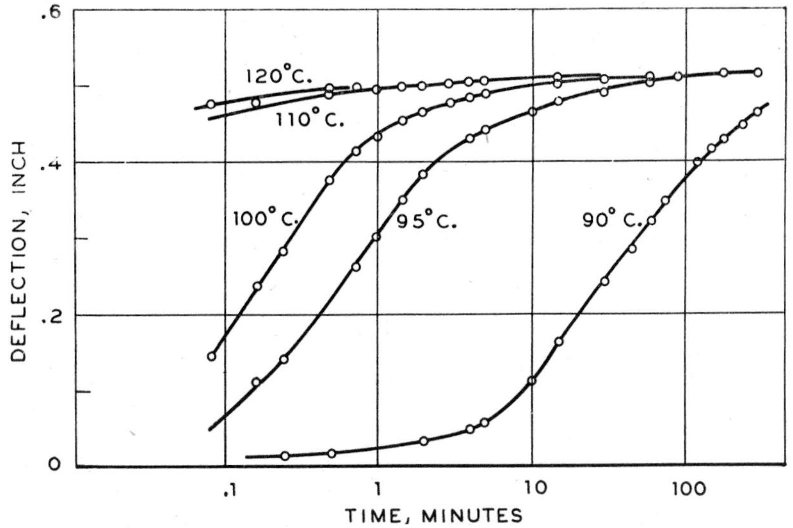

Fig. 116. Deflection of Bakelite beams in bending under constant load as a function of time (curves after Leaderman, data of Hetényi).

3. Wool

Oddly enough, one of the most complete studies of the effects of cross linking on viscoelastic behavior has been made with a natural polymer, wool. The structural material in wool consists of protein chains which are cross-linked by cystine units. Harris and coworkers have broken the S—S cross link chemically without otherwise changing the wool fiber. Then they have reintroduced cross links into the structure, varying the length and flexibility of the cross link. The properties of these various chemically modified wools were compared with those of the original wool. This important work is discussed in the following chapter.

V. CHEMICAL CHANGE ACCOMPANYING VISCOELASTIC RESPONSE

In all previous sections, viscoelastic response has been considered as a purely physical process, involving inter- and intramolecular arrangements of position and shape, but no chemical changes. The sample was assumed to possess a definite molecular structure, and during mechanical deformation each molecule was assumed to retain its identity although not its shape.

We shall now consider a more complicated behavior—where chemical reaction accompanies mechanical deformation. In principle, such a discussion could have been appended to the chapter on amorphous linear polymers; in practice, however, the cases of interest fall in the realm of cross-linked materials. We are mainly concerned with changes in the number or the spatial distribution of covalent cross links due to chemical reaction during deformation, but van der Waals' "cross links" are also discussed.

The treatment is divided as follows:

1. Additional cross linking during deformation.
2. Rupture of cross links during deformation.
3. Breaking and re-forming of cross links.
4. Dynamic interchange of van der Waals' linkages.

1. Additional Cross Linking during Deformation

When an incompletely cured cross-linked polymer is subjected to environmental conditions favorable to a continuation of the curing process, additional chemical reaction take place resulting in an increase in the degree of cross linking. If a stress is present, the viscoelastic response of the original structure becomes complicated by the structural change which is taking place.

2. Rupture of Cross Links during Deformation

Many high polymers are susceptible to chemical degradation—especially under oxidizing conditions. Rubber, for example, is attacked by oxygen and even more readily by ozone. The rate of such degradation reactions is often extremely sensitive to the presence of mechanical stress. Thus ozone attacks stressed rubber much more rapidly than it attacks unstressed rubber. If chemical degradation occurs in a cross-linked polymer, the effect is a reduction of the degree of cross linking—regardless of whether the cross links themselves or the linear chains connecting the cross links are broken.

The mechanical result of such a degradation reaction is a slow relaxation of stress. An idealized (permanent) network of polymer chains possesses a viscoelastic spectrum $J(\tau)$. At any definite deformation, the stress changes with time for a while, but eventually elastic equilibrium is established; the molecular network bears the entire stress, which is given by:

$$S = \frac{1}{\int_0^\infty J(\tau)\, d\tau} \gamma \tag{204}$$

This equilibrium stress should be supported by the network for an infinite time. If the network is actually being ruptured by a degradation reaction, the viscoelastic spectrum $J(\tau)$ is continually changing. The stress decays away, asymptotically approaching zero.

3. Breaking and Re-forming of Cross Links during Deformation

We have considered two irreversible chemical processes—irreversible increase in cross linking and irreversible breakdown. A third possible case is that of a dynamic equilibrium between polymerization and depolymerization (these words being used in the broader sense). Consider, for example, a cross-linked polymer resulting from the reaction between glycerin and a dibasic acid. Even while the total extent of reaction remains constant, individual ester linkages may be formed at one place and broken at another. At high temperatures or in the presence of an esterification catalyst this certainly occurs. The esterification equilibrium is a dynamic equilibrium. In addition, ester interchange reactions continually take place.

As long as no stress acts, these reactions do not affect the mechanical properties of the polymer. The network structure continually changes—but the various detailed forms are essentially equivalent. The cross links are formed in a random fashion, and the statistical description of the network is unchanged.

In the presence of a stress, all this is changed. The deformed network is no longer in its most probable configuration. Thus when a new cross link is formed, it is not randomly arranged relative to the unstrained configurations, and when a link is broken, the neighboring chains are given new freedom which allows the sample to relax the stress upon it somewhat. Eventually, if the sample is held at constant strain, the processes of condensation and rupture result in a structural reorganization which leads to the equilibrium network for the strained shape. The "strained" shape is now the equilibrium shape, and no stress is required to maintain it.

In contrast to cases 1 and 2, a polymer which undergoes such a dynamic equilibrium may still be represented by a mechanical model. The simplest form of such a model is the retarded elastic model which the polymer would exhibit if no chemical reaction occurred, plus a dashpot which represents the relaxation due to dynamic chemical change. The material reponds to a constant stress as follows: (*a*) instantaneous elastic deformation; (*b*) retarded elastic deformation (configurational changes of the original network); and (*c*) network reorganization, which appears as viscous flow.

Both dynamic chemical equilibrium and irreversible breakdown result in stress relaxation at constant deformation. They differ, however, in

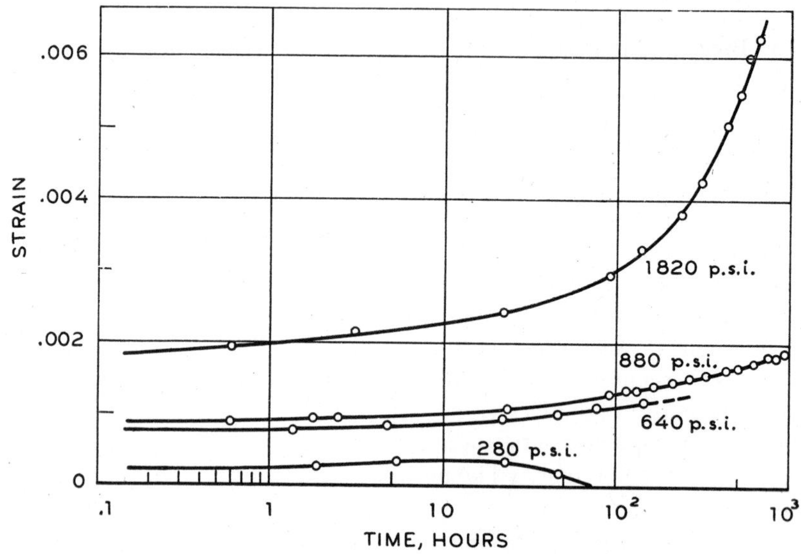

Fig. 117. Set of creep curves for rag-filled phenolic resin.

the following respect: Irreversible degradation has a permanent effect on the statistical nature of the network; the entire viscoelastic spectrum is affected. Dynamic equilibrium, on the other hand, ultimately leaves the network in a structure which is indistinguishable locally from the original structure, even when permanent deformation has taken place.

Only two examples are given below of chemical reaction during mechanical deformation, but these suffice to indicate the widespread occurrence of the phenomenon in practical applications of cross-linked polymers: (A) continued cure of phenolic resins during creep; and (B) relaxation of stress by vulcanized rubbers.

A. Continued Cure of Phenolic Resins during Creep

Telfair, Carswell, and Nason (*40a*) studied the creep of various commercial phenolic resins at elevated temperatures. Some of their results are indicated in figures 117 through 120. Figures 117 and 118 show the creep of rag-filled and tire-cord-filled phenolic, respectively, at various loads and at 90° C. In both cases, the samples which are subjected to small loads (around 300 p.s.i.) show practically no retarded elongation for several hours—and then actually *decrease* in length. The samples

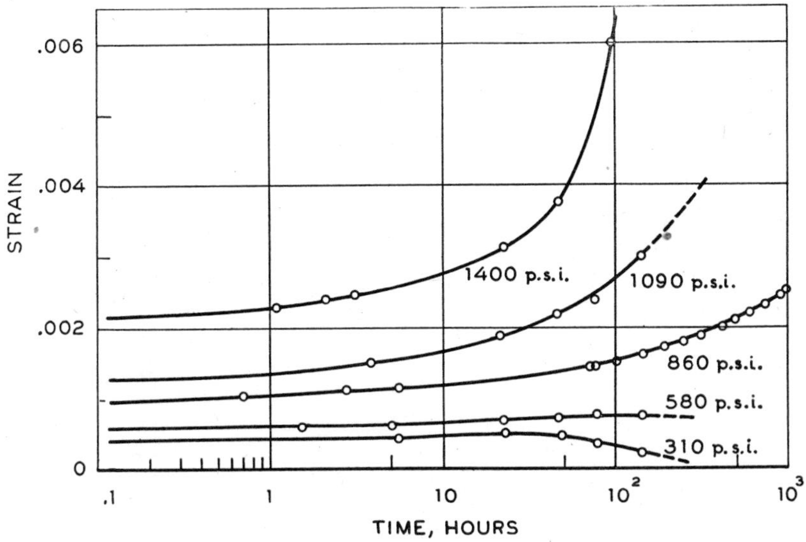

Fig. 118. Set of creep curves for tire-cord-filled phenolic resin.

subjected to larger loads behave in a more normal fashion. This effect is due to a *volume shrinkage* which takes place at the high temperature. In a later study, this effect was investigated in detail. Unstressed samples were placed alongside the stressed samples, and the shrinkage was measured simultaneously with the creep. In figure 119, the linear shrinkage of an unstressed sample is plotted as well as the net change in length of a stressed sample. By difference, the elongation due to creep is calculated and plotted. In this case the shrinkage dominates the creep so that the net effect is a contraction. In Figure 120, similar short-time creep curves at various loads are compared with the shrinkage curve of an unloaded sample. It is seen that the shrinkage dominates the creep when the load is small.

The shrinkage observed here is presumably a continuation of the curing process. "The specimens used in this work were molded at 165° C. with a cure time of 10 minutes. Assuming that rate of cure doubles with a 10 degree rise in temperature, the reaction during molding proceeds only about 180 times as fast as during the creep test. The total time at the molding temperature was only 1/6000 of the time the specimens were subjected to creep. It is only reasonable to suppose that the material continued to cure during the tests."

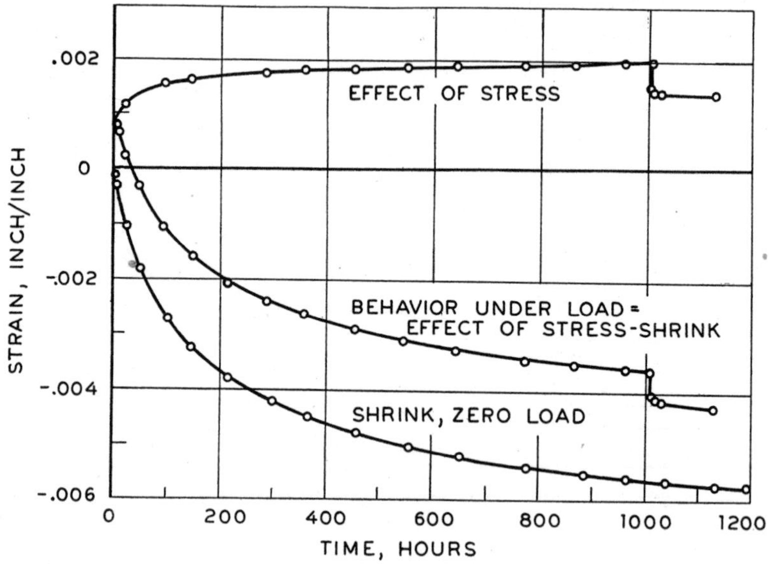

Fig. 119. Behavior under load of woodflour-filled phenolic resin.

At the end of 1000 hours, the samples were removed and subjected to stress–strain tests under standard conditions. In each case the modulus was found to increase as a result of the 1000 hours at 90° C. This substantiates the conclusion that the resins underwent additional curing simultaneously with the creep test.

B. Stress Relaxation in Vulcanized Rubbers

Tobolsky, Prettyman, and Dillon (*43*) have made a very thorough experimental and theoretical study of stress relaxation in vulcanized rubbers. When a sample of rubber is suddenly stretched, and is held at constant elongation, the stress relaxes in the fashion indicated in figure 121. The left hand part of this curve represents the retarded establish-

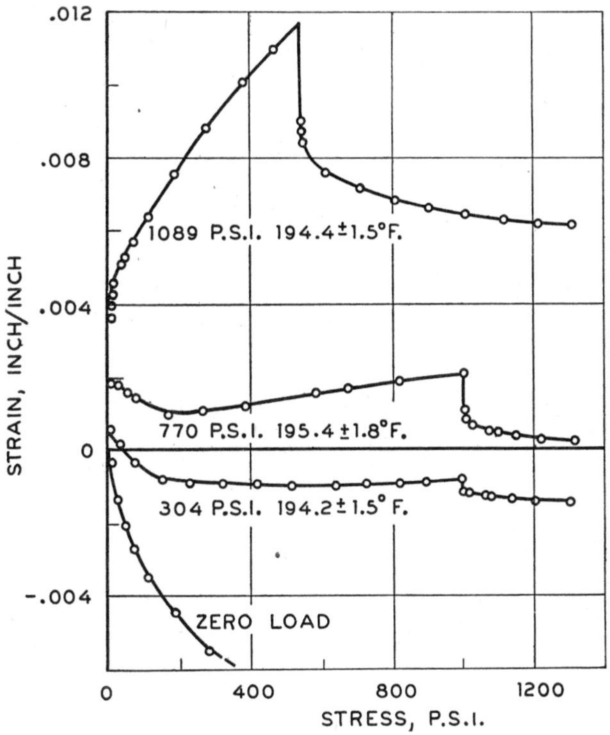

Fig. 120. Behavior under load of tire-cord-filled phenolic resin.

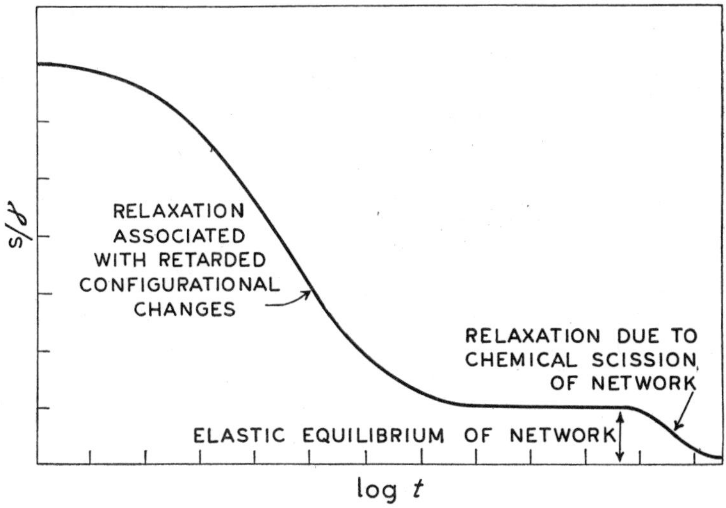

Fig. 121. Stress relaxation curve of vulcanized rubber (schematic).

ment of configurational elastic equilibrium for the network. This process has already been discussed and is of no interest here. The right hand portion of the curve represents a chemical change in which the network structure is altered. This chemical change takes place much more slowly than the retarded elastic changes; in fact, it becomes appreciable only at elevated temperatures where the configurational elastic equilibrium is attained in much less than a second.

Apparently the chemical reaction involved here is a "bond rupture by oxidative scission at some point along the molecular chains or at the network junctures." The authors found that the rate of stress relaxation was the same in an atmosphere of commercial nitrogen as in air, but they report the findings of Schneider and Magat that in an atmosphere of highly purified nitrogen the rate is reduced by fortyfold. The authors point out, however, that, taken by itself, stress relaxation could be explained by: (*1*) bond rupture by oxidative scission, or (*2*) spontaneous bond rupture at or adjacent to the cross-linking bonds put in by vulcanization. They proceed to predict theoretically the nature of the stress relaxation curve, on the basis of ordinary chemical kinetics:

From the kinetic theory of elasticity, the stress is given by:

$$\tau = \mathrm{s}kT\left[\frac{l}{l_0} - \left(\frac{l_0}{l}\right)^2\right] \tag{205}$$

where τ is the tension, s the number of chains per unit volume supporting the stress, k is Boltzmann's constant, T the absolute temperature, and l/l_0 the ratio of stretched to unstretched length. Although equation (205) is not exact, it shows what is important in the discussion; namely, that the stress is proportional to the number of effective chains per unit volume.

Alternatively, one can write

$$\tau = (\mathrm{S}_1 + \mathrm{S}_2)kT\left[\frac{l}{l_0} - \left(\frac{l_0}{l}\right)^2\right] \tag{206}$$

where S_1 is the number of chains per unit volume terminated at both ends by primary cross bonds and S_2 the number of chains per unit volume terminated by at least one secondary bond.

The relaxation of secondary network bonds plays a role in the initial portion of the experiment at sufficiently low temperatures. These postulated bonds have a natural time of relaxation; that is, the bonds break and remake in new positions which allow the molecular chains to resume coiled configurations and thus release the stress. This phenomenon is distinguished from the breaking of primary bonds by being completely reversible.

In large part, the observable decay of stress at high temperatures is due to the breaking of bonds of the kind postulated in mechanisms (205) and (206) above. These bonds do not remake, and the processes are not reversible, as was seen by the fact that the tensile strength of the rubber bands decayed concomitantly. At fairly high temperature the number of secondary bonds holding the stress has decayed practically to zero in the time before the first measurement is taken. In this case the number of chains per unit volume supporting the stress is reduced by bond rupture somewhere along these chains by the following law:

$$-\frac{1}{S_1}\frac{dS_1}{dt} = K'_{S_1} \tag{207}$$

where K'_{S_1} is a reaction rate constant which by the theory of absolute reaction rates is given by:

$$K'_{S_1} = kT/h \exp\left(-\Delta F_1\ddagger/RT\right) \tag{208}$$

where k is Boltzmann's constant, h is Planck's constant, R the gas constant, $\Delta F_1\ddagger$ the free energy of activation per mole, and T the absolute temperature.

Integration of equation (207) and substitution in (205) gives:

$$\tau = S_{1,0} \exp\left(-K'_{S_1}t\right)kT\left[\frac{l}{l_0} - \left(\frac{l_0}{l}\right)^2\right] \tag{209}$$

where $S_{1,0}$ is the initial number of chains per unit volume. Otherwise stated:

$$\tau = \tau_0 \exp\left(-K'_{S_1}t\right) \tag{210}$$

where τ_0 is the initial stress. More generally, the expression that should be valid for low temperatures is:

$$\tau = (S_{1,0} \exp[-K'_{S_1}t) + S_{2,0} \exp(-K'_{S_2}t)]kT\left[\frac{l}{l_0} - \left(\frac{l_0}{l}\right)^2\right] \tag{211}$$

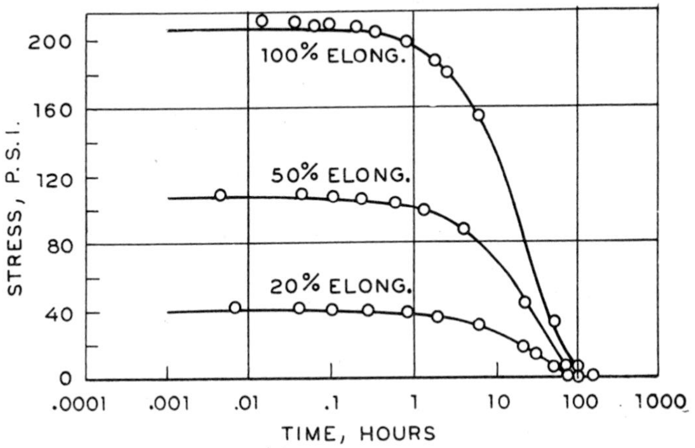

Fig. 122. Stress relaxation curves. Hevea gum stock; 100°C. Note agreement between experimental points and theoretical curves.

Equation (210) agreed remarkably well with the observed relaxation of stress for natural gum rubber (see Figs. 122 and 126). The reaction rate constants K'_S turned out to be nearly independent of the elongation of the rubber (and therefore independent of the stress in the network). In the range studied, the temperature dependence of K'_S

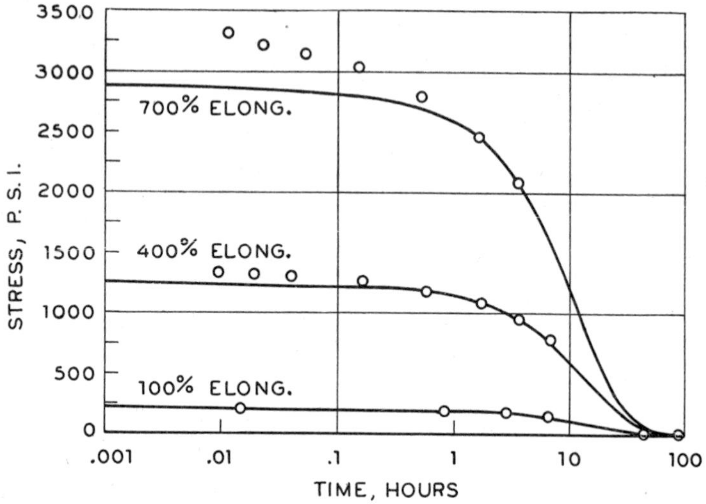

Fig. 123. Stress relaxation curves of Hevea gum stock at 100°C. Note agreement between experimental points and theoretical curves.

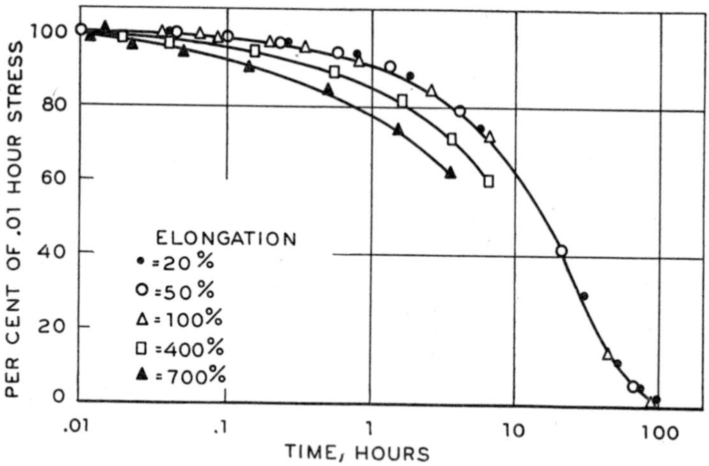

Fig. 124. Stress relaxation curves. Effect of elongation on relaxation rate for Hevea gum at 100°C.

was given with great exactness by equation (208) with $\Delta F\ddagger$ being entirely energy of activation (no entropy of activation). $\Delta F\ddagger$ for natural gum rubber turned out to be 30.4 kcal. per mole and the exactness of the temperature relationship of K_S' is shown by figure 126 which gives theoretical curves and observed data. The theoretical curves were all obtained by assuming $\Delta F\ddagger = 30.4$ kcal. per mole, taking the observed values for τ_0 (with a slight correction of less than three percent for secondary bond slippage), and determining the curves from equations (208) and (210).

The independence of $\Delta F\ddagger$ on the elongation is shown in figures 122 to 125 where theoretical curves are plotted against observed points for Hevea gum at 100°C. and at different elongations. At the very high elongations (400 and 700 percent) the theoretical equations did not fit the data with the same exactness as at the lower elongations (Fig. 123). Also the specimens broke before the decay of stress was very considerable. It appears reasonable from the observed data to say that the relaxation rate was greater than at 100 percent elongation, but certainly not more than three times as great. It is possible that for these very high elongations, the valence angles of the long chain molecules were somewhat stretched, thus hastening reaction. For 20, 50, and 100 percent elongations, the relaxation rates were practically identical.

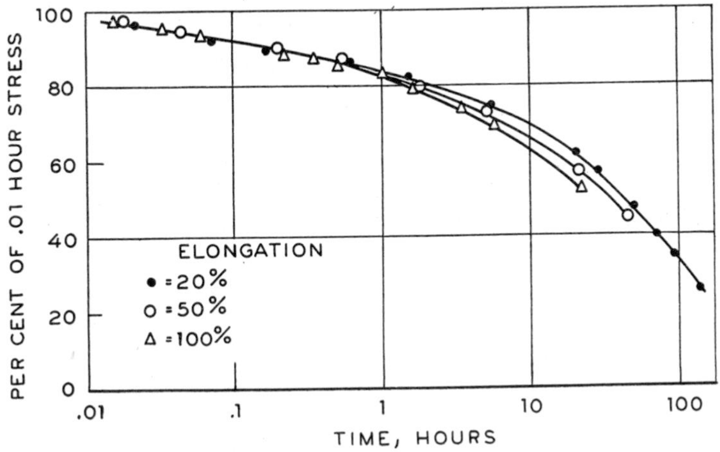

Fig. 125. Stress relaxation curves. Effect of elongation on relaxation rate for GR–S tread at 100°C.

This oxidative scission of chains is not the only chemical reaction which takes place at high temperatures, however. There is in addition an oxidative cross-linking reaction which *increases* the tightness of the network structure.

. . . Most frequently these reactions occur simultaneously, and in some cases the cross-linking effect follows very closely after scission. The physical appearance of the samples exposed to air at high temperatures in the relaxation apparatus is indicative of this behavior, some samples going through a tacky stage and then a brittle stage. The tackiness is of course to be associated with scission of chains and stress decay. In the case of natural rubber the tacky range is quite large; in the case of GR-S, quite transient. It appears that occurring simultaneously with the scission of chains, a cross-linking reaction occurs which tends to produce hardness and brittleness. This reaction is initially slower than the scission reaction in Hevea, but in GR-S the hardening reaction is always faster.

The physical appearance of specimens of Hevea and GR-S in the temperature box for 20 hours at various temperatures is shown in Table XI. These varying behaviors for different type stocks may have important implications in the wearing and cracking of rubber articles, such as tires, subjected to stress at high temperatures.

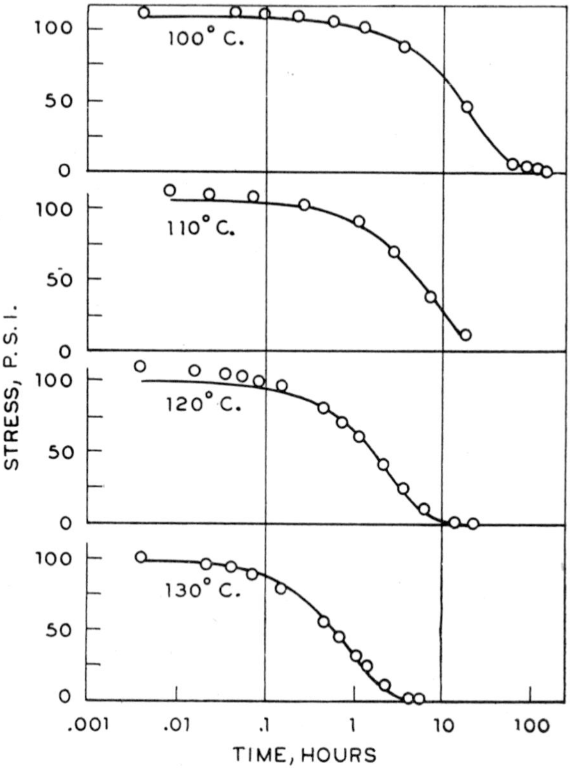

Fig. 126. Stress relaxation curves for Hevea gum stock at 50% elongation. Note agreement between experimental points and theoretical curves.

The importance of the relaxation of stress method is that it measures exclusively the rate of chain cutting at high temperatures. Inasmuch as the cross linking occurs between relaxed chains, this chemical phenomenon is not reflected in the physical measurement of stress decay at constant elongation.

If instead of keeping the rubbers at constant elongation, they are left in a relaxed state and the stress required to elongate these a definite amount is measured from time to time, then the net rate of cross linking minus chain scission is measured. In the case of Hevea gum and tread, the stress required to attain a certain elongation (50 percent at 130°C. for this experiment) decreases as a function of time, though not quite so rapidly as if the elongation were maintained constant. In the case of GR-S gum and tread

TABLE XI

CHANGE IN PHYSICAL APPEARANCE OF RING SAMPLES AS A FUNCTION OF TEMPERATURE AFTER 20 HOURS AT 50% ELONGATION

Polymer	Stock type	Temperature of test, ° C.	Change in appearance after treatment
Hevea	Gum	110	Slightly tacky
		120	Tacky
		130	Very brittle
	Tread	110	No change
		120	Slightly tacky
		130	Very brittle
GR-S	Gum	110	No change
		120	No change
		130	Quite brittle
	Tread	110	Slightly hard
		120	Slightly hard
		130	Brittle

stocks, the stress required to attain 50 percent elongation at regular intervals increased as a function of time, indicating that the cross-linking reaction is faster than scission for these rubbers. This of course agrees with the observations of the physical appearance of the samples. The results of this experiment are shown in figure 128, which should be compared with figure 127 (see page 334).

The authors included in their study, in addition to natural rubber, a large number of synthetic polymers. They comment:

All the synthetic rubber stocks, gum, and tread studied, including the Buna-S types, the Butaprene-N types, Neoprene-GN, and the Butyl types, showed behavior in these experiments not far different from that of Hevea. Equation (210) did not apply as well to any of the other stocks as it did to Hevea gum, but the general relaxation behavior was the same. Although the times necessary for nearly complete relaxation of stress varied by about tenfold between the various rubbers, the free energy of activation for the process did not vary from 30.4 kcal. per mole (the value for Hevea gum) by more than ±2.0 kcal. per mole. This is a strong indication that whatever chemical reaction was responsible for the decay of stress it must have been common to all the rubbers, the slight difference in energies having been caused by the perturbing influence of the side groups which differed in the various rubbers . . .

For the case of the synthetic rubbers and for Hevea tread, although equation (210) did not apply over the entire course of the stress–log time plot as well as it did for Hevea gum, if one assumes that the rate constant k' is equal to the reciprocal of the time that it takes for the stress to reach $1/e$ th (36.8 percent) of its initial value, one can calculate values of $\Delta F\ddagger$ from the data at any given temperature.

The best values of $\Delta F\ddagger$ for Hevea gum and tread and GR-S gum and tread were, respectively, 30.37, 30.05, 31.83, and 31.44 kcal. per mole. Assuming that $\Delta F\ddagger$ is independent of temperature, one can compare the observed and the calculated values for the

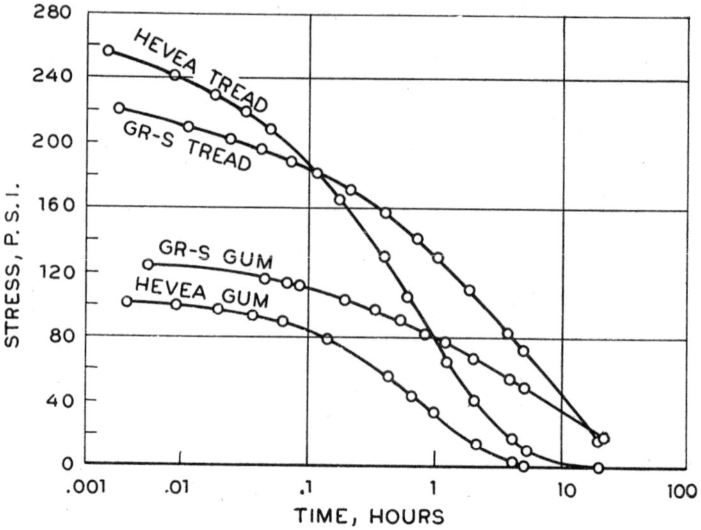

Fig. 127. Stress relaxation curves for Hevea and GR-S stocks at 130°C. and 50% elongation.

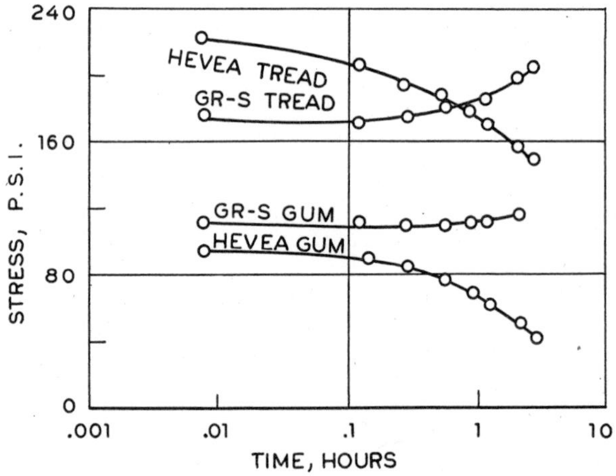

Fig. 128. Stress required to attain 50% elongation (intermittent measurements, 130°C.).

time it took the stress to decay to 36.8 percent of its initial value. The close agreement between observed and predicted values is shown in table XII . . .

Several problems presented themselves as a result of these experiments. If oxidation was the cause of deterioration, which bonds in the postulated network structure did the oxygen attack, the double bonds, the cross bonds, or perhaps special bonds such as the

TABLE XII

COMPARISON OF OBSERVED AND CALCULATED TIMES FOR RELAXING TO $1/e$ TH OF INITIAL STRESS

Polymer	$\Delta F\ddagger$, kcal. per mole	Temp., ° C.	t_e (calc.)	t_e (obs.)
R 198 (Hevea gum)	30.37	100 110 120 130	22.6 hr. 7.50 2.63 0.993	26.2 7.40 2.55 0.900
R 199 (Hevea tread)	30.05	100 110 120 130	11.7 4.94 1.75 0.841	13.0 4.60 1.79 0.785
R 202 (GR-S gum)	31.83	100 110 120 130	162.0 51.0 16.9 6.14	165.0 46.5 17.4 6.40
R 203 (GR-S tread)	31.44	100 110 120 130	96.2 30.8 10.4 3.80	85.0 28.0 11.5 4.25

double bonds adjacent to the cross bonds. Experiments with Butyl rubber at temperatures of 100°C. and 120°C. showed that, at least for the polymers used in these studies, the relaxation of stress behavior was very similar to that of GR-S. This might of course indicate that there is still appreciable residual unsaturation in vulcanized Butyl stocks, even though only small amounts of butadiene are polymerized with isobutylene in synthesizing the raw Butyl polymer. This amount of unsaturation should, nevertheless, be small, compared to that occurring in the other rubbers studied here.

The rate constants defined by equation (207) and subsequent equations include within them as a multiplicative factor the number of places along the chain that are subject to scission. If this number is larger than unity, it would show up in the calculated free energies of activation as an entropy of activation, which would of course make $\Delta F\ddagger$ temperature dependent. As was seen by the results of Table XII, a temperature independent $\Delta F\ddagger$ appeared to give very satisfactory agreement with experiment in the temperature range between 100°C. and 130°C. This would appear to indicate that even for the case of Hevea and GR-S, the number of places along the chain that are subject to scission is not very large. However, such a far-reaching conclusion requires further experimental verification.

Experiments were conducted on specially prepared GR-S stocks to determine the effect of antioxidant on the stress relaxation curves. The results definitely indicated that relaxation occurred more slowly in the presence of antioxidant. This is an added confirmation of the belief that oxidative scission of chains is the mechanism of the stress decay.

The authors summarize their results as follows (for the items not reproduced in the preceding discussion, the reader is referred to the original paper, *43*):

1. The complete decay of stress in the rubbers studied, held at constant elongation, appeared to involve the rupturing of a definite bond either at some point along the molecular chain or at the cross-linking bond put in by vulcanization. In the case of a Hevea rubber gum stock the data could be fitted very well by ordinary reaction-rate theory, leading to the conclusion that the free energy of activation required for breaking the bond is 30.4 kcal. per mole of bonds. This result was found to be practically independent of the elongation, and of the presence of carbon black in a Hevea rubber tread stock. This is to be compared to a strength of about 90 kcal. per mole for the C—C bond.

2. In the case of other rubbers (Buna-S, Butaprene-N, Neoprene-GN, and Butyl) the activation free energy for breaking the bond did not vary by more than 2.0 kcal. per mole from that of Hevea rubber. However, these differences were quite definite. For example, the relaxation of stress in GR-S was slower than in Hevea; a small difference in energy corresponding to a 2:1 ratio in the respective times of decay.

3. The effect of temperature on the relaxation of stress appeared to be of the general type characteristic of chemical reactions. By use of the ordinary formula for expressing rate of reaction in terms of energy of activation, one could predict very closely the behavior of the stress–log time curves at different temperatures.

4. Natural rubber and GR-S vulcanized with paraquinone dioxime and lead dioxide showed relaxation curves very similar to those of the sulfur vulcanized stocks.

5. Relaxation experiments in an ordinary air atmosphere and in an atmosphere of commercial nitrogen showed no appreciable differences.

6. Examination of stretched rubber bands in which the stress had decayed nearly completely (at 100°C.) gave no evidences of gross oxidation, such as would make the rubber bands sticky or hard, or of surface deterioration. At higher temperatures, however, the rubber could be observed getting sticky, and then brittle. Specimens in which the stress had completely decayed showed very low tensile strength (by hand test).

7. Antioxidant added to a sulfur-stabilized Buna-S stock caused a definite retardation of the rate of relaxation.

8. Comparison of the results of these experiments with previously recorded observations in the literature indicated that the chemical reaction which ruptured the rubber structure and caused the decay of stress in these experiments (and concomitantly a lowering of tensile strength) was an oxidation of the rubber by small amounts of oxygen, the reaction rate being independent of the oxygen pressure in the range between that present in an ordinary air atmosphere and in a commercial nitrogen atmosphere.

4. Dynamic Interchange of van der Waals' Linkages

We have previously considered as networks only those polymers which contain a three-dimensional net of primary valence bonds. It is, however, quite possible for linear polymer molecules which contain strong polar groups to form van der Waals' bonds which are strong enough to be considered as temporary cross links. We could then visualize a three-dimensional net structure in which the cross links were strong van der

Waals' forces, rather than primary valence bonds. Since we can expect, at ordinary temperatures, an appreciable rate of breaking and reforming of such intermolecular bonds, this type of network would exhibit the same general properties as those outlined in case 3 (pages 323–336). In general, however, van der Waals' links would break and reform much more rapidly than primary valence bonds. Hence the range of timescale in which the system would act as a single permanent network would be smaller than in the case of a primary valence network. (In vulcanized rubber, for example, the relaxation of stress due to chemical change is observable only over much longer periods of time than the time necessary for initial elastic equilibrium to be essentially established.) The usefulness of such a concept as that of van der Waals' cross links clearly depends upon mean lifetime of a given van der Waals' bond as compared with the time necessary for shape changes of the linear chains. It cannot be said that there is any satisfactory quantitative theory which describes the mechanical response of such a polymer.

BIBLIOGRAPHY

BOOKS

(*1*) Carothers, W. H., *Collected Papers on High Polymeric Substances* (High Polymers, Vol. I). Interscience, New York, 1940.

(*2*) *First Report on Viscosity and Plasticity.* Royal Netherlands Academy of Sciences, Noord-Hollandsche, Amsterdam, 1935.
Second Report on Viscosity and Plasticity. Royal Netherlands Academy of Sciences, Noord-Hollandsche, Amsterdam; Interscience, New York, 1938.

(*3*) Houwink, R., *Physikalische Eigenschaften und Feinbau von Natur-und Kunstharzen.* Akadem. Verlagsgesellschaft, Leipzig, 1934.

(*4*) Houwink, R., *Elasticity, Plasticity, and the Structure of Matter.* Cambridge Univ. Press, London, 1937.

(*5*) Leaderman, H., *Elastic and Creep Properties of Filamentous Materials and Other High Polymers.* Textile Foundation, Washington, 1943.

(*6*) Mark, H., *Physical Chemistry of High Polymeric Systems* (High Polymers, Vol. II). Interscience, New York, 1940.

ARTICLES

(*7*) Carswell, T. S., Telfair, D., and Haslanger, R. U., "Effects of Continuous Heat on Phenolics," *Modern Plastics*, **20**, No. 6, 79–82, 126 (1943).

(*8*) Carswell, T. S., Telfair, D., and Haslanger, R. U., "The Influence of Temperature on the Mechanical Properties of Molded Phenolic Materials," *Modern Plastics*, **19**, No. 11, 65–69 (1942).

(*9*) Davies, J. M., Miller, R. F. and Busse, W. F. "Dielectric Properties of Plasticized Polyvinyl Chloride," *J. Am. Chem. Soc.*, **36**, 361–9 (1941).

(*10*) Dawson, T. R., and Scott, J. R., "Effect of Stain on the Aging of Vulcanized Rubber," *Trans. Inst. Rubber Ind.*, **6**, 198–210 (1940).

(*11*) Dillon, J. H., Prettyman, I. B., and Hall, G. L., "Hysteretic and Elastic Properties of Rubberlike Materials under Dynamic Shear Stresses," *J. Applied Phys.*, **15**, 309 (1944).

(*12*) Eley, D. D., "The Kinetics of Rubber-like Elasticity," *Trans. Faraday Soc.*, **38**, 299 (1942).

(*13*) Eley, D. D., "The Kinetics of Rubberlike Elasticity," *Rubber Chem. Tech.*, **15**, 438 (1942).

(*14*) Fikentscher, H., and Mark, H., "Ueber ein Spiralmodell des Kautschuks," *Kautschuk*, **6**, 2–6 (1930).

(*15*) Flory, P. J., "Network Structure and the Elastic Properties of Vulcanized Rubber," *Chem. Revs.*, **35**, 51 (1944).

(*16*) Flory, P. J., "Molecular Size Distribution in Three Dimensional Polymers. I. Gelation," *J. Am. Chem. Soc.*, **63**, 3083 (1941); "II. Trifunctional Branching Units," *ibid.*, 3091; "III. Tetrafunctional Branching Units," *ibid.*, 3096.

(*16a*) Flory, P. J., and Rehner, J., "Statistical Mechanics of Cross-Linked Networks," *J. Chem. Phys.*, **11**, 512–520 (1943).

(*17*) Garvey, B. S., Alexander, C. H., Küng, F. E., and Henderson, D. E., "Mixed Polymers and Vulcanizable Plasticizers. Relation to the Vulcanization of Rubber," *Ind. Eng. Chem.*, **33**, 1060 (1941).

(*18*) Guth, E., and James, H. M., "Elastic and Thermoelastic Properties of Rubberlike Materials," *Ind. Eng. Chem.*, **33**, 624 (1941).

(*19*) Hahn, S. H., and Gaydik, I., "The Creep of Natural and Synthetic Rubber Compounds in Shear," *India Rubber World*, **103**, 51 (1914).

(*20*) Hauk, V., and Neumann, W., "The Dependence of Stress in Rubber at Constant Extension on Temperature," *Z. Physik. Chem.*, **A182**, 285–94 (1938); "The Dependence of the Stress on the Temperature of Rubber Elongated to a Constant Degree," *Rubber Chem. Tech.*, **12**, 520 (1939).

(*21*) Hauser, E. A., and Cze, M. C., "Chemical Reactions during Vulcanization," *J. Phys. Chem.*, **46**, 118–31 (1942).

(*22*) Hetényi, M., "The Fundamentals of Three-Dimensional Photoelasticity," *Trans. Am. Soc. Mech. Engrs.*, **60**, **A149** (1938); "Application of Hardening Resins in Three-Dimensional Studies," *J. Applied Phys.*, **10**, 295–300 (1939).

(*23*) Holt, W. L., and McPherson, A. T., "Change of Volume of Rubber on Stretching. Effects of Time, Elongation and Temperature," *J. Research Natl. Bur. Standards*, **17**, 657–78 (1936).

(*24*) James, H. M., and Guth E., "Theoretical Stress-Strain Curve for Rubberlike Materials," *Phys. Rev.*, **59**, 111 (1941).

(*25*) James, H. M., and Guth, E., "Theory of Rubber Elasticity for Development of Synthetic Rubber," *Ind. Eng. Chem.*, **34**, 1365 (1942).

(*25a*) James, H. M., and Guth, E., "Theory of the Elastic Properties of Rubber," *J. Chem. Phys.*, **11**, 455–481 (1943).

(*26*) Kienle, R. H., "Observations as to the Formation of Synthetic Resins," *Ind. Eng. Chem.*, **22**, 590 (1930); "Structural Chemistry of Synthetic Polymerides and Their Films," *J. Soc. Chem. Ind.*, **55**, 229T (1936).

(*26a*) Kirkwood, J. G., "Elastic Loss and Relaxation Times in Cross-Linked Polymers," *J. Chem. Phys.*, **14**, 51–56 (1946).

(*27*) Kobeko, P. P., Kuvshinskü, and Gurevich, G., "Investigation of the Amorphous State," *Tech. Phys. U.S.S.R.*, **4**, 622–37 (1937).

(*28*) Kohlrausch, F., "Experimental-Untersuchungen über die elastische Nachwikrung bei der Torsion, Ausdehnung und Biegung," *Ann. Physik Chem.*, **158**, 337 (1876).

(*29*) Kuhn, W., "Über die Gestalt fadenförmiger Moleküle in Lösungen," *Kolloid-Z.*, **68**, 2–15 (1934).

(*30*) Mack, E., Jr., "Molecular Structure and van der Waals Forces," *J. Phys. Chem.*, **41**, 221–31 (1937).

(*31*) Meyer, K. H., and Ferri, C., "The Elasticity of Rubber," *Helv. Chim. Acta*, **18**, 570–89 (1935); "The Elasticity of Rubber," *Rubber Chem. Tech.*, **8**, 319–34 (1935).

(*32*) Midgley, T., "Critical Examination of Some Concepts in Rubber Chemistry," *Ind. Eng. Chem.*, **34**, 891 (1942).

(*33*) Mooney, M., "A Theory of Large Elastic Deformation," *J. Applied Phys.*, **11**, 582 (1940).

(*34*) Ostwald, W., "Zur Theorie des Röntgeneffektes gespannter Gele, im besonderen des Kautschuks," *Kolloid-Z.*, **40**, 58–73 (1926).

(*35*) Peterson, L. E., Anthony, R. L., and Guth, E., "Equation of State of Some Synthetic Rubbers," *Ind. Eng. Chem.*, **34**, 1349 (1942).

(*36*) Powell, R. E., Roseveare, W. E., and Eyring, H., "Diffusion, Thermal Conductivity, and Viscous Flow of Liquids," *Ind. Eng. Chem.*, **33**, 430 (1941).

(*37*) Roseveare, W. E., Powell, R. E., and Eyring, H., "The Structure and Dynamics of Liquids," *J. Applied Phys.*, **12**, 669 (1941).

(*38*) Roth, F. L., and Wood, L. A., "Some Relations between Stress, Strain, and Temperature in a Pure-Gum Vulcanizate of GR-S Synthetic Rubber," *J. Applied Phys.*, **15**, 749 (1944).

(*39*) Scott, J. R., "The Plastic Behavior of Ebonite," *Rubber Chem. Tech.*, **15**, 826–34 (1942).

(*40*) Stockmayer, W. H., "Theory of Molecular Size Distribution and Gel Formation in Branched-Chain Polymers," *J. Chem. Phys.*, **11**, 45 (1943).

(*40a*) Telfair, D., Carswell, T. S., and Nason, H. K., "Creep Properties of Molded Phenolic Plastics," *Modern Plastics*, **21**, No. 6, 137–144 (1944).

(*41*) Tobolsky, A. V., and Eyring, H., "Mechanical Properties of Polymeric Materials," *J. Chem. Phys.*, **11**, 125–34 (1943).

(*42*) Tobolsky, A., Powell, R. E., and Eyring, H., "Elastic-Viscous Properties of Matter," Chapter V in *The Chemistry of Large Molecules*. Interscience, New York, 1943.

(*43*) Tobolsky, A. V., Prettyman, I. B., and Dillon, J. H., "Stress Relation of Natural and Synthetic Rubber Stocks," *J. Applied Phys.*, **15**, 380 (1944).

(*44*) Treloar, L. R. G., "The Elasticity of A Network of Long-Chain Molecules—II," *Trans. Faraday Soc.*, **39**, 36 (1943).

(*45*) Treloar, L. R. G., "Stress-Strain Data for Vulcanized Rubber under Various Types of Deformation," *Trans. Faraday Soc.*, **40**, 59 (1944).

(*46*) Wall, F. T., "Statistical Thermodynamics of Rubber. I," *J. Chem. Phys.*, **10**, 132 (1942); "II," *ibid.*, 485; "III," *ibid.*, **11**, 527–30 (1943).

(*47*) Wiegand, W. B., and Snyder, J. W., "The Rubber Pendulum, the Joule Effect and the Dynamic Stress-Strain Curve," *Trans. Inst. Rubber Ind.*, **10**, 234–62 (1934).

(*48*) Wildschut, A. J., "The Stress-Strain Relation of Natural and Synthetic Rubbers," *Rubber Chem. Tech.*, **17**, 826 (1944).

D. CRYSTALLIZATION OF HIGH POLYMERS

The preceding chapters have dealt with the plastoelastic behavior of amorphous high polymers.

It has been emphasized that (in the range of small strains) the mechanical behavior of an amorphous polymer can be represented by a mechanical model, consisting of a series of retarded elastic elements, a flow element, and an instantaneous elastic element. Mathematically, this behavior can be expressed in terms of a distribution of elastic retardation times, $J(\tau)$, or by an impedance function $Z(\omega)$. Such relatively simple behavior cannot be expected to extend over all experimental ranges (*e.g.*, large deformations, large rates of straining, *etc.*). However, the emphasis in chapter B was placed upon that important range of conditions where such simple behavior does prevail. Experimental evidence in the field of amorphous polymers would seem to justify such an approach as a useful first approximation.

It was pointed out that whenever specific orienting forces compelled the polymer molecules to take on ordered configurations of low entropy, such "amorphous" behavior could not be expected to hold. In this section, the most definite and extreme example of specific forces, namely, forces causing crystallization, are discussed.

In the case of crystalline polymers there are serious objections to the use of mechanical models. Undoubtedly, such models (or their mathematical equivalents) can be successfully used in certain experimental ranges with crystalline polymers. The ranges where this is possible, however, are much narrower than in the case of amorphous polymers and do not coincide with the ranges which are of paramount practical interest. It would be unwise, in the case of crystalline polymers, to focus our attention on these ranges. This is particularly true in the case of *oriented* crystalline fibers. For this reason, this chapter would fall far short of its purpose if it consisted merely of the application of the methods and concepts developed in chapter B to a new class of materials.

The reason for the insufficiency of these concepts and methods in the case of crystalline, and particularly oriented crystalline, polymers are many. A few of the more important reasons are listed below:

(1) A "crystalline" polymer is a mixture of regions of different degrees of order, ranging from completely ordered crystallites to completely amorphous regions. The viscoelastic spectrum of such a material obviously depends upon the relative amounts and spatial arrangement of the regions of different degrees of order—for example, upon the percentage of crystalline material. Hence we would have to consider not one mechanical model to describe a given polymer, but a whole series of models, each corresponding to a definite stage of crystallization. Even this is not sufficient, however, for in general a deformation of such a polymer is accompanied by *phase changes* which are incompletely reversible. Thus we must admit that as the sample is deformed its fundamental structure changes and the governing mechanical model consequently changes. If we wish to describe such a polymer by a model, we must allow the elastic and flow elements of the model to change in character during a deformation. With this extra freedom, the model loses much of its value as a quantitative tool, although it may still retain its usefulness as a qualitative aid to discussion.

(2) One of the attractions of the mechanical model in the case of amorphous polymers lies in the fact that the function $J(\tau)$ for behavior in shear is sufficient to determine the behavior in tension, in combined stress and strain, and in nonhomogeneous combined stress and strain. This fact depends upon the isotropy of the polymer in the unstrained state. An oriented crystalline fiber is *not* isotropic. As a result, even if a mechanical model were developed to describe the behavior in tension, this model would not permit the calculation of response to other types of stress. Perhaps this is not so serious an objection, since practical interest in the case of fibers is after all more or less limited to behavior in tension.

(3) In any material—even an amorphous polymer—it is an oversimplification to assume that a homogeneous macroscopic stress is evenly divided over a given cross-sectional area all the way down to molecular dimensions, so that each individual molecular segment is acted upon by the same biasing stress field. In an amorphous material, however, we can expect the local stress nonhomogeneity on the atomic scale to be relatively small. Furthermore, if the viscoelastic spectrum of the material is linear, the response from regions of high and low stress tend to just balance each other out. The assumption that stress homogeneity extends down to

molecular dimensions would seem to be admissible even in fairly refined treatments of the mechanical behavior of amorphous materials.

This is not true in the case of crystalline polymers. In a material which is made up of regions of definitely different mechanical properties, the stress is strongly concentrated in certain regions and almost entirely absent in others. There is an enormous nonhomogeneity of the local stress even where the macroscopic stress is completely uniform. Not only is the magnitude of the local-stress nonhomogeneity exaggerated by the structural heterogeneity but also the effects are exaggerated. There is no tendency for the response in regions of high stress to balance out that in regions of low stress since there is a definite correlation between the stress concentration in a region and the properties of the material in that region.

The importance of this point cannot be categorically stated on the basis of our present knowledge. The writer feels, however, that it is so extremely important that it must be recognized, in one way or another, in any molecular theory of the mechanical behavior of crystalline polymers. In the case of amorphous polymer, local-stress nonhomogeneity can be neglected until extremely refined theories are developed. In the case of crystalline polymers, it should be considered at a relatively crude early stage of theoretical development.

However, before discussing the mechanical properties of crystalline and crystallizable polymers, it is necessary to discuss in detail the structure of crystalline high polymers, the thermodynamics and kinetics of high polymer crystallization, and the specific molecular factors which influence crystallization.

I. STRUCTURE

To begin, let us define a crystallite as a piece of matter in which the structural units are arranged in a far-reaching, regular geometric pattern. This definition is extremely loose and requires further specification before we can talk about the crystallization of high polymers.

First of all, are there any limitations upon the nature of the structural units which make up a crystallite? For our purpose let us consider that a sufficiently well ordered aggregate will be called a crystallite, whether the structural units are atoms, ions, molecules or repeating molecular segments.

Second, how nearly perfect must the geometric pattern be in order to justify the use of the term "crystallite"? Let us take the position which is commonly assumed in the case of nonpolymeric crystals, recognizing the fact that no crystal ever exhibits completely perfect order. Even at absolute zero there are lattice vibrations, and at higher temperatures every crystal possesses lattice imperfections. The important thing is that these imperfections are local; they do not destroy the long range order of the system. In some crystals, the structural units are fixed with respect to the positions of their centers of gravity but not with respect to their angular orientations. Thus, in ammonium chloride the ammonium ion, and in other cases the entire molecule, can rotate within the lattice of what is still called a crystal. The same criterion of long range positional order is used in this chapter.

Third, how large must an ordered region be before it can be called a crystallite? Even in a liquid, there exist tiny regions where a few structural units are arranged in a crystal-like array (see chapter A on the local structure of liquids). These extremely small regions will not be called crystals. They are too small to give sharp X-ray diffraction diagrams, and they do not behave thermodynamically as a distinct phase. We will call a polymer "crystalline" if it satisfies two requirements. There must be enough unit cells in each individual ordered region to cause definite X-ray interference spots, and the crystalline polymer must possess the thermodynamic properties associated with a distinct phase. We do *not* require that the crystallites be large enough to be seen, even with a microscope, or that the crystal boundaries be of any particular shape.

In the sense of the above definition, crystallization is a common phenomenon among high polymers. The structural units in a high polymer crystallite are not molecules but rather segments of molecules—monomeric units. The structures of many such crystallites have been determined by X-ray diffraction. It appears that some polymers possess several different crystal structures—in fact, polymorphism may possibly be more common with high polymers than with small molecules. A knowledge of the "structure" of a crystalline high polymer means knowing the following:

(1) The unit cell of the crystallites.
(2) The polycrystalline character of the sample.
  (a) Percentage crystallized.
  (b) Size of crystallites.
  (c) Arrangement and orientation of crystallites.

A high polymer is never completely crystalline. Regions of high order (crystallites or micelles) are separated by more or less amorphous regions. A single polymer molecule may extend through several phases. For one part of its length it may lie in a crystalline region, then it may pass through an amorphous region, enter another crystallite, etc. Figure 129 indicates the structural relationships between amorphous, crystalline, and oriented crystalline polymers.

It is not to be expected that every volume element of a "crystalline" polymer lies either in a completely crystalline or a completely amorphous region. There are certainly portions of the polymer in which the degree of order is not entirely sufficient or the size of the ordered region is too small to justify the unqualified use of the term "crystalline" and, yet, in

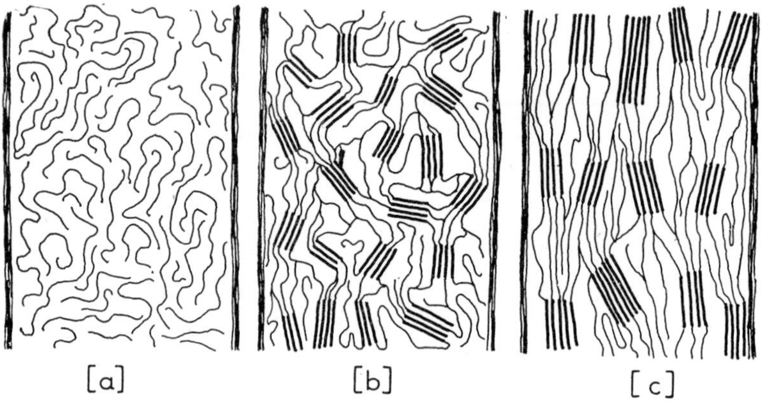

Fig. 129. Schematic representation of an amorphous polymer [a], a crystalline polymer [b], and an oriented crystalline polymer [c].

which there is too much crystal-like order to permit the use of the term "amorphous." Definitely crystalline and definitely amorphous regions represent the simple extremes of order and disorder. In some cases, the mechanical properties of the polycrystalline polymer can be sufficiently explained on the basis of these simple extremes. In general, however, it must be recognized that there are present in a polycrystalline polymer regions possessing all degrees of order, from complete randomness to complete crystallinity. A polymer possessing such quasi crystalline regions—"frozen in" by the accidental course of the crystallization process—is, of course, in a metastable state.

Not only is the fraction of crystalline material in a sample important but also the size of the individual crystalline regions, their relative positions, and their *orientations*. In a fiber, the crystallites are oriented more or less parallel with the fiber axis; in a crystallized melt, the crystallite orientation may be completely random.

An important characteristic of the crystallization of a polymeric material is the fact that it is greatly facilitated by the presence of a tensile stress. Thus amorphous rubber can be crystallized at room temperature if stretched to an extension of a few hundred per cent. The crystallites formed by this means have the same internal structure (unit cell) as rubber crystallites formed by *cooling* rubber to a few degrees below 0°C. The polycrystalline nature is different, however. The crystallites formed by stretching are oriented parallel to the direction of tension; stretched rubber gives a typical fiber X-ray diagram. The crystallites formed by cooling are arranged at random; the frozen sample gives a typical powder X-ray diagram.

II. THERMODYNAMICS OF HIGH POLYMER CRYSTALLIZATION *(8–10)*

Phase equilibrium in high polymers is a somewhat more complex subject than phase equilibrium in low molecular weight materials. The same fundamental thermodynamic and kinetic principles govern the transition between crystalline and amorphous rubber as between solid and liquid benzene. Because of the long-chain nature of the polymer molecules, however, these fundamental laws result in what appears at first sight to be very complicated behavior. It is the purpose of this section to show that the following peculiarities of high polymer crystallization derive in a logical fashion from what is known of the molecular and crystalline structures involved:

(1) *The unsharp melting points of crystalline high polymers:* At a given pressure, the crystals of a pure low molecular weight material have a definite, sharp melting point. Below this temperature the sample is completely crystalline; above it, completely liquid. Crystallite can exist in equilibrium with liquid only *at the melting temperature.* High polymers, on the other hand, are never observed to be 100% crystalline. Some amorphous material is always present. As the temperature is increased, the crystallinity does not disappear suddenly but over a range of temperature.

(2) *Variation of melting range:* Even the melting *range* is not unique but may depend upon the conditions under which the sample was originally crystallized.

(3) *Effect of tensile stresses upon phase equilibrium:* In all crystals, the melting point is somewhat dependent upon the pressure, *i.e.*, compressive stress. The effect is rather small; an enormous stress is required to shift

the melting point appreciably. In a high polymeric system, there is a much more important stress effect. Relatively small tensile stresses shift the crystalline-amorphous equilibrium enormously.

Equilibrium Considerations

Systems of two or more components exhibit, in general, melting ranges rather than sharp melting points. Since any high polymer is made up of molecules which are not identical in chain length, one may be tempted to ascribe the unsharp melting point of a polymer to its multicomponent nature. It is possible, for example, to consider the polymer as a mixture of many fairly homogeneous fractions. Unfortunately, if we apply ordinary thermodynamic considerations to such a mixture, we are still unable to explain the observed properties of crystalline polymers. The inapplicability of this point of view has been foreshadowed in the discussion of micellar structure. It was pointed out that the crystallites in high polymers are not made up of entire linear macromolecules but of parts of them. A succession of monomer units from a given long chain may be lined up as part of one particular crystallite; at the point at which the crystallite ends, the molecule extends on into an amorphous area. Still another section of the same chain may lie in another crystallite, and so on. In materials of ordinary molecular weight, the molecule itself can be considered as the kinetic unit, which is definitely in one of the phases under consideration. This is not true of high polymers. It has repeatedly been shown that segments of high polymer molecules move about more or less independently of each other and that such independent segments, rather than the molecules themselves, should be considered the kinetic units for any statistical treatment in the concentrated state. The behavior of a given segment in entering or leaving a crystalline phase does not depend to any great extent on the total length of the molecule of which it is a part. It cannot be said, therefore, that the melting range of the polymer can be explained on the basis of molecular nonhomogeneity.

On the other hand, the long chain nature of polymer molecules results in surface effects of a more complex type than the interphase surface energy and entropy which are ordinarily encountered. The fact that single molecules may extend from one crystallite to another opens the possibility of mutual crystal interference as an important contributing factor. This crystal interference seems to be the most likely explanation for the unsharp melting points (*9*):

> It is well known, in the case of metals, that the shape of crystal grains in a quenched melt is determined not by the natural crystalline structure, but by the random man-

ner in which growing grains meet each other and restrain further growth. In the case of rubber, such interaction probably sets in long before two growing crystallites actually meet. Both crystallites may contain segments of common molecules and, in general, the alignment of one crystal will prevent the complete growth of the other. This interference would begin as soon as the crystallites were formed, and would become more and more pronounced as they grew toward each other. This would result, not in a shape restriction, as in the case of metals, but in a vagueness of melting point. Each successive group is less easily fitted into the crystal lattice. This is because crystal growth limits not only the mobility of the entering group, but also the mobility of the amorphous hydrocarbon chain connecting the two crystallites. The change in energy ΔE is the same for the last link as for the early ones, but the change in entropy ΔS is greater for the later groups. In addition to the entropy decrease, or loss of randomness, due to the fixing of the group, which actually enters the lattice, there is an associated decrease in the randomness of the amorphous connecting chain, due to the choking action of the two growing crystallites. This mechanism would, of course, lead to the sort of unsharp melting point at given tension which is observed experimentally.

The effect of stress on the crystalline-amorphous equilibrium is also understandable. The *entropy* of a stretched amorphous polymer has been seen to be less than that of an unstretched polymer. The energy and entropy of the crystalline phase and the energy of the amorphous phase are not markedly affected by small stresses. Thus ΔH of melting remains much the same, but ΔS of melting becomes *smaller* upon the application of a tensile or shear stress. The melting point is shifted to a higher temperature.

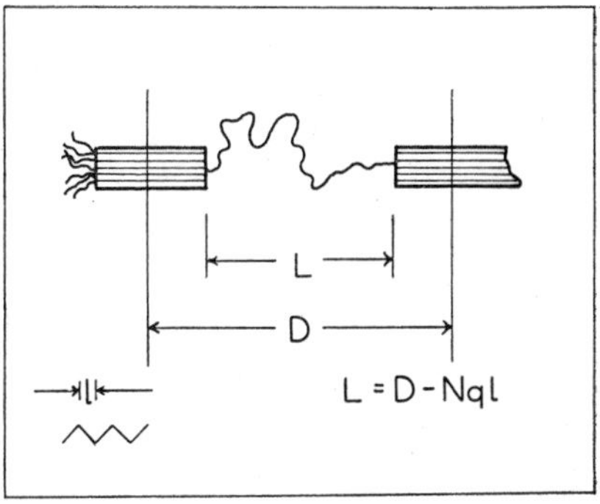

Fig. 130. Schematic representation of the portion of a polymer chain connecting two crystallites.

In nonthermodynamic language, a stress *partly* straightens out the amorphous chains, and makes it easier for the intermolecular forces to straighten them out *completely* into the crystalline configuration.

A rough theoretical treatment of this problem has been made, using the model sketched in figure 130 (*10*). A sample of partially crystallized polymer under tension is represented by a portion of a single polymer chain extending from the interior of a crystallite to an amorphous region and through this amorphous region into another crystallite. The question is: how does the crystalline fraction of this model system depend upon temperature and upon the separation of the two ends? In this treatment, increase of crystalline content is considered entirely as *growth* of crystallites, which are already present, at the expense of the intermicellar amorphous polymer. No allowance is made for the appearance of *new* crystallites. The predictions of such a model are therefore inapplicable to a *first* crystallization, during which not only the size but also the *number* of crystallites are changing. Indeed, it will be shown that *no* strictly equilibrium treatment is applicable to the crystallization of an amorphous polymer for the first time. Such a model is much more applicable to the *melting* of a crystalline polymer and/or the subsequent recrystallization (see section III, page 353).

The predictions of such a treatment are as follows:

(1) A polycrystalline sample of a high polymer does not melt at sharply defined temperature but over a temperature range. If the number of crystallites remains unchanged, this equilibrium can be described by a function $q_\nu(T)$, where q_ν is the equilibrium fraction of crystalline material (subject to the restriction that ν, the *number* of crystallites per unit volume, remains fixed).

(2) The larger the value of ν, the lower is the temperature range of melting, *i.e.*, the crystal-crystal interference is more extreme among many small crystallites than among a few larger crystallites.

(3) In the presence of a tensile stress, $q_\nu(T)$ is shifted to larger amounts of crystallization or, in other words, the melting range is shifted to higher temperatures.

Quantitative experimental studies of the thermodynamics of crystallization in high polymers have been most complete in the case of rubber. The heat of fusion, for example, has been reported by Bekkedahl and Matheson (*15*) to be 16.71 joules per gram. This value was determined from the area under the peak in the specific heat curve for crystallized rubber (Fig. 131). The entropy of fusion was calculated to be 0.059 joules per gram per degree C., using 284°K. as the melting temperature. These values represent the enthalpy and entropy changes which result when one gram of "crystalline rubber" is melted. Since the "crystalline" samples were probably somewhat short of 100% crystallinity, the "true" value would presumably be somewhat higher.

Bekkedahl (*14*) has also used the volume–temperature relation of rubber as a tool in the study of rubber crystallization. Figure 132 shows the volume–temperature curve for supercooled amorphous rubber, and for crystalline rubber relative to that of amorphous rubber at 0°C. The absolute scale of these curves can be fixed by the density of amorphous rubber at − 10°C. (0.93). The curves indicate that rubber increases in

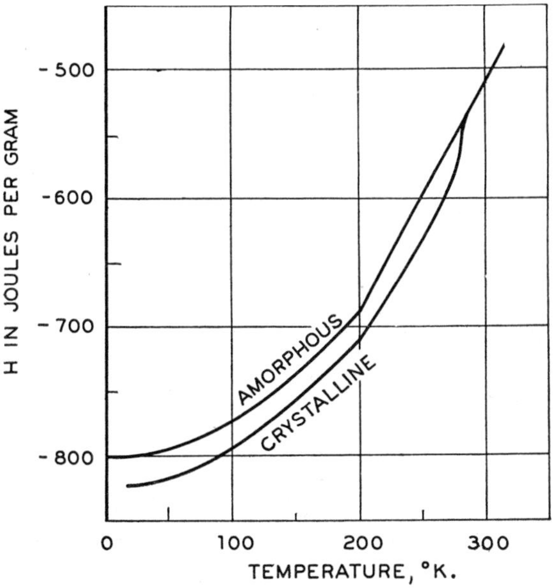

Fig. 131. Enthalpy–temperature curves for amorphous and crystalline rubber.

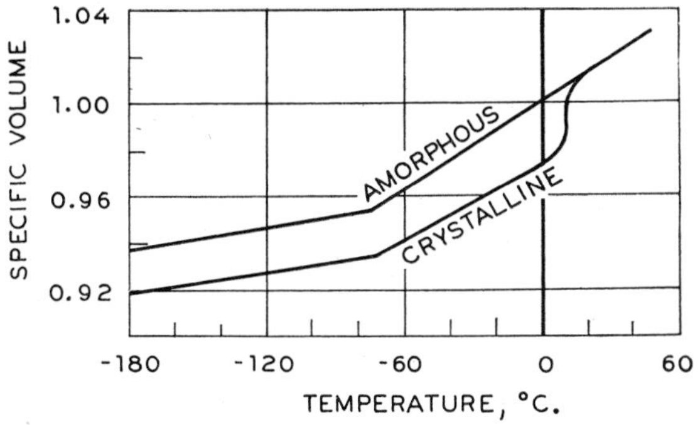

Fig. 132. Volume–temperature curves for amorphous and crystalline rubber.

density by about 2.6% when it crystallizes. Again it must be remembered that after this amount of volume contraction the rubber is still not 100% crystallized. The "true" volume change on crystallization should be somewhat greater than this. Treloar (*56*) has estimated that the increase in density during crystallization is at least 3.75%. Smith and

Hanna (*55*), after an extended analysis of the question, conclude that amorphous rubber has a density of 0.93 at − 10°C. and that completely crystalline rubber would have a density of 0.965 to 0.97.

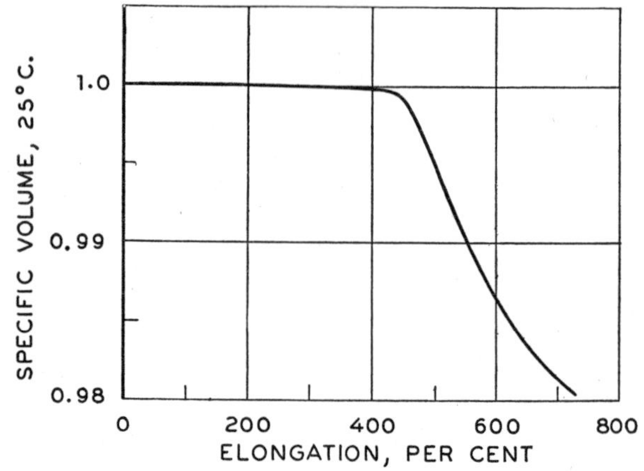

Fig. 133. Specific volume of rubber as a function of elongation.

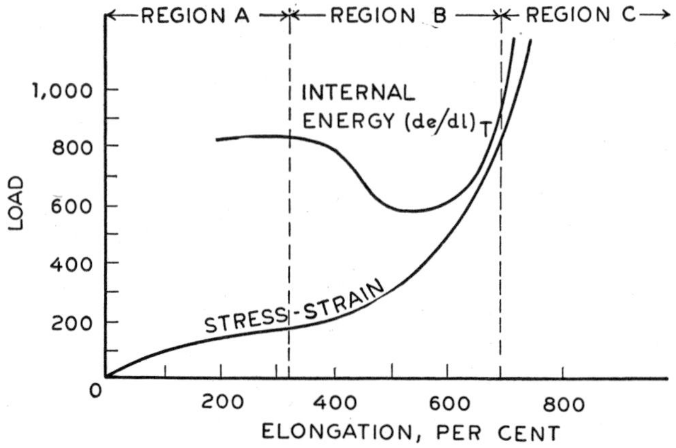

Fig. 134. Energy changes during the extension of rubber.

The effect of tensile strain upon crystallization has also been extensively studied in the case of rubber. Figures 133 and 134 indicate the volume change and the thermal change which result when rubber is stretched. Figure 135 shows the volume as a function of temperature for stretched (600%) and unstretched rubber. The samples of rubber used by these various investigators were not identical. Furthermore, as we shall see in the next section, none of these curves represent true thermodynamic equilibrium; competitive rate phenomena can serve to shift significantly the amount of crystallization under a given set of conditions.

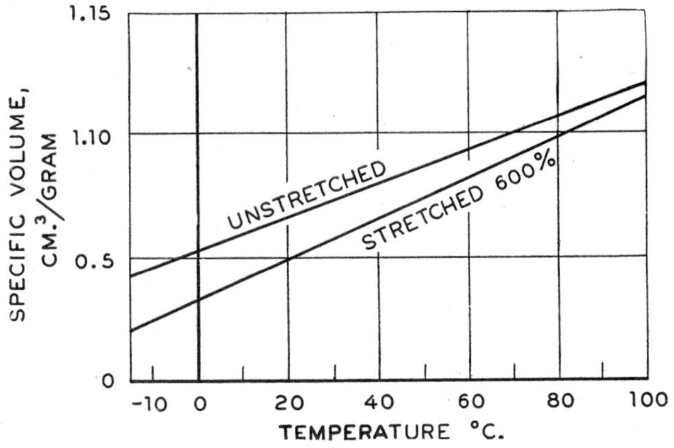

Fig. 135. Specific volume of stretched and unstretched rubber as a function of temperature.

Even so, these curves, which relate to entirely different properties of rubber, agree very well with regard to the way crystallization changes with elongation. Rubber can be stretched several hundred per cent before crystallization begins, then the degree of crystallization increases rapidly with further elongation.

III. KINETICS OF HIGH POLYMER CRYSTALLIZATION

The rate of crystallization of any liquid below its freezing point depends upon the rates of two distinct processes—the formation of crystal nuclei and the growth of these nuclei to large dimensions. The rate of the first process generally has its maximum value at a temperature much below the melting point, whereas the second process goes fastest at temperatures only a little below the melting point and progressively slower at lower temperatures. The over-all rate of crystallization depends upon the rates of the two separate processes. The polycrystalline nature of the final product depends upon the relative values of the two rates and, hence, upon the temperature of crystallization. If crystallization is carried out at the low temperature at which the rate of nucleus formation has its maximum, then many nuclei are formed and the final product is composed of many small crystals. At a higher temperature, nuclei are created more slowly but once formed grow rapidly giving a polycrystalline mass composed of a few large crystals. (It is, of course, impossible to hold the temperature of a crystallizing liquid below the equilibrium melting point unless the *over-all* velocity of crystallization is very slow compared with the rate of heat transfer with the surroundings.)

These general rate considerations seem to apply in the case of high polymers as well as low molecular weight compounds. Figure 136 shows the progress of rubber crystallization with time at constant temperature

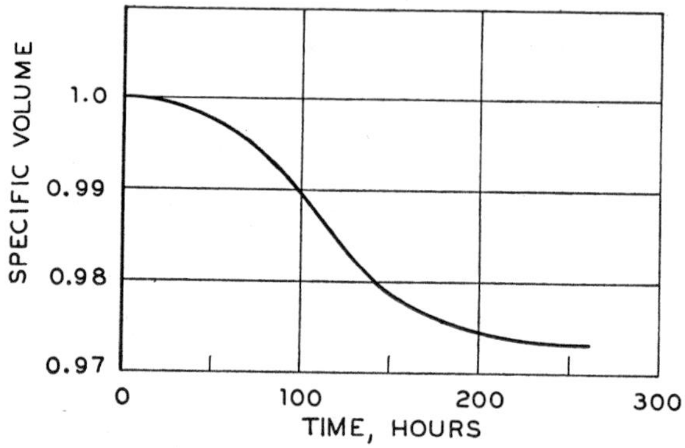

Fig. 136. Decrease in volume with time. Rubber changes from the amorphous to the crystalline form at a temperature of 0°C. (after Bekkedahl).

(*44*). The form of this curve indicates that two processes, rather than one, determine the over-all velocity of crystallization. The over-all rate of crystallization depends on temperature roughly as follows (*15*): crystallization time is a matter of days at 0°C. Crystallization rate is greatest between − 15°C. and − 25°C. At these temperatures crystallization takes place in a few hours. At liquid air temperatures amorphous rubber can be kept indefinitely without crystallization. The velocity of crystallization is increased by the presence of a tensile stress. When rubber is stretched several hundred per cent at room temperature, an appreciable fraction of the resulting crystallization takes place in less than a minute. See figure 138 (page 354).

For the process of nucleus formation to have an appreciable velocity, it is necessary for there to be an appreciable thermodynamic driving force favoring crystallization. If the crystallization is carried out by cooling the sample, the temperature must be lowered well below the point where crystallization becomes thermodynamically possible. In crystallization by stretching, the sample must be stretched well beyond the extension which makes crystallization thermodynamically possible. This is not true of the growth process, whose rate depends more upon the temperature itself than upon the amount of supercooling or overstretching.

Similar considerations apply in the reverse process of *melting.* The rapid and complete destruction of a crystal nucleus, as well as its original creation, requires an appreciable thermodynamic driving force. This means that if a crystalline sample is heated slightly above the equilibrium melting point, the crystallites melt down to very small size—but do not disappear completely in a reasonable time unless the system is considerably *over*heated. (Even if the sample is not superheated, it *appears* to be

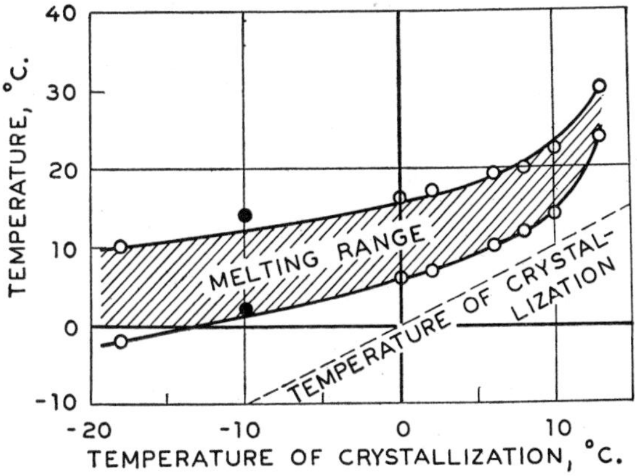

Fig. 137. Melting range of crystalline rubber as a function of the temperature of crystallization. The lower points represent the beginning of melting, the upper points the ending of melting.

completely amorphous. The residual nuclei are too small a fraction of a sample to give a crystalline X-ray pattern or to affect the volume, enthalpy, etc. appreciably. Their presence can be detected if the sample is cooled again. Crystallization can now proceed simply by means of crystal growth; the nuclei are already present. The process is therefore much more rapid than it would be if the nuclei had completely disappeared.)

It seems, therefore, that the *polycrystalline character* of rubber frozen at − 25°C. should differ from that of rubber frozen at − 5°C. Even after a sample is melted, it *retains* a certain "memory" of its original polycrystalline character in the crystal *nuclei* which remain.

Bekkedahl and Wood (*16*) have observed that the melting range of crystalline rubber is markedly dependent upon the temperature at which it was crystallized. This is indicated in figure 137. "More complete data not yet published show that, when crystallization occurs between − 40°C. and + 10°C., melting begins at a temperature of from 4° to 7° above that at which the crystals were formed, and the melting continues over a range of from 10° to 30° more." It should be recorded here that the experimental investigations of Bekkedahl and Wood preceded, and indeed were the stimulus for, the theoretical analysis of the problem just presented.

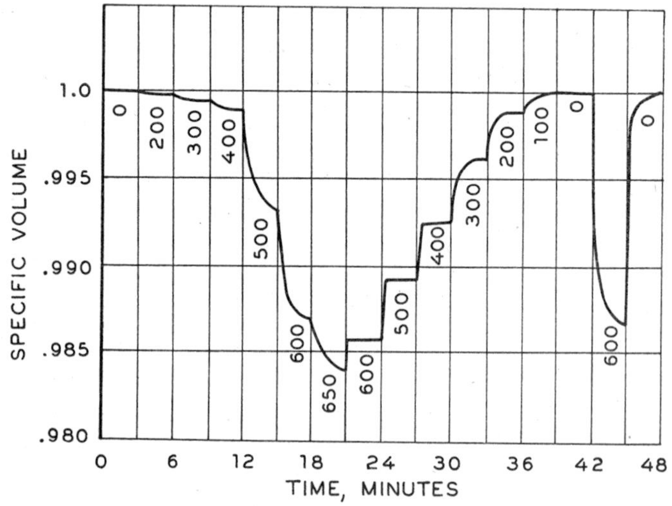

Fig. 138. Successive volume changes during the stepwise extension and retraction of rubber, showing crystallization hysteresis.

Holt and McPherson (*44*) have made an intensive study of effects of time, elongation, and temperature on rate of crystallization of rubber, using volume change as a criterion of crystallization. Figure 138 shows the volume changes which occur when a sample is stretched for successively larger amounts (being held for three minutes at each elongation) and then released in a similar stepwise manner. This gives a vivid picture of the rate of crystallization of stretched rubber and shows as well two other significant features: (1) the hysteresis of crystallization for a complete strain cycle, and (2) the greater rate of melting than of crystallizing.

Figure 139 shows the results of long time tests in which rubber samples were held for several weeks at elongations of 550 and 600%, and temperatures of 0°C. and 25°C., respectively. It is seen that, although a large amount of crystallization takes place in a few minutes, complete equilibrium is not reached in a day.

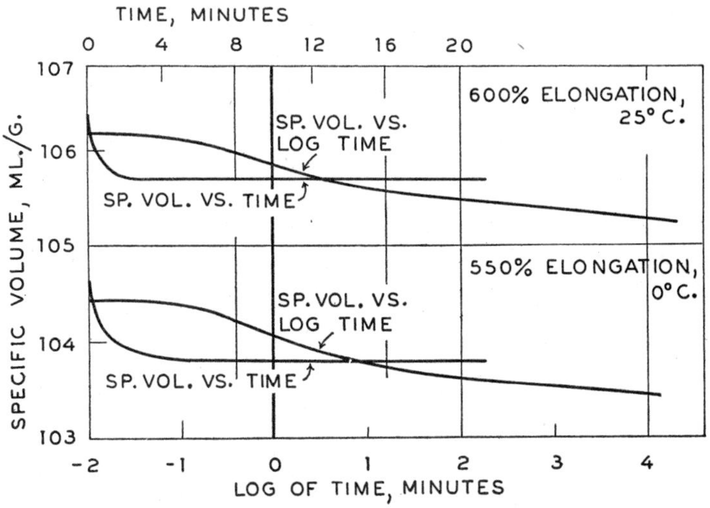

Fig. 139. Specific volume *vs.* time and log time for rubber held at two different elongations.

Let us summarize the kinetics and thermodynamics of high polymer crystallization as follows:

(1) When an amorphous polymer is crystallized for the first time, whether by cooling or by stretching, the velocity of crystallization depends upon the rate of nucleus *formation* and the rate of *growth*. The over-all velocity shows a *maximum* with temperature.

(2) Such a first crystallization is never an equilibrium process. The final polycrystalline character cannot be predicted on the basis of thermodynamic considerations, but is the result of competitive rate processes.

(3) A polymer frozen at a very low temperature should be composed of many small crystallites, whereas one frozen at a higher temperature should be composed of a smaller number of *larger* crystallites.

(4) Since the processes both of nucleus formation and of nucleus destruction require either a strong driving force or a long time, a sample which has once been crystallized retains a "memory" of its polycrystalline character for some time after melting, unless it is superheated.

(5) Such a sample, containing residual crystal nuclei from a previous crystallization, can be recrystallized by the single process of crystallite *growth.*

(6) Such a second crystallization process is much more nearly an equilibrium phenomenon than the *first* crystallization. A third or fourth recrystallization is still closer to an equilibrium process.

(7) Therefore a theoretical treatment of high polymer crystallization along the general lines laid down in the previous section is presumably fairly valid for a second or third crystallization, although it does not apply for a first crystallization.

(8) Such a treatment considers the *number* of crystallites as a fixed parameter for a given sample. This parameter depends, however, upon the nonequilibrium conditions during the initial crystallization. Thus a sample frozen at − 50°C. has a different *melting range* than a sample frozen at − 5°C. The former, with many small crystallites, should melt in a lower temperature range than the latter, since the crystal-crystal interference should be greater.

(9) The number of crystallites can itself change over a long period of time (or quickly, if extreme conditions are present). Such changes in *number* of crystallites are never equilibrium phenomena. (The *equilibrium* state as far as polycrystalline character is concerned would be a single enormous crystal or a single large, amorphous region. The former state has never been observed in a high polymer.)

IV. EFFECT OF SPECIFIC MOLECULAR STRUCTURE FACTORS ON THE CRYSTALLIZATION OF HIGH POLYMERS

The general process of high polymer crystallization has been described in some detail, but nothing has as yet been said concerning the specific structural factors which govern the tendency toward crystallization. It is an experimental fact that different polymers exhibit widely different crystallization tendencies. In some cases, relatively small structural differences result in marked differences in crystallizability. In this section an attempt is made to correlate differences in crystallizability with differences in structure.

The principal factor determining the melting point of a low molecular weight crystal is the (molar) heat of crystallization, since different substances of the same molecular symmetry have roughly the same entropy of fusion. The heat of fusion is dependent upon the potential energy of interaction of the molecules in the crystal lattice, since a fairly definite fraction of this potential energy is removed in the melting process. The potential energy of a crystal is a large negative quantity; that of a liquid is a somewhat smaller negative quantity. The heat of fusion consists principally of this increase in potential energy.

The potential energy of molecular interaction in a crystal obviously depends upon the molecular structure. Molecules possessing polar groups exert stronger forces upon each other than nonpolar molecules. Furthermore, molecules which can pack closely together can satisfy their intermolecular forces more completely than can molecules of irregular shape which cannot be fitted so closely together. A molecule which fits well with its neighbors is in close contact with others over its whole surface. A molecule which fits poorly has much of its surface somewhat isolated and hence will exhibit a reduced potential energy of interaction with its neighbors.

The *entropy* of fusion of many low molecular weight materials is roughly the same, but much wider variations are observed than in the case of the entropy of vaporization. Particularly among molecules of different symmetry, marked variations in entropy of fusion occur. Dietz and Andrews (*26*) have pointed out the effect of symmetry on the melting points of benzene and the hydrogenated benzenes. All of these molecules have the same general shape and do not differ much in heat of fusion. Yet, because of their higher symmetry, benzene and cyclohexane have much higher melting points than dihydro- and tetrahydrobenzene. An unsymmetrical molecule gains more orientational randomness or entropy by going from the crystalline to the liquid state than a symmetrical molecule. If n is the symmetry number of a molecule (the number of indistinguishable orientations), then the entropy of fusion contains a term $(-\text{R} \ln n)$.

Mark (*5*, *48*, *49*) has pointed out that the crystallizability of organic high polymers is determined by the same general structural factors as the crystallizability of low molecular weight compounds. A good first approximation to the crystallization characteristics of a polymer can be obtained if one ignores symmetry and fitting factors and considers only the polarity of the repeating monomeric residues. Mark has estimated the specific cohesional energy of various polymers per unit of chain length by the simple process of adding together terms for all groups in the unit length. This assumes that fitting is so good that every part of the molecular surface is at an optimum distance from its neighbors. These cohesional energies are tabulated in table XIII (*49*). Mark points out that polymers possessing calculated cohesional energies of less than 2000 calories tend to be amorphous and rubbery at room temperature and those possessing energies above 5000 calories tend to be highly crystalline and to fit into the category of textile fibers.

TABLE XIII

EFFECT OF INTERMOLECULAR FORCES OF SOME HIGH POLYMERS ON MECHANICAL BEHAVIOR

Substance	Covalent bond along chains	Dissociation energy, cal./mole	Groups responsible for attraction	Molar cohesion per 5 Å. chain length with coordination number of 4, cal./mole
Polyethylene	—C—C—	70–80,000	(CH_2)	1000
Polyisobutylene	—C—C—	70–80,000	(CH_2), (CH_3)	1200
Polybutadiene	—C=C—	70–120,000	(CH_2), (CH=CH)	1100
Rubber	—C=C—	70–120,000	(CH_2), $(CH{=}CCH_3)$	1300
Polystyrene	—C—C—	70–80,000	(CH_2), (C_6H_5)	4000
Polychloroprene	—C=C—	70–120,000	(CH_2), (CH=CCl)	1600
Polyvinyl chloride	—C—C—	70–80,000	(CH_2), (CHCl)	2600
Polyvinyl acetate	—C—C—	70–80,000	(CH_2), $(COOCH_3)$	3200
Polyvinyl alcohol	—C—C—	70–80,000	(CH_2), (CHOH)	4200
Cellulose	—C—O—C—	80–90,000	(OH), (—O—)	6200
Cellulose acetate	—C—O—C—	80–90,000	$(OOCCH_3)$, (—O—)	4800
Polyamides	—C—N—C—	70–90,000	(CH_2), (CONH)H	5800
Silk fibroin	—C—N—C—	70–90,000	(CHR), (CONH)H	9800

Mark has also emphasized the importance of fitting factors. He points out that gutta-percha and rubber, which are both polyisoprenes, exhibit decidedly different melting ranges. Rubber (*cis*-polyisoprene) is amorphous at room temperature in the unstretched condition, whereas gutta-percha (*trans*-polyisoprene) is naturally crystalline. This results from the fact that gutta-percha fits more perfectly into a crystal lattice than does rubber. Polyethylene also exhibits a much greater crystallization tendency than is indicated by the estimated value for the cohesion energy in table XIII. The regular zig-zag form of polyethylene in its crystal lattice allows very efficient packing together, so that each unit of the chain can lie at the optimum distance from its neighbors. Thus the potential energy of the lattice is a large negative quantity. In the lattice built up of more irregularly shaped linear molecules packing is less efficient. One part of a given molecule will protrude and be forced into the repulsion range of its nearest neighbor. Other parts will be held away, so that internal strains are set up within the molecule itself. As a result, the potential energy of the lattice is not so large a negative quantity. This effect is indicated schematically in figure 140.

It is clear that in order to allow efficient packing in a crystal lattice one requirement is a regularity of groups along the polymer chain. A copolymer in which two different monomeric residues are arranged at random along the chain is obviously unable to fit into a crystal lattice as readily as a uniform polymer with only one kind of repeating group. On the other hand, a copolymer in which the two types of groups alternate

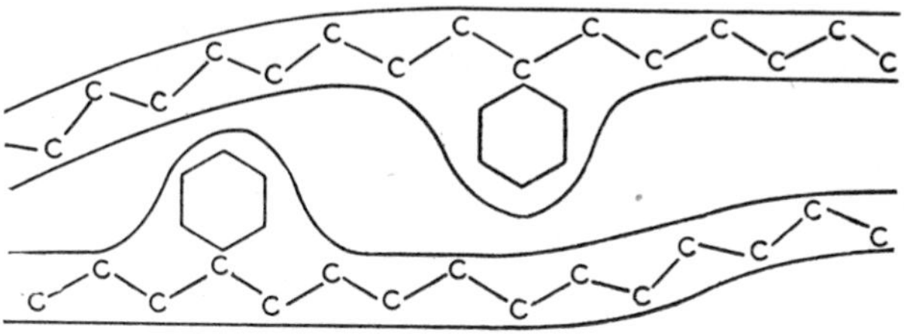

Fig. 140. Steric effect of bulky groups on the packing of polymer molecules.

regularly may well exhibit a tightly packed crystal lattice, particularly if the two groups complement one another geometrically. Not only the presence of more than one type of monomeric group, randomly arranged, but also random variations in head-to-head and head-to-tail orientations of the neighboring groups can be expected to reduce the ease with which a polymer molecule fits into a crystal lattice.

Mark (*5*, *48*, *49*) has tabulated the crystallization characteristics of a number of vinyl polymers; Baker and Fuller (*11–13*) have reported similar characteristics for a number of condensation polymers; and Meyer (*6*) has described a group of natural polymers.

1. Effect of Molecular Weight and Cross Linking on Crystallization

Since the structural units involved in high polymer crystallization are segments of molecules, rather than whole molecules, it is to be expected that such crystallization will be more or less independent of the molecular weight of the polymer. As long as the polymer chains are much longer than the individual crystallites the precise chain length is unimportant. A given segment in a very long polymer chain is influenced very little by far distant segments of the same chain and has much the same tendency to enter or leave the crystalline phase if it is a member of a molecule of 1000 units as one of 2000 units. This independence of crystallization upon molecular weight could not be expected to extend downward to extremely low molecular weights, however. For very short polymer chains, where the chain length is of the same order as the crystallite length, the crystalline-amorphous phase change must be markedly dependent upon chain length of the polymer. As a corollary to the above conclusions, it is to be expected that changes in molecular weight distribution curve of a linear polymer should have very little effect on the crystallization process as long as material of high molecular weight is predominant.

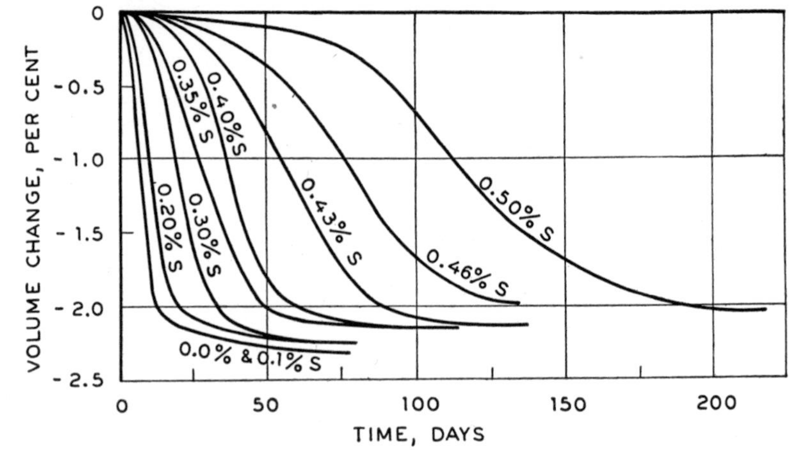

Fig. 141. Crystallization rates of vulcanized rubbers as indicated by volume–time relationships.

On the other hand, *cross linking* has a marked effect, particularly on the rate of crystallization. This is to be expected, since each cross link represents a geometric constraint upon two chains, which may interfere with the alignment which the crystallization process entails. Holt and McPherson (*44*) observed the crystallization of rubber, with various amounts of vulcanization, at 0°C. (see Fig. 141). Large amounts of cross linking completely prevent crystallization.

2. Effect of Low Molecular Weight Materials on High Polymer Crystallization

The presence of a foreign material of low molecular weight in a high polymeric sample should lower the equilibrium melting range of the crystalline polymer. However, it is difficult to predict theoretically the magnitude of the shift. In the case of many low molecular weight mixtures, there is a simple thermodynamic relation between concentration of the second component and lowering of the freezing point.

$$\Delta T_m = KC \tag{1}$$

Here the K is the cryoscopic constant for the component which is present in large excess and which crystallizes. No matter what the second component is, the ΔT_m depends only on the molal concentration. The relationship holds only at low concentration of the second component, and under the condition that the crystalline phase is composed only of the component in excess; no solid solutions form.

For a given material, the cryoscopic constant, K, depends upon the heat of fusion:

$$K = \mathrm{R}T_m^2/\Delta\mathrm{H} \tag{2}$$

These two relations, (1) and (2), arise in the following manner. The melting point of a material is the temperature at which $\Delta\mathbf{F}_{\text{melting}} = 0$.

$$\Delta\mathrm{H} - T\Delta\mathrm{S} = 0 \tag{3a}$$

$$T_{\text{melting}} = \frac{\Delta\mathrm{H}_{\text{melting}}}{\Delta\mathrm{S}_{\text{melting}}} \tag{3b}$$

Now the presence of a small amount of a second component in the liquid phase changes the value of $\Delta\mathrm{S}_{\text{melting}}$. Neither the enthalpy nor the entropy of the *crystalline* phase is affected if the crystals are one-component. Further, the partial molal *heat* of solution for the solvent is zero for low solute concentrations. Thus the presence of the solute does not change the heat of crystallization, $\Delta\mathrm{H}$. Furthermore, the partial molal entropy of solution of the solvent is given by the classical expression for the entropy of mixing:

$$\left(\frac{\partial \mathrm{S}}{\partial N_1}\right) = -\mathrm{R}\ln n_1 \tag{4a}$$

$$\Delta\mathrm{S}_{\text{melting}} = \Delta\mathrm{S}^0_{\text{melting}} - \mathrm{R}\ln n_1 \tag{4b}$$

$$T_m = \frac{\Delta\mathrm{H}}{\mathrm{A} - \mathrm{R}\ln n_1} = \frac{\Delta\mathrm{H}}{\dfrac{\Delta\mathrm{H}}{T_0} - \mathrm{R}\ln(1 - n_2)} \tag{4c}$$

In short, a crystal of the solvent gains more entropy by melting into a two-component liquid phase than into pure solvent. On the other hand, the $\Delta\mathrm{H}_{\text{melting}}$ is the same in both cases. As a result, the equilibrium melting point is lowered according to equations (1) and (2).

An analogous relation must hold for a high polymeric crystalline-amorphous equilibrium. The introduction of a small amount of low molecular weight material should increase the entropy of the amorphous phase, without affecting strongly the enthalpy of the amorphous phase or the enthalpy or entropy of the crystalline phase. However, even at quite low concentrations, the partial molal entropy of mixing for an amorphous polymer and a low molecular weight component is very different from the classical entropy of mixing. Therefore one should not expect relation (4c) to hold for high polymeric systems. However, the following general picture is probably justified.

If to a crystalline-amorphous high polymeric system, in equilibrium, there is added a small amount of a miscible low molecular weight component, this component enters the *amorphous* regions of the system. As these regions are swelled, the crystallites melt somewhat, increasing the relative amount of amorphous polymer and establishing a new crystalline-amorphous equilibrium. If enough low molecular weight material is added, the crystallites may be completely dissolved or melted.

It is, of course, possible for the low molecular weight component actually to enter the crystal lattice, as well as the amorphous regions, resulting in a new, modified lattice structure.

V. EFFECT OF CRYSTALLINITY AND THE CRYSTALLIZATION PROCESS ON THE MECHANICAL PROPERTIES OF HIGH POLYMERS

1. Mechanical Properties of the Crystallites

An individual high polymer crystallite must be a highly rigid structure, especially in the direction of the long axis. A cellulose crystallite, for example, can be elongated only by stretching primary valence bonds and opening valence angles. The Young's modulus in the direction of the molecular chains is therefore very high. The crystal can be enlarged in the transverse directions more easily by pulling apart neighboring chains against van der Waals' forces. In the particular case of cellulose even these intermolecular forces are very strong, but in a crystal of rubber the transverse Young's modulus should be significantly lower. In some high polymer crystallites, the molecule is folded back and forth rather than extended in the most elongated manner. This should reduce the longitudinal modulus considerably. In the case of wool, for example, a tensile stress seems to change the crystalline portion from one crystal modification to another. In general, however, it is probably safe to consider the crystallites themselves as ideal elastic regions, of relatively high elastic moduli, and not readily subject to flow.

2. Mechanical Properties of a Polycrystalline Polymer, without Phase Change

We have seen that a "crystalline" high polymer is not a homogeneous material but a mixture of amorphous and crystalline regions and, in general, of regions of intermediate degrees of order. In section 1, above, it was observed that the crystallites themselves can be considered as rigid, flowless regions of high elastic moduli. The amorphous regions which lie between the crystalline micelles may also be quite rigid (if the temperature is below the amorphous "brittle point"). On the other hand, if the temperature is high, the intermicellar amorphous regions may be rubbery or may exhibit retarded elasticity.

The simplest set of assumptions which we could make in an attempt to predict the mechanical behavior of a polycrystalline polymer mass would be the following:

(1) The polycrystalline polymer consists of definite crystallites embedded in an amorphous matrix. Refinements such as the presence of mesomorphic regions are neglected.

(2) When the sample is deformed by means of imposed stresses, no phase change occurs. The crystallites do not grow at the expense of the amorphous matrix; neither do they melt out.

(3) The crystallites are much more rigid than the amorphous matrix and can be considered as perfectly rigid inclusions. The small elastic deformations of the crystallites are thus neglected.

(4) The amorphous matrix can be considered as a continuum with the mechanical properties of the pure amorphous polymer.

If these four assumptions were justified, it would be possible to deduce in a straightforward fashion the mechanical properties of a polycrystalline polymer from its structure. Where the shear properties of the amorphous polymer are representable by a completely linear mechanical model, this problem would be purely geometric. The result would be that the polycrystalline polymer could be represented by a mechanical analog identical with that of the amorphous polymer, except that every elastic modulus and every "viscosity" of the latter would be multiplied by a factor (the same factor for all mechanical elements). This factor, to repeat, would depend upon the polycrystalline structure of the sample. For example, for a low degree of crystallinity, and where the crystallites were fairly isometric, the multiplicative factor would be given roughly by:

$$1 + (2.5) \text{ (volume fraction of crystalline material)}$$

The simplicity of such an approach certainly makes it tempting. Unfortunately, however, a critical analysis of assumptions (1), (2), (3), and (4) leads to the conclusion that this is a very poor approximation to the behavior of real polycrystalline polymers.

Assumption (1) introduces an approximation to begin with. The range of mesomorphic regions, of different degrees of crystalline order, is replaced by the simple extremes of amorphous and crystalline regions. As a first approximation, this is probably justified, so that assumption (1) can be considered as acceptable. Assumption (3) also would seem to be satisfactory for many polycrystalline polymers. The major difficulties arise from assumptions (2) and (4).

For assumption (4) to be correct, it must be possible to divide the amorphous material into volume elements which are small compared with the crystallites and yet large enough to include a representative sample of the amorphous polymer. If the polycrystalline polymer were made up of a few very large crystallites separated by large distances in the amorphous matrix, then this condition would be satisfied. We have seen, however, that the polycrystalline structure of high polymers is not of this nature. Since, in general, the crystallites are shorter in length than a single completely extended polymer molecule, it is manifestly impossible to consider the amorphous matrix as a continuum possessing the mechanical properties of the pure amorphous polymer. The amorphous matrix is composed of intermicellar molecular *sections*, not of whole molecules; and the interaction between amorphous matrix and crystallite is too intimate and discrete to approximate by means of a continuum.

Finally, assumption (2) is in direct contradiction with a great deal of experimental evidence concerning the deformation of polycrystalline polymers. In general, such a deformation cannot be resolved simply into shape changes of crystallites and of amorphous matrix; rather, *phase change* accompanies mechanical deformation.

These facts would seem to indicate that the mechanical properties of a polycrystalline polymer can be deduced only from a basic model which includes both amorphous and crystalline molecular sections and which permits phase change to take place. The principles of statistics must be applied directly to such a model, rather than separately to an amorphous and a crystalline model.

Even on the basis of a static model, however, it is easy to understand one effect of crystallization. This is the inhibition of flow. It is clear that if the polymer molecules are laced together in a polycrystalline structure, the crystallites serve as effective cross links and the polycrystalline mass represents a three-dimensional molecular network. Indeed, if no phase change takes place, a highly crystalline polymer can hardly exhibit true flow at all.

3. Mechanical Properties of a Polycrystalline Polymer, with Phase Change

A tentative theoretical approach to this subject has been outlined in section II (pages 345–351). In this section, the emphasis is upon experimental observations. Specific examples are considered, and in each case an attempt is made to evaluate the role played by crystallization.

A. Crystallization during Elastic Deformation

It was pointed out in section II (pages 345–351) that a tensile stress serves to favor crystallization, both from the standpoint of equilibrium and of rate. The effect of the crystallization process is an additional elongation, *i.e.*, a reduction in the stress necessary to cause a given elongation. The intermolecular forces, which act in crystallization, are striving to elongate the sample and thus act in the same direction as the tensile stress. This effect is very apparent in the case of slightly vulcanized rubber.

It has been pointed out that the extension curve of rubber can be considered as made up of three parts, as indicated in figure 142. Early in the process of elongation, rubber exhibits mainly gaslike elasticity. In this range, the entropy decrease is the predominant factor in opposing extension. In the middle range, the process of crystallization begins to affect the curve, acting in the same direction as the externally applied tension. In this region, the stress–strain curve becomes somewhat flat since small stresses, aided by the crystallization process, can produce large changes in length. After crystallization has proceeded as far as possible, further extension must involve the stretching of crystallites and of highly constrained amorphous regions. In this last range, rubber exhibits the elastic behavior typical of all crystalline substances—high coefficient of elasticity and small range of extension.

The identification of the extreme S-shaped nature of the extension curve as the effect of crystallization is supported by experimental evidence. Gehman (*34*) has shown that most of the crystallization of rubber takes place in the intermediate extension range.

The phenomenon of spontaneous extension is proof that the crystallization process acts to facilitate the elongation. Gehman and Field (*35*) have shown that, if a stretched rubber sample is cooled at constant

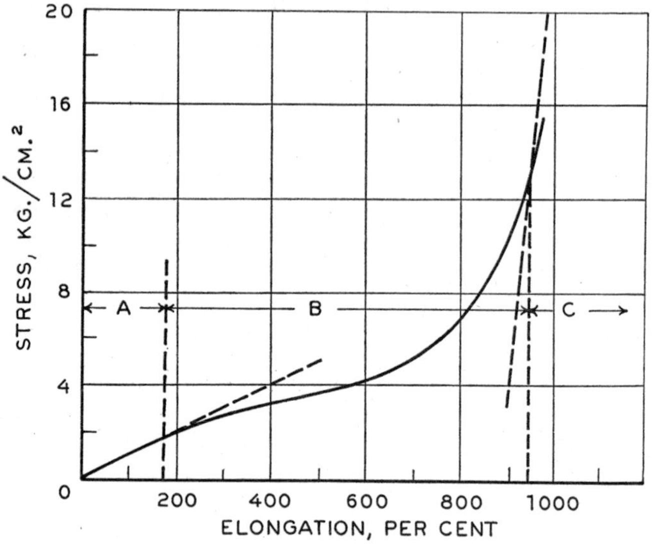

Fig. 142. Schematic representation of the stress–strain curve for rubber showing three regions: (A) region of "gas-like elasticity"; (B) region in which crystallization occurs; (C) region in which crystallization is essentially complete.

elongation, additional crystallization takes place. The result of this crystallization is to reduce the tensile stress. If cooling is carried far enough, the tension decreases to zero and becomes a compressive stress. The rubber then elongates without the application of any external tensile stress. Spontaneous elongations as great as 50% of the original (unstretched) length were observed.

A complete theory of rubber extension should predict both the effect of the crystallization process on the apparrent coefficient of elasticity and the variation of crystalline content with tension. It is possible, however, to treat the first problem by itself and to correlate, in a rough manner, the extension curve with the experimentally observed crystallization curve. Hauser and Mark (*40*), Clark and co-workers (*22–24*), and Gehman and Field (*35*) have measured crystallization as a function of elongation. It can be represented in a crude first approximation as a straight line, starting at about 200% extension. Such a straight-line approximation (as shown in Fig. 143) of the crystallization curve leads to the general shape required of the extension curve.

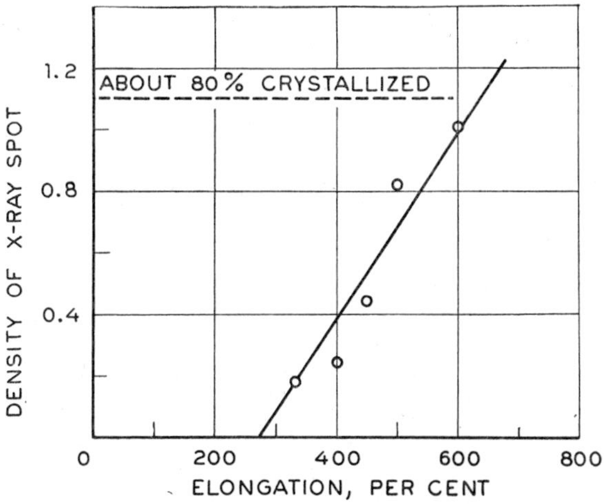

Fig. 143. Crystallization of rubber as a function of elongation, as indicated by X-ray data (after Hauser and Mark).

Let us assume that the broken straight line in figure 143 approximates closely the actual curve in the region between 250 and 600% elongation. Then q, the fraction of crystalline material, can be expressed in this range by the relation:

$$q = (\gamma - 250)(0.002) \tag{5}$$

where γ is the elongation in percentage.

If, now, the only effect of the crystallization process is the extra extension, we may write a differential stress–strain relationship as follows:

$$d\gamma = \frac{1}{k}\,ds + \alpha\,dq \tag{6}$$

Here γ is the elongation, k the coefficient of elasticity (gaslike), s the stress and α the fractional elongation due to crystallization of 1% of the material. This may be written as:

$$d\gamma = \frac{1}{k}\,ds + 0.002\alpha\,d\gamma \tag{7}$$

Figure 144 shows a set of extension curves, calculated in the foregoing way, for different values of the constant α. At the point at which crystallization begins, the coefficient of elasticity suddenly changes to a new value.

The crystallization process not only increases the elongation but also reduces the amount of amorphous phase. In the higher ranges of crystallization, this becomes important, since the quantity of material which can

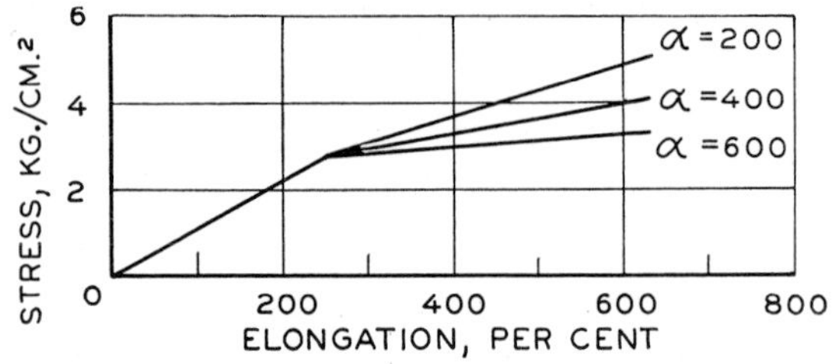

Fig. 144. Theoretical stress–strain curves (first approximation of the effect of crystallization).

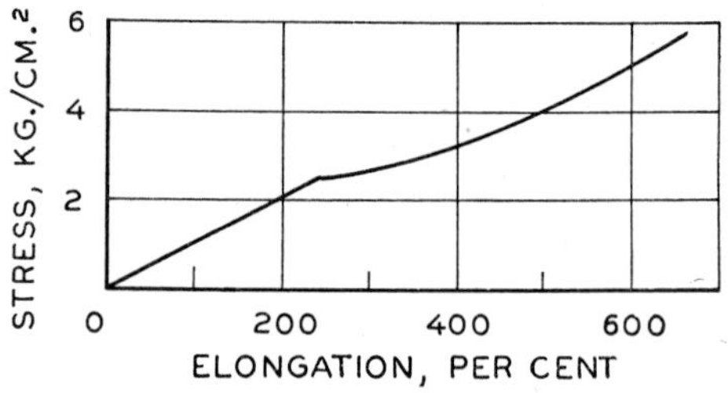

Fig. 145. Theoretical stress–strain curve for rubber (second approximation of the effect of crystallization).

undergo gaslike elastic deformation becomes smaller and smaller. It seems reasonable, therefore, to replace equation (7) by an expression of the following type:

$$d\gamma = \frac{1}{k}(1 - q)ds + 0.002\alpha\, d\gamma \tag{8}$$

This equation obviously coincides with equation (7) for small values of q. When crystallization has proceeded to a great extent, however, equation (8) predicts an increase in the coefficient of elasticity. Figure 145 shows the form of stress–strain curve which results from equation (8).

The sharp break in the curve (Fig. 145) is explained by the assumption that crystallization suddenly begins to take place at 250% extension and proceeds linearly. This approximation is, of course, not in accord with experimental observations, and a more refined analysis would smooth away the corner on the extension curve.

The differential stress–strain equation could be written in the following more general form:

$$d\gamma = (1 - q)\frac{1}{k}\,ds + \alpha\frac{\partial q}{\partial \gamma}\,d\gamma \tag{9}$$

or

$$d\gamma\left(1 - \alpha\frac{\partial q}{\partial \gamma}\right) = (1 - q)\frac{1}{k}\,ds \tag{10}$$

Instead of substituting for q a linear function of γ, as in equation (8), it would be possible either to evaluate q and $\partial q/\partial \gamma$ directly from experimental curves or to substitute an analytic expression for q which closely approximates the observed values. Gehman and Field (*35*) have obtained a distinctly S-shaped curve relating degree of crystallization to extension. However, no experimental stress–strain curves have been made under conditions corresponding to those of their X-ray study. It would, therefore, be of little value to calculate a stress–strain curve based on the finer details of Gehman's curve.

Just as the elasticity of rubber in the early stages of extension is thermodynamically very similar to the elasticity of an ideal gas, so the behavior of rubber in the intermediate range of extension where crystallization occurs is analogous to the condensation of a real gas. When a gas is compressed, the early resistance to compression is due to the random molecular motion (in thermodynamic terms, to the entropy decrease accompanying the volume decrease). When the pressure reaches the value of the vapor pressure exerted by liquid, condensation occurs. While this phase change takes place, the gas can be compressed enormously with no additional pressure. The intermolecular attractive forces, which favor a small volume, act in the same direction as the external pressure. Finally, when the phase change is completed, further compression is very difficult. These three portions of the P–V isotherm of a condensable vapor correspond to the three portions of the stress–strain curve of rubber. (In the latter case the phase change does not occur at one sharply defined stress but over a range of stress, and hence the S–γ curve does not possess the abruptness of the typical P–V plot.)

One interesting result of crystallization during elastic deformation is the effect on Poisson's ratio. It can be proved that the maximum possible value of ν for a homogeneous material which undergoes no phase change during deformation is 0.5. This is the value which corresponds to a constant volume during deformation. If crystallization takes place, however, a net contraction is observed, even though the sample is being subjected to a dilative stress. As a result ν takes on values in excess of the "theoretical limit" of 0.5.

Several authors have proposed that the S-shaped stress–strain curve can be explained without recourse to the effects of crystallization. As a matter of fact, Guth and James (*38*) have extended the original kinetic theory of rubber elasticity to cover the whole range of extension. They find that even without crystallization, a cross-linked rubberlike material should exhibit a stress–strain curve which is S-shaped to a certain extent. Furthermore, their theoretical considerations are born out experimentally, both in the case of synthetic copolymers which cannot crystallize and in the case of vulcanized rubber samples in which crystallization was delayed. Crystallization, therefore, actually causes additional extension in a material whose stress–strain curve would be somewhat S-shaped even in the absence of crystallization. Since the above rough treatment of crystallization cannot pretend to predict the stress–strain curve quantitatively, it must be admitted that, taken by itself, the S-shape of the stress–strain curve of rubber is not a conclusive proof that crystallization affects the ease of extension. On the other hand, the extremely S-shaped stress–strain curves which have been reported by several authors, the phenomenon of spontaneous extension, and the correlation between stress–strain hysteresis and crystallization hysteresis, all indicate that the general thesis of the above discussion is correct. Not only does a tensile stress facilitate crystallization, but the crystallization process in turn aids the stress in extending the sample.

Mack Elasticity.—Once it is established that an elastomeric material belongs in the class of linear or slightly cross-linked high polymers, it is a kinematic certainty that the long range elasticity of the material is achieved through the elongation and orientation of molecular chains. It must necessarily be true that in the unstressed equilibrium state the molecular chains follow some definite distribution law as far as their shapes and orientations are concerned—not necessarily the idealized "amorphous" distribution law of the previous chapter but *some* distribution law. In the presence of a tensile stress, some new distribution law must represent the new equilibrium state of the system. In this new distribution, the molecular configurations of large extension and orientation in the direction of the stress must appear with greater frequency than in the unstressed equilibrium distribution. In simple terms, a tensile stress causes the individual polymer molecules or molecular chains to become, on the average, more extended and aligned in the preferred direction. When the stress is removed, the molecules return from these extended and aligned configurations.

What is not obvious and, moreover, cannot be established on purely kinematic grounds is the *reason* for the molecular opposition to the above process of extension and orientation. *How* does the chain molecule resist being stretched? Where does the work done on the sample during extension go? Why is there a free energy difference between the stretched and the unstretched sample, and what is the molecular basis for this difference? These are all equivalent ways of expressing the fundamental question involved here.

It is perhaps natural that in the first attempts to answer this question, a somewhat static model was used. These early attempts usually involved the rubber molecule. It was assumed by a number of workers that certain specific coiled or folded forms of this molecule best satisfied the intermolecular, or intersegmental, forces. When the sample was stretched, the molecules must be forcibly pulled out from these curled forms. Hence, according to such a picture, the elongation of rubber is opposed by molecular forces. Thus Mark and Fikentscher (*28*) assumed that in the unstressed state the rubber molecule is in the form of a tightly coiled spiral, which under the action of an external force can be uncurled. The stability of the spiral form was assumed to arise from the attractions among double bonds. This general point of view was further developed by Mack (*47*), who rejected the particular role of the double bond attractions and substituted the attractions between hydrogen atoms attached to carbon atoms.

In this volume, the term "Mack elasticity" is applied to all cases in which intersegmental forces cause specific folded or coiled molecular forms to possess particularly low energies so that extension is opposed by these forces. Thermodynamically, the stretching process in such a case entails an increase of energy.

We have already seen that, in the case of rubber, thermodynamic studies of the extension process show that an entropy decrease, rather than an energy increase, contributes mainly to the free energy change on stretching. This indicates that the rubber molecule gravitates not so much to specific curled forms (because of intersegmental forces) as to random, half-curled shapes (because of their statistical predominance).

Rubber itself would seem to fit the pattern of the amorphous polymer (in the early range of extension), rather than the pattern of Mack elasticity. There are many other cases, however, where the energetic preference for specific curled or folded forms must be considered as an important factor and may indeed outweigh in importance the statistical preference for the randomly kinked forms. This is particularly true of polymer chains which possess localized spots of high attraction and even more particularly when these localized attractive spots exert a strong directional selectivity. Such molecules may well be of a structure which allows the attractive forces to be more completely satisfied by specific intramolecular contacts than by intermolecular contacts.

The folding of a polymer molecule into a definite type of configuration can be considered as a sort of intramolecular crystallization, and the process of stretching such a sample involves something of the character of a first-order phase change. It seems very likely that as the scientific study of high polymers advances, "intramolecular crystallization" or "Mack elasticity" will assume a more and more important role. At the present time, a thorough discussion of this important question is very difficult for several reasons:

(1) A polymer possessing strong, specific intersegmental attractions almost necessarily becomes easily frozen in metastable configurations. The purely equilibrium aspect of deformation may well be hidden by time effects. In the case of an amorphous polymer it is possible, as we have seen, to carry out an experimental study of the thermodynamics of extension and recovery by operating in a temperature range where retardations are unimportant. In general, this would not be feasible in an extreme case of Mack elasticity.

(2) An attempt to deduce from molecular structures even the equilibrium behavior of a sample exhibiting Mack elasticity is inherently much more difficult than the corresponding problem in the case of an amorphous polymer. We have seen that the detailed molecular structure of an amorphous polymer does not greatly affect the general nature of the equilibrium elastic behavior. (That is, the assumption of free rotation about C—C bonds leads to essentially the same result as the assumption of three equally probable torsional orientations of each bond.) The very essence of Mack elasticity, on the other hand, lies in the *energies* of polymer molecules as functions of their configurations. In order to compute the equilibrium stress–strain behavior from molecular structure, it is necessary to calculate the potential energy of an aggregate of polymer molecules in different types of packing. This is not easy.

(3) Molecules with localized, directed points of attraction, such as tend most strongly to undergo specific intramolecular folding, are quite likely to undergo intermolecular crystallization once they are straightened

out by an external force. During an extension the process of intermolecular crystallization may take place continuously and simultaneously with the "melting out" of the intramolecular folds. This would further complicate matters and make it more difficult to isolate the phenomenon of Mack elasticity for individual study or theoretical treatment.

B. Effect of Crystallization on Flow in Rubber

It has already been pointed out that the crystallites in a polycrystalline polymer sample serve to link the linear polymer chains together, and that this cross-linking effect can be expected to retard the flow of the polymer. This is true whether the material is naturally crystalline or whether it crystallizes only in the presence of a tensile stress. If a sample of uncross-linked rubber is subjected to a small tensile stress, it slowly flows and finally breaks. If the tensile stress is made larger, the initial flow rate is greater but crystallization soon takes place and reinforces the sample. This results in the interesting fact that, after the same (long) period of time, the sample with the small stress has flowed *more* than the sample with the larger stress. See also section III (pages 355–356). Field (*27*) has analyzed the effect of crystallization on creep in vulcanized rubber. He finds that the rate of creep increases with the stress for low stresses and reaches a maximum at just about the value for which crystallization starts. As the percentage of crystallization increases, the creep decreases.

The stress–strain curve of unvulcanized rubber has an extremely large hysteresis loop on the first cycle. Upon removal of the stress, a large permanent set is observed. The second and subsequent cycles show much less hysteresis, and very little additional permanent set. Figure 146 shows stress–strain curves for raw rubber, as reported by Hock and Boström (*43*). These curves have been interpreted as indicating that in raw rubber which has not been previously deformed a structure is present which is broken down when the rubber is first extended. The form of these curves may, however, be connected with the crystallization process, as follows. During the early part of the first deformation a good deal of flow takes place along with the configurational elastic response. After the stress has increased to a certain point, crystallization begins and facilitates the extension and, at the same time, inhibits the flow. The large permanent deformation at the end of the first cycle is thus due to the flow which takes place before the rubber is reinforced by crystallization. In the second cycle, the rubber is more easily deformed, because of the presence of seed crystallites, but flow is inhibited from the beginning. This interpretation, however, cannot be considered as satisfactorily established as long as the proper sequence of crystalline-amorphous phase changes is merely inferred, rather than observed by means of auxiliary experiments. See also pages 500 *et seq.* for the effect of the crystallization process on the breaking time of rubber as a function of stress.

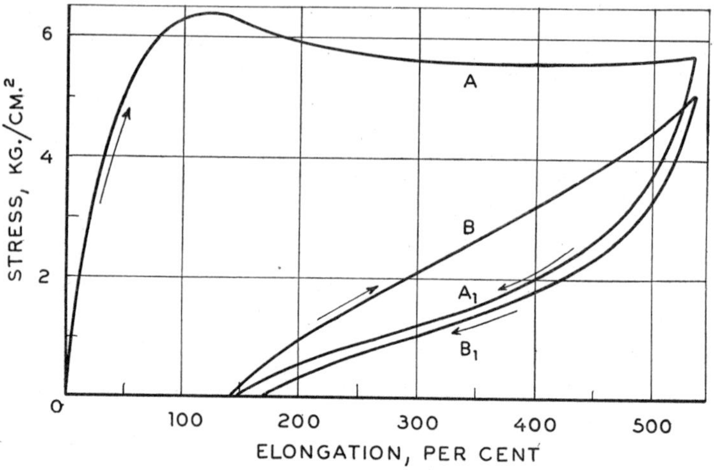

Fig. 146. Stress–strain curves for raw rubber. A, B = strain curves. A_1, B_1 = recovery curves.

C. Crystallization of Polyvinylidene Chloride (Saran) (*37*)

Polyvinylidene chloride, —CH_2—CCl_2—CH_2—CCl_2—, has a crystalline melting point well above room temperature. Present commercial polymers of this type are rather low in molecular weight, possessing polymerization degrees of about 200. As a result, once the crystalline structure is melted out the polymer becomes extremely fluid. The crystalline material of course exhibits very little flow because of the "cross-linking" effect of the crystallites.

In the molten state, polyvinylidene chloride can be extruded or injection molded. Immediately after molding or extrusion the polymer is amorphous; on cooling, crystallization takes place. The crystallization-time curve at a given temperature (Fig. 147) has the same S-shaped character as figure 136 (p. 352) for rubber. *Rate* of crystallization depends of course on temperature. At room temperature it is slow; at higher temperatures it is faster. Figure 148 shows the time necessary for essentially complete crystallization as a function of temperature. This curve would apply only for a particular formulation; both the thermodynamic equilibrium and the kinetics of crystallization are naturally affected by the presence of foreign materials such as plasticizers.

If molten polyvinylidene chloride is cooled quickly to room temperature (quenched), a supercooled amorphous product is obtained which crystallizes only slowly. The amorphous polymer is soft, weak, and

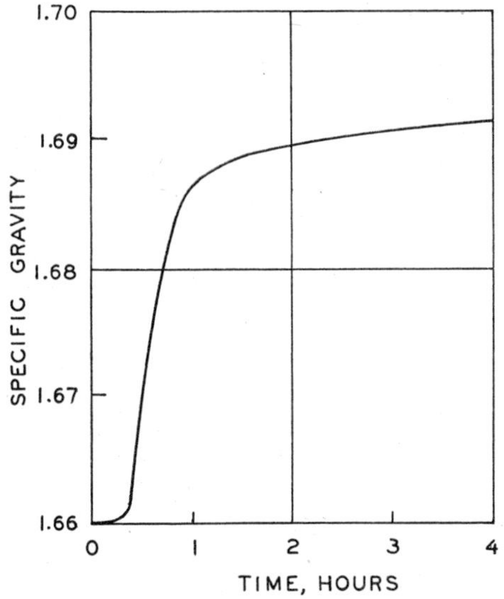

Fig. 147. Crystallization as a function of time for polyvinylidene chloride at 20°C. (after Goggin and Lowry).

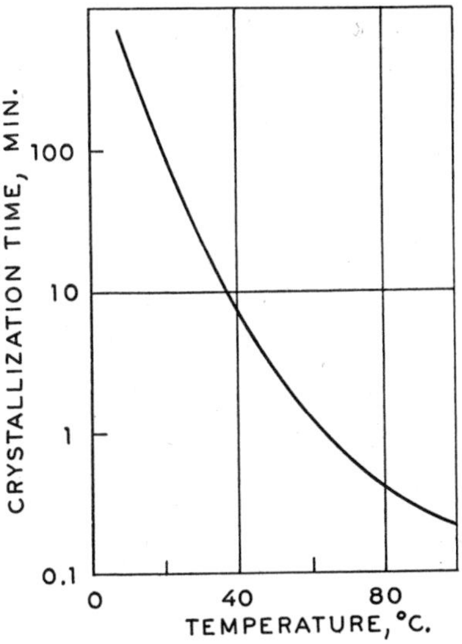

Fig. 148. Effect of temperature on the rate of crystallization of polyvinylidene chloride (after Goggin and Lowry).

pliable at room temperature. The polycrystalline mass which results after long standing or from annealing at higher temperature is much harder and stronger.

"The injection molding of Saran is unique. With other commercial thermoplastics the use of cold dies hastens the cooling of the plastic part and shortens the cycle. With Saran the reverse is true. Cold dies produce soft, flexible, amorphous pieces. Rapid hardening is accomplished by heat treatment (heated dies) to produce recrystallization. For normal sections this permits short cycles." (*37*)

In a polycrystalline mass produced in the above manner, the crystallites are of course oriented completely at random. If the supercooled amorphous polymer is stretched, however, rapid crystallization accompanies the plastic flow. Since the sample is below its equilibrium melting point even in the absence of the tensile stress, the crystals once formed are stable. The sample does not tend to retract with melting when the stress is removed, as rubber does at room temperature. The stress serves to increase the *rate* of crystallization. Of course, only the formation of crystallites *parallel* to the tensile stress is favored kinetically. Therefore, in the polycrystalline mass resulting from cold drawing, the crystallites are oriented parallel to the direction of stretch.

Of the three distinct forms of the polymer—amorphous, crystalline, and oriented crystalline—the latter has the best unidirectional physical properties. Thus the unoriented crystalline polymer exhibits a tensile strength of from 4000 to 12,000 p.s.i., depending upon formulation and heat treatment. The *oriented* crystalline polymer exhibits a tensile strength *in the fiber direction* of as high as 56,000 p.s.i. Presumably the *transverse* tensile strength is much lower but, since the oriented polymer finds its use in fiberlike applications where little transverse loading is to be expected, the longitudinal strength is the important factor.

It must be remembered that the cold drawing of amorphous Saran is not thermodynamically equivalent to the crystallization of rubber by stretching at room temperature. The crystalline phase in stretched rubber is stable only as long as the tensile stress is imposed; when the stress is removed, the crystallites melt out. Crystalline Saran is stable at room temperature; the crystallization is merely accelerated by the tensile stress. The crystallization of rubber by stretching is thus analogous to the increase in melting point of a crystalline solid when a homogeneous pressure is applied. The cold drawing of Saran is analogous to the (hypothetical) crystallization of a *supercooled* liquid by means of external pressure.

D. Effect of Crystallization on the Elastic Behavior of Nylon

Busse and co-workers (*21*) investigated the response of various cords to constant loads. They found that cords loaded by a weight which was about twenty per cent of their tensile strength extended linearly with log of time. The higher the temperature, the greater the rate of extension. After the cords had been under load for several hours, so that the rate of growth was small, an increase in temperature produced an immediate and reversible *decrease* in length. Figure 149 shows the results when a cotton cord was held under a constant load (about 1/30 of its normal tensile strength) for two hours at 300°F., and then the temperature was changed back and forth between 200° and 300°F. Figure 150 shows

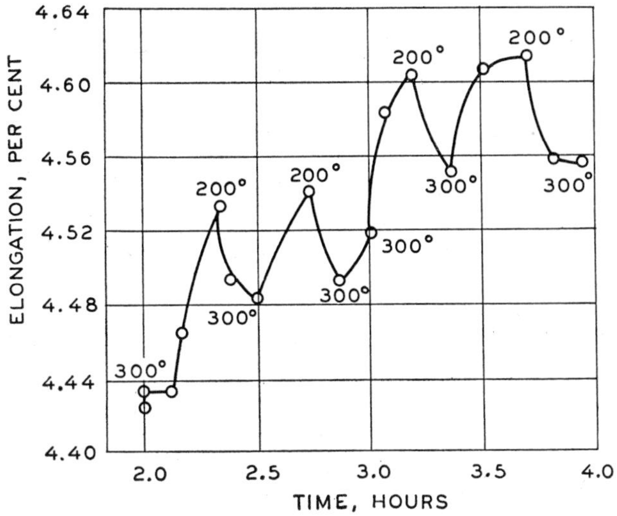

Fig. 149. Change in length of cotton cord with temperature.

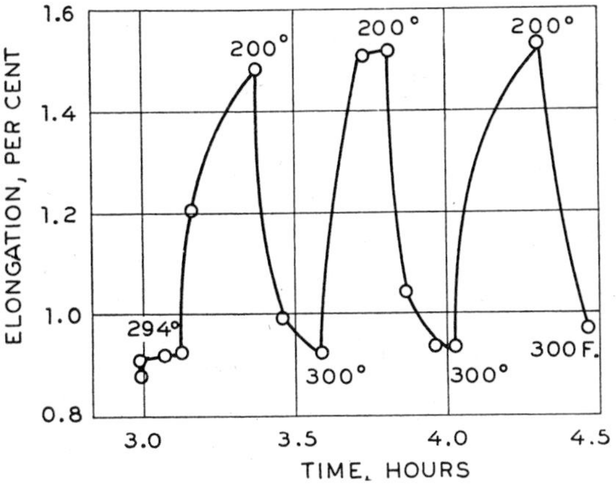

Fig. 150. Change in length of nylon cords with temperature.

the results of a similar test with nylon. The effect in the case of cotton is rather small and can be explained without postulating any phase change on the basis of the kinetic theory of elasticity. In the case of nylon, on the other hand, the contraction caused by going from 200° to 300°F. amounts to almost 50% of the total extension. The kinetic theory of elasticity could account for only a small fraction of this contraction since the kinetic Young's modulus should be directly proportional to absolute temperature. It is clear that specific forces are being overcome by thermal agitation, and that these forces favor extension. It would seem reasonable to suppose that upon going from 300° to 200°F. a certain amount of additional crystallization takes place, resulting in extension, and upon going from 200° to 300°F., some melting out of crystallites occurs. The amorphous regions, of course, contract according to the kinetic theory but the phase change, which changes the relative amounts of crystalline and amorphous material, is responsible for the large magnitude of the contraction.

E. Other Examples

In the previous examples, the role of crystallization was more or less clear cut and definite. In some cases, direct evidence of crystallization during deformation was available in the form of X-ray patterns, volume changes, etc. In other cases, the mechanical effects were pronounced enough and of such a nature that they could safely be attributed to crystallization even though the evidence was more indirect. In many cases, however, the precise effects of the crystallization process are less definitely understood. It is well known that the creep and recovery properties of textile fibers do not follow the simple pattern of chapter B. It seems reasonable to attribute the more complicated behavior of such materials to the fact that they are often crystalline and oriented and to the other fact that additional crystallization may take place during deformation. Any detailed conjectures as to the effects of crystallinity and crystallization upon a creep curve must necessarily remain somewhat more tentative than similar conjectures in the case of a stress–strain curve or a strain–temperature effect (or a stress–temperature effect), particularly if such a curve or effect is reversible or nearly reversible. (It is nearly always easier to supply a satisfactory molecular explanation of an equilibrium phenomenon than of a rate phenomenon.) In spite of this difficulty, there have been in recent years a number of attempts to interpret creep curves of textile filaments in terms of crystallization. The remainder of this chapter is devoted largely to such studies.

Press (*52*) has reported a rather detailed study of the creep and recovery properties of viscose rayon yarn, in which the logarithmic creep is analyzed as being partly due to retarded elasticity in the amorphous regions and partly due to additional crystallization which accompanies the deformation. A large part of this paper is quoted below.

. . . Thus we arrive at a loose, tangled, net-like structure of disordered long chain molecules interlocking at the few points where the segments happen to be suitably disposed for strong interaction. The regions of strong interaction (relatively crystalline) contribute mostly to high modulus and strength. The regions of weak interaction (relatively amorphous) contribute to long-range elasticity and the ability to distribute stresses.

Upon the application of an external force the regions with varying degrees of order approach new equilibrium positions of higher order by slippage, stretching, orientation, and rotation. The time-extension test under constant load is the simplest type of experiment with which to study such phenomena.

A sample of commercial viscose rayon (150 denier multifilament yarn) was used in the following experiments as representative of the more complicated type of composite high-polymeric system. The conditions of 70°F. and 65 percent R.H. (relative humidity) were used for two reasons. (1) They yield internal viscosities great enough satisfactorily to spread the superimposed relaxation and retardation times characterizing the regions of varying degrees of order and size. (2) These conditions are fairly representative of industrial practice, and therefore possibly of some immediate value.

TABLE XIV

EXTENSIONS AFTER VARYING LENGTHS OF TIME UNDER A CONSTANT LOAD OF 0.67 GRAMS PER DENIER

Time, sec.	Extension, %	Time, sec.	Extension, %	Time, sec.	Extension, %
0.01	0.67*	250	6.0	11,000	7.55
1	2.6	400	6.1	68,000	8.45
5	3.2	700	6.4	75,000	8.5
10	3.6	1,000	6.6	97,200	8.6
20	4.2	1,500	6.8	183,600	8.8
40	4.9	2,000	6.9	327,600	8.9
60	5.1	3,000	7.1	356,400	8.95
80	5.3	4,000	7.2	414,000	9.05
120	5.55	5,000	7.25	442,800	9.08
180	5.8	7,500	7.35		

* Calculated from elastic modulus.

Table XIV gives the results of such a time-extension test under a moderate load of 0.67 g/d for the time range of 10^{-2} to 4.5×10^{5} seconds. These data are plotted in figure 151 as the logarithm of time *versus* the extension. The extension at 10^{-2} second represents the instantaneous elastic elongation (0.67 percent) characteristic for the elastic modulus (1.33×10^{11} dynes/cm^2) of the material. From 10^{-2} to 10^{3} seconds the curve indicates a fairly complicated change in equilibrium within those regions possessing low relaxation or retardation times. A low relaxation time is synonymous with ease of viscous flow, while a low retardation time corresponds to a slightly retarded elasticity. From 10^{3} to 4.5×10^{5} seconds the results are fairly well characterized by a straight line in the semilogarithmic graph indicating a more uniform change in equilibrium in regions having much higher relaxation and retardation times.

This fairly sharp change at about 10^{3} seconds, characteristic of all loads above 0.4 g/d, indicated the advisability of studying separately the regions from 10^{-2} to 10^{3} seconds and from 10^{3} to 10^{6} seconds . . .

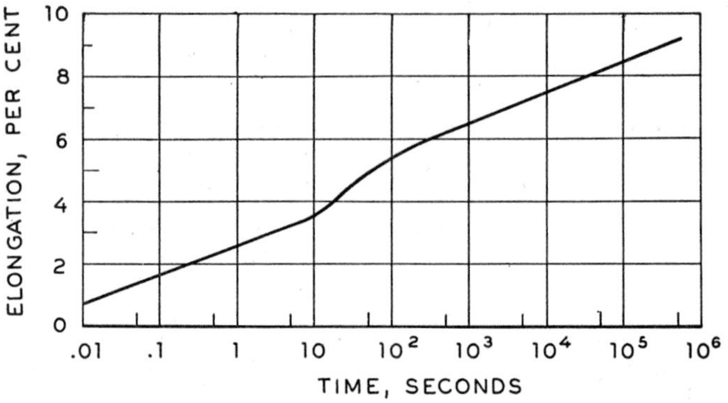

Fig. 151. Creep curve for commercial viscose rayon at 70°F. and 65 percent relative humidity at a load of 0.67 gram per denier (after Press).

TABLE XV

COMPARATIVE ELASTICITY MODULI OF VISCOSE RAYON YARN

Condition	Method	Modulus in dynes per sq cm $\times 10^{10}$
Air dried	Supersonics	11.5
− 190°F.	Static, extrapolated	13.2
70°F. and 65% R.H.	Short time static	13.3
Air dried	Normal static	8.3
—	Normal static	5.9
—	Normal static	6.9
50% R.H.	Normal static	6.9

TABLE XVI

EXTENSION (SHORT TIME) UNDER LOAD FOR 1000 SECONDS, AFTER RECOVERY FOR 1000 AND 86,400 SECONDS, AND AFTER WETTING AND DRYING. EACH VALUE IS AN AVERAGE OF FIVE TESTS

Load (grams/denier)	Extension 1,000 seconds	Recovery length		
		1,000 seconds	86,400 seconds	Wet and dried
Blank				−0.50%
0.2	0.50%	0.01%		
0.3	0.71	0.02	−0.02%	−0.46%
0.4	1.19	0.19	0.02	−0.42
0.5	2.98	1.09	0.58	−0.45
0.65	5.66	3.13	2.39	−0.16
0.8	8.64	5.20	4.30	0.25
1.0	10.97	6.96	6.18	0.85

The short time tests consisted in measuring the extension of individual samples after 1000 seconds loading, after 1000 and 86,400 seconds recovery, and after wetting the samples and reconditioning at 70°F. and 65 percent R.H. The loads ranged from 0.1–1.0 gram/denier. The results of these tests are given in table XVI and figure 152.

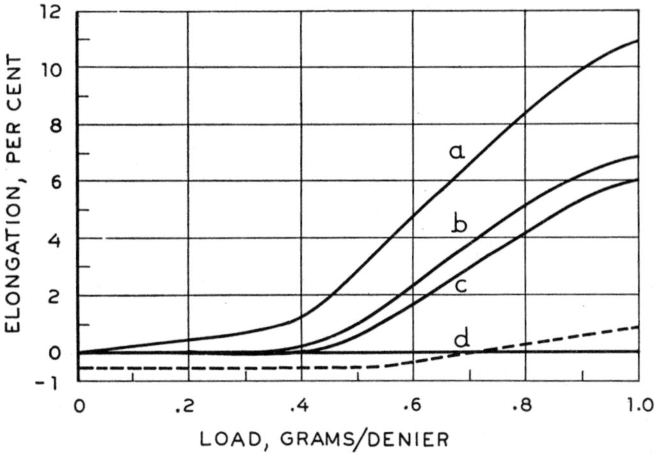

Fig. 152. Short time tests (after Press): (a) amount of creep after 1000 seconds, as a function of load; (b) residual deformation after 1000 seconds recovery; (c) residual deformation after 86,400 seconds recovery; (d) residual deformation after wetting and drying.

An examination of figure 152 discloses some very interesting relationships. Up to 0.3 g/d and 3/4 percent extension the time for complete recovery (1000 seconds) is the same as the time for the extension (1000 seconds). This range, although retarded, is completely elastic, involving no permanent change in the sample. It probably represents the maximum movement (mostly in the relatively amorphous regions) of various molecular segments before the weaker secondary bonds begin to break.

From 0.3 g/d and 3/4 percent extension to 0.55 g/d and 4 percent extension the time for complete conditioned recovery is much longer than the time for extension. However, after wetting and reconditioning, the samples do recover completely to the same extension (− 0.5 percent) as the blank after similar wetting and reconditioning. The greatly retarded conditioned recovery indicates an increase in viscosity, while the complete recovery after wetting to remove internal strains and then reconditioning indicates that no permanent deformation has taken place. The 0.5 percent shrinkage of the blank after wetting and reconditioning is due to residual internal strains in this sample of yarn.

Above 0.55 g/d and 4 percent extension the conditioned recovery is retarded and the recovery even after wetting and reconditioning is still not complete. Here again the greatly retarded recovery indicates an increase in viscosity, while the incomplete wet recovery represents permanent deformation.

Long time tests were then run in which the extensions were checked periodically under load (0.1–0.8 g/d), during recovery, and after wetting and drying. The results of these tests are shown in table XVII and are summarized in figure 153. We see here several features which show surprising similarity to some features of the short time tests (Fig. 152).

TABLE XVII

EXTENSION (LONG TIME) UNDER LOAD, DURING RECOVERY AND AFTER WETTING AND DRYING

Time (seconds)	Load (grams/denier)						
	0.1	0.2	0.3	0.4	0.5	0.65	0.8
(loaded)	Extension (%)						
100	0.0%	0.28%	0.5%	0.73%	1.33%	4.61%	7.73%
1,000	0.0	0.28	0.67	1.00	3.67	6.06	9.06
10,000	0.06	0.33	0.89	2.33	4.50	7.62	10.16
20,000	0.06	0.33	1.27	2.83	4.83	7.95	10.33
86,400	0.12	0.62	1.62	3.50	5.50	8.50	11.00
108,000	0.12	0.67	1.67	3.67	5.57	8.62	11.00
194,400	0.17	0.67	1.83	3.83	5.83	8.83	11.33
345,600	0.17	0.67	2.00	4.06	6.00	9.00	11.62
540,000	0.17	0.73	2.16	4.33	6.16	9.16	11.84
691,200	0.23	0.83	2.22	4.33	6.33	9.28	12.00
864,000	0.28	0.83	2.33	4.39	6.33	9.33	12.17
950,400	0.28	0.83	2.33	4.45	6.39	9.33	12.33
(load removed)	Recovery length (%)						
100	0.0	0.5	1.78	3.67	5.39	8.00	10.06
1,000	0.0	0.495	1.67	3.56	5.16	7.51	9.62
10,000	0.0	0.33	1.50	3.28	4.73	7.00	9.00
20,000	0.0	0.33	1.45	3.16	4.67	6.67	8.73
259,200	0.0	0.28	1.17	2.83	4.06	6.16	8.33
518,400	0.0	0.28	1.12	2.67	4.00	6.06	8.28
950,400	−0.05	0.23	1.06	2.67	3.95	6.06	8.22
(soaked and dried)	−0.67	−0.62	−0.33	−0.33	−0.17	0.83	1.39

The composite results may be outlined as follows:

1. The recovery rate for extension up to 3/4 percent is practically the same as the extension rate. Thus, we have a retarded, completely elastic range involving no permanent change in the sample and limited by a *yield extension of 3/4 percent.* This probably represents the maximum movement of molecular segments before the weaker secondary bonds in the relatively amorphous regions begin to break.

2. Between 3/4 percent and 4 percent extension, we have an elastic region in which the conditioned recovery is greatly retarded; however, after wetting to remove internal strain and then reconditioning, the recovery is complete. The extension is the important factor in this range. The incomplete conditioned recovery indicates an increase in recovery viscosity or a decrease in the restoring forces while the complete recovery after

wetting to remove internal strain and then reconditioning indicates that no permanent deformation has taken place. In the relatively amorphous regions some secondary bonds probably have been broken and some segments have begun to change positions, but do not have sufficient translational and rotational freedom to move into new equilibrium positions of strong interaction. There are still strong internal restoring forces due to molecular entanglement and cross bonding, however, they are now not strong enough to overcome the steric hindrance produced by the movement of some segments to new positions. Upon wetting, water penetrates the amorphous regions, pushes apart

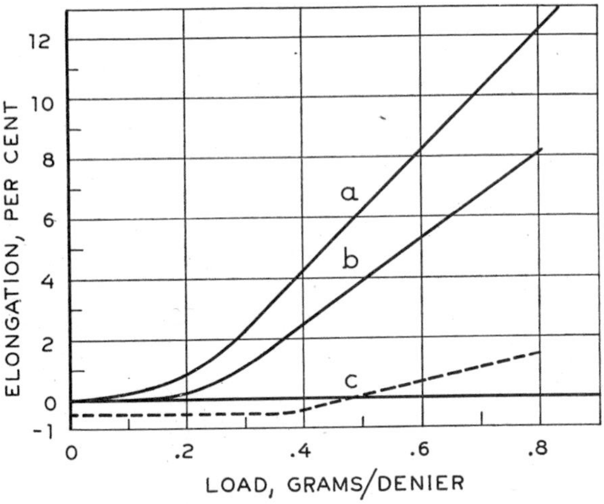

Fig. 153. Long time tests (after Press): (a) creep in 950,400 seconds as a function of load; (b) residual deformation after 950,400 seconds recovery; (c) residual deformation after wetting and drying.

the molecular segments and reduces the steric hindrance so that now the weakened restoring forces can bring the segments back to their original state of lower order. The 0.5 percent shrinkage of the blank after wetting and reconditioning indicates that the sample was dried during production or was wound afterwards under a tension which counteracted part of the internal restoring forces and left the material with some residual strain.

3. Above 4 percent extension the conditioned recovery is greatly retarded and the sample *does not* recover completely even after wetting and reconditioning. There is, in this region, an increase in recovery viscosity or a decrease in restoring forces with some molecular segments now having sufficient energy to move into new equilibrium positions. The extension of 4 percent appears to be associated with a *critical energy level* in the amorphous regions, which is sufficiently great to allow some segments to move into new equilibrium positions.

4. The logarithmic rate of extension (Fig. 154) for each load from 10^3 to 10^6 seconds can be fairly well represented by a straight line described by the equation $\gamma = A + b \log (t + 1)$. Here γ is the extension at time t, A is a constant, and b is the

slope of the line. A plot of slope b against load in grams/denier (Fig. 154A) shows that the logarithmic rate of extension increases proportional to load up to 0.2 g/d, very rapidly for loads from 0.2 to 0.4 gram/denier, and then remains fairly constant for the loads above 0.4 g/d. Referring these load ranges back to figure 154, we see that each

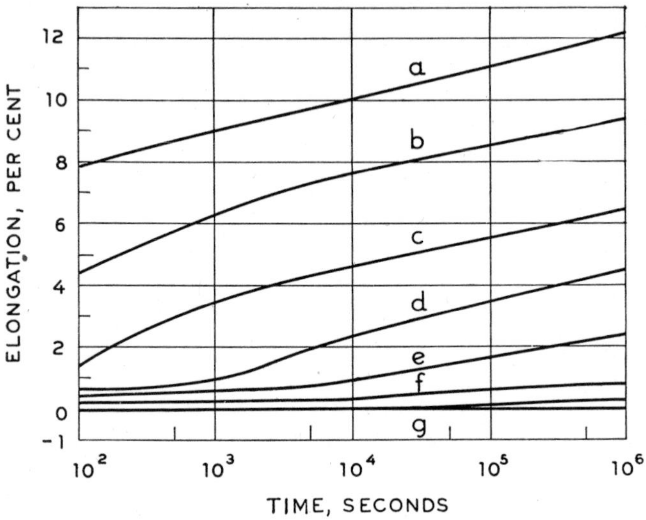

Fig. 154. Creep curves for viscose rayon at different stresses (after Press): (a) 0.80; (b) 0.65; (c) 0.50; (d) 0.40; (e) 0.30; (f) 0.20; and (g) 0.10 gram per denier.

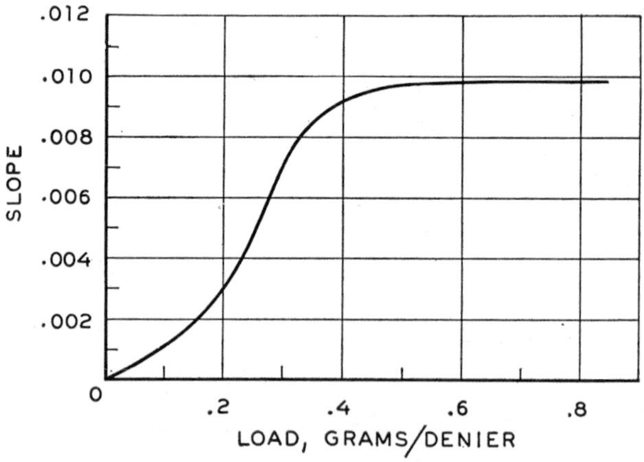

Fig. 154A. Slope b of logarithmic creep curve *vs.* load for viscose rayon (after Press).

one corresponds exactly to one of the ranges of extension which characterize the material. The slopes (*b*) for loads up to 0.2 g/d, proportional to load, have reached a maximum extension of 3/4 percent for the 0.2 g/d load at 10^6 seconds. This range, therefore, is within the 3/4 percent limiting extension (see paragraph 1) of retarded, completely elastic behavior and involves no permanent changes in the material. The slopes (*b*) for loads of 0.2 g/d to 0.4 g/d, increasing rapidly with load, cover roughly the range from 3/4 percent to 4 percent extension. This is the range (see paragraph 2) previously associated with incomplete conditioned recovery and complete wet recovery, with the incomplete conditioned recovery being ascribed either to an increase in recovery viscosity with extension or to a decrease in the restoring forces. The rapid increase in slope (Fig. 154A) for this range represents a sharp drop in viscosity, indicating that the incomplete conditioned recovery is due mostly to a decrease in the internal restoring forces resulting

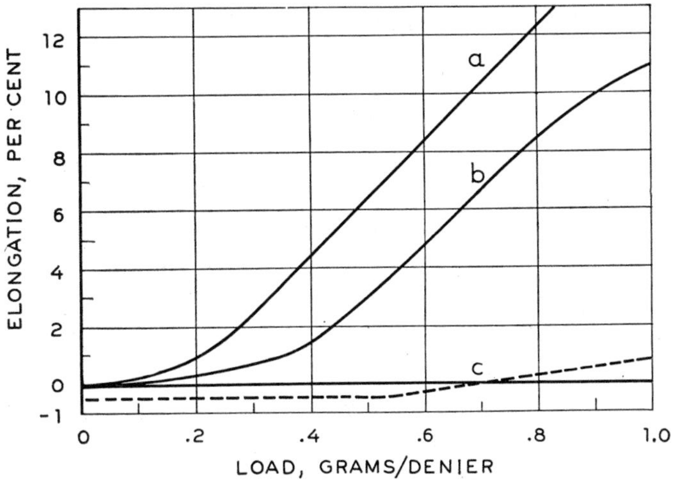

Fig. 154B. Long and short time deformations as a function of load: (a) extension in 950,400 seconds; (b) in 1,000 seconds. (c) Residual deformation after wetting and drying.

from the breaking of many secondary bonds in the amorphous regions. The slopes (*b*) for the loads above 0.4 g/d, remaining fairly constant, cover roughly the range of extension above 4 percent. This was the range (see paragraph 3) associated with incomplete conditioned recovery and incomplete wet recovery, with the incomplete conditioned recovery being ascribed either to an increase in viscosity or to a decrease in restoring forces. The fairly constant slope (Fig. 154A), for this range, indicates an increase in viscosity proportional to both load and extension. From this it appears likely that the incomplete conditioned recovery for this range is due not as much to a decrease in the original restoring forces as it is to an increase in viscosity resulting from segments in the relative amorphous regions moving into new equilibrium positions of higher order.

The short time (10^3 seconds) and long time (10^6 seconds) data were then arranged (Fig. 154B) in an effort to determine whether the permanent deformation and increase

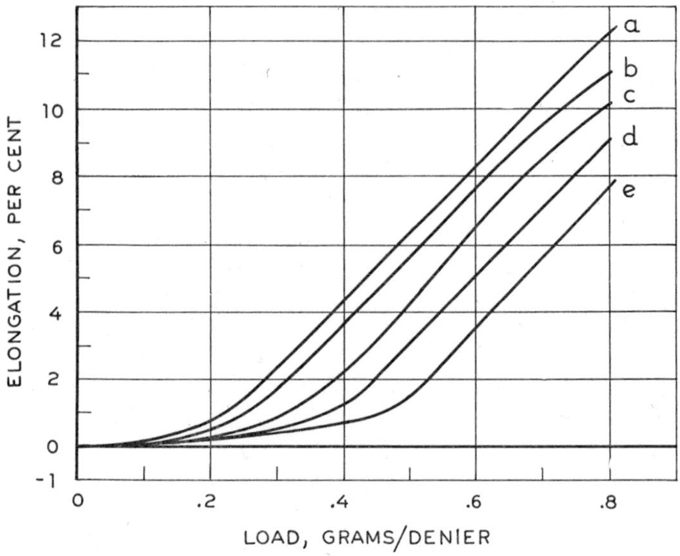

Fig. 154C. Extension *vs.* loads for various times of loading (after Press): (a) 950,400; (b) 108,000; (c) 10,000; (d) 1,000; and (e) 100 seconds.

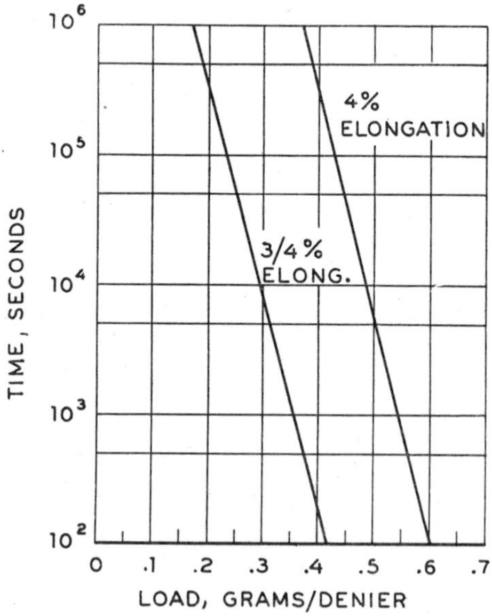

Fig. 154D. Time to reach 3/4 and 4 percent elongation as a function of the load (after Press).

in viscosity for extension above 4 percent was due to translational movement (viscous flow) or to rotational movement (crystallization) of segments. Upon calculation, the percent deformation for extensions *above 4 percent* remained fairly constant in the short time (10^3 seconds) tests at about 19 percent of the extension (0.65, 0.80, and 1.0 g/d gave values of 19.3 percent, 17.8 percent, and 19.4 percent), while in the long time (10^6 seconds) tests the percent increase in permanent deformation based on the increase in extension from 10^3 to 10^6 seconds showed an increase in percent permanent deformation with load (0.50, 0.65, and 0.80 g/d gave values of 19.2 percent, 27.2 percent, and 31.2 percent). The constancy of the percent permanent deformation for the short time (10^3 seconds) tests indicates that the mechanism is probably one of translational movement which is proportional to the extension. This represents mostly the disentangling of parts of molecules in the amorphous regions and the sliding of some segments over other segments along the fiber axis, producing an increased steric hindrance to recovery. The increase of the percent permanent deformation with load in the long time (10^6 seconds) tests indicates that here the increase of rotational freedom, with increasing energy stored in the molecular segments, is beginning to play an important part. The percent permanent deformation (19.2 percent) for the smallest load (0.5 g/d) is similar to the fairly constant value (approximately 19 percent) for the short time tests and is probably mostly translational movement (viscous flow). Above 0.5 g/d the percent permanent deformation in the long time tests (10^6 seconds) increases with load (27.2 percent at 0.65 g/d and 31.2 percent at 0.8 g/d) suggesting that rotational movement (crystallization) is occurring simultaneous with translational movement (viscous flow). The higher load stores more energy in the sample and increases the rotational energy level of the segments. For rotational movement the increase in recovery viscosity results mostly from the establishment of new secondary intermolecular forces which oppose the recovery forces.

The greater rotational freedom of the long time (10^6 seconds) tests as compared to the short time (10^3 seconds) tests suggests the possibility of a shift in the internal load distribution with time either from regions of strong interaction (relatively crystalline) to regions of weaker interaction (relatively amorphous) or in the amorphous regions to fewer segments as the reinforcement between segments relaxes and the load distribution becomes less regular.

An attempt to check the decrease in viscosity and the change in load distribution, in going from 3/4 to 4 percent extension, was made by calculating the very short time (10^{-2} second) elastic modulus at 3/4 and 4 percent extension. The loads required to produce extensions of 3/4 percent and 4 percent, respectively, after 10^2, 10^3, 10^4, 10^5, and 10^6 seconds were approximated from the curves of figure 154C and plotted in figure 154D as load (grams/denier) against log time (seconds). The points for both 3/4 percent and 4 percent extension are fairly well represented by straight lines described by an equation of the type, $S = A - b \log (1 + t)$. S is the load in grams/denier required to produce the extension (3/4 percent or 4 percent) in time t, A is a constant, and b is the slope of the line.

3/4 Percent Extension

$$b = \frac{2.35}{4} = 0.59$$

at = 10^3;

$$0.35 \text{ g/d} = A - 0.59 \log (10^3 + 1)$$
$$A = 5.27$$
$$S = 5.27 - 0.59 \log (t + 1)$$

at $= 10^{-2}$;

$$S = 5.27 - 0.59 \log (10^{-2} + 1)$$
$$= 5.27 \text{ g/d}$$
$$\therefore E_{3/4\%} = \frac{5.27 \times 1.33 \times 10^{9*}}{0.75\%}$$
$$= 3.8 \times 10^{11} \text{ dynes/cm}^2$$

4 Percent Extension

$$b = \frac{2.25}{4} = 0.56$$

at $= 10^3$;

$$0.55 \text{ g/d} = A - 0.56 \log (10^3 + 1)$$
$$A = 7.18$$
$$S = 7.18 - 0.56 \log (t + 1)$$

at $= 10^{-2}$;

$$S = 7.18 - 0.56 \log (10^{-2} + 1)$$
$$= 7.18$$
$$\therefore E_{4\%} = \frac{7.18 \text{ g/d} \times 1.33 \times 10^{9*}}{4\%}$$
$$= 0.74 \times 10^{11} \text{ dynes/cm}^2$$

Comparing the determined (small loads: t approximately 10^{-2}) short time static modulus with the calculated moduli ($t = 10^{-2}$) we get:

Determined modulus:

$$E = 1.33 \times 10^{11} \text{ dynes/cm}^2$$

Calculated moduli:

$$E_{3/4\%} = 3.8 \times 10^{11} \text{ dynes/cm}^2$$
$$E_{4\%} = 0.74 \times 10^{11} \text{ dynes/cm}^2$$

The modulus apparently increases with extension up to a maximum of about 10^{12} dynes/cm^2 at 3/4 percent extension, decreases to about 2.5×10^{11} dynes/cm^2 at 4 percent extension, and then probably starts to increase again. The modulus increases with extension up to 3/4 percent as the load is distributed amongst an increasing number of regions and segments, from 3/4 percent to 4 percent extension the modulus and viscosity decrease as more and more of the weaker secondary bonds in the relatively amorphous regions break, and then above 4 percent extension the modulus and viscosity increase as reinforcement takes place in the relatively amorphous regions. Several other observations on the relation of time to tenacity have some bearing on this problem. The short time tests (Fig. 154B) show a slightly stronger reinforcement for the 1.0 g/d test as compared with the 0.80 g/d test. The long time 1.0 g/d tests were impossible to complete, all samples breaking before 10^6 seconds. This indicates a strong short time reinforcement which gradually relaxes until the sample breaks. Possibly the short time reinforcement of segments in the amorphous regions allows these regions at first to support a high load, then gradually the reinforcement relaxes, fewer and fewer segments are in a position to support the load and finally the sample breaks. From this we may obtain a value of 0.8–1.0 g/d for the low limiting tenacity of the material with minimum reinforcement. The normally determined tenacity for this material is about 2.0 g/d conditioned and about 1.0 g/d wet. The long time tenacity of 0.8 to 1.0 g/d checks fairly well with the normal wet tenacity of about 1.0 g/d and indicates a possible similarity in internal load distribution and breaking mechanism. In the wet tensile test, because of the presence of water molecules in the amorphous regions, the material is not able to reinforce itself significantly. Further work is in progress on the tenacity aspect of the problem.*

* 1 gram/denier = 1.33×10^9 dynes per cm^2.

Press summarizes his results as follows:

1. The relation of load and time to the elastic properties of viscose rayon varies with the range of extension and up to at least 12 percent may be roughly divided into three ranges; to 3/4 percent, from 3/4 percent to 4 percent, and above 4 percent.

2. Extensions to a *3/4 percent yield extension* are retarded and completely elastic. The elastic modulus increases from 1.33×10^{11} (determined) to 3.8×10^{11} dynes/cm^2 (calculated). This range represents the maximum movement of molecular segments before weaker secondary bonds in the relatively amorphous regions begin to break.

3. The second range from 3/4 percent to 4 percent extension is not completely recoverable until the sample is swollen with water. The elastic modulus decreases from 3.8×10^{11} dynes/cm^2 (calculated) at 3/4 percent extension to 0.74×10^{11} dynes/cm^2 (calculated) at 4 percent extension. Numerous secondary bonds in the relatively amorphous regions are broken resulting in a decrease in restoring forces and viscosity. Molecular chain segments have begun to change positions, but do not have sufficient translational and rotational energy to move into new equilibrium positions of strong interaction. Swelling in water reduces the steric hindrance and allows the weakened restoring forces to bring the segments back to their original state of lower order.

4. Above 4 percent the extensions are not completely recoverable even after swelling in water. The further decrease in viscosity with breakage of additional secondary bonds in the relatively amorphous regions is overshadowed by the increase in viscosity resulting from some molecular segments now having sufficient translational (viscous flow) and rotational (crystallization) energy to move into new equilibrium positions of higher order. For short times (10^3 seconds) the translational movement predominates and the permanent deformation is proportional to the extension above a critical value of about 4 percent. For longer times (10^3 to 10^6 seconds) the rotational movement, which is proportional to load, becomes apparent and is superimposed over the translational movement.

5. With loads of 1.0 grams/denier (approximately 19,000 lb. per sq. inch) this sample of viscose rayon shows strong reinforcement in the short time (10^3 seconds) tests and breaks in the long time (10^3 to 10^6 seconds) tests. The short time reinforcement in the amorphous regions allows them at first to support a high load, then gradually the reinforcement relaxes until a low limiting tenacity of 0.8–1.0 gram/denier is reached for the material with minimum reinforcement. The normally determined tenacity is about 2.0 grams/denier dry and about 1.0 g/d wet. The similarity of the long time tenacity with the normal wet tenacity indicates a possible similarity in internal load distribution and breaking mechanism.

These papers have been quoted at some length because they represent a very ambitious step toward a thorough molecular interpretation of the creep of a "crystalline" polymer. Some of the more detailed conclusions should perhaps be considered as primarily heuristic in nature, but there can be little doubt that the general point of view, in which retarded elasticity, additional crystallization, etc., are explicitly considered, represents an important contribution.

Press and Mark (*50*) have made a similar study of acetate rayon, in which a specific molecular interpretation is placed on each part of the creep curve and comparisons are made with viscose.

The total elongation γ of a stretched fiber or film has recently been represented as a function of time by the following contributions:

(a) An instantaneous elastic elongation γ_0 computed from the stress by means of S/E_0, where E_0 represents an appropriate average of the moduli, the relaxation times of which are short as compared with the time of the experiment.

(b) A delayed or retarded elastic elongation γ_1, which has the form

$$\gamma_1 = \frac{S - S_1}{E_1}(1 - e^{-k_1 t}) \tag{11}$$

S_1 = yield value for this retarded elasticity, E_1 = modulus value for this retarded elasticity, $k_1 = 1/\tau_1$ = rate constant (reciprocal time of relaxation).

In the sense of our discussion, it seems appropriate to replace (11) by the more general expression

$$\gamma_1 = \int_0^{\infty} \frac{S - S(\lambda)}{E(\lambda)} [1 - e^{k(\lambda)t}]d\lambda \tag{12}$$

$S(\lambda)$ = distribution curve of yield values for the various species λ of retarded elastic elements, $E(\lambda)$ = distribution curve of moduli, $k(\lambda)$ = distribution curve of rate constants.

Equation (12), giving γ_1 as a function of time, can be computed in principle if the distribution curves are known.

(c) A Bingham flow term

$$\gamma_3 = \frac{S - S_3}{\eta}t \tag{13}$$

where η represents an appropriate average of the viscosity for all elements of isolated viscous flow and S_3 is a corresponding average over value for the yield point.

(d) Recently it has been pointed out by Alfrey, Fourt, Harris, Press, and others, that as soon as a phase transition takes place, it is necessary to add a fourth term, the rate of which is commensurable with the reciprocal time of the experiment. If one assumes a second-order mechanism for the rate of crystallization, as has been successfully done by Taylor for silicate glass one arrives at a term

$$\gamma_2 = k_2 \log (t + 1) \tag{14}$$

for sufficiently large values of t (above 100 seconds) this gives

$$\gamma_2 = k_2 \log t \tag{15}$$

Fourt, Harris, Holt, Leaderman, McPherson, Press, and Steinberger have observed that the flow curves of many high polymers follow the relationship (15) over a fairly long period.

There exist cases (rubber, swollen viscose rayon, undrawn nylon) in which certain analyses (X-ray diffraction, birefringence) indicate additional crystallization. We have observed that in such cases the dynamic modulus of the fiber increases with elongation. Under such conditions equation (14) represents a fair mechanism to account for the logarithmic flow over comparatively long periods. We have, however, observed that in other cases (air dry viscose rayon, acetate rayon, drawn nylon) the elongation which corresponds to the logarithmic period of creep is partly reversible. This suggests that the total logarithmic creep is built up by *two* contributions.

(1) A series of retarded elastic elements, as represented in equation (12). It can be shown that certain distribution functions $E(\lambda)$ and $k(\lambda)$ make γ_1 either exactly, or nearly so, a linear function of $\log (t + 1)$.

(2) A crystallization term according to (14).

It seems that creep and recovery measurements over a sufficient range of experimental conditions (time, stress, moisture, temperature) should permit a splitting of the total logarithmic creep into these two contributions . . .

The creep [of acetate] was observed between 0.25 and 86,400 seconds at 70°F. and 65 percent R.H.; the initial length of the yarn was 500 mm, its cross-section 375 denier. The initial stress was 9.1×10^8 dynes per square centimeter (about 0.15 g/d). The modulus E_0 as determined from short time measurements is 2.9×10^{10} dynes/cm², which is in reasonable agreement with other values obtained with cellulose acetate. The instantaneous elastic extension is therefore 3.1 percent. At times longer than 10^5 seconds very slow viscous flow was observed, which follows the expression $\gamma_3 = 1.5 \times 10^{-5}\ t$. Between $t = 100$ and $t = 6000$ seconds, the creep is a fair linear function of log $(t + 1)$ with a slope of 1.5×10^{-2}. At shorter periods retarded elasticity with $\tau_1 = 25$ seconds takes place; its range is 3.4 percent. This leads to the following equation for the total elongation γ as a function of time.

$$\gamma = 3.1 + 3.4[1 - \exp(-t/25)] + 1.5 \log(t + 1) + 1.5 + 10^{-5}t \qquad (16)$$

Table XVIII contains in column 1 the observed values of γ over a period from 0.25 seconds to 1 day (86,400 seconds) as listed in column 2. Columns 3, 4 and 5 show how the differential contributions of the retarded elastic mechanism gradually decrease from 0.5 at 5 seconds to 0.1 at 75 seconds and then completely disappear. Superimposed is from the beginning the instantaneous elasticity (column 6) of 3.1 percent and the logarithmic creep (column 7). After 100 seconds instantaneous and retarded elasticity together contribute the constant amount of 6.5 percent and the further elongation is only due to the logarithmic creep. Column 8, which will later contain the viscous flow, does not yet contribute measurably to γ. Column 9 contains the sum of γ_0, γ_1, γ_2 and γ_3, which in column 10 is corrected for the increase of stress due to the reduced cross section. This correction is carried out under the simplifying assumption of constant density. Although this is presumably not quite correct, the changes of the specific volume during elongation are so small that their influence would be far below the accuracy of our measurements and considerations. The final computed values (column 10) which resulted from equation (16) show a rather fair agreement with the observed figures in column 1. Around $t = 9000$ viscous flow starts to become noticeable and influences the elongation from then on to an increasing extent.

Attempting a molecular interpretation of the values in table XVIII, one may argue as follows:

(a) Modulus and range of the instantaneous elasticity point to the fact that the immediate response of the sample to the external force consists in stretching of van der Waals' bonds or hydrogen bridges which extend throughout the material and act between the entangled chains of the acetylated cellulose. As soon as the stress ceases, this elongation of 3.1 percent disappears at once.

(b) As times goes on (around 5 seconds) certain loose portions in the sample start to move. They seem to be fairly large, because their average relaxation time is 25 seconds. This is in line with an observation of S. S. Kistler, who found large moving volumes in cellulose acetate films. Presumably there exist highly entangled clusters of chain molecules, which are slowly disentangled, straightened out and parallelized. They provide for the retarded elasticity up to about 100 seconds, which recovers upon relaxation after a sufficiently long period (half recovery time around 150 seconds).

TABLE XVIII

CREEP OF CELLULOSE ACETATE RAYON UNDER STANDARD CONDITIONS WITH AN INITIAL STRESS OF 9.1×10^8 DYNES PER SQ. CM.

1	2	3	4	5	6	7	8	9	10
Observed in %	Time in seconds	$e^{-t/25}$	$(1-e^{-t/25})$	$3.4(1-e^{-t/25})$	$\gamma_0+\gamma_1$	γ_2	γ_3	γ calculated	γ corrected for cross sect. decrease
3.4	0.25	1.00			3.1	0.1		3.2	3.3
3.6	1.0	0.96	0.04	0.1	3.2	0.4		3.6	3.7
5.0	5.0	0.82	0.18	0.6	3.7	1.1		4.8	5.0
6.2	10	0.67	0.33	1.1	4.2	1.5		5.7	6.1
7.5	20	0.45	0.55	1.9	5.0	1.9		6.9	7.4
8.4	30	0.30	0.70	2.4	5.5	2.2		7.7	8.3
9.1	45	0.17	0.83	2.8	5.9	2.5		8.4	9.1
9.6	60	0.09	0.91	3.1	6.2	2.7		8.9	9.7
9.9	75	0.05	0.95	3.2	6.3	2.8		9.1	9.9
10.3	100	0.03	0.97	3.3	6.4	3.0		9.4	10.3
10.6	125	0.02	0.98	3.3	6.4	3.1		9.5	10.5
10.9	160	0.01	0.99	3.4	6.5	3.3		9.8	10.9
11.2	200		1.00	↓	↓	3.4		9.9	11.0
11.6	260		↓			3.6		10.1	11.3
11.9	350					3.8		10.3	11.6
12.3	500					4.1		10.6	11.9
12.5	700					4.3		10.8	12.1
12.8	1,000					4.5		11.0	12.4
13.1	1,500					4.8		11.3	12.8
13.2	2,000					4.9		11.4	12.9
13.4	3,000					5.2		11.7	13.2
13.6	4,000					5.4		11.9	13.6
13.9	6,000					5.7		12.2	13.9
14.2	9,000					5.9	0.1	12.5	14.2
14.3	13,000					6.2	0.2	12.9	14.7
14.8	18,000					6.4	0.3	13.2	15.1
15.2	25,000					6.6	0.4	13.5	15.5
17.6	86,400					7.4	1.3	15.2	17.8

(c) While process (b) takes place, and after it is concluded, the logarithmic creep continues. In the case of cellulose acetate, one has no indication (X-rays, specific volume changes, etc.) for crystallization and it is therefore difficult to decide which of the two mechanisms as discussed before can be made responsible for this logarithmic creep. Relaxation experiments have been made at different times and it turned out that one part of the logarithmic extension recovers, while another is permanent. It seems reasonable to attribute the recoverable part of the logarithmic creep to a wide distribution function of retarded elastic elements and the permanent fraction to crystallization or at least strong interaction between the parallelized chains. Such additional crystallization of the material should lead to an increase of the dynamic modulus during process (c). Actually the modulus increases continually during the creep period and reaches values around 5.0×10^{10} dynes per square centimeter after 3000 seconds.

(d) Finally, there is a very slow viscous flow, which is due to the existence of poorly organized and weak volume elements throughout the yarn and which ultimately leads to the rupture of the sample if one waits long enough (around 10^6 seconds).

It seems that this interpretation, as suggested by the relatively good agreement between equation (16) and the experiments (compare columns 1 and 10 of table XVIII) reflects in a fair way the textile properties of an acetate rayon yarn. γ_0 and γ_1 together provide for a certain springiness . . . of the material, which at low stresses (between 0.5 and 1.0 grains per denier) provide for about 5 percent elongation, which recovers within a few seconds. As long as the stresses are small and their duration is short, the yarn shows excellent recovery. However, these two highly elastic mechanisms are overshadowed by the logarithmic creep, which does not amount to much at low stresses and over short periods, but which plays an important role at longer times. This creep provides for a reinforcement of the material and is not identical with viscous flow. It is a re-arrangement of increasingly larger volume elements, during which elastic energy is continuously stored in the yarn and can be partly recovered after unloading. However, this recovery is slow and causes the limited springiness of acetate rayon in the range of higher elongation. True viscous flow sets in only after two or three hours. However, it continues even at small loads if one waits sufficiently long (several days or weeks) and is responsible for the slow, continuous growth of acetate rayon.

TABLE XIX

CREEP OF VISCOSE RAYON TEXTILE YARN AT 70°F., 65% R.H., AND AN INITIAL STRESS OF 8.9×10^8 DYNES PER SQ. CM.

1	2	3	4	5	6	7	8
γ observed in %	t in seconds	γ_0	$\gamma_0+\gamma_{10}$	γ_1	γ_2	γ calc.	γ corrected for cross-section
0.67	0.01	0.6	0.6	0.0	0.0	0.6	0.6
2.6	1.0		2.5	0.0	0.0	2.5	2.5
3.2	5.0		2.5	0.1	0.6	3.2	3.3
3.6	10			0.2	0.9	3.6	3.7
4.2	20			0.3	1.2	4.0	4.2
4.9	40			0.5	1.5	4.5	4.7
5.1	60			0.7	1.6	4.8	5.0
5.3	80			0.8	1.7	5.0	5.3
5.6	120			0.9	1.9	5.3	5.6
6.0	250			1.0	2.2	5.7	6.0
6.1	400			1.0	2.4	5.9	6.2
6.4	700				2.5	6.0	6.3
6.6	1,000				2.7	6.2	6.6
6.8	1,500				2.9	6.4	6.8
6.9	2,000				3.0	6.5	6.9
7.1	3,000				3.2	6.7	7.2
7.2	4,000				3.3	6.8	7.3
7.3	5,000				3.4	6.9	7.4
7.6	11,000				3.7	7.2	7.7
8.5	75,000				4.4	7.9	8.5
8.8	183,000				4.8	8.3	9.0
9.1	442,000				5.0	8.5	9.3

Corresponding medium and long time flow and recovery measurements were carried out with viscose textile rayon yarns. They can be subjected to a similar analysis. Table XIX shows the results of an experiment run at 70°F., 65 percent R.H., and 8.9×10^8 dynes per square centimeter initial stress extending from 0.01 to 442,000 seconds. The dynamic modulus of the material was found to be about 15×10^{10} dynes per square centimeter, which leads to an instantaneous elongation γ_1 of 0.6 percent. The elongation of 0.67, which was observed at $t = 0.01$ second, is in fair agreement with this computed value. Between $t = 0.01$ and 1.0 second, the sample undergoes another 1.9 percent elongation (γ_{10}) which is a very slightly retarded elastic extension, the relaxation time of which must be somewhere below 1.0 second. Its numerical value could only be determined if a number of measured points were available between 0.01 and 1.0 seconds; its modulus is 4.7×10^{10} dynes per square centimeter. Above $t = 120$ one has mainly logarithmic creep with a k_2-value of 0.91, which extends until $t = 450{,}000$. In order to represent the six experimental values between $t = 1.0$ and $t = 120$ seconds, one has to introduce a retarded elastic mechanism with a relaxation time of 50 seconds, which contributes 1.0 percent elongation. In this way one is led to the following equation

$$\gamma = 0.6 + 1.9 + 1.0(1 - e^{-t/50}) + 0.9 \log (t + 1) \tag{17}$$

the results of which are introduced in column 8 of table XIX. Comparison with the experimental values (column 1) shows that the agreement is rather fair.

Interpreting again (17) in terms of the suggested molecular mechanisms one arrives at the following picture:

The initial response (0.01 second) of the yarn to the external stress reveals the presence of comparatively strong intermolecular forces (E_0 = around 15×10^{10}), which presumably are due to frequent hydrogen bridges between the chains. Immediately afterwards, however (within about 1.0 second), the material responds with a fast elastic mechanism, which has a modulus of about 5×10^{10} and a range of about 2.0 percent. Recovery experiments make it probable that it represents rubber-like elasticity of randomly kinked and curled up chains in the amorphous regions. The moderate stretching, which such a filament undergoes during its formation seems to provide for the presence of a certain amount of such rubbery constituents in the sample. The recovery of this elongation is not as fast as in rubber, because the strong intermolecular forces increase the viscosity of the viscous elements, which are arranged parallel to the elastic elements of this composite mechanism.

Both fast elasticities together provide only for 2.5 percent elongation, (with comparatively high modulus) and are responsible for the stiffness which viscose rayon (and cellulose in general) exhibits in comparison with cellulose acetate or wool.

Also the next process—considerably retarded elasticity with $\tau_1 = 50$ seconds—provides only for another 1.0 percent elongation and represents high modulus extension ($E_1 = 8 \times 10^{10}$ dynes/cm^2). During its operation larger units—micellae, or clusters of entangled chain molecules—are displaced and provide for strong retardation and slow recovery.

All three elastic mechanisms together create the impression of a comparatively stiff and rigid material, which can only be elongated to a limited extent (3.5 percent as compared with 6.5 percent in the case of cellulose acetate) and returns only slowly to its original state.

Superimposed to these processes is a logarithmic creep having a slope of only 0.9 as compared with 1.5 for cellulose acetate rayon. Apparently the reinforcement through additional crystallization takes place more effectively in the presence of the free hydroxyl groups distributed along the chains. In fact the dynamic modulus increases up to 20×10^{10} dynes/cm.^{2}, a large proportion of the elastic creep is not recoverable and there is no evidence for any true viscous flow up to times around 10^6 seconds.

The most thorough experimental study of creep in fibers has been made by Leaderman (*4*). In his recent book, Leaderman reports intensive investigations of silk, viscose rayon, acetate rayon, and nylon. Leaderman points out that many filaments exhibit a different creep and recovery behavior in the first test as compared with subsequent tests. During a first long duration creep test a certain amount of deformation takes place which does not recover under the same experimental conditions upon removal of the stress. In later creep tests (at the same or smaller load) there is no such nonrecoverable creep. The fiber can therefore be considered to be in a "mechanically conditioned" state. Since Leaderman was interested in isolating the delayed elastic response, he followed the practice of mechanically conditioning his fibers before carrying out creep tests.

(The "nonrecoverable" deformation which occurs in the conditioning of a fiber is not viscous flow. When such a mechanically conditioned fiber is steamed under no load and then dried, most or all of the previously observed set disappears. Furthermore, the conditioned character of the fiber is destroyed.)

Even when the retarded elastic response (or "primary creep," in Leaderman's terminology) is isolated from nonrecoverable effects by mechanical conditioning, this response does not exhibit the simple character typical of amorphous polymers. We have seen that such materials as rubber, hard rubber, and bakelite can be represented by linear mechanical models. As a result, the creep of such materials follows the Boltzmann superposition principle. Leaderman, as well as other investigators, points out that the creep curve of an oriented crystalline polymer is not directly proportional to stress. He finds, however, that the creep at constant stress can be expressed as a function of stress times a function of time. The stress dependency is expressed by a scale factor, which is defined as the difference between the deformation ninety minutes after application of the load and that one minute after application of the load. This scale factor would be directly proportional to the stress for a material which exhibits a *linear* viscoelastic spectrum; for an oriented filament the scale factor is a nonlinear function of stress. It is interesting that Leaderman comes to the conclusion that "the nonproportionality of creep and load must be attributed to the existence of a highly oriented structure."

In figure 155 the scale factors for various filaments are plotted as functions of the stress. These curves in general have an upward curvature, indicating that creep increases faster with load than a direct proportionality. At high stresses, however, there is a downward bend in the

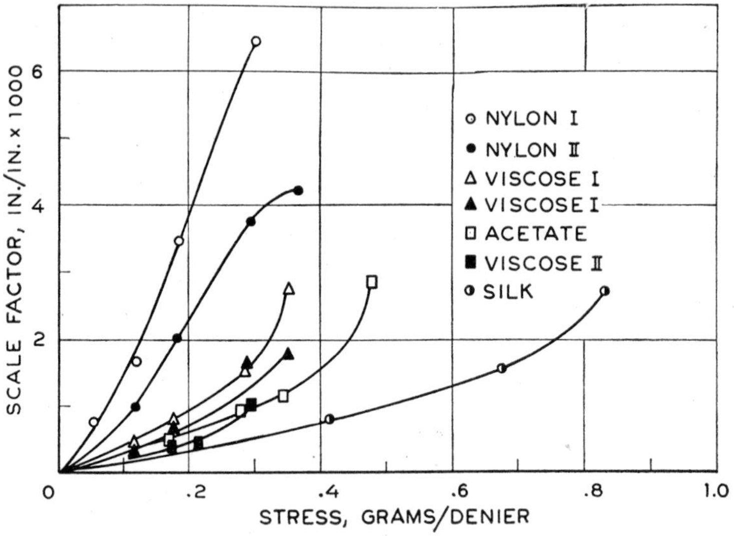

Fig. 155. Stress and scale factors for "primary creep" (after Leaderman).

curve for one nylon sample, indicating a *slower* increase of creep with stress at high stresses. We shall see that at still higher stresses the curves for nylon are flattened out almost completely so that further increases in stress do not increase the creep. One might also infer from the work of Press (*e.g.*, Fig. 154A) that viscose rayon would show a similar leveling off at higher stresses. Leaderman reports such a leveling off for viscose under the condition of 100% relative humidity.

Leaderman has formulated a "modified superposition principle" to replace the original Boltzmann principle for silk and rayon, and for nylon at low stresses. According to the Boltzmann principle, which applies to materials with linear stress dependence, the deformation as a function of time can be derived from the stress as a function of time as follows:

$$\gamma(t) = \frac{S(t)}{E} + \beta \int_{\infty}^{0} \frac{dS(t - \omega)}{d\omega} \phi(\omega)\, d\omega \tag{18}$$

where $\phi(t)$ gives the time dependence of the creep at constant load. (The creep at constant load will be given by:

$$\gamma(t) = (S/E) + \beta S \, \phi(t) \tag{19}$$

and equation (18) merely represents the superposition of strains arising from the entire past stressing history.)

Leaderman's suggested modification to this principle involves the fact that the creep curve at constant stress for the filaments under consideration can be resolved into a (nonlinear) function of stress times a function of time.

$$\gamma(t) = S/E + \beta \, f(S) \, \phi(t) \tag{20}$$

He then assumes that the creep contributions arising from various stress increments are simply superimposed upon each other, keeping in mind the nonlinearity of the stress dependence. He then writes, for the case of varying stress, the following deformation function:

$$\gamma(t) = \frac{S(t)}{E} + \beta \int_{\infty}^{0} \frac{df(S[t - \omega])}{d\omega} \, \phi(\omega) \, d\omega \tag{21}$$

Two important predictions follow from this modified superposition principle:

(1) The recovery curve taken after a long time creep curve should duplicate that creep curve.

(2) It should be possible to compute the form of the long duration creep curve from a sequence of short duration creep and recovery curves, just as in the case of the ordinary superposition principle (Fig. 80, page 199).

Leaderman has tested both of these predictions and has found that they are satisfactorily obeyed by rayon and silk, and by nylon at small loads. He concludes that the modified superposition principle holds for these materials. It seems to the writer that equation (21) is much more general than either of the above specific predictions and, while the above agreement is consistent with the modified superposition principle, it does not constitute positive evidence of the general validity of equation (21). Henceforth when we report that a given material "obeys the modified superposition principle," this should be taken to mean that it behaves according to predictions (1) and (2) above, rather than that it obeys equation (21). The converse statement, however, can be more definite, since failure to obey these two specific predictions necessarily means that (21) cannot apply.

Leaderman investigated the effect of temperature on the creep of dry acetate rayon. These tests were made on a filament of length 3.94 inches and nominally of 3 denier. Four series of tests were made, which differed briefly as follows:

Series I. 1.053 gram load, temperatures of 51° to 75°C.

Series II. 0.856 gram load, temperatures of 67° to 90°C. (Between the second and third series of tests, the filament was disturbed, resulting in a permanent increase in length of 0.052 inch.)

Series III. 1.480 gram load, temperatures 51.5° to 75.5°C.

Series IV. Same conditions as Series I.

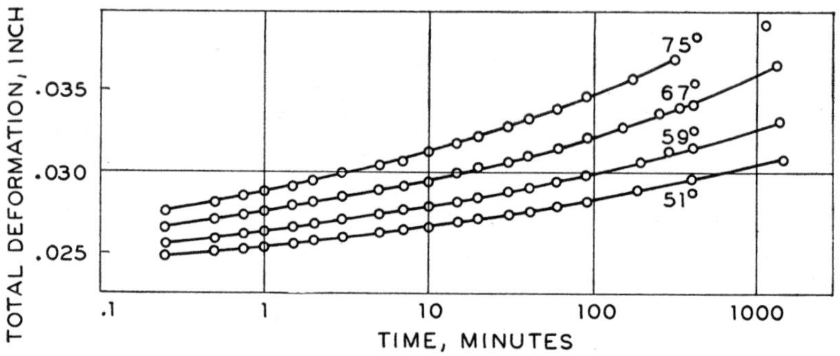

Fig. 156. Total deformation curves for acetate filament under load of 1.053 grams.

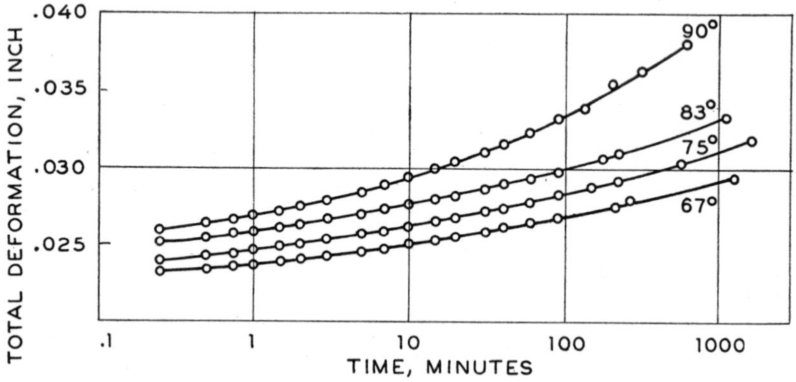

Fig. 157. Total deformation curves for acetate filament under load of 0.856 gram.

The results of these tests are shown in figures 156 to 163. The first four figures are the actual creep curves; in the last four curves, the log of the time necessary to reach specified deformations is plotted against

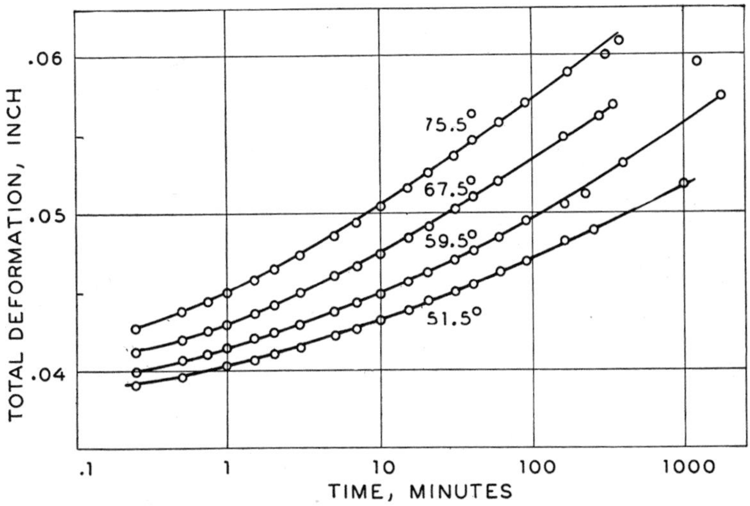

Fig. 158. Total deformation curves for acetate filament under load of 1.480 grams.

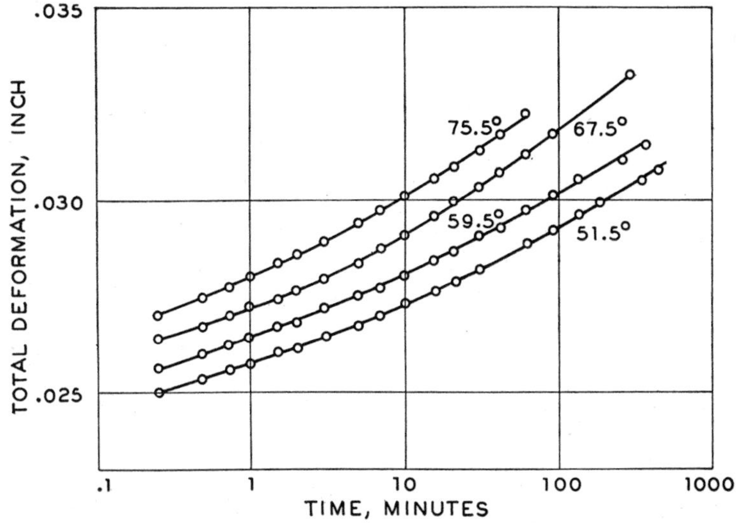

Fig. 159. Total deformation curves for acetate filament after mechanical conditioning load, 1.053 grams.

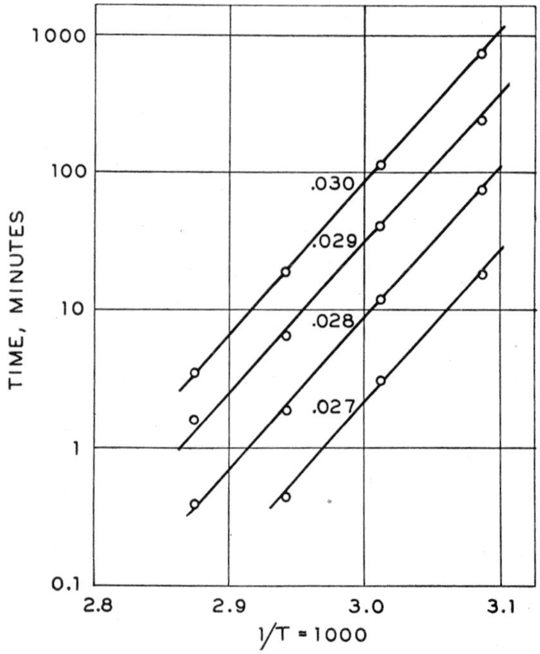

Fig. 160. Times to attain specified deformations in Series I tests.

the reciprocal of the absolute temperature. The slopes of these lines were used to calculate activation energies for the creep process. These are given in table XX (*4*).

TABLE XX

ACETATE FILAMENT: ENERGY OF ACTIVATION FOR PRIMARY CREEP

Series	Load, g.	Temperature range, °C.	*Q*, cal./mole
I	1.053	75–51	49,200
II	0.856	90–67	51,200
III	1.480	75.5–51.5	31,500–39,000
IV	1.053	75.5–51.5	29,400

Leaderman comments as follows:

Comparing first the activation energies from the tests of Series I and Series II, it is observed that these values are very similar; in these two series of tests the filament was practically in the same state. In the tests of Series IV the state of the filament was identical with that in Series III, since in the later series of tests the same temperature range but a smaller load was used. In the Series IV tests the effect of temperature on the primary creep behavior can be expressed simply by an energy of activation. The results of the tests in Series III cannot be expressed in this way, the energy of activation apparently increasing with the deformation.

From the tests of Series IV and corresponding tests in Series III the relative delayed deformations have been obtained for a time of 90 minutes. This is of course the difference between the total deformation at a time 90 minutes after load application and that for a time of 1 minute . . . the ratio of the relative delayed deformations at any given

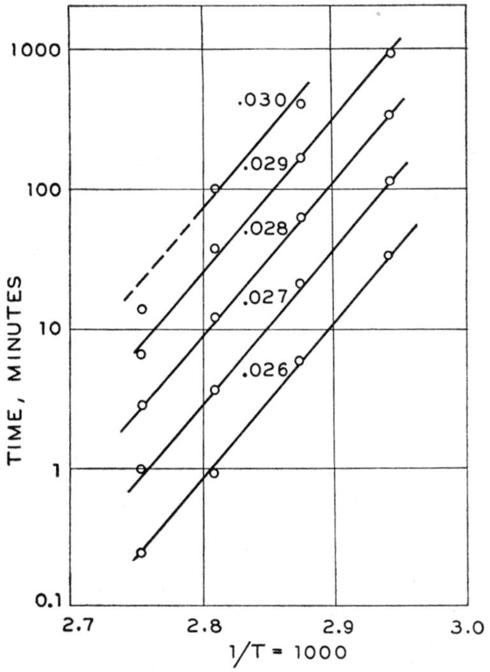

Fig. 161. Times to attain specified deformations in Series II tests.

temperature is greater than the ratio of the loads, and . . . increases with increase of temperature. This suggests that, at any given temperature, the primary creep properties of the acetate rayon filament are given by the modified form of Boltzmann's Superposition Principle.

It should finally be remarked that the energy of activation from the tests of Series IV is much less than that from the tests of Series I, carried out under almost identical conditions (Table XX). Between these two series of tests the filament had suffered a permanent set of about 0.078 inch. The stretch of about 2% under dry conditions causes a marked reduction in the energy of activation for primary creep, and so this activation energy appears to be a function of the physical state of the filament.

Leaderman carried out a "superposition test," of the type of figure 80, on acetate rayon at 75.5°C. He concluded that "the close agreement between the computed and observed deformations indicates that the primary creep properties of an acetate filament, under dry conditions and at an elevated temperature, obey the modified Superposition Principle."

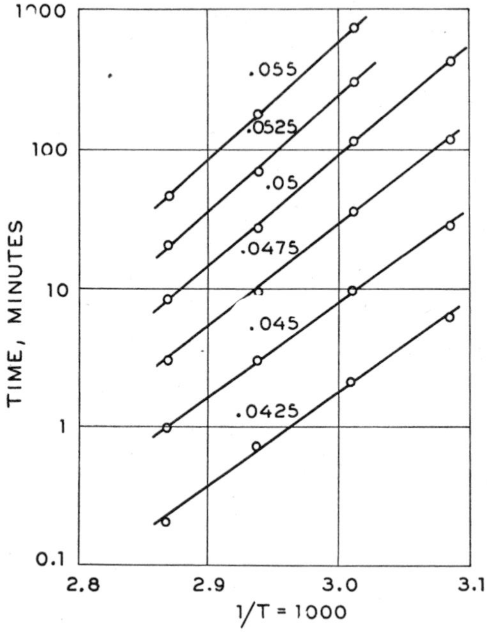

Fig. 162. Times to attain specified deformations in Series III tests.

The Creep and Recovery Behavior of Nylon.—Leaderman (*4*) carried out a detailed study of creep of nylon under both small and large loadings, at a series of temperatures, and under various conditions of humidity. The effects of load under standard conditions (70°F., 65% R.H.) are extremely interesting. For small loads, nylon was found to follow the pattern previously described, which is characteristic of rayon and silk. That is, nylon under small loads obeys the modified superposition principle, and the scale factor *vs.* load curve has an upward curvature, indicating that the creep increases more rapidly with load than by direct proportion. At high loads the behavior is very different. The modified superposition principle is not obeyed (for example, the long time creep curve is not identical with the recovery curve which follows). Furthermore, the scale factor curve flattens out and becomes parallel with the load axis. This means that after a certain stress has been reached, the rate of creep is not increased by further increases in stress.

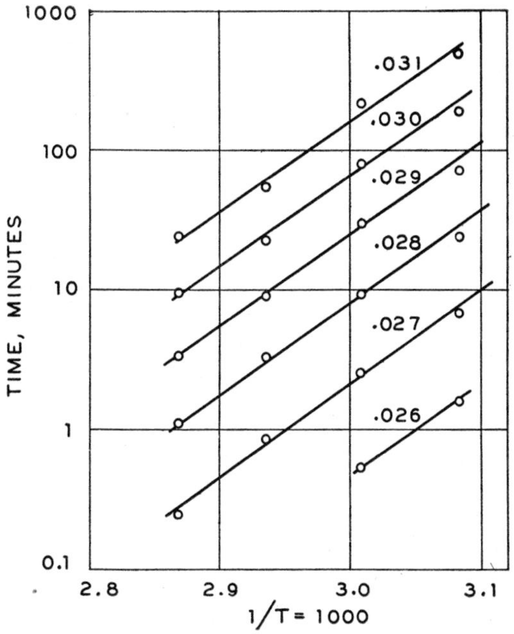

Fig. 163. Times to attain specified deformations in Series IV tests.

The failure of the modified superposition principle for nylon under large loads is shown in figure 164, where the total deformations during three successive creep and recovery experiments are plotted against log *t*.

. . . The total deformation in any long-duration creep or recovery test is of course the difference between the cathetometer scale reading at any given instant and the reading just before application or removal of load. The first three tests were carried out using the maximum load employed in this investigation; the total deformation curves are shown in figure 164. In the time allowed for recovery in the first two of these tests, the filament did not return to its length at the beginning of the test; it appears from figure 164 that this would still have been true even for a much longer recovery time. On the other hand, in Test No. III the specimen returned at the end of the experiment practically to its length at the beginning of this experiment. Consequently Tests Nos. I and II may be regarded as preliminary mechanically conditioning tests, and Test No. III as representing the creep and recovery of the filament in a mechanically conditioned state.

The first point to remark concerns the relationship between the total-deformation curves for creep and recovery. In the usual behavior we have been considering earlier, these curves were very nearly the same, the curve for recovery falling slightly below that for creep as the value of time approached the time of duration of the creep test. In the present case the total-deformation curve for recovery is seen to lie very much below the curve for creep; the recovery is on the whole more rapid than the preceding creep. In Test No. III, carried out under a load of 6.186 grams (approximately 2.1 grams per denier) the extension at a time one-half minute after application of load amounted to 6.78% of the original length of the filament; this extension increased to 7.23% after 20 hours under load. One-half minute after removal of load the contraction of the filament

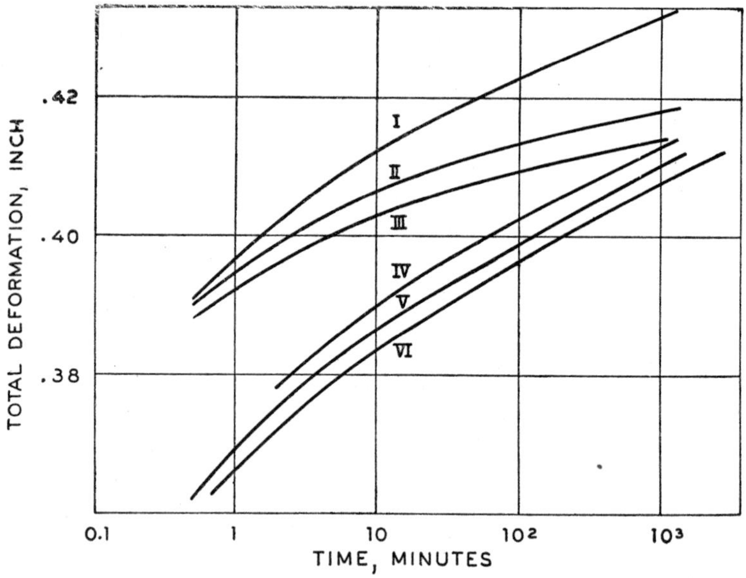

Fig. 164. Successive creep and recovery curves for nylon filament under a 6.19-gram load: (I) first creep test; (II) second creep test; (III) third creep test; (IV) first creep recovery; (V) second creep recovery; (VI) third creep recovery.

amounted to only 6.27% of the original length; however, after 50 hours the filament had returned to its original length. The "stiffness" of the filament was consequently somewhat greater on removal of load following long-duration creep compared to the stiffness on the original load application.

We can offer an explanation for this behavior in terms of the fringe theory of the structure of quasi-crystalline high polymers. In a material such as nylon, we assume that each long molecular chain traverses regions where it is arranged in a regular parallel fashion with similar chains; these are the crystalline or micellar regions. In passing from one micelle to the next the chain traverses, in a more or less random manner, a region of the fiber similarly occupied by other molecular chains; such are the amorphous regions of the fiber. It is reasonable to assume that in nylon the flexible chains in the fringe regions are highly kinked due to their thermal agitation. Secondary bonds hold the chains together in the micellar regions; similar bonds exist between the chains in the amorphous regions. We have previously interpreted primary creep phenomena as being due to a *migration* or *directed* rearrangement of the secondary bonds in the amorphous regions; such is presumably the explanation of the primary creep properties of nylon under small loads. When a *large* constant load is applied to a nylon filament, the filament suffers a large (reversible) extension; there must be consequently an appreciable straightening of the chains in the amorphous regions to give rise to this extension. The chains which branch out at the ends of each crystalline region [as in Fig. 129] are thus brought closer together. It seems reasonable to assume under these circumstances that the micelles grow along their length during the course of a creep test under constant

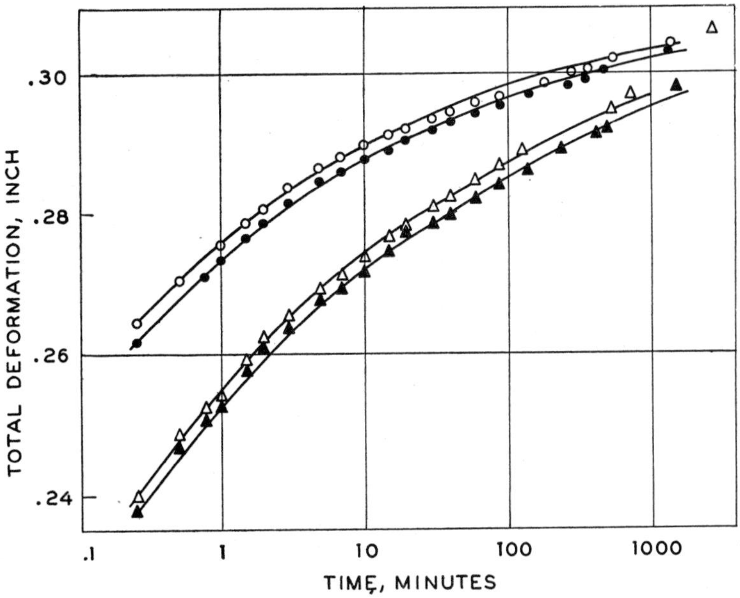

Fig. 165. Successive creep and recovery curves on mechanically conditioned filament of nylon, using a load of 3.42 grams. Open circles, first creep; open triangles, first recovery; black circles, second creep; black triangles, second recovery.

load. Hence the proportion of material in the amorphous regions gradually decreases, and new secondary bonds are formed between the now parallelized segments of chain which augment the micellar regions. When the load is removed, the filament is "stiffer," since the amount of material in the amorphous regions has been reduced. In the course of time, as a result of the thermal agitation of the molecular chains in the amorphous regions, the new bonds in the augmented portions of the micelles gradually break up, and creep recovery takes place while the fiber gradually reverts to its initial state at the beginning of the test.

In this explanation of the creep and creep recovery properties of nylon under large loads we have assumed that a gradual increase in the degree of crystallinity takes place in the filament while under load, and that new secondary bonds are formed. Following load removal decrystallization takes place accompanied by a gradual disappearance of these bonds.

Concerning the tests at different large loads (Figs. 165 and 166), Leaderman observes:

. . . It is seen that the predominant effect of alteration of load is to displace the total-deformation curves for creep and recovery along the deformation axis. Thus at any given time after load application (or removal) the rate of creep (or recovery) is independent of load, in this load range. The absolute deformation is however very much

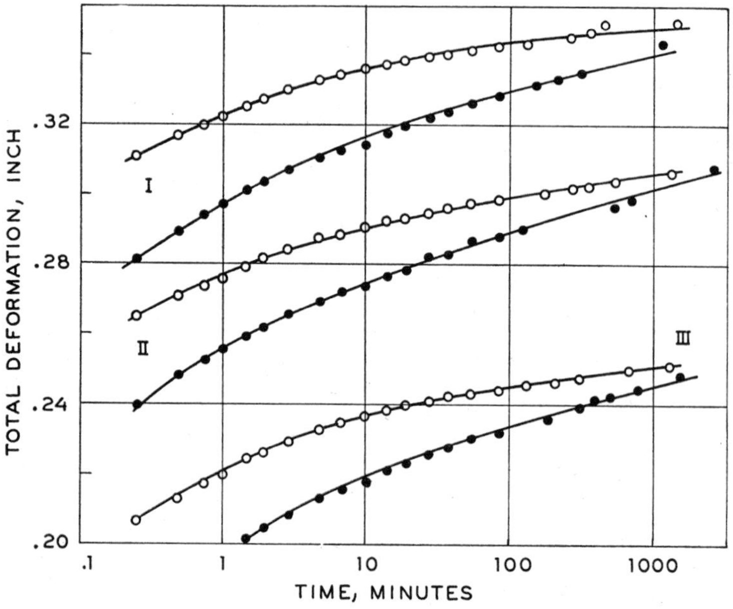

Fig. 166. Creep and recovery curves of nylon at different loads. (I) 4.26 grams; (II) 3.42 grams; (III) 2.54 grams. Open circles, creep; solid circles, recovery.

affected by change of load. . . The creep and recovery behavior of a nylon filament under large loads differs thus in two major respects from its behavior under small loads: the creep and recovery total deformation curves are no longer nearly identical, and the rate of creep is independent of load, instead of being a function of the load.

The two types of behavior are represented diagrammatically in figure 167. The load–time diagram of a long-duration creep test followed by recovery is represented in [a] for a load A and for a larger load B. In [b] and [c] are shown the corresponding changes in length of a filament subjected to the loading history of [a]. The creep and recovery behavior of a filament obeying the modified Superposition Principle is shown in [b].

For each load the deformation–time curve for creep is the mirror-image of the curve for recovery; the instantaneous extension is equal to the instantaneous contraction. The instantaneous deformation is proportional to the load; the delayed deformation is proportional to a function of the load, but increases more rapidly than the load. The

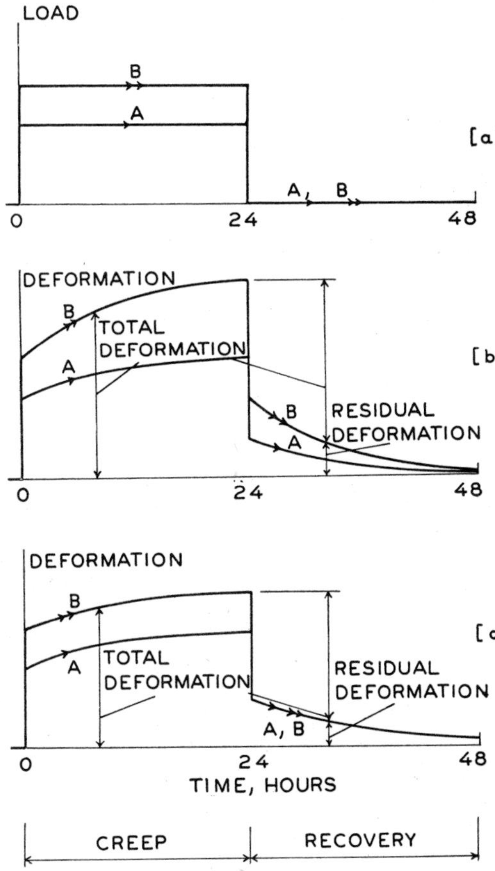

Fig. 167. Schematic representation of creep and creep recovery behavior of textile filaments in long duration tests: [a] load–time diagram; [b] behavior of nylon under small loads, and of silk and rayon; [c] behavior of nylon under large loads.

corresponding behavior of a nylon filament under large loads is represented in figure 167[c]; the recovery curve is no longer the mirror-image of the creep curve, and a somewhat longer time (more than 24 hours) must be allowed for complete recovery to the initial length. It is seen from figure 167[c] that increase of load causes merely a constant arithmetical increase in the total deformation for creep and recovery. Expressed in another way, the residual deformation as a function of recovery time following removal of load should be independent of the load. In the ideal behavior represented in figure 167[c], the cathetometer scale observation (representing the length of the filament) at a given time following removal of load in a long-duration test should therefore be independent of the magnitude of that load. The cathetometer scale readings obtained in the recovery stage of tests under four different loads are plotted as a function of recovery time in figure 168. These curves are seen to be very nearly of the same shape; there is

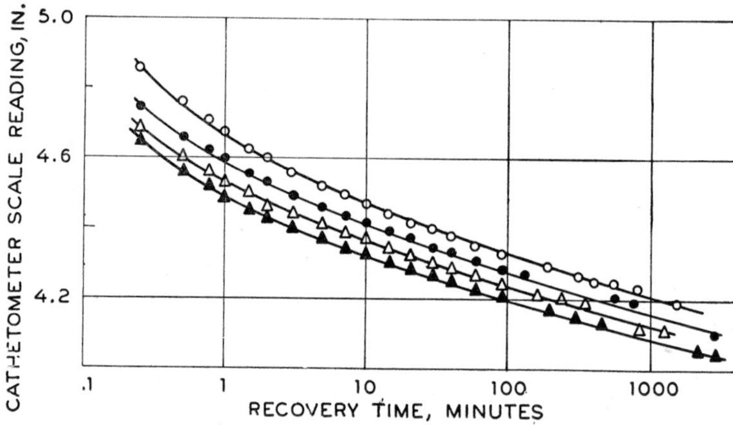

Fig. 168. Cathetometer scale readings in recovery tests following long duration creep of nylon under various loads. Open circles, 2.54 grams; black circles, 3.42; open triangles, 4.26; black triangles, 6.19.

however a progressive displacement, the later curves lying above the earlier ones. This slight displacement is due to the fact that insufficient time was allowed in the tests for the filament to recover completely to its initial length. In the tests in figure 168 the magnitude of the largest load used was more than twice as great as that of the smallest load. . .

When the scale factor *vs.* load curve for nylon (see Fig. 155) is extended to larger loads, it flattens out parallel to the load axis. This is shown in figure 172.

Figures 169–171 show the effect of temperature on the creep properties in this load region of the nylon filament at 65% relative humidity. In figure 169 the total-deformation curves are shown for a long-duration test carried out at 76°F. . . and a subsequent test at 70°F. . . Increase of temperature is seen to displace vertically upwards the total-deformation curves. Figure 170 shows the results of similar tests performed with a smaller load. The effect of increase of temperature, holding the load constant, appears to be very similar to the effect of increase in load, keeping the temperature constant. . . Figure 171 shows the effect of decrease of temperature below standard conditions. . .

In connection with his studies on creep, Leaderman investigated the effects of temperature changes on the lengths of nylon filaments. The

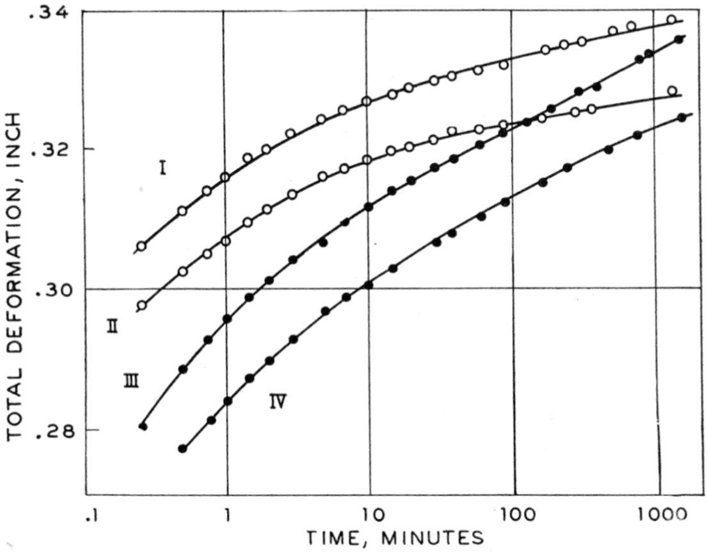

Fig. 169. Total-deformation curves for nylon in long-duration tests (load 4.26 grams) at 76°F. (I, III) and 70°F. (II, IV).

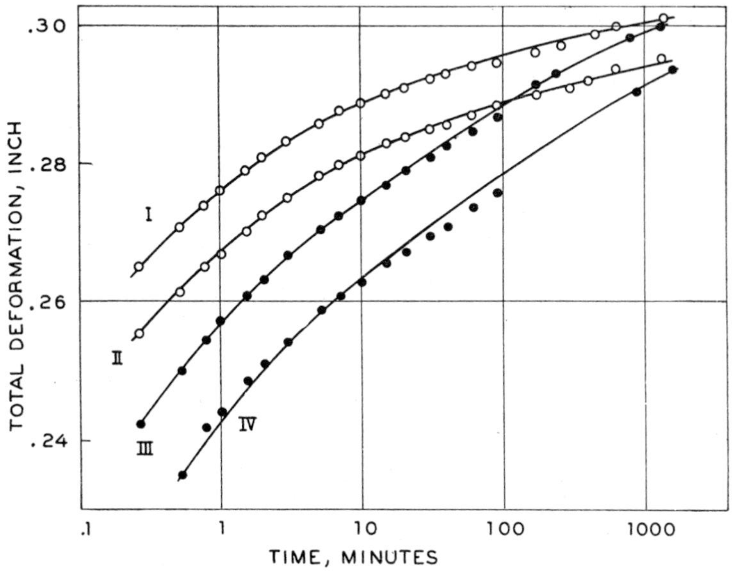

Fig. 170. Total-deformation curves for nylon in long-duration tests (load 3.42 grams) at 76°F. (I, III) and 70°F. (II, IV).

results of one of many such experiments are shown in figure 173. The filament, under no load, was subjected to the sequence of temperatures indicated in figure 173[a]. The resulting motion of the free end of the

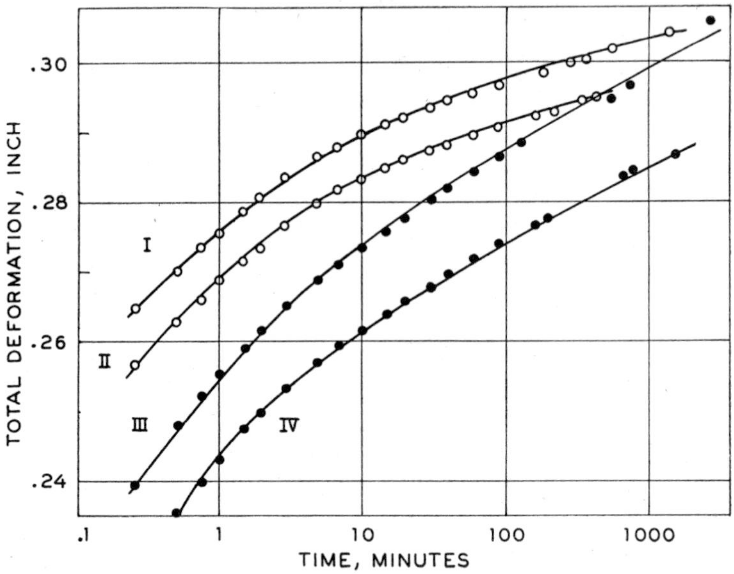

Fig. 171. **Total-deformation curves for nylon in long-duration tests (load 3.42 grams) at 70°F. (I, III) and at 64°F. (II, IV).**

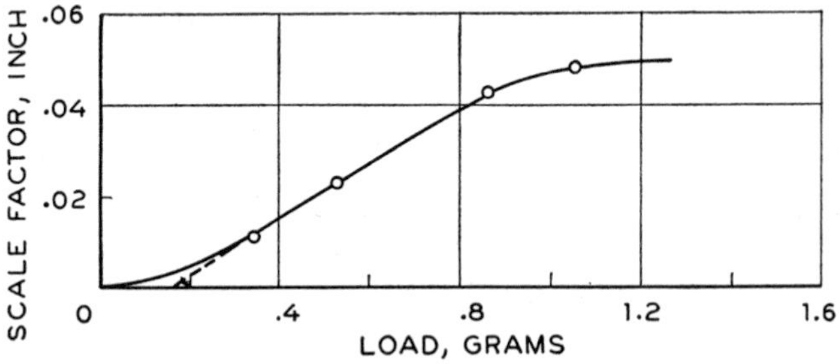

Fig. 172. Scale factor *vs.* load for nylon.

filament is shown in figure 173[b]. (An increase in the scale reading corresponds to an elongation, a decrease to a contraction.) As the temperature is lowered from 51.5° to 21.5°C., the filament elongates slightly. This appears to be a reversible extension, since the sample contracts to its original length when reheated to 51.5°C. Upon heating to 90.5°, a much larger contraction occurs. This is not a reversible effect; upon cooling to the original temperature only a small elongation is observed. The sample is about 1% shorter than at the beginning of the experiment. Subsequent temperature changes result in reversible changes in length, however, temperature increases causing contractions and decreases causing elongation. (In the subsequent changes the temperature was not raised beyond 90.5°C.)

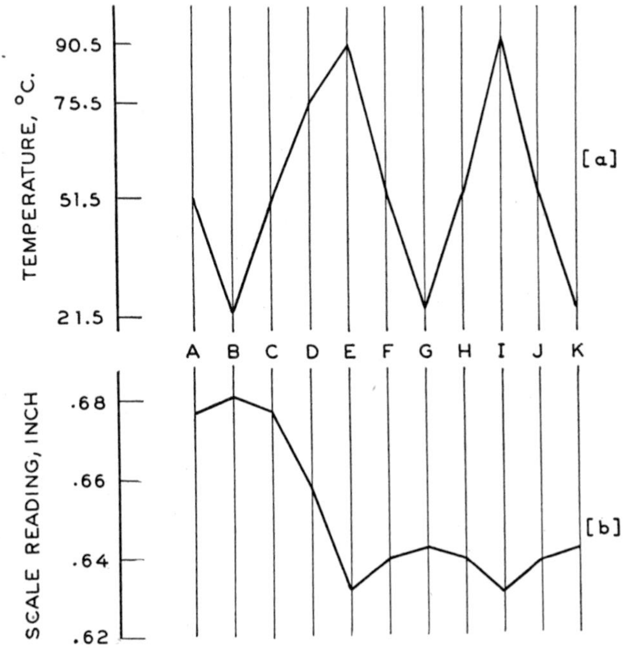

Fig. 173. Change in length of nylon filament resulting from temperature changes under zero load.

Leaderman interprets these results as follows:

A body can be given an apparent permanent set by applying a large extension for a short duration of time, or alternatively by mechanically conditioning with a relatively small longitudinal load in a long-duration creep and recovery test. If subsequently the temperature of the body is raised slightly, part or all of the 'permanent' deformation disappears (thermorecovery). Thus the contraction due to thermorecovery may mask the normal thermal expansion of the body. In general, a nylon filament free from load contracts on being heated in dry air; however, on subsequent cooling an increase in length takes place. If creep recovery is absent, the change in length with temperature may be rapid and reversible, and so the filament can be said to have a negative longitudinal thermal expansion, since increase of temperature causes a decrease in length and *vice versa*. Under these circumstances the contraction on heating is not of the nature of thermorecovery but is due to another process, namely, the increased thermal agitation of the flexible molecular chains in the amorphous regions of the fiber.

That is, the *reversible* contraction on heating is attributed to increased molecular activity of the amorphous region, while the irreversible effects are attributed to changes in the degree of crystallization. The writer cannot agree with this interpretation. When the sample is under no load, its equilibrium shape is that which maximizes the entropy of the amorphous regions. An increase in temperature increases the thermal activity, it is true, but since the amorphous regions are already in a state of maximum configurational entropy, there should be no marked contraction as a result of this increase in temperature. The following analysis is suggested. Both the reversible and the irreversible changes in length are the result of crystallization changes. The reversible changes involve the growth or melting out of crystallites which are already present, without changes in the "polycrystalline structure." The irreversible changes involve alterations in the polycrystalline structure.

If this interpretation is correct, it presumably applies as well to the creep behavior. There, too, crystallization effects of two kinds should be recognized: fairly rapid crystallization with no change in polycrystalline character, which would also be recoverable, and reorganization of the polycrystalline structure, yielding effects which would recover only very slowly. Certain further experiments of Leaderman with nylon may lend credence to this view.

. . . the filament was allowed to creep under a load of 2.54 g. at a temperature of 51.5°C. for 24 hours. After this time the length of the filament had nearly reached equilibrium. It was then subjected, without removing the load, to the temperature cycle shown in Fig. 174[a]; the corresponding changes in length are shown in Fig. 174[b]. A reversible change in length occurred when the filament was cooled from A to B and reheated from B to C. On heating the filament above the original temperature an *increase* in length occurred (C to D, Fig. 174), and a further increase on cooling. From E to G the filament was heated to a temperature below the previous maximum (at D) and then cooled again from G to J. In this process the length again varied reversibly with temperature. The length of the filament at H and J was much greater (0.61%) than at the corresponding temperatures in the beginning of the test (A and B). This increase in length is due to the fact that the filament was heated above its original temperature while under load . . . Presumably an increase in the proportion of material in the micellar regions occurred during this heating process. In the absence of such crystallization phenomena and of creep we conclude that nylon possesses a negative temperature coefficient of expansion also when under constant load.

In terms of our interpretation of the previous experiments, we would replace these last two sentences by the following: "Presumably a change in *polycrystalline character* occurred during this heating process. In the absence of such changes in *polycrystalline character*, we conclude that nylon has a negative temperature coefficient of linear expansion *in the fiber direction* (*because of the ordinary process of crystallization*) even when under a constant load."

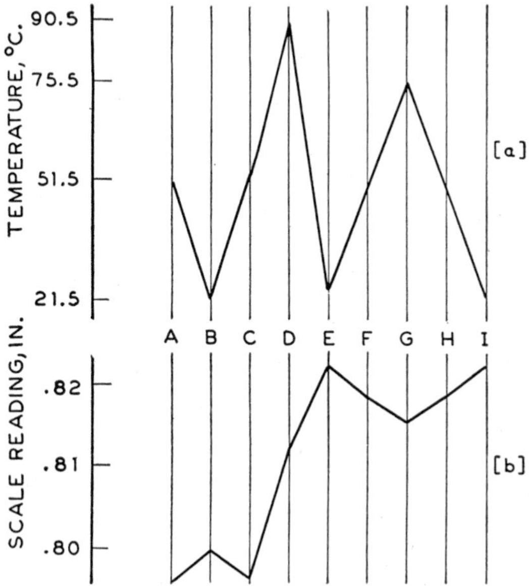

Fig. 174. Change in length of nylon filament resulting from changes in temperature under a 2.54-gram load.

In a third and more extensive series of tests Leaderman established that he could eliminate irreversible changes in length, as follows:

> . . . In this investigation creep and recovery have been eliminated by allowing sufficient time after application or removal of load for the length of the filament to come to equilibrium; thermorecovery has been eliminated by working at temperatures below the starting temperature. Under these circumstances nylon possesses a negative longitudinal thermal expansion over the load and temperature range investigated. The rate of change of length with temperature increases with temperature, but decreases for increase of load.

VI. MECHANICAL BEHAVIOR OF WOOL

Animal hairs, in particular wool, are largely composed of protein molecules which are built up by polycondensation of different amino acids.

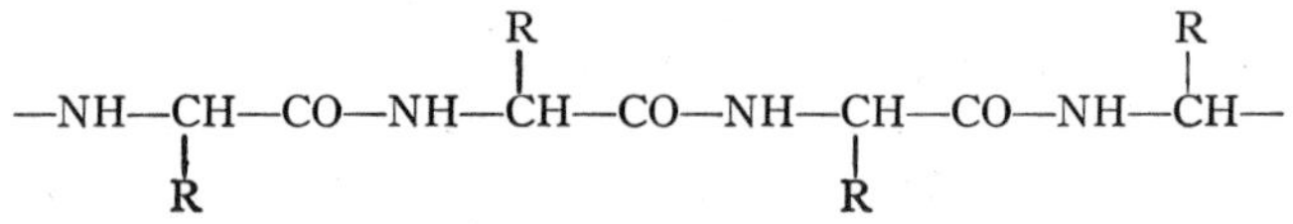

Harris, Mizell, and Fourt (*39*) report that various amino acids are present in the amounts given in table XXI. They further point out the following four characteristics of the protein chains:

(1) They exhibit great flexibility, which enables them to assume a large number of configurations.

TABLE XXI

AMINO ACIDS IN WOOL

Amino acid	Per cent	Amino acid	Per cent	Amino acid	Per cent
Glycine	6.5	Cystine/2	12.72	Histidine	0.7
Alanine	4.4	Leucine isomers	11.3	Hydroxylysine	0.21
Serine	9.41	Aspartic acid	7.27	Phenylalanine	3.75
Proline	6.75	Lysine	3.3	Arginine	10.4
Valine	4.72	Glutamic acid	15.27	Tyrosine	5.8
Threonine	6.76	Methionine	0.71	Tryptophane	0.7

(2) They possess a large number of highly polar peptide linkages, which can give rise to intra- and intermolecular hydrogen bonding. Such a preponderance of polar groups would lead to high strength but also to inflexibility and brittleness were it not for the following factor.

(3) The protein chains possess relatively large side chains (R groups above), which prevent close chain packing and thus decrease the extent of hydrogen bonding. From table XXI, it can be seen that close to 50% of the weight of wool is in the side chains.

(4) Covalent cross links are provided between the protein chains by the amino acid, cystine. "Wool may thus be considered a network of polypeptide chains linked together by the disulfide groups of the amino acid, cystine." (It should be recognized that covalent cross links may also be formed by a peptide linkage between glutamic acid and arginine.)

In the unstressed state, these polypeptide chains exist in collapsed, curled, or folded forms. In the presence of a tensile stress, they can be straightened out into an extended form. Astbury (*1*) concluded that unstretched wool protein was mainly in a specific folded shape, in which the polar peptide linkages formed strong intramolecular bonds. According to Astbury, this specific folded configuration, the α-keratin form, went over (upon stretching) into a specific extended configuration, the β-keratin form, in which the polypeptide chains were parallelized. The elongation of wool thus assumed something of the character of a change from one crystalline form to another.

The original picture advanced by Astbury has been the subject of several suggested revisions. For one thing, the specific form originally chosen to represent the α-keratin structure has been replaced by others in which the intramolecular fold is nonplanar. Furthermore, Harris *et al.* (*39*) point out that "such structures have been suggested on the basis of X-ray data, and should accordingly be found principally in the 'crystalline' regions of the fiber. Since, as also is indicated by the X-ray diffraction patterns, these regions account for only a relatively small proportion of the total wool fiber, it appears that one may assume a more or less random type of folding in the 'amorphous' regions which make up the bulk of the fiber."

In unstretched wool, then, the polypeptide chains are curled and kinked—but, unlike the ideal "amorphous" polymers of chapter B, they do not distribute themselves completely at random among all possible configurations. Instead, the polar peptide linkages make a folded form, with many intramolecular hydrogen bonds, the most stable from the standpoint of potential energy. These specific forms are therefore statistically favored. There is still, however, a great deal of randomness in the chain arrangement; the precisely folded chain segments account for only a fraction of the material.

Upon stretching, all chains are straightened out so that eventually the extended, crystalline β-keratin form predominates. This stretching opens up the specific folds as well as the more random kinks of the polypeptide chains. Astbury emphasized the change of the specific α-keratin folds to the β configuration. Harris *et al.*, on the other hand, emphasize the change of the "amorphous fraction"—*i.e.*, the less perfectly folded chains —to the extended form.

One final factor which must be considered is the action of water on wool. It is clear that the strong intra- and intermolecular hydrogen bonds make it difficult for bone-dry wool to change from one molecular configuration to another. The energy of activation for segmental diffusion should be high and the rate of such diffusion slow, as compared with a hydrocarbon like rubber. On the other hand, water molecules can swell the wool and solvate the polar peptide linkages. This results in a reduction of the interchain forces and an increase in the rate of segmental diffusion. It is thus much easier to stretch wet wool than dry wool; the elastic recovery is also facilitated by moisture. Astbury reports that absolutely dry wool can usually be stretched only about 20%. At normal humidities from 20–40%, and at 100% relative humidity extensions of 70% can be attained. Figure 175 shows stress–strain curves for wool at various humidities. The extreme S-shapes of the curves at high humidities suggest the process of crystallization, and Astbury (*1*) reports that X-ray data indicate the transformation from α-keratin to β-keratin to take place in the range of easy extensibility:

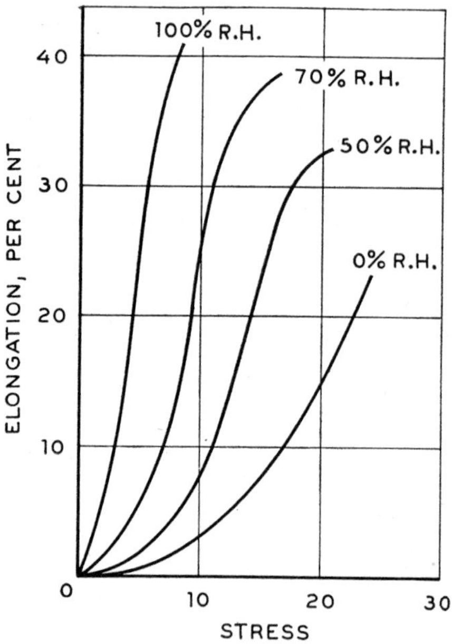

Fig. 175. Stress–strain curves for wool at different relative humidities.

It can be shown by precision X-ray methods that in the Hooke's Law region all that happens is that the crumpled molecular chains of α-keratin suffer a general, perfectly reversible, extension of about 2 percent. without any actual unlocking of the folds; but that when this limit is overstepped, suddenly the intramolecular transformation sets in, and the chains are rapidly unfolded one after another in the elongated form which we have called β-keratin.

The rate of relative recovery of wool is also extremely dependent upon the moisture content (*1*):

Provided it has not been submitted in the stretched state to the action of steam or certain other reagents, wet, stretched wool will always return to its initial length when given the opportunity, that is to say, on the removal of the conditions which caused the stretching. But it requires complete wetness or saturated water vapour—100 percent. relative humidity—to bring about the full contraction. When stretched wool is absolutely dry—0 percent. R.H.—it shows practically no tendency to contract, while at intermediate humidities it shows a continuous range of contractile powers, varying from zero at 0 percent. R.H. up to perfect recovery at 100 percent. R.H. . . . At 100 percent. R.H. there are present sufficient water molecules to leave the cohesive forces almost helpless, and full contraction to the original unstretched length rapidly ensues. At intermediate humidities, intermediate effects take place: there is a partial contraction, fairly quick at first, which never entirely ceases, but which grows slower and slower as time goes on, with the result that, to all intents and purposes, the fibre is left with a permanent elongation so long as the humidity is not increased. This elongation will vanish at the first suitable—that is, wet—opportunity.

The precise role of the covalent (cystine) cross links in the mechanical response of wool has been thoroughly investigated by Harris, Mizell, and Fourt, who prepared and studied a number of chemically modified wools. The methods used involve the reduction of the disulfide groups of the

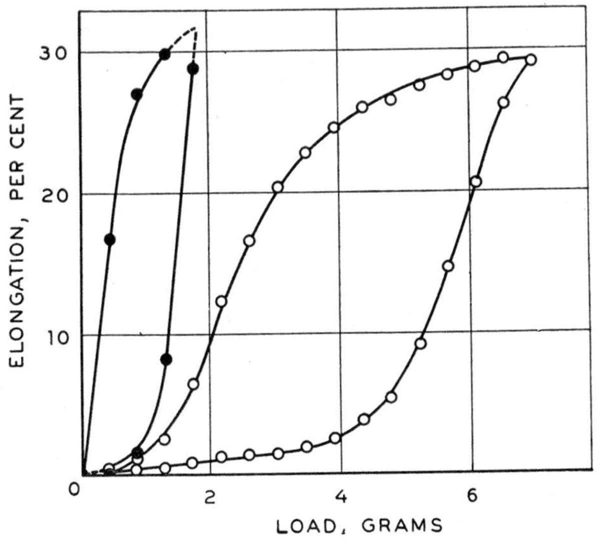

Fig. 176. Effect on the stress–strain cycle of opening five-sixths of the cross linkages by reduction and alkylation with methyl iodine. Open circles, untreated; solid circles, reduced and methylated.

cystine units with thioglycolic acid, followed by treatment of the reduced product with an alkyl halide. When a monohalide is used, the cross link is replaced by two alkyl thioether side groups; when a dihalide is used, a new cross link replaces the original cross link. The authors represent the reactions by the equations:

$$\text{W—S—S—W} + 2\,\text{HS—CH}_2\text{—COOH} \rightarrow 2\,\text{W—SH} + (\text{S—CH}_2\text{—COOH})_2$$

$$\text{W—SH} + \text{RX} \rightarrow \text{W—SR} + \text{HX}$$

$$2\,\text{W—SH} + (\text{CH}_2)_n\text{X}_2 \rightarrow \text{W—S—(CH}_2)_n\text{—S—W} + 2\,\text{HX}$$

where W represents the portions of the wool chains connected (originally) by a disulfide group, R an alkyl group, and X a halogen atom.

The effects of these treatments are shown in figures 176 to 179. When wool is reduced and then methylated, the original (S—S) cross links are replaced by unlinked —S—CH_3 groups. The uncross-linked wool is much more easily extensible, as shown in figure 176. Reduction followed by reoxidation replaces original cross links by new cross links, and the stress–strain curve is very similar to that of the original wool. Reduction followed by alkylation with trimethylene bromide replaces the original —S—S— cross links by longer —S—CH_2—CH_2—CH_2—S— cross links. The network structure is somewhat looser than in untreated wool. The stress–strain curve is definitely affected by this chemical treatment—not so much as by reduction and methylation, yet more than by reduction and reoxidation.

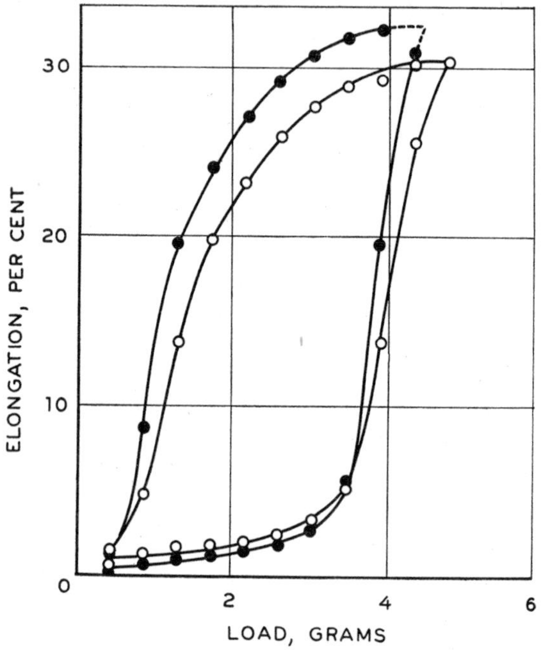

Fig. 177. Effect on the stress–strain cycle of reduction of one-half of the cross linkages, followed by rebuilding by oxidation with oxygen. Open circles, untreated; solid circles, reduced and reoxidized.

When wool is reduced and benzylated, disulfide cross links are replaced by benzyl side groups. The bulky benzyl side groups increase the "internal viscosity" of the wool, even while they reduce the cross linking. The stress–strain curve of the benzylated wool exhibits an extreme hysteresis—while extension is facilitated, recovery is slow (*39*).

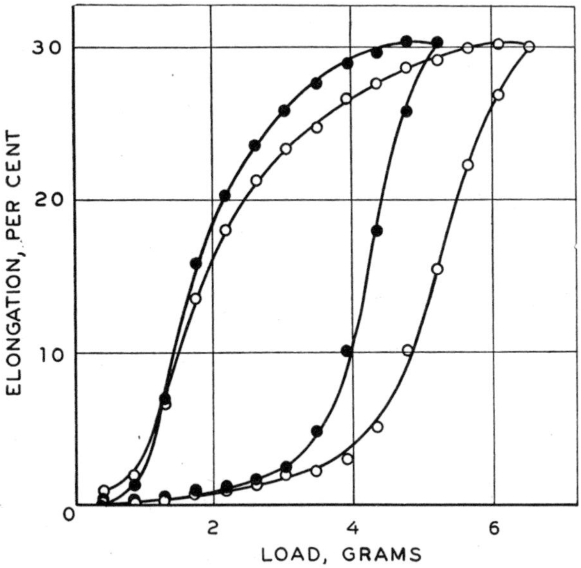

Fig. 178. Effect on the stress–strain cycle of rebuilding of five-sixths of the cross linkages as bis-thioethers by reduction and alkylation with trimethylene bromide. Open circles, untreated; solid circles, reduced and alkylated with $(CH_2)_3BR_2$.

It may be that benzyl groups on adjacent sulfur atoms exhibit mutual interaction of a van der Waals' type, or that there is an attraction between benzyl groups and a portion of a neighboring polypeptide chain. At the point of maximum extension the benzyl groups appear to form new interactions which resist the tendency of the fiber to return to its original length. An alternative explanation could be that the large volume of the benzyl group increases the energy of activation required for flow.

We have already discussed the phenomenon of chemical scission and cross linking of the network in vulcanized rubber. It is possible that similar breaking and re-forming of cross links can take place when wool is subjected to extreme conditions of heat, moisture, and tension. Certainly the long time mechanical behavior of wool under these conditions is such as to indicate that some permanent structural change is taking place. Astbury comments as follows (*1*):

The lubricating action of water on the molecular chains of the wool fibre, whereby their mutual cohesion is considerably decreased and the simpler stresses and strains of elongation and contraction are gradually dissipated, does not by any means comprise the whole of its activities in this field. We must now turn to the consideration of a far-reaching and valuable effect which finally culminates in the phenomenon known as "permanent set." *A stretched wool fibre, when moist, tends to lose its state of tension.*

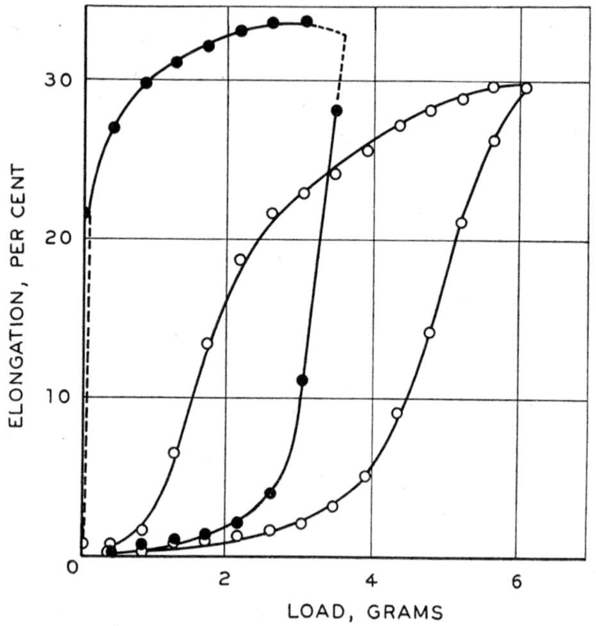

Fig. 179. Effect on the stress–strain cycle of opening of five-sixths of the cross linkages by reduction and alkylation with benzyl chloride. Open circles, untreated; solid circles, reduced and benzylated.

In view of what we have now learnt of the way water can interfere with the operation of the cohesive forces, this is not surprising: what is striking is the fact that this weakening of the elastic powers can persist after the original length has been regained and every change of recovery has been offered by resting the unstretched fibre in water or even by submitting it to the action of steam. . . . It seems clear *that the application of tension to a wool fibre in the presence of water or water vapour results in permanent structural changes which increase with prolongation of the time of extension, and also with increasing extension, humidity, or temperature.* These changes manifest themselves in the first place by a loss of tension and by a slowing down of the rate of contraction to the original length when the stretching force is removed.

These changes are associated, it would seem, with rupture (possibly followed by re-forming) of covalent cross links between wool chains—*e.g.*, disulfide linkages of cystine; salt linkage or peptide linkage between glutamic acid and arginine.

We have already seen that we cannot extend a wool fibre much beyond 20 per cent. without the aid of water at ordinary temperatures, or much beyond 70 per cent. without the aid of steam, so that we are led to the conclusion . . . that full extension can be realized only after the loosening or complete break-down of certain side-chain linkages involving either one and the same main chain or neighbouring main chains, or both these possibilities. The necessary loosening is only partially achieved by the use of cold water, but it is brought about almost immediately by the application of steam and certain other reagents, such as caustic soda solutions. If we stretch a wool fibre in steam *quickly*, even to double its original length, it is possible to make it recover almost completely by leaving it in steam after the tension is removed, and thereafter to demonstrate, simply by stretching it again in water at ordinary temperatures, that the folded chains of α-keratin are truly elastic, not merely over a range of extensions of the order of 70 per cent., but over the full range of 100 per cent. of the initial length. We thus arrive at the concept of what we may call "free" keratin chains, that is, chains which are no longer subject to the more obstinate of those restraining linkages which form an essential part of the structure of the normal wool fibre. Wool that is built of "free" keratin chains is different from either the α-keratin of normal unstretched wool or the β-keratin of normal stretched wool—a "new" wool, if you like, as we see at once from the remarkable property which we shall now discuss.

If we stretch a Cotswold wool fibre in cold water, say to an extension of 50 per cent., and then while held stretched place it in steam *for no more than two minutes*, we find that it will remain stretched without tension when removed from the steam, *but it left without tension in the steam it will contract to about one-third shorter even than its original unstretched length!* If now we repeat the experiment, but this time hold the fibre stretched in steam for about twenty minutes, we find that leaving it afterwards without tension in steam will bring it back only to about its original unstretched length; while if once again we carry out the experiment and this time expose the stretched fibre to steam for about two hours, then it will recover, on subsequent removal of the tension and leaving in steam, only to a length which is about one-third *longer* than the unstretched length. It is quite clear what is happening. The first action of the steam on the stretched keratin chains is a freeing or break-down of certain restricting side-chain linkages: this action is over in two minutes, and its effect is to leave the chains in what we have called the "free" state. In this state the original unstretched length of the fibre means nothing—it has lost completely its former significance—so that, under the further stimulating and lubricating action of water molecules at high temperature, the chains now coil up more than ever before, that is to say, the fibre contracts to a length much shorter even than what was its "normal" length at the beginning of the experiment. *But the loosening action of steam is followed immediately by a new binding action which is at first wholly reversible.* This new binding action shows itself most simply in the fact that, if at any time we remove the elongated fibre from the steam, it remains elongated without the necessity of maintaining the tension. If the fibre has been held stretched in the steam for only a short time, then this "setting" effect can be reversed by further application of steam without tension, that is to say, the fibre still retains its power of contraction, given the right conditions; but if it has been held stretched in steam for any length of time, then a permanent binding action comes into play which holds up the contraction to an extent depending on the length of time the stretched fibre has been steamed. We may call this first "setting" phase, "temporary set," and the second, "true permanent set."

These phenomena, of which the interpretation is so clear in the light of fundamental investigations of molecular structure, are so important from the point of view of textile finishing processes that it will be well worthwhile to emphasize once more the various points by the following summary:

Definitions. "Temporary set" is an elongation which is not reduced by the action of water at ordinary temperatures, while "true permanent set" is an elongation which is not reduced even by the prolonged action of steam in the absence of all tension.

(1) The first action of steam or hot water on stretched wool is a break-down of certain side-chain linkages which leaves the main chains in a much freer state than is found in the normal fibre and confers on them the power of contracting much below their original unstretched length.

(2) Wool that has been treated while stretched to the action of hot water at a temperature not exceeding about 90°C. can always be made to return to its original unstretched length if placed without tension in water at least as hot as that in which it was held stretched. If placed in *steam* it can always be made to contract *below* its original unstretched length ("super-contraction").

(3) The side-chain break-down is followed almost immediately by the formation of new linkages which tend to "set" the fiber at the new stretched length ("temporary set"). If this action takes place in water not hotter than 90°C., it follows from (2) that it is completely reversible in water at least as hot.

(4) If the side-chain break-down and temporary set is brought about by the action of steam, it is reversible only for the first few minutes of the action. Thereafter, more permanent linkages are built up which oppose the contraction ("true permanent set").

(5) There is thus a certain time of steaming under tension, about fifteen or twenty minutes—the precise time, and also the magnitude of the contraction and setting effects, vary somewhat with the type of wool—for which the "super-contraction" and the permanent set cancel each other. *For times of steaming shorter than this, a contraction below the original unstretched length can always be realized by sufficient further steaming in the absence of tension;* for longer times, there is produced a permanent increase of the original length.

(6) For extensions in water at ordinary temperatures, that is, extensions not exceeding about 70 per cent., the maximum possible true permanent set is of the order of only 35 per cent. Its magnitude is a function of both the extension and the time of steaming under tension.

These contraction and setting effects in wool are summarized graphically in figure 180.

Wool is unique in the recognized number of complicating factors in its mechanical behavior. (Many other polymers would no doubt present as complicated a picture if as thoroughly investigated, but in wool the complications have actually been described and isolated for study.)

(1) Wool exhibits time effects in its behavior. Hence the considerations of chapter B are necessary as a starting point. These fall down, however, because of the added complications:

(2) The viscoelastic response of wool is far from being directly proportional to stress.

(3) Wool is cross-linked and has cross links of more than one kind (covalent, salt, hydrogen bond).

(4) Wool exhibits crystallization and undergoes phase change during deformation.

(5) The configurational elasticity of even the "amorphous" wool must be largely Mack elasticity.

(6) The plasticizing action of water must always be considered.

(7) Water and heat not only accelerate configurational changes. They also cause permanent structural changes—chemical breaking and re-forming of cross links during the experiment.

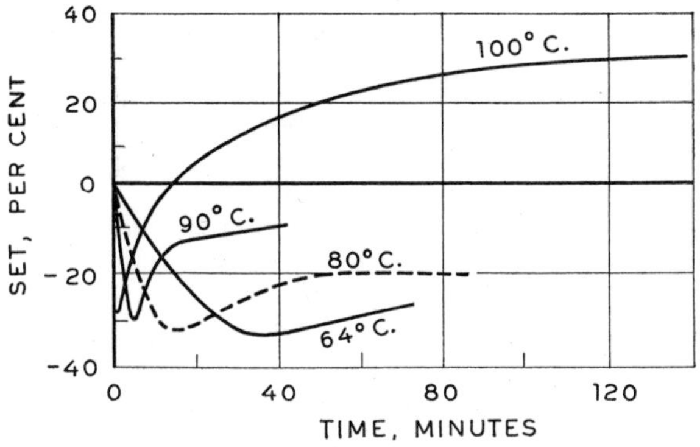

Fig. 180. Contraction and setting effects in wool.

In view of this array of complicating factors, it is indeed remarkable that the investigators who have studied wool have succeeded in learning as much as they have about the relationships between its molecular structure and mechanical behavior—even though the picture is still far from complete. For more detailed discussions of the properties of wool, the reader is referred to the papers of these investigators.

BIBLIOGRAPHY

BOOKS

(*1*) Astbury, W. T., *Fundamentals of Fiber Structure.* Oxford Univ. Press, London, 1933.

(*2*) Houwink, R., *Elasticity, Plasticity, and the Structure of Matter.* Cambridge Univ. Press, London, 1937.

(*3*) Houwink, R., *Physikalische Eigenschaften und Feinbau von Natur- und Kunstharzen.* Akadem. Verlagsgesellschaft, Leipzig, 1934.

(*4*) Leaderman, H., *Elastic and Creep Properties of Filamentous Materials and Other High Polymers.* The Textile Foundation, Washington, D. C., 1943.

(*5*) Mark, H., *Physical Chemistry of High Polymeric Systems* (High Polymers, Vol. II), Interscience, New York, 1940.

(*6*) Meyer, K. H., *Natural and Synthetic High Polymers* (High Polymers, Vol. IV), Interscience, New York, 1942.

(*7*) Ott, E., *Cellulose and Cellulose Derivatives* (High Polymers, Vol. V), Interscience, New York, 1943.

ARTICLES

(*8*) Alfrey, T., "Equilibria and Rates in Crystallization of High Polymers," *Polymer Bull.*, **1**, 40–46 (1945).

(*9*) Alfrey, T., and Mark, H., "Phase Transitions in Rubber and Their Connection with the Stress–Strain Curve," *Rubber Chem. Tech.*, **14**, 525–543 (1941).

(*10*) Alfrey, T., and Mark, H., "A Statistical Treatment of Crystallization Phenomena in High Polymers," *J. Phys. Chem.*, **46**, 112 (1942).

(*11*) Baker, W. O., and Fuller, C. S., "Macromolecular Disorder in Linear Polyamides. Relation of Structure to Physical Properties of Copolyamides," *J. Am. Chem. Soc.*, **64**, 2399 (1942).

(*12*) Baker, W. O., and Fuller, C. S., "Intermolecular Forces and Chain Configuration in Linear Polymers—The Effect of N-Methylation on the X-Ray Structures and Properties of Linear Polyamides," *ibid.*, **65**, 1120 (1943).

(*13*) Baker, W. O., Fuller, C. S., and Pape, N. R., "Effects of Heat, Solvents and Hydrogen-Bonding Agents on the Crystallinity of Cellulose Esters," *ibid.*, **64**, 776 (1942).

(*14*) Bekkedahl, N., "Forms of Rubber as Indicated by Temperature–Volume Relationship," *J. Research Natl. Bur. Standards*, **13**, 411–431 (1934).

(*15*) Bekkedahl, N., and Matheson, H., "Heat Capacity, Entropy, and Free Energy of Rubber Hydrocarbon," *ibid.*, **15**, 503 (1935).

(*16*) Bekkedahl, N., and Wood, L. A., "Influence of the Temperature of Crystallization on the Melting of Crystalline Rubber," *J. Chem. Phys.*, **9**, 193 (1941).

(*17*) Bekkedahl, N., and Wood, L. A., "Crystallization of Vulcanized Rubber," *Ind. Eng. Chem.*, **33**, 381 (1941).

(*18*) Bunn, C. W., "The Crystal Structure of Long-Chain Normal Paraffin Hydrocarbons. The 'Shape' of the $>CH_2$ Group," *Trans. Faraday Soc.*, **35**, 482 (1939).

(*19*) Bunn, C. W., "Molecular Structure and Rubber-like Elasticity. I. The Crystal Structures of β Gutta-percha, Rubber and Polychloroprene," *Proc. Roy. Soc. London*, **A180**, 40 (1942); "II. The Stereochemistry of Chain Polymers," *ibid.*, 67; "III. Molecular Movements in Rubber-like Polymers," *ibid.*, 82.

(*20*) Bunn, C. W., "The Stereochemistry of the Rubber Molecule," *Rubber Chem. Tech.*, **15**, 704 (1942).

(*21*) Busse, W. F., Lessig, E. T., Loughborough, D. L., and Larrick, L., "Fatigue of Fabrics," *J. Applied Phys.*, **13**, 715–724 (1942).

(*22*) Clark, G. L., "X-Ray Structure of Vulcanized Rubber," *Ind. Eng. Chem.*, **31**, 1397 (1939); "Analysis by X-Rays of Ultimate Structures of Living Materials," *Radiology*, **30**, 180–190 (1938).

(*23*) Clark, G. L., Kabler, M., Blaker, E., and Ball, J. M., "Hysteresis in Crystallization of Stretched Vulcanized Rubber from X-Ray Data," *Ind. Eng. Chem.*, **32**, 1474 (1940).

(*24*) Clark, G. L., Wolthius, E., and Smith, W. H., "X-Ray Diffraction Patterns of Sol, Gel and Total Rubber When Stretched, and When Crystallized by Freezing and from Solutions," *J. Research Natl. Bur. Standards*, **19**, 479–491 (1937).

(*25*) Davies, J. M., Miller, R. F., and Busse, W. F., "Dielectric Properties of Plasticized Polyvinyl Chloride," *J. Am. Chem. Soc.*, **63**, 361 (1941).

(*27*) Field, J. E., "An X-Ray Study of the Proportion of Crystalline and Amorphous Components in Stretched Rubber," *J. Applied Phys.*, **12**, 23 (1941).

(*28*) Fikentscher, H., and Mark, H., "Über ein Spiralmodell des Kautchuks," *Kautschuk*, **6**, 2 (1930).

(*29*) Frith, E. M., and Tuckett, R. F., "The Melting of Crystalline Polymers," *Trans. Faraday Soc.*, **40**, 251 (1944).

(*30*) Frohlich, H., "Phase Transitions of Solid Paraffins and the Flexibility of Hydrocarbon Chains," *ibid.*, **40**, 498 (1944).

(*31*) Fuller, C. S., "The Investigation of Synthetic Linear Polymers by X-Rays," *Chem. Revs.*, **26**, 143 (1940).

(*32*) Fuller, C. S., Baker, W. O., and Pape, N. R., "Crystalline Behavior of Linear Polyamides. Effect of Heat Treatment," *J. Am. Chem. Soc.*, **62**, 3275 (1940).

(*33*) Fuller, C. S., Frosch, C. J., and Pape, N. R., "Chain Structure of Linear Polyesters —Trimethylene Glycol Series," *ibid.*, **64**, 154 (1942).

(*34*) Gehman, S. D., "The Contribution of X-Ray Research to the Knowledge of Rubber," *Chem. Revs.*, **26**, 203 (1940).

(*35*) Gehman, S. D., and Field, J. E., "Colloidal Structure of Rubber in Solution. Effects of Precipitants," *Ind. Eng. Chem.*, **30**, 1031 (1938); "An X-Ray Investigation of Crystallinity in Rubber," *J. Applied Phys.*, **10**, 564 (1939); "Observations on the X-Ray Structure of Rubber and the Size and Shape of Rubber Crystallites," *ibid.*, **15**, 371 (1944).

(*36*) Hermann, K., Gerngross, O., and Abitz, W., "Zur röntgenographischen Strukturerforschung des Gelatinemicells," *Z. physik. Chem.*, **B10**, 371 (1930).

(*37*) Goggin, W. C., and Lowry, R. D., "Vinylidene Chloride Polymers," *Ind. Eng. Chem.*, **34**, 327 (1942).

(*38*) Guth, E., and James, H. M., "Elastic and Thermoelastic Properties of Rubber-like Materials. A Statistical Theory," *ibid.*, **33**, 624 (1941); "Theory of Rubber Elasticity for Development of Synthetic Rubbers," *ibid.*, **34**, 1365 (1942); "Theoretical Stress–Strain Curve for Rubber-like Materials," *Phys. Rev.*, **59**, 111 (1941).

(*39*) Harris, M., Mizell, L. R., and Fourt, L., "Elasticity of Wool. Relation to Chemical Structure," *Ind. Eng. Chem.*, **34**, 833 (1942).

(*40*) Hauser, E. A., and Mark, H., "Zur Kenntnis der Struktur gedehnter Kautschukproben," *Kolloid-Beihefte*, **22**, 63 (1926).

(*41*) Hermans, P. H., "The Analogy between the Mechanism of Deformation of Cellulose and That of Rubber," *J. Phys. Chem.*, **45**, 827 (1941).

(*42*) Herrmann, K., and Gerngross, O., "Die Elastizität des Kautschuks" *Kautschuk*, **8**, 181 (1932).

(*43*) Hock, L., and Boström, S., "Die quantitative Bestimmung der Joule'schen Dehnungswärme am Rohkautschuk," *Gummi-Ztg.*, **41**, 1112 (1927).

(*44*) Holt, W. L., and McPherson, A. T., "Changes of Volume of Rubber on Stretching: Effects of Time, Elongation, and Temperature," *J. Research Natl. Bur. Standards*, **17**, 657 (1936).

(*45*) Jeffrey, G. A., "The Structure of Polyisoprenes. Part II. The Structure of β-Gutta-percha," *Trans. Faraday Soc.*, **40**, 517 (1944).

(*45a*) Kistler, S. S., "The Thermoplastic Behavior of Linear and Three-Dimensional Polymers," *J. Applied Phys.*, **11**, 769 (1940).

(*46*) Leaderman, H., "Textile Materials and the Time Factor. I. Mechanical Behavior of Textile Fibers," *Textile Research*, **11**, 171–193 (1941).

(*47*) Mack, E., Jr., "Remarks on Molecular Structure and van der Waals' Forces," *J. Phys. Chem.*, **41**, 221 (1937).

(*48*) Mark, H., "Progress in High Polymer Plastics," *Ind. Eng. Chem.*, **34**, 449 (1942).

(*49*) Mark, H., "Intermolecular Forces and Mechanical Behavior of High Polymers," *ibid.*, **34**, 1343 (1942).

(*50*) Mark, H., and Press, J. J., "Elasticity, Creep and Recovery of Acetate and Viscose Rayon Yarns," *Rayon Textile Monthly*, **24**, 297, 339, 405 (1943).

(*51*) Müller, A., "A Further X-Ray Investigation of Long-Chain Compounds (*n*-Hydrocarbon)," *Proc. Roy. Soc. London*, **120**, 437 (1928).

(*52*) Press, J. J., "Flow and Recovery Properties of Viscose Rayon Yarn," *J. Applied Phys.*, **14**, 224 (1943).

(*53*) Sisson, W. A., and Saner, W. R., "The Effect of the Temperature and the Concentration of Sodium Hydroxide on the X-Ray Diffraction Behavior of Raw and of Degraded Cotton," *J. Phys. Chem.*, **45**, 717 (1941).

(*54*) Smallwood, H. M., "Limiting Law of the Reinforcement of Rubber," *J. Applied Phys.*, **15**, 758 (1944).

(*55*) Smith, W. H., and Hanna, N. P., "Comparison between the Observed Density of Crystalline Rubber and the Density Calculated from X-Ray Data," *J. Research Natl. Bur. Standards*, **27**, 229–236 (1941).

(*56*) Treloar, L. R. G., "Crystalline Phenomena in Raw Rubber," *Trans. Faraday Soc.*, **37**, 84 (1941).

(*57*) Weber, W., "Über die Elasticität fester Körper," *Ann. Physik Chem.*, **54**, 1 (1841).

(*58*) Wiegand, W. B., and Snyder, J. W., "The Rubber Pendulum, the Joule Effect and the Dynamic Stress–Strain Curve," *Trans. Inst. Rubber Ind.*, **10**, 234–262 (1934).

E. PLASTICIZATION AND SOLUTION

Systems Containing High Polymers and Materials of Low Molecular Weight

I. INTRODUCTION

The preceding chapters have dealt almost entirely with systems consisting only of high polymer molecules. This chapter, on the other hand, deals with mixtures of high polymers with low molecular weight materials. From a practical standpoint, such mixtures are extremely important. Many polymers are never used alone, but are always "plasticized" by the addition of tricresyl phosphate, camphor, glyceryl tributyrate, dioctyl phthalate, dibutyl sebacate, or some such material. Precisely what effect does a plasticizer have upon the viscoelastic behavior of a high polymer? Before discussing this question, it is necessary, as in preceding chapters, to discuss the *structures* of the systems concerned. In this case, this is largely a question of the arrangement of the polymer and plasticizer molecules in a mixture of the two.

II. ARRANGEMENT OF MOLECULES IN AMORPHOUS MIXTURES

The simplest case of molecular arrangements in binary liquid mixtures is where both types of molecules involved are roughly spherical and of about the same size, and where there is no heat of mixing. In such a case there results a completely *random* molecular arrangement. There are no preferential attractive forces which would tend to cause clustering of the two molecular types. Thus in a 50:50 mixture, any given molecule is surrounded, on the average, by six molecules of each kind (assuming a total coordination number of 12).

If the heat of mixing for the solution is different from zero, on the other hand, there is some clustering together. Consider the two kinds of molecules, A and B, where both types are roughly spherical and roughly the same size. Consider further that the intermolecular forces are not highly localized. Let E_{AA} be the energy of interaction of a pair of adjacent A molecules, E_{BB} the energy of interaction of a pair of neighboring B molecules, and E_{AB} the interaction energy of an A—B pair of neighbors. Now if $E_{AB} = (E_{AA} + E_{BB})/2$, then we have the simple case already discussed. The energy of the whole mixture is not affected by the nature of the intermolecular packing arrangement. Therefore the *most random* mixing is obtained. The number of "A—B" pairs of neighbors is given by:

$$[(N_A)(N_B)/(N_A + N_B)]z$$

where N_A is the number of A molecules, N_B is the number of B molecules, and z is the coordination number.

If $E_{AB} > (E_{AA} + E_{BB})/2$, then the energy* of the system is *increased* by the process of mixing. The mixing of pure A and pure B is an *endothermic* process. Furthermore, in the final mixture, the most random packing cannot be attained. The A molecules tend to cluster together with other A molecules; the B molecules cluster with other B molecules. There are fewer A—B pairs than in the case of random arrangement. If $[E_{AB} - (E_{AA} + E_{BB})/2]$ becomes too great, separation into two phases occurs.

If $E_{AB} < (E_{AA} + E_{BB})/2$, then the mixing process is *favored* by the resulting energy change. The process is exothermic. The number of A—B pairs of neighbors is *greater* than in the case of complete randomness. The limiting cases are the following:

Completely random mixing. The random thermal activity of the mixture tends to shake it into this structure of maximum entropy. When $E_{AB} > (E_{AA} + E_{BB})/2$, the *energy* of the system would be a minimum in this separated condition.

Regular *alternating* structure (checkerboard). Number of A—B pairs as high as geometrically possible. When $E_{AB} < (E_{AA} + E_{BB})/2$, this would be the stable structure from only the *energetical* considerations. When $E_{AB} > (E_{AA} + E_{BB})/2$, the actual structure is somewhere between cases (1) and (2), determined by the competition between energy and entropy factors (*i.e.*, between *forces* and thermal agitation). When $E_{AB} < (E_{AA} + E_{BB})/2$, the actual structure is somewhere between cases (1) and (3) and is governed by the same general competition.

Localized and Directed Forces

The more polar liquids are not only characterized by stronger intermolecular forces, but also by localized and directed forces. For them the

* It should be noted that, if two particles attract one another, strongly, the condition attained when they are close neighbors is one of low potential energy. Thus, if the force of attraction between A and B is greater than between A and A, E_{AB} is less than E_{AA}.

above relations do not hold. Consider, for example, a solution of benzoic acid in benzene. Each benzoic acid molecule possesses a strong dipole moment, which is *localized* at one part of the accessible surface of the molecule. There is a strong tendency for benzoic acid molecules to cluster in one specific manner—to form pairs; see figures 181 and 182. Once a pair has been formed, the strong attractive forces are essentially saturated, and no further clustering occurs. That is, in a dilute benzene solution of benzoic acid, there is an exceptionally large number of paired acid molecules, but not an exceptionally large number of triplet clusters. In water, on the other hand, the polar group of the benzoic acid molecule is solvated. Thus, in water solution there is little clustering tendency of the type exhibited in benzene. However, in water solution, the energy of the mixture can be lowered by a clustering of the *hydrocarbon* portions of the benzoic acid molecules, as shown in figure 182. In either case, an increase in temperature should reduce the amount of clustering.

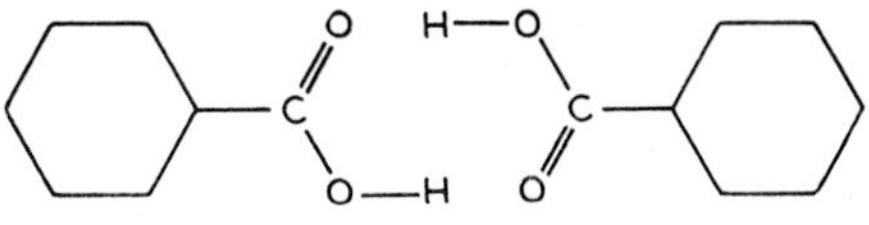

Fig. 181. Clustering of benzoic acid molecules in benzene solution.

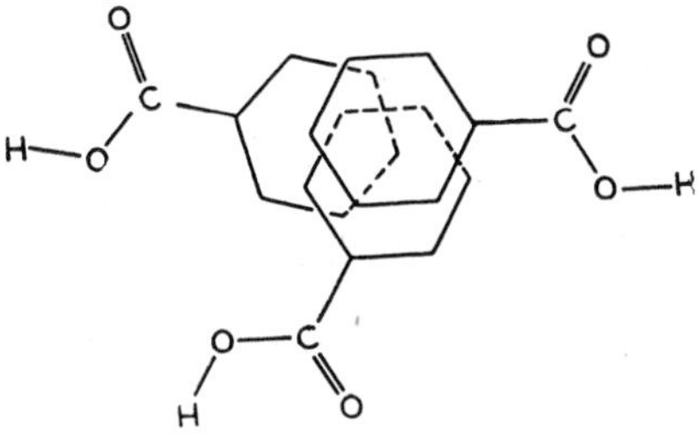

Fig. 182. Clustering of benzoic acid molecules in aqueous solution.

Similar considerations apply to the packing of low molecular weight molecules among the chains in an amorphous high polymer. Consider first the case of random packing, to be expected when a polymer possessing no specific points of strong, localized intermolecular attraction is mixed with a low molecular weight material of great chemical similarity. For simplicity, consider a portion of the polymer chain which is of about the same size as the low molecular weight (or solvent) molecule, and call this chain portion a "submolecule." In a random mixture, solvent molecules and polymeric submolecules are packed together in a fashion very similar to the packing of two chemically indifferent low molecular weight species. However, the submolecules must follow the necessary constraint of being strung together in chains. Any submolecule (except end groups) of necessity have two other submolecules as nearest neighbors. Huggins (*37*) and Flory (*25*) have discussed in detail the consequences of such a random packing of polymeric submolecules and solvent molecules, with this constraint. They have succeeded in explaining on this basis the thermodynamic properties of high polymer solutions, which for some time had been considered as anomalous.

Just as in the case of binary mixtures of low molecular weight liquids, completely random packing can only be expected when the energy of molecular interaction of the mixture is independent of the configuration. In general, this will not be true, and clustering of one type or another will occur (*9*). One particularly important type of clustering occurs in the typical plasticized polar polymer. Consider a polymer molecule which possesses certain specific points which are capable of exerting strong intermolecular forces (*e.g.*, localized dipoles), and a low molecular weight molecule consisting of an inactive hydrocarbon chain with either a localized dipole or a localized polarizability. Such a binary mixture certainly does not exhibit random packing. There is a tendency for the dipole or the polarizable group of the low molecular weight molecule to lie adjacent to a localized dipole of the polymer, and saturate its field of force. On the other hand, there is also a tendency for two polymer dipoles to cluster together and neutralize their fields in this fashion. There is thus a competition between the strong points of the small molecules and of the neighboring polymer chains, for the positions neighboring any given polymer dipole. The outcome of this competition depends upon the relative shapes of the molecules involved, the magnitudes of the forces, etc. In cellulose, for example, the polymer molecules can themselves fit together so neatly, and can neutralize their dipoles by polymer–polymer interaction so completely, that most low molecular weight molecules are unable to squeeze into the structure. In other cases, low molecular weight molecules fit so well into the spaces next to certain parts of the polymer chain that definite "compound formation" takes place. In such a case, the partial molal heat and entropy of solution may depend upon concentration in a more discontinuous fashion than in the case of random and near-random mixing. The first small molecules may be particularly anxious to enter the polymeric structure, and yet after the localized dipoles of the polymer are saturated, the small molecules may be forced to cluster among themselves, even to the extent of forming a separate phase.

A complete thermodynamic study of any given binary mixture of a polymer with a low molecular weight component throws much light upon the nature of the intermolecular packing. Thus the more definite the compound formation between the two components, the sharper is the break in the curve relating partial molal heat of solution with concentration; the break resulting from the saturation of the available active spots.

It is clear that, to be effective as a plasticizer, a low molecular weight component must be able to overcome the polymer–polymer interaction and to pack around the polar groups of the polymer, to some extent at least.

III. EFFECT OF LOW MOLECULAR MATERIALS ON VISCOELASTIC PROPERTIES OF HIGH POLYMERS IN CONCENTRATED SYSTEMS

Having considered the structure of mixtures of high polymers with low molecular weight components, the next question is the effect of such components upon the viscoelastic behavior of a polymer. Two cases are discussed: the random mixture, in which there is no preferential clustering; and the typical plasticized polar polymer structure, in which the low molecular weight component is attracted to specific points on the polymer chains.

The Random Mixture.—The ideal example of a random mixture of amorphous polymer with swelling agent would presumably be a saturated polyhydrocarbon, such as polyisobutylene, swollen with a paraffin of low molecular weight, such as gasoline. Polystyrene swollen with an aromatic hydrocarbon presumably represents another extremely random mixture and is used in this discussion because of the large amount of data available for mixtures of this type.

In a mixture of polystyrene and toluene, of high toluene content, the toluene molecules can wander about easily from place to place. It is no longer necessary for a large polymer segment to find a large hole in order to move. Instead, the random diffusional motion of the surrounding toluene molecules produces a slow diffusional motion of the polymer segments by displacement (just as the diffusion of water molecules results in a slow Brownian movement of a dissolved sugar molecule). The polymer molecule undergoes a micro-Brownian and a macro-Brownian motion, as in the unswollen state, but by means of a different elementary process. Because of the extreme rapidity of the new elementary diffusion process—the diffusion of toluene—the macro- and micro-Brownian motions for the swollen polymer is much faster than for the unswollen polymer.

The temperature dependence of a multiple process, such as polymer diffusion, is determined by the *energy of activation* of the *elementary molecular process*—here toluene diffusion. Hence the observed "activation energy" governing the viscosity, η_3, and the retarding internal resistance to configurational changes (η_2) is smaller for a swollen than for an unswollen polymer.

The progressive change in properties of polystyrene upon the addition of xylene have been investigated by Ferry (*24*), who used high frequency sinusoidal shear stresses. Briefly, the polymer changes from a hard, inflexible polymer to a retarded elastic material, then to a rubbery, flexible material (with flow), then to a viscous liquid with marked elastic effects, and finally to a liquid with no elastic effects which can be detected by ordinary methods. As one would expect, these transitions can be shifted to lower polymer concentrations by decreasing the temperature or by shortening the timescale of experimental observation.

Ferri found that a four-parameter model of the Maxwell type could be used to approximate the viscoelastic behavior of these solutions in the range studied. Table XXII shows the dependence of G_1, G_2, τ_1, and τ_2 with concentration at 25°C.

TABLE XXII

ANALYSIS OF RIGIDITY MECHANISMS IN POLYSTYRENE–XYLENE

Polystyrene concentration, %	$G_0 \times 10^{-4}$	$G_1 \times 10^{-4}$	$G_2 \times 10^{-4}$	η	$\tau_2 \times 10^4$	$\tau_1 \times 10^2$
15	0.75	0.16	0.59	13.1	4.0	0.73
20	1.66	0.22	1.44	52.5	4.0	2.12
25	2.82	0.28	2.54	209.	4.0	7.1
30	4.80	0.33	4.47	660.	4.0	19.5
35	9.34	0.39	8.95	2,000.	4.0	50.
52.3	38.	1.2	36.8	116,000.	4.0	950.

At low polymer concentration, every polymer segment is surrounded by an environment which is essentially made up of solvent. Hence solvent diffusion can be considered as the *sole* elementary diffusion mechanism, and the observed "energy of activation" for configurational retardation, as well as the "energy of activation" for the solution viscosity, should be very close to the energy of activation for pure solvent diffusion. Furthermore, the retardation time for a given configurational elasticity contribution should be independent of polymer concentration in this range. At *high* polymer concentration, the polymer cannot be considered as surrounded by an environment of solvent alone, and the pure solvent-diffusion mechanism goes over continuously into the polymer segment elementary process characteristic of 100% polymer. At high polymer concentration, therefore, the "energies of activation" governing micro- and macro-Brownian polymer diffusion should be intermediate between the flow activation energy for pure polymer and the diffusion activation energy for pure solvent. Further, the retardation time for a configurational change should be dependent upon polymer concentration in this region.

Ferry (*24*) has shown that the critical stress frequency for polystyrene–xylene mixtures is independent of polymer concentration at moderate concentrations, but must decrease at high concentrations to the value for pure polystyrene at the same temperature. It has also been observed that the "second order transition point" for polystyrene is reduced by the addition of paraffin swelling agents. Houwink has studied the plasto-elastic behavior of polystyrene–monostyrene mixtures. Ferry (*24*) reports the investigation of the system polybutene–heptane. All of these investigations are consistent with the general picture presented here.

From a practical standpoint, the significant characteristic of the random mixture is that it shifts the *entire viscoelastic spectrum* to a shorter timescale, with very little selectivity. Thus the *retarded elasticity* of polystyrene can be shifted to so short a timescale as to make the polystyrene nonrigid; but this is done at the expense of also accelerating the *irrecoverable viscous flow*. As we shall see, the situation is quite different in the case of plasticized polar polymers such as polyvinyl chloride.

The Typical Plasticized Polar Polymer.—We have seen that a typical plasticizer for a polar high polymer is not distributed at random in the polymer–plasticizer mixture, but is particularly attracted to the polar groups of the polymer. The polymer–plasticizer bond may often be very strong. If the mean lifetime of a particular polymer–plasticizer complex is long compared with the time between elementary diffusion steps, then as far as the plastoelastic properties are concerned, we may consider this as a true compound formation. It is clear that diffusion of the plasticizer alone is not a rapid process in this case and does not introduce a new mechanism for plastoelastic response. On the other hand, the plasticizer screens off the field of force originally associated with the polar group of the polymer. Strong polymer–polymer interactions are eliminated. The polymer is no longer strongly polar, but can be considered as a new polymeric chemical species, with an inactive side group in place of the original polar group. The result is a softening action which is similar to the softening of polystyrene by means of toluene or xylene, even though the mechanism of softening is (presumably) different.

On the other hand, it is possible that the mean lifetime of a polymer–plasticizer complex is *short* as compared with the experimental timescale. In this case, the dynamic solvation-desolvation process will play a significant role in the plasticizing action. It is difficult to determine, on the basis of present data, which of these cases represents more closely the mechanism of plasticization when typical plasticizers like tricresyl phosphate are added to polar polymers like polyvinyl chloride.

One thing, however, is certain. The nonrandomness of the structure is extremely significant from the standpoint of viscoelastic properties. The polymer–plasticizer mixture forms a sort of *gel structure* quite unlike the random structure of a system such as polystyrene–toluene. The result is that the system exhibits high elasticity without undue flow. To put it very crudely, toluene "plasticizes both the configurational elastic response and the flow" of polystyrene, whereas a typical plasticizer "plasticizes the configurational elastic response of polyvinyl chloride without plasticizing the flow."

TABLE XXIII

YOUNG'S MODULUS OF ELASTICITY OF POLYVINYL CHLORIDE PLASTICIZED WITH TRICRESYL PHOSPHATE

TCP, per cent by volume	Modulus, p.s.i.			
	−10°C.	32°C.	70°C.	105°C.
0		180,000	97,000	3,000
10		130,000	9,700	1,000
20		91,000	1,400	
30	250,000	17,000	850	
40	52,000	1,100	440	
50	17,000	460	290	
60	1,100	170	160	

Davies, Miller, and Busse (*16*) have measured the modulus of rigidity of plasticized polyvinyl chloride at different temperatures and different concentrations of plasticizer (tricresyl phosphate), but holding the experimental timescale constant. Their results are given in table XXIII. It is clear that addition of plasticizer changes polyvinyl chloride from a hard material with a modulus in the neighborhood of 10^{10} to a rubbery material with a modulus in the neighborhood of 10^6 to 10^7, and that an increase in temperature shifts the transition to higher polymer concentrations. Busse found similar results with the system polyvinyl chloride–diphenyl. Sack (*50*) has investigated the effect of experimental timescale (frequency of sinusoidal stress) on the modulus of plasticized polyvinyl chlorides, obtaining similar results.

Aleksandrov and Lazurkin (*9*) have investigated the plastoelastic properties of plasticized polymethylmethacrylate by means of alternating stresses. Figure 183 illustrates their results. The amplitude of the strain depends upon whether the configurational elasticity can "follow the stress." At low frequencies and high temperatures, large strains are

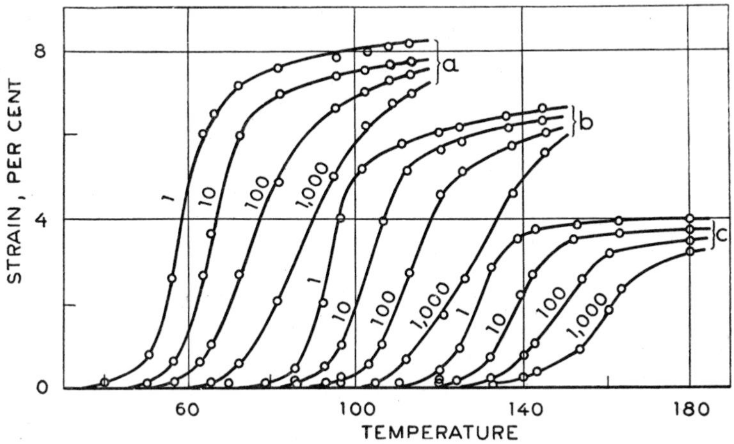

Fig. 183. Strain amplitude as a function of temperature at different frequencies of stressing for plasticized polymethylmethacrylate; a, b, and c represent three different concentrations of plasticizer.

observed. At high frequencies and low temperatures, small strains are observed. Eley (*22*) has computed, from the data of Aleksandrov and Lazurkin, the following values for the activation energy of the configurational elasticity of plasticized polymethylmethacrylate:

30% plasticizer, $\Delta H = 52$ kcal.
10% plasticizer, $\Delta H = 59$ kcal.
0% plasticizer, $\Delta H = 75$ kcal.

Clash and Berg (*14*) have studied the "stiffness" of nonrigid vinyl chloride-acetate copolymer formulations, as a function of temperature and plasticizer content. Stiffness was measured in two ways: (*a*) Tentative Method of Test for Stiffness in Flexure of Non-rigid Plastics (A.S.T.M. Designation D747). (*b*) Bakelite Corporation torsion test for stiffness in torsion. In both tests, the total retarded elastic (plus instantaneous) deformation which occurs in about five seconds is observed. The apparent Young's modulus for this timescale is computed from the deformation and the stress. This apparent Young's modulus, for a timescale of about five seconds, is termed the "stiffness" of the material. It was found that the stiffness values as measured by the two methods were in good agreement. This is in complete harmony with the conclusions arrived at in Chapter B. Clash and Berg have also measured the "brittle temperature" of each material. This was the temperature at which the sample gave a brittle fracture at a fixed rate of loading.

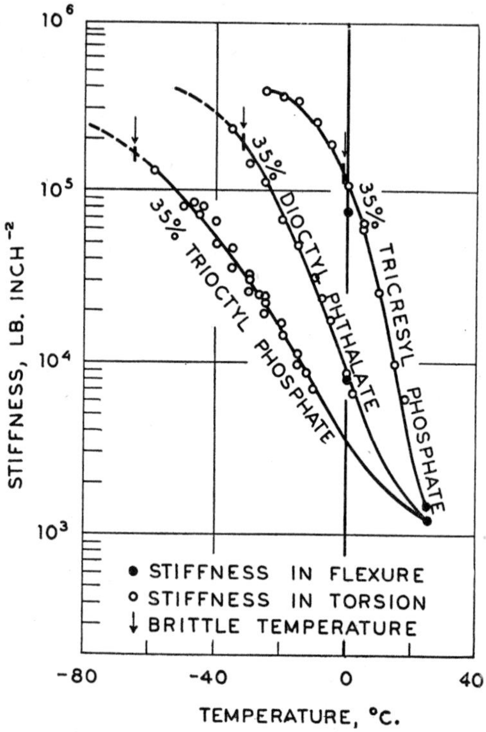

Fig. 184. "Five-second" stiffness of plasticized Vinylite as a function of temperature (after Clash and Berg).

Figure 184 shows how the stiffness of three plasticized samples of Vinylite VYNW varies with temperature. In each case 35% plasticizer was used—tricresyl phosphate, dioctyl phthalate, and trioctyl phosphate, respectively. Although all three samples had very nearly the same stiffness at room temperature, they differ enormously in low temperature flexibility. The sample plasticized with trioctyl phosphate exhibited a brittle point which was more than 60°C. below that plasticized with tricresyl phosphate—and this brittle point relation is also characteristic of the flexibility relation.

An idea of the effect of plasticizer concentration on flexibility can be obtained from figures 185 and 186. The addition of more plasticizer serves to shift the stiffness curve along the temperature axis, by an amount which is roughly proportional to the amount of plasticizer added, without markedly changing the shape of the curve. In figure 187, the stiffness–temperature relationship of unplasticized Vinylite VYNS is compared with that for a sample plasticized with 30% of dioctyl phthalate. (It is clear, however, that the effect of plasticizer cannot in all cases be so simple as merely to shift the stiffness–temperature curve of the pure resin without changing its shape, since the highly plasticized samples exhibit stiffness–temperature curves whose shapes are characteristic of the plasticizer used.)

A really satisfactory experimental study of the effects of plasticizers must go much further than those reported above. The real question to which we would like to know the answer is the following: How does a

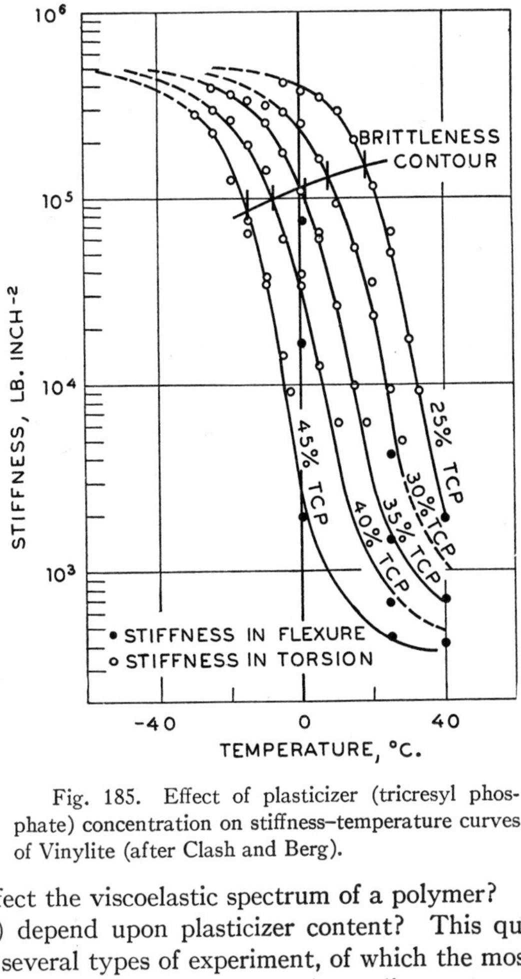

Fig. 185. Effect of plasticizer (tricresyl phosphate) concentration on stiffness–temperature curves of Vinylite (after Clash and Berg).

plasticizer affect the viscoelastic spectrum of a polymer? How does the function $J(\tau)$ depend upon plasticizer content? This question can be answered by several types of experiment, of which the most obvious is a creep study. If complete creep curves (extending over a wide timescale range such as 10^{-1} second to 10^7 seconds are taken for samples containing from 0 to 100% plasticizer, at a number of different temperatures, the resulting information represents a thorough knowledge of the polymer–plasticizer system under consideration.

While we can predict, very roughly, what the trends among these creep curves must be, any really detailed analysis is beyond the scope of present theoretical methods. We know from chapter B that the curve

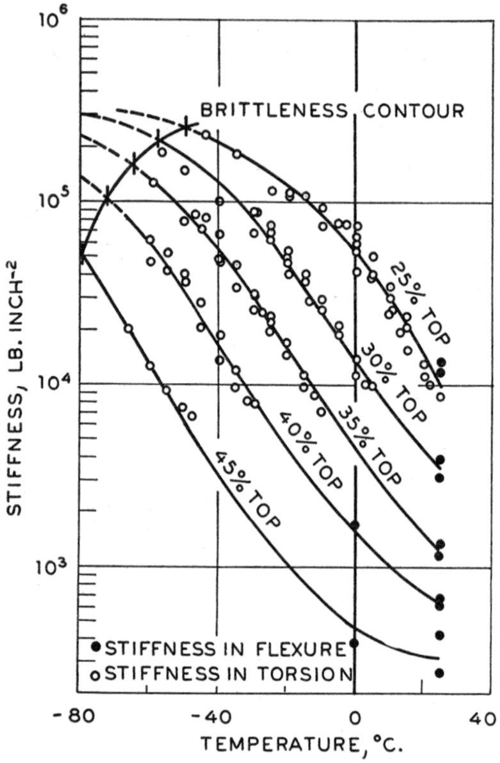

Fig. 186. Effect of plasticizer (trioctyl phosphate) concentration on stiffness–temperature curves of Vinylite (after Clash and Berg).

for the unplasticized polymer, when plotted as (γ/S) *vs.* log t, is a sigmoidal curve (retarded elasticity) plus an exponential curve (true viscous flow). At a higher temperature, the curve is shifted to shorter times. To a first approximation the curve is rigidly shifted, with no change of shape. If plasticizer is added to the polymer, the effect is crudely the same as if the temperature were raised; the creep curve is shifted to shorter times (faster response). But what are the answers to the following more detailed questions?

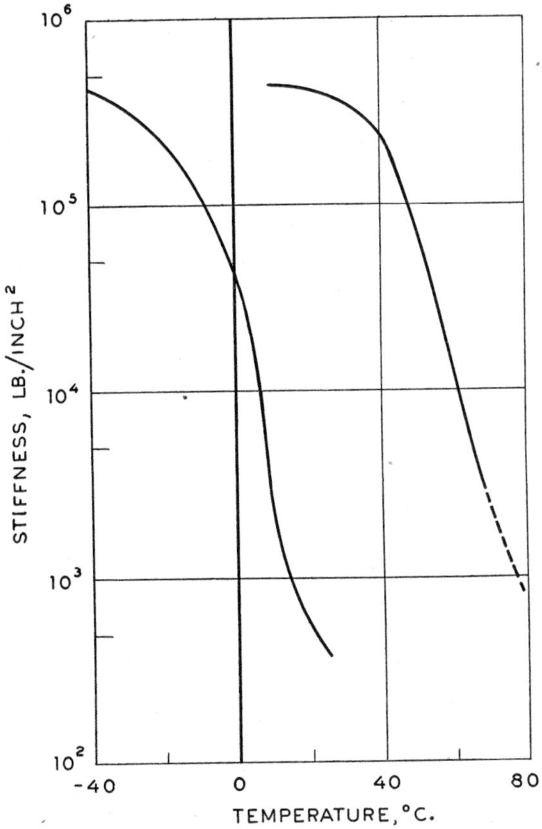

Fig. 187. Stiffness–temperature curves for Vinylite VYNS (after Clash and Berg): unplasticized (at right); plasticized with 30% dioctyl phthalate (at left).

(1) How much is the creep curve shifted by the addition of a given amount of plasticizer? Is the shift proportional to the quantity of plasticizer?

(2) Is the shift in the creep curve actually "rigid," or does the plasticizer affect the retardation times for local kinks to a different extent than those of large convolutions?

(3) Comparing results at different temperatures, how does the energy of activation for retarded elasticity and flow vary with plasticizer content?

(4) In what ways do different plasticizers differ from each other? Is it in the shapes of the creep curves, or in the activation energy, or what?

Unfortunately, even so thorough a study as that of Clash and Berg cannot give unequivocal answers to such questions. These authors observed the amount of elastic deformation which took place in five seconds, *i.e.*, one point on a creep curve. Thus there is no way of deciding the effects of plasticizer on the *shape* of the creep curve. Figure 188, taken from the paper of Clash and Berg, apparently indicates that the effect of plasticizer is far from a linear function of concentration. If we return to the basic sigmoidal creep curves, however, it is clear that figure 188 is in no way inconsistent with the hypothesis that the creep curve is shifted along the log time axis by an amount which is directly proportional to plasticizer concentration.

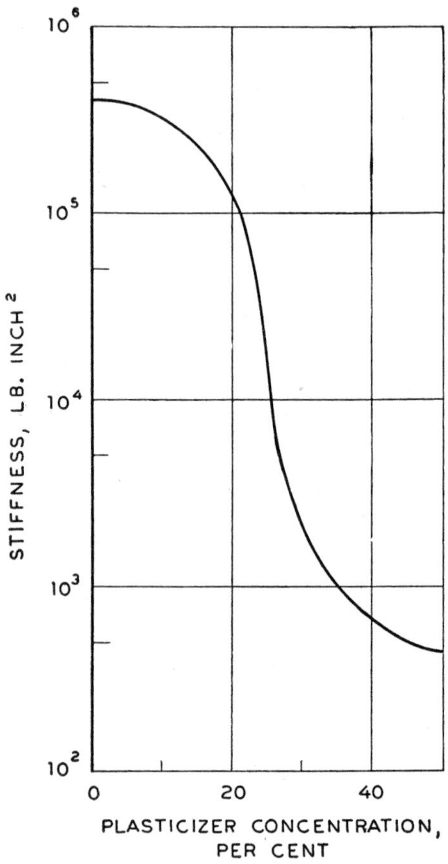

Fig. 188. Effect of plasticizer concentration on stiffness at room temperature (after Clash and Berg).

As far as temperature effects are concerned, there is no doubt that the stiffness–temperature curves of the tricresyl phosphate compositions are much steeper than those of the trioctyl phosphate compositions. This can be interpreted in more than one way, however:

(1) The creep curves of trioctyl phosphate and tricresyl phosphate formulations are of the same shape, but the tricresyl phosphate formulations have larger activation energies.

(2) The activation energies are about the same, but the creep curves for trioctyl phosphate samples are flatter (represent a wider distribution of retardation times) than for tricresyl phosphate samples.

These two interpretations must lead to entirely different hypotheses concerning the molecular mechanisms of these plasticizations, and hence it is important that we be able to distinguish between them. This can only be done if complete creep curves are obtained.

The studies of Busse, and of Alexandrov and Lazurkin, exhibit much the same difficulty. They represent only a single timescale or, at most, only a small range in timescale and hence cannot be used to answer the questions just posed.

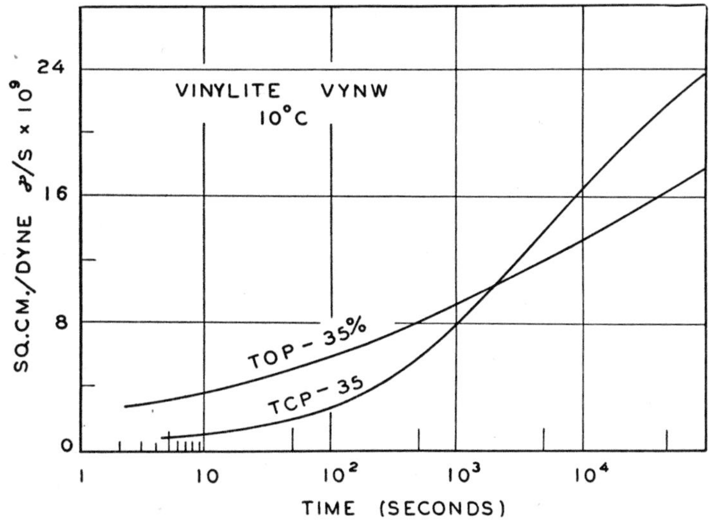

Fig. 189. Creep curves illustrating differences between tricresyl phosphate and trioctyl phosphate.

Such a study has been carried out recently by Aiken, Alfrey, Janssen, and Mark (7).* They report:

1. It was found that for small and moderate stresses the creep curves of plasticized vinyl films were directly proportional to the tensile stress used. The effect of using a larger stress is to multiply the strain at every time by a factor proportional to the stress. As a result of this simple variation with stress, it was found convenient to refer all creep curves to a unit stress, *i.e.*, plot strain *divided* by *stress*, rather than strain itself, against log time. When this is done, the creep curves at different (small) stresses become identical, within experimental error.

2. If all plasticizers gave creep curves of about the same shape, they would only differ in the *amount of displacement* of the creep curves along the log t axis. In this case, it

* For a more detailed discussion of viscoelastic properties of plasticized vinyl resins, see Aiken, Alfrey, Janssen, and Mark (*8*).

would be satisfactory to represent a creep curve by a single number, *e.g.*, the amount of creep after some single arbitrary time. Our experiments, however, indicate that different plasticizers impart different *shapes* to the creep curves. It appears, for example, that creep curves of films plasticized with trioctyl phosphate (TOP) are *flatter* than those of films plasticized with tricresyl phosphate (TCP).

In figure 189 the creep curves are shown for VYNW plasticized with 35% TCP and 35% TOP, at 10°C. The trioctyl phosphate sample stretches more in any given *short* period of time, *i.e.*, it is more "flexible" in a hand feel test or the Clash-Berg test. On the other hand, the tricresyl phosphate sample will deform more in response to stresses of extremely long duration. This indicates the possibility of increasing the short-time flexibility of a resin without increasing too much the long-time creep.

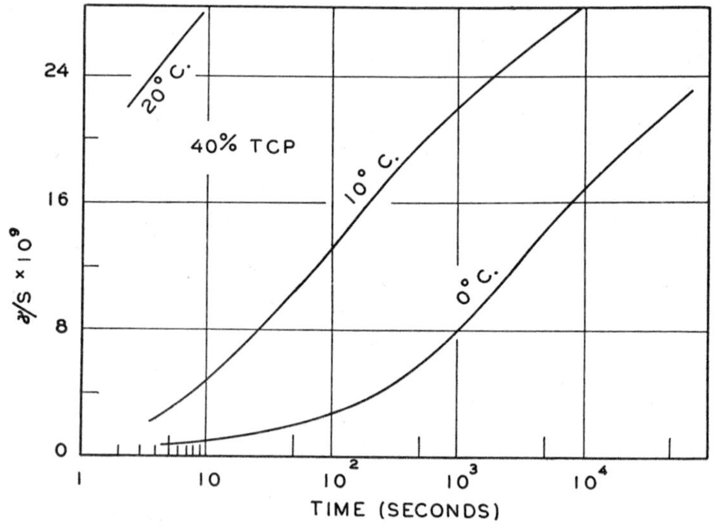

Fig. 190. Effect of temperature on creep behavior of Vinylite VYNW plasticized with 40% tricresyl phosphate.

Figure 190 shows a series of creep curves (at different temperatures) of samples plasticized with 40% TCP. Figure 191 shows a similar set of curves for samples plasticized with 40% TOP. It can be seen that at each temperature the TCP curves exhibit a low flat tail followed by a steep rise, whereas the TOP curves are relatively flat, although fairly high. The differences between TCP and TOP can perhaps be seen best when the creep curves are plotted against time, rather than against log t (figures 192 and 193). It is clear that a TOP sample has a larger *quick elastic response*, but that a TCP sample has a larger amount of *slow* creep response. When plotted together, as in figure 194, the TCP curve crosses two of the TOP curves, and after a somewhat longer period will cross the third. Thus in a quick test (*e.g.*, five seconds), the TCP sample at 10°C. is stiffer than the TOP sample at − 10°. If a longer time (*e.g.*, fifty seconds) is allowed to elapse, the creep of the TCP sample at 10°C. will be between that of the TOP sample at − 10° and 0°C. Finally, after a period of a few thousand seconds, the TCP sample will have deformed more than the TOP sample at the same temperature.

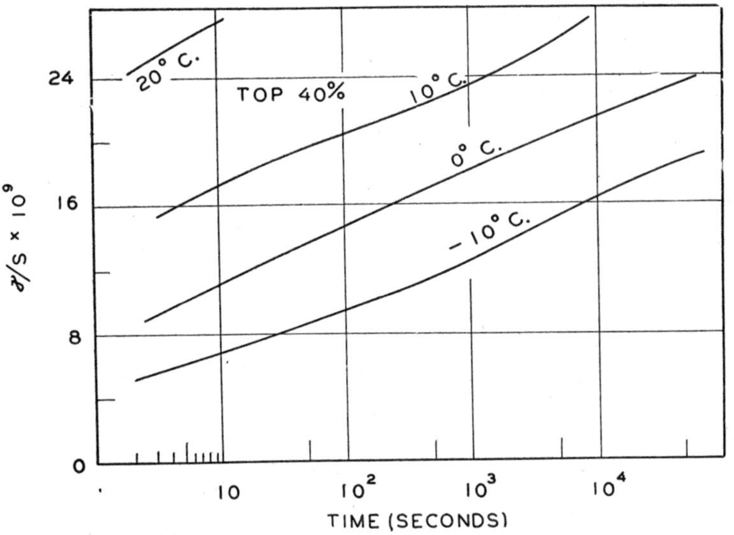

Fig. 191. Effect of temperature on creep behavior of Vinylite VYNW plasticized with 40% trioctyl phosphate.

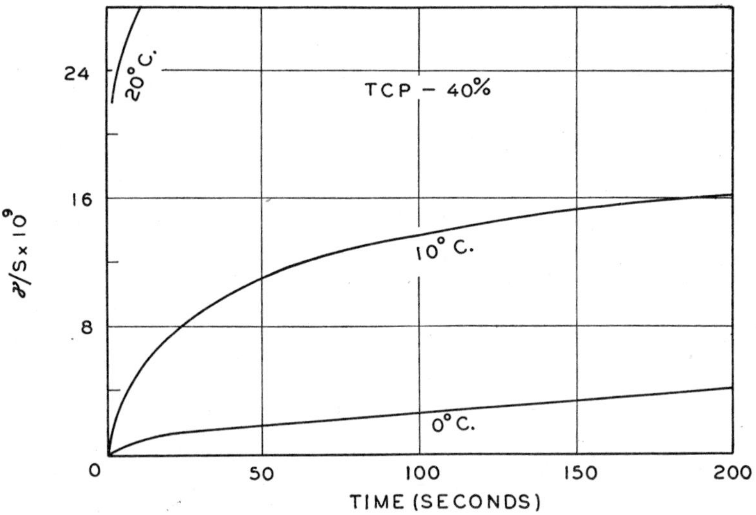

Fig. 192. Creep curves of Figure 190 plotted against time.

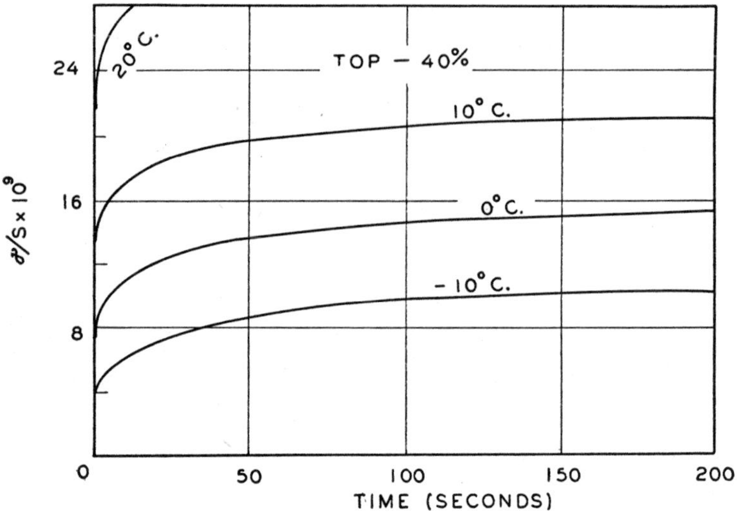

Fig. 193. Creep curves of Figure 191 plotted against time.

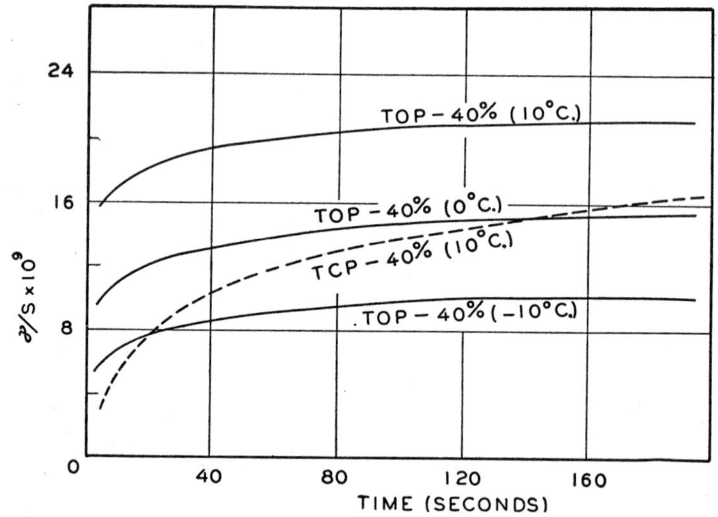

Fig. 194. Comparison of creep curves of tricresyl phosphate and trioctyl phosphate samples.

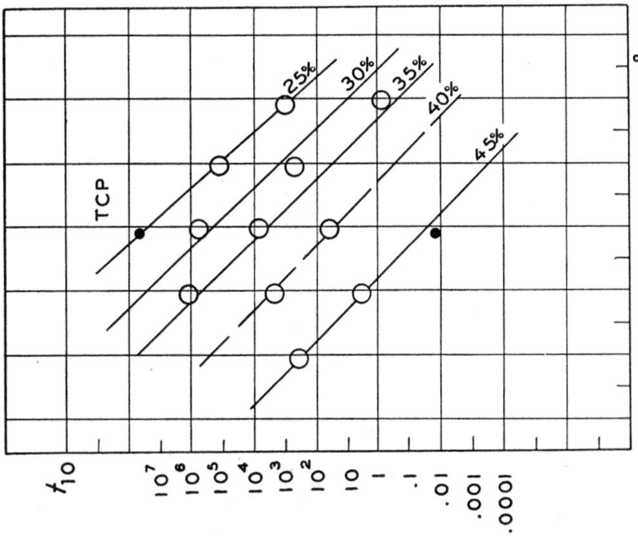

Fig. 195. Dependence of t_{10} on temperature and tricresyl phosphate concentration.

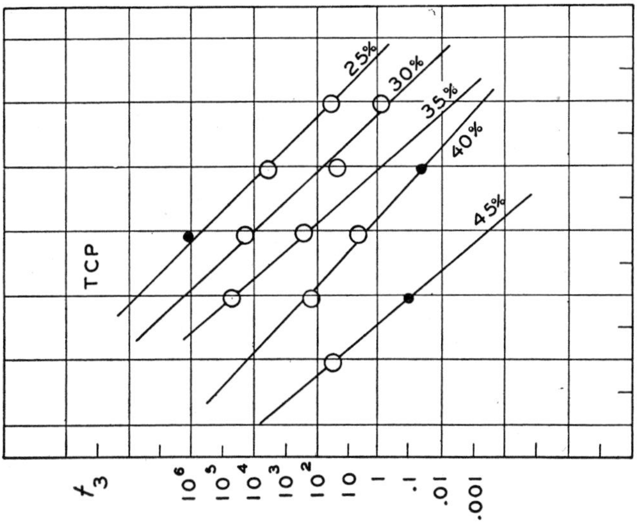

Fig. 196. Dependence of t_3 on temperature and tricresyl phosphate concentration.

The results of many such tests can be generalized as follows: At low temperatures and/or for stresses of short duration, TOP films are more flexible than TCP films of same plasticizer content. At high temperatures and/or for stresses of long duration samples plasticized with TCP creep more than those plasticized with TOP. DOP (dioctyl phosphate) is intermediate in character between TCP and TOP.

3. A creep curve can be partially represented by a single number in either of two ways: (*a*) The strain per unit stress which results in the course of a specified time (*e.g.*, five seconds) as by Clash and Berg. (*b*) The time required to reach a strain per unit stress of some specified amount.

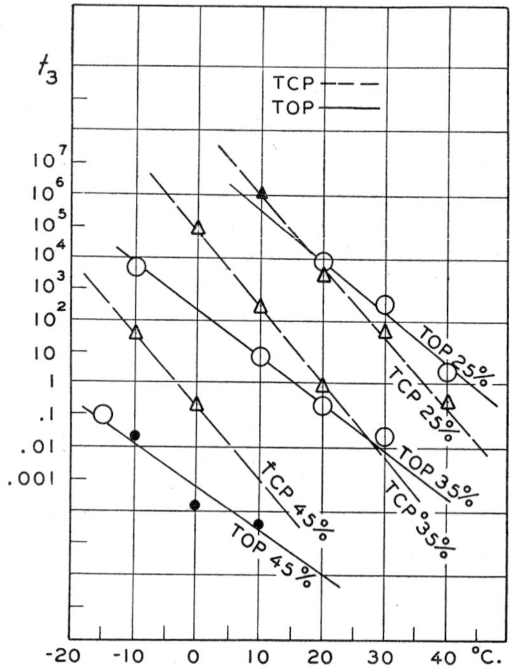

Fig. 197. Comparison of t_3 *vs.* temperature curves for tricresyl phosphate and trioctyl phosphate.

The latter type of condensation is sometimes very useful, with the following nomenclature. The symbol t_{10} will refer to the time required to reach a γ/S value of 10×10^{-9}; the symbol t_3 will refer to the time required to reach a γ/S value of 3×10^{-9}; etc. Figures 195 and 196 show how t_{10} and t_3 vary with temperature for samples plasticized with different amounts of TCP. In figure 197, t_3 *vs.* T curves are shown for TOP and TCP. It is seen that (using t_3 as a criterion of plasticization) TOP is more effective at low temperatures, and DOP more effective at high temperatures.

4. Mixtures of TCP and TOP have also been investigated. The general pattern of behavior is indicated in figure 198. The rapid response with a 50:50 TOP-TCP mixture lies between the high TOP curve and the low TCP curve. The slow response of the

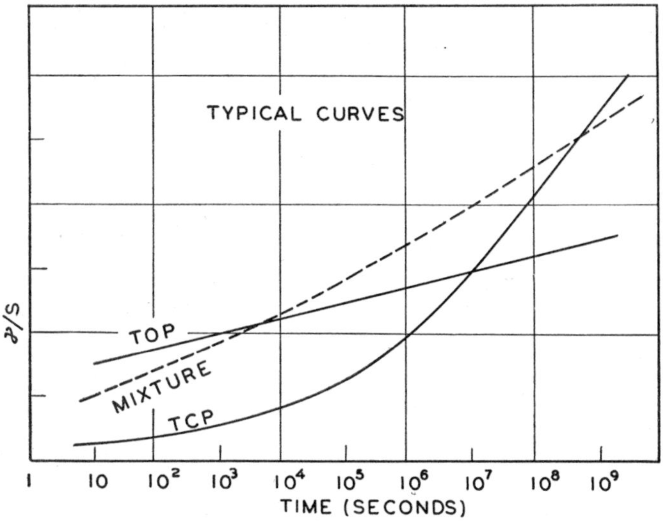

Fig. 198. Schematic representation of creep behavior of samples plasticized with mixtures of trioctyl phosphate and tricresyl phosphate.

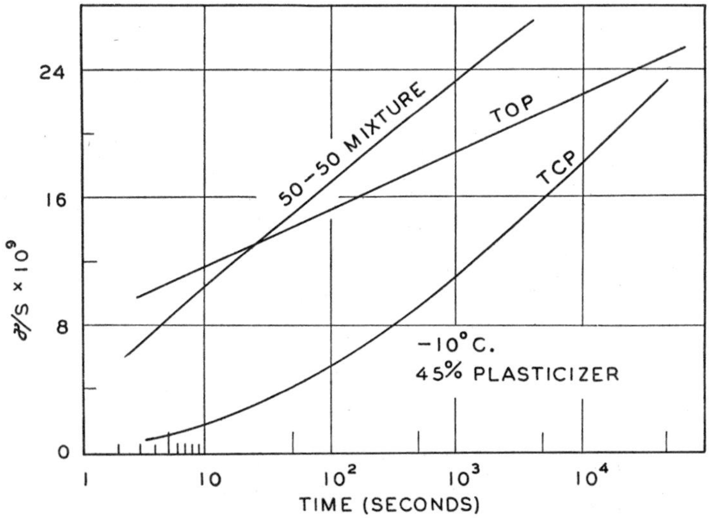

Fig. 199. Creep curves at -10°C. for Vinylite VYNW plasticized with 45% of tricresyl phosphate, trioctyl phosphate, and a 50–50 mixture.

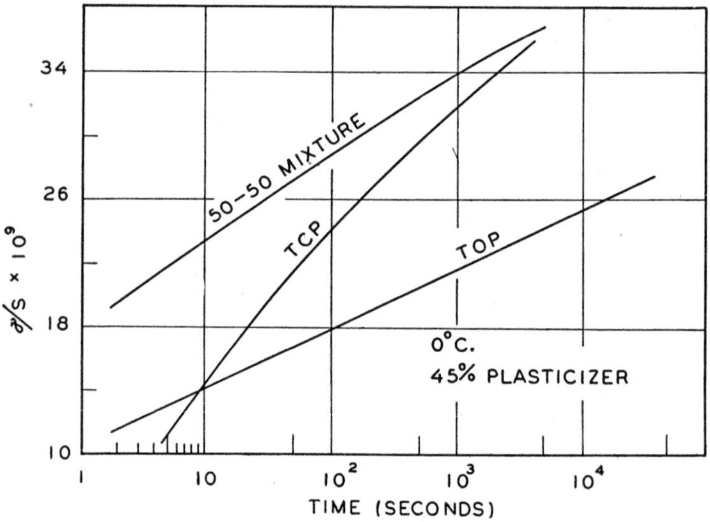

Fig. 200. Creep curves at 0°C. for Vinylite VYNW plasticized with 45% of tricresyl phosphate, trioctyl phosphate, and a 50–50 mixture.

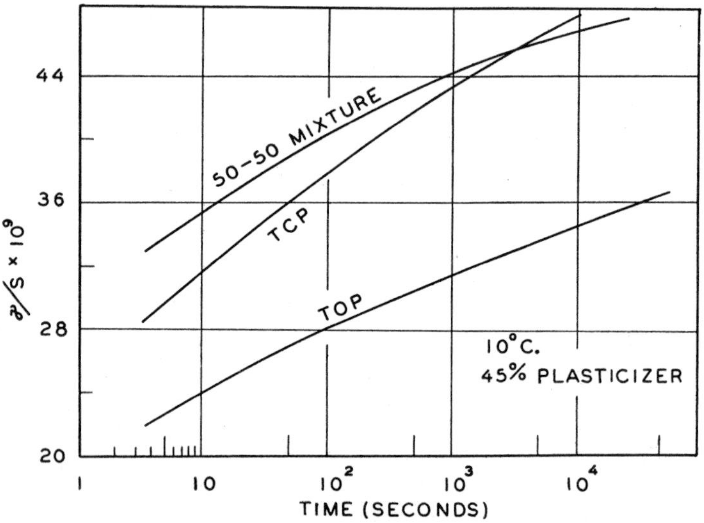

Fig. 201. Creep curves at 10°C. for Vinylite VYNW plasticized with 45% of tricresyl phosphate, trioctyl phosphate, and a 50–50 mixture.

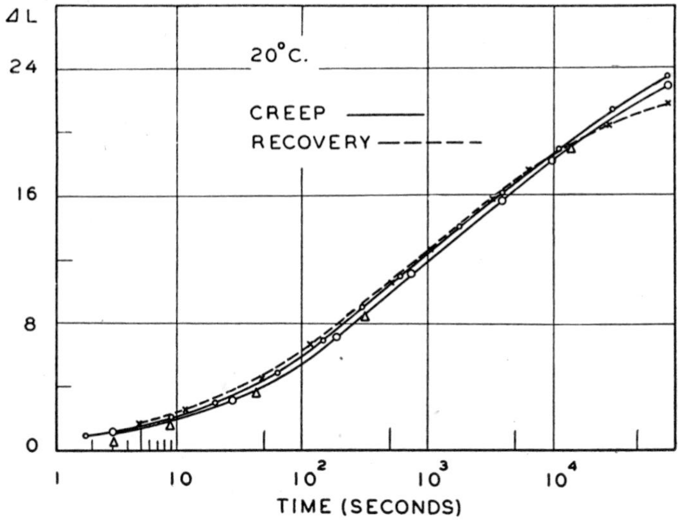

Fig. 202. Creep and creep recovery curves at 20°C. for Vinylite VYNW plasticized with 30% tricresyl phosphate.

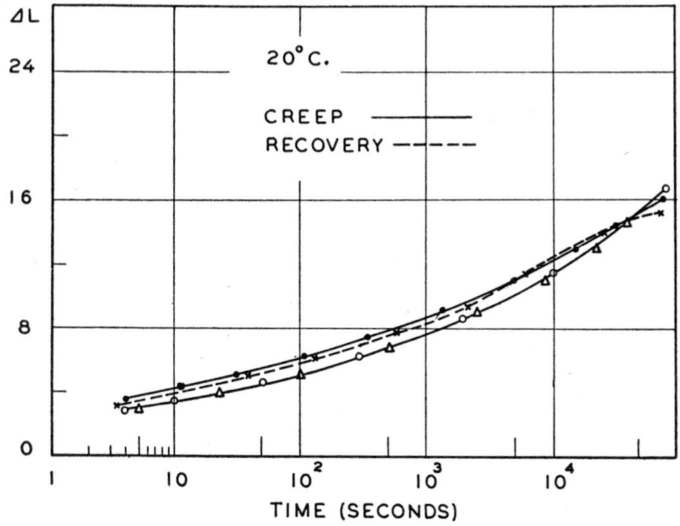

Fig. 203. Creep and creep recovery curves at 20°C. for Vinylite VYNW plasticized with 30% trioctyl phosphate.

mixture likewise lies between the high TOP and the low TCP curve. In between, there is a period of time during which the mixture gives a larger creep response than either pure plasticizer (see broken line of figure). At different temperatures different parts of these creep curves become dominant. Figures 199, 200, and 201 show experimental curves for three different temperatures.

5. The deformation which takes place during a creep test (under our conditions) is not flow, but rather retarded elastic deformation. This can be shown by studying the recovery as well as the creep behavior. It is found that if a sufficient time is allowed, essentially all of the elongation will recover. Furthermore, the *rate* of creep recovery closely parallels the rate of creep. If the creep curve is plotted as ΔL *vs.* log t, and the recovery curve as amount of recovery *vs.* log t, then theory predicts that the creep and recovery curves should be identical up to about the last decade of log t, after which the recovery curve should drop below the creep curve. Figure 202 shows two creep curves (solid lines) and two recovery curves (superimposed) for a sample plasticized with TCP. Figure 203 shows similar curves for a TOP sample. It is clear that within experimental error the recovery curve *can be predicted* from a knowledge of the creep curve. Thus a knowledge of creep behavior (for these materials) means also a knowledge of recovery behavior. This is an important means of simplifying the experimental investigation.

SUMMARY:

1. The "five-second stiffness" of a plasticized formulation gives an incomplete picture of its flexibility. A TOP sample and a TCP sample with the same five-second stiffness are actually quite different both in their very quick response and their long-time response to stresses. In a test lasting only 0.1 second, the TOP sample may be several times as flexible as the TCP; in a test of long duration, the TCP sample will creep more than the TOP. This indicates that increases in the quick flexibility of a resin are not necessarily accompanied by too much lowering of the long-time stiffness. It also indicates the desirability of carrying out complete creep (or relaxation) studies in the evaluation of a series of plasticizers.

2. The effects of temperature observed in this study are entirely consistent with those reported by Clash and Berg.

3. DOP seems to be intermediate in character between TCP and TOP. This is again in agreement with the results of Clash and Berg.

4. Mixtures of TCP and TOP show behavior which is "intermediate" between the behaviors of the individual plasticizers. In certain ranges of temperature and timescale, however, the mixture imparts greater flexibility to the film than either individual plasticizer.

5. In the range of stresses studied, the plasticized films obey the Boltzmann superposition principle; recovery curves are identical with creep curves.

Effect of Molecular Structure of the Plasticizer

Little can be said with absolute certainty of the effect of the molecular structure of plasticizer and its mechanical effects.

Kirkpatrick (*40*) points out the highly specific nature of plasticizer action. It can never be hoped to correlate the action of a plasticizer with its own molecular structure alone. This action depends upon the structures of both the plasticizer and the polymer with which it is incorporated. Kirkpatrick summarizes the structural characteristics which determine plasticizer action as follows:

(1) Presence in both plasticizer and plastic of groups that afford points of mutual attraction.

(2) Proper location of these groups in relation to each other so as to permit the attractive forces to function.

(3) Proper shape of the plasticizing molecules.

He explains, on the basis of fitting possibilities, the unique place of camphor among nitrocellulose plastics, and its lack of similar effect elsewhere.

Fuoss and co-workers (*28–32*) have made a thorough study of the effect of various plasticizers upon the dielectric relaxation times of polyvinyl chloride, and have correlated these effects with the purely mechanical effects of the plasticizers. Their conclusions are (*28*, XII):

. . . (2) Plasticization is essentially a separation of chain molecules by the plasticizer molecules, accompanied by a rapid decrease in microscopic and macroscopic coefficients of friction.

(3) A simple empirical relationship connecting loss factor and plasticizer concentration is given. Very roughly, the viscosity varies inversely as the third or fourth power of the relative concentration, depending on the temperature.

(4) The concentration at which a given plasticizer produces a given internal viscosity as measured by a characteristic electrical response, depends on the size and shape of the plasticizer molecule. A long cylindrical molecule is more effective in reducing viscosity than a spherical molecule of the same molecular weight.

(5) Plasticizers of about the same size and shape are about equally effective as plasticizers, regardless of their chemical structure. For polyvinyl chloride, however, a polar or polarizable group must be present in the plasticizer in order for it to interact with the polymer.

Aiken, Alfrey, Jannsen, and Mark (*7*) have studied a large number of plasticizers in Vinylite VYNW, using the creep test discussed. Some typical creep curves are shown in figure 204. Presence of cyclic groups seems to lead to *steep* creep curves of the TCP type. Thus tricresyl phosphate, dibenzyl sebacate, and tetrahydrofurfuryl sebacate all give steep creep curves, as compared with trioctyl phosphate, dioctyl sebacate, etc.

These conclusions emphasize the importance of geometric considerations in determining the effectiveness of a given plasticizer with a given polymer. The greater softening action of long, cylindrical plasticizer molecules than of spherical molecules of the same molecular weight reminds one of the similar effect in the case of chemically bonded side chains in the acrylate and methacrylate series.

On the basis of our present knowledge, it is impossible to *predict* whether the optimum plasticizer shapes for one polymer will also be best for use in another polymer (where the packing requirements may be different). Experimentally, however, this seems to be the case among the various vinyl chloride polymers. Aiken *et al.* also studied a series of Vinylites plasticized with the same concentration of TCP and TOP.

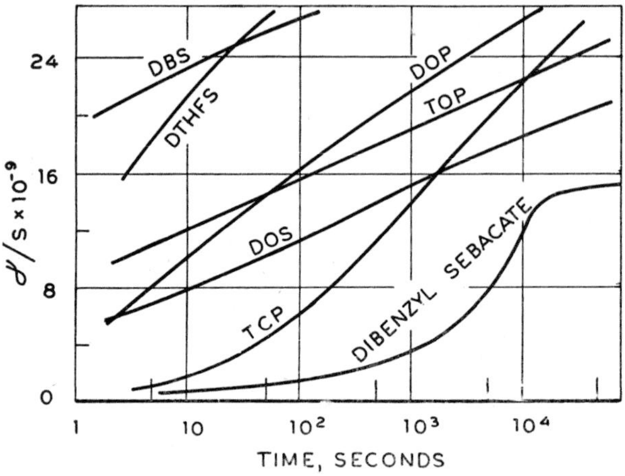

Fig. 204. Comparison at $-10°C.$ of a series of plasticizers (45% concentration) in Vinylite VYNW.

At room temperature, the various Vinylites differed markedly in their creep response (see Fig. 205). The amount of creep (softness) increased with decreasing molecular weight and decreasing vinyl chloride content (increasing vinyl acetate content). The differences between TCP and TOP, previously discussed in the case of VYNW, also appear in the other resins, as shown in figure 206.

Fuoss and co-workers also found that a smaller *weight* concentration of a low molecular weight plasticizer than of a plasticizer of higher molecular weight is required to produce a given reduction in viscosity. They obtained a fairly good linear relation between plasticizer action (amount of plasticizer for a given effect) and molecular weight. Two plasticizers, dibenzyl sebacate and dioctyl phthalate, deviate markedly from this relation. If the former is computed on the basis of one-half of its molecular weight, it conforms to the general pattern. In other words, one molecule

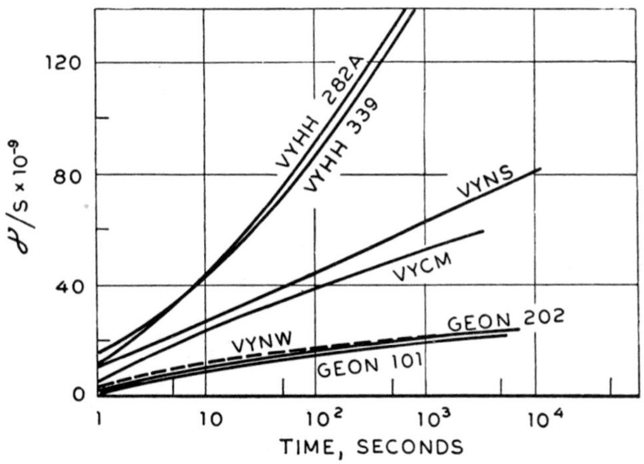

Fig. 205. Creep curves for various vinyl chloride type resins plasticized with 30% tricresyl phosphate at 30°C.

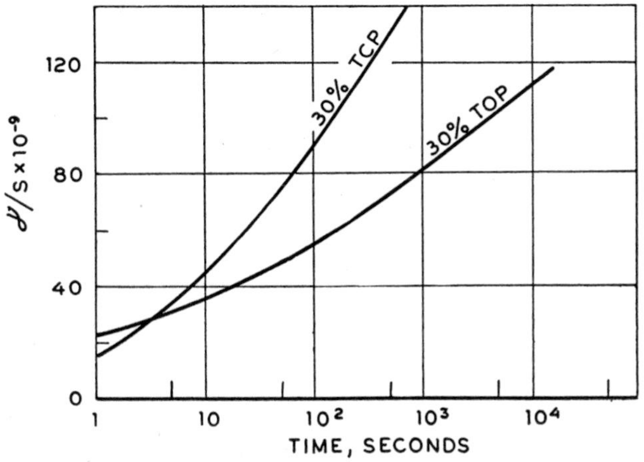

Fig. 206. Comparison of tricresyl phosphate and trioctyl phosphate in Vinylite VYHH 339 at 30°C.

of $C_6H_5CH_2CO_2(CH_2)_8CO_2CH_2C_6H_5$ acts like two independent molecules of plasticizer, because of the long, flexible, nonpolar methylene chain between the two polar ends. Dioctyl phthalate, which did not fit into the relation at all, is very different in structure from the other compounds of the group. Any simple empirical relation between molecular weight and plasticizer action can only be expected to hold within a series of plasticizers whose structures are fairly similar.

IV. DILUTE POLYMER SOLUTIONS

Dilute solutions of high polymers in low molecular weight solvents represent a limiting case of the mechanical properties just discussed. Such solutions exhibit elastic as well as viscous effects. At extreme dilution, of course, the elastic character becomes less and less important compared with the viscous character. It was pointed out in Chapter B that in such a case the elastic response is noticeable only while the stress is changing. If the stress on a volume element is constant, only the steady-state flow is observed. Thus the conditions for which the elastic aspects of the flow of dilute polymer solutions can be neglected are similar to the conditions for which the *inertial* aspects can be ignored.

The passage of a dilute polymer solution through a capillary tube of proper dimensions, for example, can be analyzed in terms only of flow. This does not mean that a volume element in such a flowing solution is not elastically deformed. It does mean that the elastic deformation is not changing. It has reached a steady-state value (which depends upon the stress), and all *motion* is due to true flow. The steady-state elastic deformation of the polymer molecules can, however, be directly observed during such a flow process, through the optical double refraction which it causes. The polymer molecules are uncurled and oriented by the flow, and therefore the flowing solution is optically anisotropic. The steady-state uncurling and orientation of the polymer molecules also reflects itself in the nonlinear character of the relationship between shear stress and steady-state rate of flow, *i.e.*, in the non-Newtonian character of the steady-state flow. When the long polymer molecules are elongated and oriented in the direction of flow, the resistance which they impart to the motion of the solvent is reduced; hence the over-all viscosity of the solution is lowered.

At this point a rather fine distinction should be drawn between a viscosity which is fundamentally a nonlinear function of the stress, and a viscosity which *depends upon the value of an elastic strain.* It seems likely to the author that the non-Newtonian character of high polymer solutions in steady-state flow is almost entirely due to this latter, indirect effect. From hydrodynamic considerations it seems likely that *for a given distribution of polymer molecules among the various molecular configurations*, (*i.e.*, for a given set of values of the configurational elastic strains), the dissolved molecules create a definite geometric interference with the motion of the solvent. Hence, if the solvent itself is a Newtonian liquid, the solution, with the polymer molecules in a definite distribution of shapes, also is a Newtonian liquid, with a viscosity coefficient somewhat increased over that of the solvent. With a different distribution among polymer configurations, a different geometric interference and, hence, a different solution viscosity result. The flow which takes place in an infinitesimal element of time, *dt*, when the shear stress S is acting, is given by:

$$d\gamma_3 = (1/\eta)S\,dt \tag{1}$$

Here η is a function of the instantaneous distribution among polymer configurations (or in simple terms, of γ_2), but η is *not* a function of the instantaneous *stress*. However, if only steady-state flow is considered, γ_2 always is defined by the stress. Thus the stress indirectly determines the *viscosity in the steady state*. We can ignore completely the elastic deformation γ_2, and simply say that the steady-state rate of flow is a nonlinear function of the stress. The two points of view differ only with reference to the transient phenomena leading up to the steady state of flow. If a high polymer solution were a simple non-Newtonian fluid, then it would begin to flow at the steady-state rate as soon as a shear stress is imposed. (The only delay in establishing the steady state would be that due to the *inertia*.) On the other hand, if the primary effect involved is a dependency of flow rate on γ_2, rather than a fundamental nonlinearity with stress, then in the first instant after the imposition of a stress, the polymer molecules would still be curled and unoriented. The true flow would therefore be somewhat slower than the steady-state value until the process of uncurling and orientation could be completed. This does not necessarily mean that the *total* rate of shear would be less than the steady-state value during this time; during this transient period the change of γ_2 with time provides an additional rate-of-shear term. If the contribution of the configurational elastic change, $d\gamma_2/dt$, to the velocity gradient, is subtracted from the total velocity gradient, the part due to true flow should rise from a finite initial value to the limiting steady-state value.

It has already been pointed out that in many cases only the steady state of flow is significant. These cases are of such great practical importance that almost all studies of the mechanical properties of dilute polymer solutions have been confined to the problem of the steady-state flow curve. The work of Ferry (*24*) represents one of the exceptions. In fact, a very great number of investigations, both theoretical and experimental, have been confined to an even narrower field—the *initial slope* of the steady-state flow curve (*i.e.*, the *viscosities* of polymer solutions at low rates of shear). This problem has already been discussed at some length in Volume II of this series (*4a*). Furthermore, a later volume will deal specifically with the viscous properties of high polymer solutions. However, the viscosities of high polymer solutions provide such an important tool in structural investigations that it is impossible to omit the subject completely. For this reason, the following brief summary of the problem is included.

1. The Staudinger Equation

Staudinger proposed that the viscosity of a high polymer solution should be governed by the expression:

$$\frac{\eta_{\text{solution}} - \eta_{\text{solvent}}}{\eta_{\text{solvent}}} = \eta_{\text{sp}} = \text{KC}M \qquad (2)$$

where M = molecular weight, C = polymer concentration in base moles* per liter, and K is a constant characteristic of a given species of high polymer. The following assumptions are contained, either explicitly or implicitly, in equation (2):

(*a*) A high polymer solution is assumed to be a Newtonian fluid. The solution viscosity is represented as independent of the shear stress.

(*b*) The specific viscosity of a polymer solution is assumed to be directly proportional to the polymer concentration in base moles per liter.

(*c*) The specific viscosity is assumed to be directly proportional to the molecular weight of the polymer.

(*d*) In the form stated above, the specific viscosity is assumed to be independent of the solvent employed and independent of the temperature.

It will be shown that none of these assumptions are unreservedly correct, although some are justified as limiting relationships. Before considering the validity of these four important assumptions, however, a few paragraphs must be devoted to the problem of explaining, theoretically, how the Staudinger equation can be even approximately valid. Staudinger advanced a quasitheoretical justification of equation (2). This early attempt need not be repeated here, since it was based upon the assumption that polymer molecules in solution are rigid, elongated structures, which is in general incorrect, and upon an incorrect hydrodynamic

* The "base molar" concentration of a high polymer is the number of moles of monomeric segments per liter of solution, *i.e.*, the number of moles of polymer per liter divided by the number average degree of polymerization.

treatment. A more fruitful line of development is that begun by Einstein and extended by Jeffery, Eisenschitz, Guth, Simha, Huggins, Flory, and others.

Einstein treated the following problem. A simple Newtonian liquid of viscosity η has suspended in it a number of rigid spherical particles. When the suspension as a whole is subjected to a shear stress, it flows in what appears to be a simple fashion. Observed on a finer scale, the flow of the viscous liquid itself in the neighborhood of a suspended particle is not homogeneous. The liquid must flow around the particle. Thus the local rate of shear of the liquid itself varies from point to point, and the average value is greater than the over-all rate of shear of the suspension as a whole. The result is that the over-all viscosity of the suspension is greater than the viscosity of the suspending liquid. Einstein considered the case of a suspension so dilute that there was no appreciable hydrodynamic interaction between different particles. He considered the solvent to be a continuum and applied the ordinary laws of hydrodynamics to its flow. This treatment leads to the conclusion that a dilute suspension of spherical particles exhibits a specific viscosity η_{sp} which depends only upon the volume concentration of suspended matter and is equal to 2.5 times the volume concentration. (The specific viscosity of a solution or suspension is defined as $(\eta - \eta_{solv})/\eta_{solv}$. This is equivalent to $1 - \eta_{rel}$, where the relative viscosity is defined as η/η_{solv}.) Thus the *relative increase* in the viscosity of the solvent due to the suspended particles does not depend upon the original solvent viscosity, or upon the sizes of the individual suspended particles, but only on the total volume concentration of the latter. The specific viscosities calculated on the basis of Einstein's equation are much smaller than those observed in polymer solutions. This is because the dissolved polymer molecules are not solid spheres.

The first theoretical attempt to extend the treatment of Einstein to nonspherical particles was made by Jeffery, who considered the case of ellipsoidal particles. Jeffery's calculations were supplemented and extended by a number of investigators. The result was a great number of relations between specific viscosity, concentration, and axial ratio according to the special assumptions and approximations made about the suspended particles and their behavior in the field of flow.

Kuhn (*43*) and Huggins (*37*) have approached the problem from a somewhat different point of view. They consider, not an ellipsoid, but a model which is perhaps a closer approximation to a high polymer molecule, namely, a long chain molecule, curled and twisted in solution.

TABLE XXIV *

DIFFERENT EXPRESSIONS FOR SPECIFIC VISCOSITY OF SOLUTIONS AND SUSPENSIONS

Type of suspension or solution		At extreme dilution			At moderate concentrations
		Without the influence of Brownian movement		With complete Brownian movement	Without Brownian movement
Rigid spheres		Einstein, Simha $2.5\,c$			Gold, Guth, Simha $2.5\,c + 14.1\,c^2$
Liquid (soft) spheres		Taylor rc, with r varying from 2.5 down to 1			—
Rigid rodlike particles	Minimum value	Jeffery $2.0\,c$	Guth, Huggins, Jeffery $2.0\,c$	Simha $\left[\frac{f^2}{15(\ln 2f - \frac{3}{2})} + \frac{f^2}{5(\ln 2f - \frac{1}{2})} + \frac{14}{15}\right] c$	—
	Maximum value	Jeffery $\left(\frac{f}{2 \ln 2f - 3} + 2\right) c$ Eisenschitz $\frac{1.15\,f}{11 \ln 2f}\,c$	Huggins, Kuhn $\left(2.5 + \frac{f^2}{16}\right) c$ Eisenschitz $\frac{f^2}{15 \ln 2f - \frac{4.5}{2}}\,c$		Gold, Guth $\left(\frac{f}{2 \ln 2f - 3} + 2\right) c + \frac{Kf^3}{(2 \ln 2f - 3)^2}\,c^2$
Rigid disks	Minimum value	Jeffery $2.06\,c$	Guth $\frac{5}{12}\frac{f}{\tan^{-1} f}\,c$	$\frac{16}{15}\frac{f}{\tan^{-1} f}\,c$	—
	Maximum value	Jeffery $\frac{4f}{3 \tan^{-1} f}\,c$	Guth, Jeffery $\left[\frac{4f}{3 \tan^{-1} f}\right]^2 c$		

* In this table, c denotes the volume concentration of the dispersed phase, f the axis ratio of the suspended particles and K a constant of the order of magnitude 1.

Huggins calculates that the intrinsic viscosity should depend on molecular weight as follows:

$$[\eta] = KM^{a} \tag{3}$$

where a varies from 0 for a tightly coiled sphere through 1 for a randomly kinked chain to 2 for a rigidly extended molecule.

2. Dependence of Viscosity on Concentration

A number of empirical equations have been advanced to represent the effect of concentration upon the viscosity of a dilute polymer solution. One very useful form is a simple power series:

$$\eta_{sp} = \alpha_0 + \alpha_1 c + \alpha_2 c^2 + \alpha_3 c^3 + \cdots \tag{4}$$

It is clear that α_0 must necessarily be equal to zero, since the specific viscosity of the pure solvent is zero.

$$\eta_{sp} = \alpha_1 c + \alpha_2 c^2 + \alpha_3 c^3 + \cdots \tag{5}$$

Staudinger's law holds only over the range of very low concentrations where the linear term predominates over all the rest. This turns out to be a very narrow range for polymers of high molecular weight. Over a much wider range, the first two terms of equation (5) are sufficient to give a good approximation, and all higher terms than the quadratic can safely be neglected. In this range, equation (5) reduces to:

$$\eta_{sp} = \alpha_1 c + \alpha_2 c^2 \tag{6}$$

If we divide through by c, we obtain:

$$\frac{\eta_{sp}}{c} = \alpha_1 + \alpha_2 c \tag{7}$$

Thus if η_{sp}/c is plotted against c, a straight line results. The slope of this line is α_2; the ordinate intercept is α_1. This intercept is often written as $[\eta]$, and referred to as the intrinsic viscosity. If a series of sharp fractions of a given chemical species of polymer are compared in this manner, a series of curves result. The *intercept* of each curve is some function of the molecular weight of the fraction—according to Staudinger, this function is a direct proportionality. In this section, however, we are concerned with the *slopes* of the curves. Huggins has predicted that the slope, α_2, of a given curve should be proportional to the *square* of the intercept:

$$\alpha_2 = k'\alpha_1^2 \tag{8}$$

The k′ in equation (8) is a constant which applies to a given chemical species of polymer in a given solvent. Once this constant is determined, a single viscosity determination will serve to define the whole early part of the η_{sp} curve:

$$\frac{\eta_{sp}}{c} = [\eta] + k'[\eta]^2 c \qquad (9)$$

This equation (9) has not been extensively tested, since it applies only to solutions of high polymer *fractions.* However, Mark reports that it is followed in the case of cellulose acetate and styrene fractions, and Fuoss and Meade report such a relation for polyvinyl chloride fractions. Huggins goes even further in his theoretical treatment, and connects the constant k′, which is characteristic of a given polymer solvent system, with a factor μ which plays an important part in the *thermodynamic* properties of the given system.

In the light of the above remarks, it may be of interest to review some of the better known empirical expressions connecting viscosity with concentration. This is particularly interesting if each is expanded as a power series which may then be compared with equation (9). The following expressions are taken from Mark (*4a*):

Arrhenius: [1]

$$\log \eta_r = kc \qquad (10)$$

In connection with this equation, see also Berl and Bütler,[2] Duclaux and Wollmann,[3] Bredée and de Booys.[4] Arrhenius: [5]

$$\log \eta_r = k \frac{100\ c}{100 - nc} \qquad (11)$$

Fikentscher: [6]

$$\log \eta_r = k + \frac{75\ k^2}{1 + 1.5\ kc} \qquad (12)$$

Papkov: [7]

$$\log \eta_r = kc^{\alpha} \qquad (13)$$

Houwink,[8] Bungenberg de Jong, Kruyt, and Lens: [9]

$$\log \eta_r = ac + bc^2 \qquad (14)$$

[1] S. Arrhenius, *Z. physik. Chem.*, **1**, 285 (1887).
[2] E. Berl and R. Bütler, *Z. ges. Schiess- u. Sprengstoffw.*, **5**, 82 (1910).
[3] J. Duclaux and R. Wollmann, *Compt. rend.*, **152**, 1580 (1911).
[4] H. L. Bredée and J. de Booys, *Kolloid Z.*, **79**, 31, 43 (1937).
[5] S. Arrhenius, *Medd. K. Vetenskapsakad. Nobelinst.*, **4**, 13 (1916).
[6] H. Fikentscher, *Cellulosechem.*, **13**, 58 (1932).
[7] S. Papkov, *Kunststoffe*, **25**, 253 (1935).
[8] R. Houwink, *Kolloid Z.*, **79**, 138 (1937).
[9] H. G. Bungenberg de Jong, H. R. Kruyt, and W. Lens, *Kolloid-Beihefte*, **36**, 429 (1932).

Fikentscher and Mark:[10]

$$\eta_{sp} = k\frac{bc}{1 - bc} \tag{15}$$

Sakurada,[11] Baker and Mardles:[12]

$$\eta_r = (1 + ac)^n \tag{16}$$

Bredée and de Booys:[4]

$$\eta_r = \left(1 + \frac{2.5\,b}{6}\,c\right)^6 \tag{17}$$

These equations were tested over the whole known concentration range on numerous sols of synthetic and natural high polymers, particularly on synthetic resin suspensions, such as polystyrenes, polyethylene oxides on proteins, gum arabic, cellulose, cellulose esters, rubber, and others. In general, it was found that equations with one and two constants prove capable of expressing the viscosity–concentration function, by suitable choice of constants (see further below). In many cases it is astonishing how great a concentration range can be covered by using a single constant; with two or more constants, particularly if they are in the exponent, the fit is so close that it is possible to express approximately the most diverse functions of concentration.

The best way to reach a basis for comparing all these equations seems to be the one adopted by Bredée and de Booys. This consists of expanding η_{sp} in a power series of the volume concentration c and obtaining

$$\eta_{sp} = Ac + Bc^2 + Cc^3 + \cdots \tag{18}$$

As in the case of osmotic pressure, all terms in higher powers than one can be neglected at very low concentrations and the first coefficient of this expansion, A, allows an approximate estimation of the size and shape of the particles under certain favorable conditions (compare the relations in table XXIV on page 458). . .

In order to show to what extent the various equations cited above differ, some of them are here expanded into series and compared:

$$\eta_{sp} = 2.30\ kc + \frac{2.30^2}{2}\,k^2c^2 + \cdots \tag{10'}$$

The second coefficient B corresponds to $(2.30^2/2)\ k^2$.

$$\eta_{sp} = \frac{2.30}{4}\,(3\ k^2 + 4\ k)c + \text{higher terms} \tag{12'}$$

B corresponds to a complicated function of k.

$$\eta_{sp} = kbc + \frac{kb^2}{2}\,c^2 + \cdots \tag{15'}$$

B corresponds to kb^2 where b is the co-volume.

$$\eta_{sp} = 2.5\,bc + \frac{15 \times 2.5}{6^2}\,b^2c^2 + \cdots \tag{17'}$$

A corresponds to a term similar to the Einstein term; B corresponds to the square of b, which denotes the co-volume.

[10] H. Fikentscher and H. Mark, *Kolloid Z.*, **49**, 135 (1930).
[11] I. Sakurada, *Z. physik. Chem.*, **B38**, 407 (1938).
[12] F. Baker and E. W. J. Mardles, *Trans. Chem. Soc.*, **103**, 1655 (1913); *Trans. Faraday Soc.*, **18**, 3 (1923).

3. Dependence of Viscosity on Molecular Weight

According to Staudinger, the limiting intrinsic viscosity, α_1, is directly proportional to molecular weight. The question as to how precisely this is true has been vigorously debated for many years and has been satisfactorily settled only very recently. Out of a myriad of experiments and discussions only a few papers are discussed which seem to the author to be particularly significant. One of the most important criteria for this choice lies in the degree of molecular weight homogeneity attained. Mark has repeatedly emphasized that a meaningful test of equation (2) requires the use of sharp molecular weight fractions, rather than of a polydisperse material. The importance of this requirement is made clear in a later paragraph (pages 493 *et seq.*).

In 1939, Fordyce and co-workers (*26, 27*) showed that the simple relation (Eq. 2), was not correct in the low molecular weight range. They prepared members of the polyoxyethylene glycol series, having uniform molecular weights, up to values around 8000 and determined with great care the specific viscosities of these substances in two solvents at three different temperatures.

If one plots the specific viscosity divided by c (intrinsic viscosity) against the molecular weight, one obtains a straight line within the molecular weight range 810 to 8200. See figure 207. Below this there is a sharp departure from linearity. Fordyce and Hibbert conclude from their experiments that the Staudinger equation is valid for high molecular weights but that it has to be replaced by:

$$[\eta] = \eta_{sp}/c = K'_m M + \beta \tag{19}$$

as soon as lower members of a given polymeric homologous series are involved. This was a most important contribution. However, a molecular weight of 8000 is relatively low, and the validity of a linear relation in the higher molecular weight range was still open.

Recently Flory has presented viscosity and osmotic pressure data on fractions of polyisobutylene ranging in molecular weight from 10^4 to 10^6. He reports that, if the log of the limiting intrinsic viscosity, $[\eta]$, is plotted against the log of the molecular weight, a straight line results whose slope is equal to 0.64, rather than 1. This means that the limiting intrinsic viscosity, $[\eta]$, is accurately given by an expression of the form:

$$[\eta] = KM^{0.64} \tag{20}$$

Furthermore, Bartovics and Mark (*13*) have reported that the limiting intrinsic viscosities of cellulose acetate fractions are given by:

$$[\eta] = KM^{0.78} \tag{21}$$

and those of polystyrene of a definite type by:

$$[\eta] = KM^{0.71} \tag{22}$$

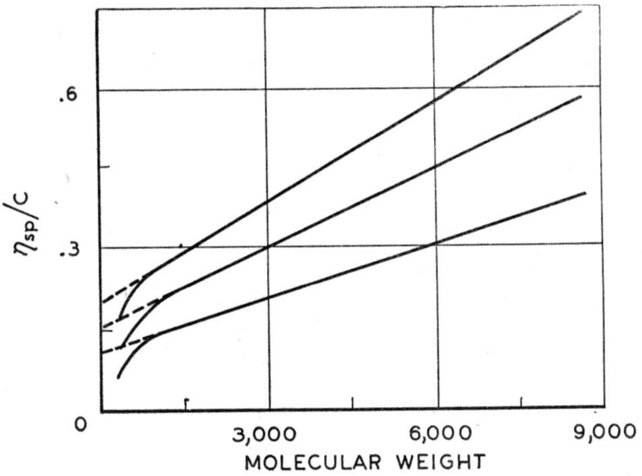

Fig. 207. Effect of molecular weight on intrinsic viscosity in polyesters (after Fordyce and Hibbert).

In the light of these investigators it seems clear that the Staudinger relation must give way to a more precise expression:

$$[\eta] = KM^{a} \tag{23}$$

where K and a are constants for any given polymer solvent system. See table XXV (*33a*) for some values of K and a.

Combining equations (23) and (9), we obtain:

$$\eta_{sp}/c = KM^{a} + k'(KM^{a})^2 c \tag{24}$$

This equation gives the relation between viscosity, molecular weight, and concentration, and has been found to hold in the case of cellulose acetate and polystyrene.

The substitution of equation (23) for (2) gives rise to a rather complex question of averaging when solutions of polydisperse polymers are involved. If Staudinger's law applied, the situation would be simple. The molecular weight computed for a polydisperse polymer on the basis of the Staudinger equation would be the *weight average* molecular weight.

TABLE XXV

VALUES FOR K AND a FOR SOME HIGH POLYMER SOLUTIONS [a]

Polymer	Viscosities in	Viscosities at °C.	k′	K ×10⁴	a	Mol. wt. range ×10⁻⁵	Remarks*
Cellulose	Cuprammonium oxide[a]	25	—	0.85	0.81		
Cellulose acetate	Acetone[b]	25	—	0.19	1.03	0.11–1.30	O,F,14
	Acetone[c]	30	0.70	9.1	0.78	0.25–1.26	O,F,5
	Acetone[d]	25		1.49	0.82	0.31–3.90	O,F,8
Cellulose acetate-butyrate	Acetone[e]	25	—	1.37	0.83	0.12–2.1	O,F,11
	Acetic acid[e]	25	—	1.46	0.83	0.12–2.1	O,F,11
	Pyridine[e]	25	—	1.33	0.83	0.12–2.1	O,F,11
Amylose	Ethylenediamine[f]	—	—	—	1.5	0.08–0.9	O,U,5
Amylose acetate	Chloroform[f]	—	—	—	1.5	0.45–0.9	O,U,3
Pectinic acid	0.155 *M* NaCl soln.[g]	25	0.41	0.014	1.34	—	Approx.
Pectin nitrate	Acetone[h]	30.5	—	5.9	1.0	—	O,F; approx.
Polyisobutylene	Diisobutylene[i]	20	—	3.60	0.64	0.056–13	O,F,23; from 4 samples
Polyisoprene	Toluene[j]	—	—	5.02	0.67	0.40–15	O,F,22; Hevea rubber
GRS copolymer butadiene and styrene	Toluene[k]	25	—	4.4	0.67		

* O = osmotic determination of molecular weight. E = end group determination of molecular weight. F = fractionated samples. U = unfractionated samples. a = bulk polymerized at 60°. b = bulk polymerized at 120°. c = bulk polymerized at 180°. Numeral = number of samples.

[a] N. Gralén and The Svedberg, *Nature*, **152**, 625 (1943).

[b] A. M. Sookne and M. Harris, *Ind. Eng. Chem.*, **37**, 475 (1945).

[c] A. Bartovics and H. Mark, *J. Am. Chem. Soc.*, **65**, 1901 (1943).

[d] W. J. Badgley, *Polymer Bull.*, **1**, 17 (1945).

[e] J. W. Tamblyn, D. R. Morey, and R. H. Wagner, *Ind. Eng. Chem.*, **37**, 573 (1945).

[f] J. F. Foster and R. M. Hixon, *J. Am. Chem. Soc.*, **66**, 557 (1944).

[g] H. S. Owens, H. Lotzkar, T. H. Schultz, and W. D. Maclay, *J. Am. Chem. Soc.*, **68**, 1628 (1946).

[h] R. Speiser and C. R. Eddy, *J. Am. Chem. Soc.*, **68**, 287 (1946). See also G. Schneider and U. Fritschi, *Ber.*, **B69**, 2537 (1936).

[i] P. J. Flory, *J. Am. Chem. Soc.*, **65**, 3172 (1943).

[j] W. C. Carter, R. L. Scott, and M. Magat, *J. Am. Chem. Soc.*, **68**, 1480 (1946).

[k] Unpublished measurements in progress at Polytechnic Institute of Brooklyn, Brooklyn, New York.

TABLE XXV—*continued*

Polymer	Viscosities in	at °C.	k'	$K \times 10^4$	*a*	Mol. wt. range $\times 10^{-5}$	Remarks*
Polystyrene	Toluene[l]	—	0.42	1.28	0.70	5.5–20.5	O,F,4[a]
	Toluene[l]	—	0.33	0.55	0.80	1.1–3.4	O,F,4[b]
	Toluene[l]	—	0.21	0.01	1.12	1.1–1.7	O,F,4[c]
	Toluene[m]	30	0.38	3.7	0.62	2.0–18	O,F,6
	Butanone[m]	40	0.54	7.0	0.53	2.0–18	O,F,6
Methyl methacrylate	Benzene[n]	25	—	0.76	0.76	0.58–9.8	O,F,12
	Chloroform[n]	20	—	0.49	0.82	0.56–9.8	O,F,12
	Chloroform[o]	20	—	0.33	0.85	0.5–10	O,F,18; from 7 samples
Polyvinyl acetate	Acetone[p]	—	0.33	—	0.83	0.61–8.5	O,U,5
	Bis(2-chloro-ethyl) ether[p]	—	0.36	2	0.63	0.61–8.5	O,U,5
	Acetone[q]	50	—	2.8	0.67	0.77–8.5	O,?,12
Polyvinyl alcohol	Water[q]	50	—	5.9	0.67	0.44–1.1	0,?,6
Poly-ε-amino caprolactam	H_2SO_4 (concd.)[r]	—	—	12	0.67	0.004–0.05	E,U,12
	H_2SO_4 (40%)[r]	—	—	24	0.51	0.004–0.05	E,U,12
(ω) Hydroxy-undeconic acid polymer	Chloroform[s]	25	0.40	0.32	1.0	0.002–0.126	E,U,7

[l] T. Alfrey, A. Bartovics, and H. Mark, *J. Am. Chem. Soc.*, **65**, 2519 (1943).
[m] A. I. Goldberg, W. P. Hohenstein, and H. Mark, *J. Polymer Sci.*, **2**, 503 (1947).
[n] J. H. Baxendale, S. Bywater, and M. G. Evans, *J. Polymer Sci.*, **1**, 237 (1946).
[o] G. V. Schulz and A. Dinglinger, *J. prakt. Chem.*, **157**, 15 (1940).
[p] R. E. Robertson, R. McIntosh, and W. E. Grummitt, *Can. J. Research*, **B24**, 192 (1946).
[q] H. Staudinger and K. Warth, *J. prakt. Chem.*, **155**, 261 (1940).
[r] H. Matthes, *J. prakt. Chem.*, **162**, 245 (1943).
[s] W. O. Baker, C. S. Fuller, and J. H. Heiss, *J. Am. Chem. Soc.*, **63**, 3316 (1941).

However, if equation (23) holds, and is used to determine the molecular weight of a polydisperse polymer, the molecular weight so obtained is intermediate between the number average and the weight average molecular weight. Specifically, it is given by:

$$\bar{M} = \left[\frac{\int_0^\infty M^a \, D(M) \, dM}{\int_0^\infty D(M) \, dM} \right]^{1/a} \tag{25}$$

where D(M) dM is the *weight fraction* of polymer in the molecular weight range M, $M + dM$.

Flory suggests calling this a "viscosity average" molecular weight. Finally, if equation (23) actually governs the viscosity, but the Staudinger equation is used to determine the molecular weight, the value obtained has no absolute meaning at all, and can serve only as an empirical value.

Mark (*4*) has predicted on theoretical grounds that the intrinsic viscosity of a high polymer solution should depend on molecular weight according to a relation of the form:

$$[\eta] = KM^{\alpha} \qquad (26)$$

According to a more elaborate treatment by Huggins (*37*), the exponential factor α should be intimately connected with the general form of the molecule in solution. If the polymer molecule in solution is coiled tightly into a spherical form, the constant α should have the value zero. This is obvious, since this special case is that previously treated in a rigorous fashion by Einstein. If the molecule is rigidly extended in the form of a rod, α should be equal to 2. This represents the extreme form from which Staudinger incorrectly deduced the value $\alpha = 1$. Finally, according to Huggins, if the polymer molecule is *extended at random*, α should have the value 1, as in the Staudinger equation. Intermediate degrees of curling should result in intermediate values of α. Huggins has used this treatment to explain the variation of intrinsic viscosity caused by a change in solvent. (For a given polymer molecule, the mean molecular extension in solution and hence α, is different in different solvents.)

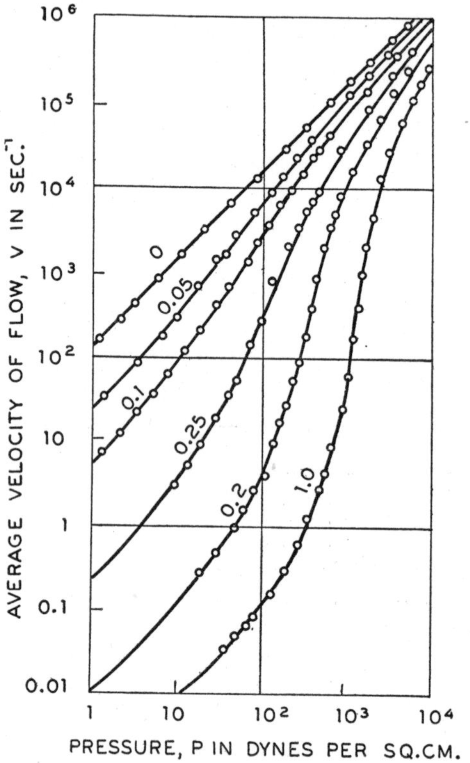

Fig. 208. Flow curves for various concentrations of cellulose trinitrate (13.7% N) in butyl acetate (after Philippoff and Hess).

4. Dependence of Viscosity on Rate of Shear

It was indicated in an earlier paragraph that the steady-state flow of a high polymer solution is not a linear function of the shear stress. Therefore a single viscosity coefficient does not serve to define the flow properties over a wide range of stress and rate of shear. Instead, the flow curve should be known explicitly. The flow curves of dilute polymer solutions are of the general form of figure 208 (page 466). Such a curve offers a striking contrast to the typical Bingham type of flow curve, discussed in Chapter B. A material exhibiting Bingham flow approximates

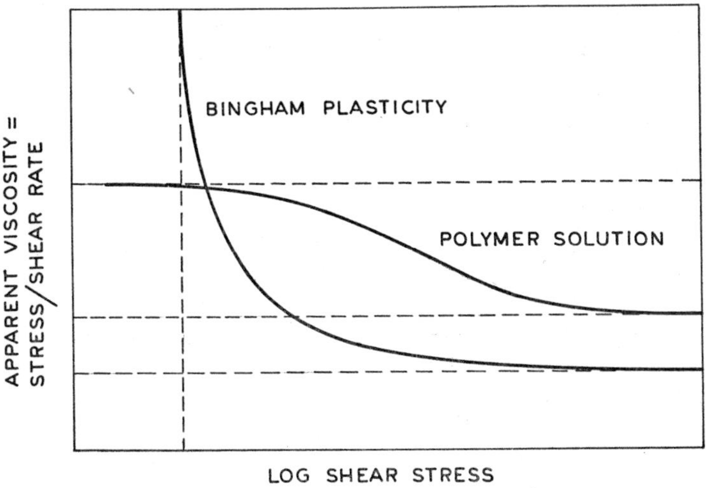

Fig. 209. Variation of apparent viscosity with shear stress (schematic).

Newtonian flow at *high* rate of shear and deviates most strongly at low rates of shear. A high polymer solution, on the other hand, behaves as a Newtonian liquid for very small rates of shear and deviates as the rate is increased. If the ratio of shear stress to rate of shear is plotted as a function of rate of shear, a Bingham material gives a curve of the form shown in figure 209, and a high polymer solution a curve of an S shape. It is clear that if various solutions are to be compared on the basis of a single viscosity value, the viscosity at very low rate of shear should be chosen. If deviations from Newtonian behavior are large, the value obtained by extrapolation to zero rate of shear should be used.

5. Effect of Temperature and Solvent Type on Intrinsic Viscosity of High Polymer Solutions

According to hydrodynamics, the specific viscosity of a Newtonian liquid containing a small amount of dissolved material should depend in first approximation only upon the volume concentration and the shapes of the suspended particles. It is an experimental fact, however, that the proportionality constant, K_m, is dependent not only upon the type of polymer concerned, but also upon the temperature and the nature of the solvent. Even in the dilute range, where specific viscosity is linear with concentration, these variations are often quite considerable. In this section, an attempt is made to treat such variations in a systematic fashion and to advance for them an explanation which is based upon changes in the average geometric shape of the particles. A reported relationship between intermolecular and intramolecular agglomeration tendency is also presented.

According to the present conception, a long chain hydrocarbon molecule in solution takes on a somewhat kinked or curled shape, intermediate between a tightly rolled up mass and the rigid linear configuration assumed by Staudinger. Presumably all possible degrees of curling are represented, owing to the internal Brownian movement of the flexible chains, but the configurations of intermediate extension predominate statistically. The average or effective value of any shape-dependent molecular property (such as hydrodynamic influences) may be obtained by summing this property over all configurational states, after each state has been given a proper weight factor. If the long chain molecule is surrounded by a continuous, energetically indifferent solvent, then the weight factor for a particular configuration is determined only by internal parameters—potential energy function for restricted rotation, prohibition of segment interpenetration, etc. The mean value of any molecular property in such an indifferent (and perhaps hypothetical) solvent might be called the "unbiased" statistical mean for the property.

If the solvent is energetically unfavorable, so that the dissolving of the high polymer is an endothermic process, then the polymer segments attract each other in solution and squeeze out the solvent between them. The curling forces in such a case are similar to those postulated in the Mack theory of rubber elasticity. Those molecular configurations which involve many contacts of the molecule with itself are weighted more heavily than in an indifferent solvent, and the mean value of any molecular property represents a more curled and contracted shape than the unbiased mean. On the other hand, if a solvent is energetically more favorable than the indifferent solvent as previously defined, then in solution the long chain molecule is surrounded by a solvated hull which tends to prevent polymer–polymer contacts. Uncurled configurations are favored, and the mean value of any property represents a more extended shape than the unbiased mean. Since an extended or uncurled configuration is associated with a high intrinsic viscosity, and vice versa, the first prediction as to effect of solvent type upon viscosity is given in the following paragraph.

Other conditions being equal, a given high polymeric material made up of flexible molecules exhibits a high intrinsic viscosity in an energetically favorable solvent and a low intrinsic viscosity in an energetically unfavorable solvent. This, of course, holds only for very diluted systems. At higher concentrations (about or more than 5% by weight), an energetically unfavorable solvent favors polymer–polymer contacts between different chains and hence leads to the danger of gelation, while an energetically favorable solvent stands a higher concentration of the polymer and yet gives a fluid, stable solution. Solvents are often classified as "good" or "bad" on the basis of the viscosity of concentrated solutions.

This effect was first suggested by Huggins (see *37*), who has since developed a theory that explicitly relates the viscous behavior of a dilute polymer solution with the thermodynamic properties of the same system. Huggins' equation relates the intrinsic viscosity with the molecular weight in a fashion which depends upon the mean molecular extension in solution. It is clear that, if this mean molecular shape varies from solvent to solvent, the magnitude of the intrinsic viscosity must also change. Furthermore, if Huggins' treatment is correct, *not only the magnitude, but also the molecular weight dependence*, of the intrinsic viscosity will vary from solvent to solvent. Huggins theoretically predicts that α should be antibatic with the thermodynamic quantity A_{12}, which is a measure of the relative cohesive energies of pairs of solvent molecules, pairs of solute submolecules or segments, and pairs consisting of a solvent molecule and a solute segment. A_{12} is also closely related with the quantity μ, which plays an important part in Huggins' well elaborated theory of the thermodynamic properties of polymer solutions. Hence it should be possible to correlate the *osmotic* properties of polymer solutions with the *viscous* properties, as far as the effect of the solvent is concerned. Huggins presents experimental evidence which is in definite concordance with this view.

If a good solvent is mixed with a precipitating agent, the resulting mixture can be expected to be energetically less favorable to a long chain molecule than is the pure solvent. A dilute solution of high polymer in a solvent–nonsolvent mixture should, therefore, exhibit a lower intrinsic viscosity than a solution of the same polymer in the pure solvent. It will be shown that a series of high polymer solutions of given polymer concentration, in mixtures of increasing nonsolvent content, shows a regular decrease in specific viscosity until the precipitation point is reached.

We have interpreted variations in the intrinsic viscosity of a given high polymer material as being due to changes in the degree of intramolecular agglomeration. If this interpretation is correct, there should be also a close connection between the intrinsic viscosity of a high polymer solution and the degree of intermolecular agglomeration. Exactly the same solvent characteristics which determine the mean geometric properties of an isolated long chain molecule should also determine the amount of association of different solute molecules into aggregates. When a nonsolvent is added to a high polymer solution, the point at which precipitation begins represents a certain definite agglomeration tendency for chain segments of different molecules. To a first approximation, therefore, it should represent a certain definite mean value for any shape dependent internal property. That solvent composition which is critical from the standpoint of solubility should correspond to a certain intrinsic viscosity, no matter what the solvent and what the nonsolvent. One would therefore conclude the following: The intrinsic viscosities of a series of solutions of a given polymer in solvent–nonsolvent mixtures of increasing nonsolvent content, should decrease to a final value at the limit of solubility. This final value should be in first approximation the same in all solvent–nonsolvent systems.

All of these effects should be more pronounced for polymer molecules of high flexibility than for more rigid chains. A paraffin chain should exhibit greater shape changes than a cellulose derivative.

The effect of temperature upon intrinsic viscosity should depend strongly upon the nature of the solvent. In a poor solvent, the effective molecular shape is more compact and curled than the unbiased statistical mean. An increase of temperature should increase the relative importance of entropy factors over energetic factors, and result in an uncurling of the molecule. In such a solvent, a temperature increase should result in an increase of intrinsic viscosity. In a very good solvent, the energetic weighting factors favor the more extended configurations; here a temperature increase should result in a downward approach to the unbiased statistical mean shape. In a very good solvent, therefore, a temperature increase should cause a decrease in intrinsic viscosity. There should be an intermediate case in which the intrinsic viscosity is independent of temperature over a limited range.

The above use of the "unbiased statistical mean" as the shape which is approached as the temperature increases is an oversimplification, since this value itself includes energetic weighting factors, arising from the internal potentials of the molecule. If we consider only the forces which depend upon the solvent, we can make the prediction: In a very good solvent, the intrinsic viscosity of a dilute solution of a flexible polymer should decrease with temperature; in a poor solvent, it should increase. Alfrey, Bartovics, and Mark (*11*) have presented some experimental data on this point:

Polystyrene, rubber, and cellulose acetate were used in the investigation. The polystyrene had a weight average molecular weight of 165,000, calculated from viscosity data and using a K_m value of 1.1×10^{-4}. The rubber was smoked crepe, with a weight average molecular weight of 223,000, based upon a k_m value of 2.7×10^{-4}. The cellulose acetate was a fraction with a molecular weight of 35,000, which had been obtained by Harris and Sookne from a sample of commercial cellulose acetate having a weight average molecular weight around 90,000.

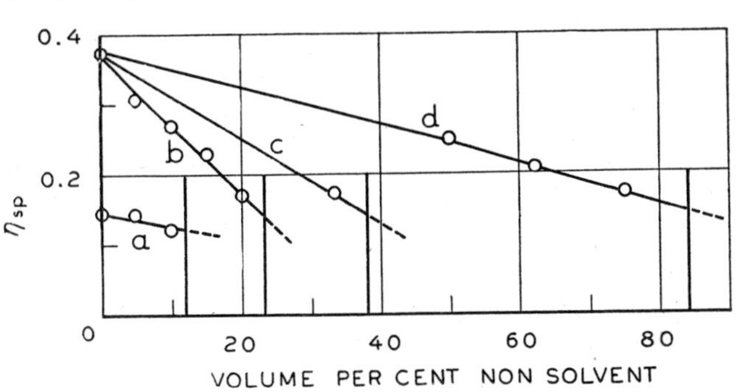

Fig. 210. Effect of solvent composition on specific viscosity of polystyrene solutions. Vertical lines represent limits of solubility.

Solutions of polystyrene at a concentration of 0.2% by volume in the following solvent–nonsolvent systems were investigated: Methyl ethyl ketone–methanol, toluene–acetone, toluene–methanol, toluene–isoamyl alcohol. Figure 210 shows the variation of specific viscosity with nonsolvent content. In each case, the specific viscosity decreases as the mixed solvent becomes less favorable until the coagulation point is reached. For all the solvent–nonsolvent systems investigated, the specific viscosity at the solubility limit is in the same range.

Solutions of rubber at a concentration of 0.0468% by volume in the following solvent–nonsolvent systems were investigated: toluene–methanol, toluene–acetone, carbon tetrachloride–methanol, carbon tetrachloride–acetone. . . Rubber was found to behave in the same general way as polystyrene.

Solutions of cellulose acetate at 0.2% by volume in the following solvent–nonsolvent systems were investigated: methylcellosolve–methanol, acetone–methanol, acetone–toluene. [Variations in specific viscosity were much less than in the cases above.] The nature of the solvent medium apparently had a smaller marked effect upon the shape of the cellulose acetate molecule in solution. It is to be expected that the cellulose chain is much less flexible than the rubber and polystyrene molecules.

TABLE XXVI

η_{sp} AS A FUNCTION OF TEMPERATURE

Sample	Temperature	
	25°C.	60°C.
Rubber in		
Toluene	0.390	0.373
Carbon tetrachloride	0.466	0.430
Toluene–14% methanol	0.205	0.243
Polystyrene in		
Toluene	0.370	0.350
Toluene–10% methanol	0.320	0.317
Toluene–20% methanol	0.160	0.185
Toluene–10% amyl alcohol	0.336	0.340
Toluene–33% amyl alcohol	0.170	0.210

Effect of Temperature.—Viscosities of many of the solutions were determined at two different temperatures, 25° and 60°. Table XXVI shows the relation between the specific viscosity at 60° and that at 25°, as a function of solvent composition, for several systems. In the pure solvents, specific viscosity decreases with temperature, while in the mixtures containing much nonsolvent, specific viscosity increases with temperature.

BIBLIOGRAPHY

BOOKS

(1) *First Report on Viscosity and Plasticity.* Royal Netherlands Academy of Sciences, Noord-Hollandsche, Amsterdam, 1935; 2nd ed., 1939.

Second Report on Viscosity and Plasticity. Royal Netherlands Academy of Sciences, Noord-Hollandsche, Amsterdam; Interscience, New York, 1938.

(2) Hatschek, E., *Die Viskosität der Flüssigkeiten.* Steinkopff, Dresden, 1929.

(3) Houwink, R., *Elasticity, Plasticity, and the Structure of Matter.* Cambridge Univ. Press, London, 1937.

(4) Mark, H., *Der feste Körper.* Hirzel, Leipzig, 1938.

(4a) Mark, H., *Physical Chemistry of High Polymeric Systems* (High Polymers, Vol. II). Interscience, New York, 1940.

(*5*) Mark, H., and Whitby, G. S., eds., *Scientific Progress in the Field of Rubber and Synthetic Elastomers* (Advances in Colloid Science, Vol. II). Interscience, New York, 1946.

(*6*) Meyer, K. H., *Natural and Synthetic High Polymers* (High Polymers, Vol. IV). Interscience, New York, 1942.

ARTICLES

(*7*) Aiken, W., Alfrey, T., Janssen, A., and Mark, H., "Effects of Plasticizers on the Viscoelastic Properties of Vinyl Resins," Rheology Society, Fall Meeting, New York, 1945.

(*8*) Aiken, W., Alfrey, T., Janssen, A., and Mark, H., "Creep Behavior of Plasticized Vinylite VYNW," *J. Polymer Sci.*, **2**, 178–198 (1947).

(*9*) Aleksandrov, A. P., and Lazurkin, IU. S., "Study of Polymers. I. Highly Elastic Deformation in Polymers," *Acta Physicochim. U.R.S.S.*, **12**, 647–668 (1940).

(*10*) Alfrey, T., Bartovics, A., and Mark, H., "Comparative Osmotic and Viscosity Measurements with Polystyrene Fractions," *J. Am. Chem. Soc.*, **65**, 2319–2323 (1943).

(*11*) Alfrey, T., Bartovics, A., and Mark, H., "The Effect of Temperature and Solvent Type on the Intrinsic Viscosity of High Polymer Solutions," *J. Am. Chem. Soc.*, **64**, 1557–1560 (1942).

(*12*) Alfrey, T., and Mark, H., "Statistical Mechanics of Binary Mixtures," *J. Chem. Phys.*, **10**, 303–304 (1942).

(*13*) Bartovics, A., and Mark, H., "Osmotic Pressure and Viscosity Measurements with Cellulose Acetate Fractions," *J. Am. Chem. Soc.*, **65**, 1901–1905 (1943).

(*14*) Clash, R. F., and Berg, R. M., "Vinyl Elastomers," *Ind. Eng. Chem.*, **34**, 1218–1222 (1942).

(*15*) Clash, R. F., and Berg, R. M., "Stiffness and Brittleness of Nonrigid Vinyl Chloride-Acetate Resin Compounds," *Modern Plastics*, **21**, 119–124 (July, 1944).

(*16*) Davies, J. M., Miller, R. F., and Busse, W. F., "Dielectric Properties of Plasticized Polyvinyl Chloride," *J. Am. Chem. Soc.*, **63**, 361–369 (1941).

(*17*) Einstein, A., "Eine neue Bestimmung der Moleküldimensionen," *Ann. Physik*, **19**, 289–306 (1906); *ibid.*, **34**, 591–592 (1911).

(*18*) Eirich, F., and Goldschmid, O., "Untersuchungen über die Viskosität von Suspensionen und Lösungen. 8. Über Trägheitseffekte suspendierter Kugeln," *Kolloid-Z.*, **81**, 7–18 (1937).

(*19*) Eirich, F., Margaretha, H., and Bunzl, M., "Untersuchungen über die Viskosität von Suspensionen und Lösungen. 6. Über die Viskosität von Stäbchensuspensionen," *Kolloid-Z.*, **75**, 20–37 (1936).

(*20*) Eirich, F., and Simha, R., "Über die Viskosität von Suspensionen und Lösungen," *Monatsh.*, **71**, 67–94 (1937).

(*21*) Eisenschitz, R., "Der Einfluss der Brownschen Bewegung auf die Viskosität von Suspensionen," *Z. physik. Chem.*, **A163**, 133–141 (1933).

(*22*) Eley, D. D., "The Kinetics of Rubberlike Elasticity," *Rubber Chem. Tech.*, **15**, 438–445 (1942).

(*23*) Eyring, H., "The Resultant Electric Moment of Complex Molecules," *Phys. Rev.*, **39**, 746–748 (1932).

(*24*) Ferry, J. D., "Studies of the Mechanical Properties of Substances of High Molecular Weight. I. A Photoelastic Method for Study of Transverse Vibrations in Gels," *Rev. Sci. Instruments*, **12**, 79–82 (1941).

(*25*) Flory, P. J., "Thermodynamics of High Polymer Solutions," *J. Chem. Phys.*, **9**, 660–661 (1941); *ibid.*, **10**, 51–61 (1942); "Thermodynamics of Heterogeneous Polymers and Their Solutions," *ibid.*, **12**, 425–438 (1944).

(*26*) Fordyce, R., and Hibbert, H., "Studies on Reactions Relating to Carbohydrates and Polysaccharides," *J. Am. Chem. Soc.*, **61**, 1910–1911, 1912–1915 (1939).

(*27*) Fordyce, R., Lovell, E. L., and Hibbert, H., "Studies on Reactions Relating to Carbohydrates and Polysaccharides," *J. Am. Chem. Soc.*, **61**, 1905–1910 (1939).

(*28*) Fuoss, R. M., "Electrical Properties of Solids. I. Experimental Methods," *J. Am. Chem. Soc.*, **59**, 1703 (1937); "II. Preliminary Report on the System Polyvinyl Chloride–Tricresyl Phosphate," *ibid.*, **60**, 451 (1938); "III. Thermal Breakdown of Plasticized Polyvinyl Chloride," *ibid.*, **60**, 456 (1938); "IV. The Influence of Thermal History on Polyvinyl Chloride Plastics," *ibid.*, **61**, 2329 (1939); "V. Their Variations at 40° with Frequency and Composition in the System Polyvinyl Chloride–Tricresyl Phosphate," *ibid.*, **61**, 2334 (1939); "VI. Dipole Rotation in High Polymers," *ibid.*, **63**, 369 (1941); "VII. The System Polyvinyl Chloride–Diphenyl," *ibid.*, **63**, 378 (1941); (and J. G. Kirkwood) "VIII. Dipole Moments in Polyvinyl Chloride–Diphenyl Systems," *ibid.*, **63**, 385 (1941); "IX. Dependence of Dispersion on Molecular Weight in the System Polyvinyl Chloride–Diphenyl," *ibid.*, **63**, 2401 (1941); "X. The System Polyvinyl Chloride–Tetrahydronaphthalene," *ibid.*, **63**, 2410 (1941); (D. J. Mead and) "XI. Polyvinyl Acetate and Polyvinyl Chloroacetate," *ibid.*, **63**, 2832 (1941); (D. J. Mead, R. L. Tichenor, and) "XII. Plasticized Polyvinyl Chloride," *ibid.*, **64**, 283 (1942); (D. J. Mead and) "XIII. Polymethyl Acrylate, Polymethyl Methacrylate, Polymethyl-α-chloracrylate and Polychloroethyl Methacrylate," *ibid.*, **64**, 2389 (1942); (D. J. Mead and) "XIV. Copolymers of Acrylonitrile and Ethyl Acrylate," *ibid.*, **65**, 2067 (1943).

(*29*) Fuoss, R. M., "Preparation of Polyvinyl Chloride Plastics for Electrical Measurements," paper presented at the Seventy-Fourth General Meeting, Electrochemical Society, Rochester, N. Y., Oct. 13, 1938; *Trans. Electrochem. Soc.*, **74**, 91–112.

(*30*) Fuoss, R. M., "The Electrical Properties of Polyvinyl Chloride Plastics," *Ann. N. Y. Acad. Sci.*, **40**, art. 5, 429–445 (1940).

(*31*) Fuoss, R. M., and Kirkwood, J. G. See reference (*28*).

(*32*) Fuoss, R. M., and Mead, D. J., "Osmotic Pressures of Polyvinyl Chloride Solutions by a Dynamic Method," *J. Phys. Chem.*, **47**, 59–70 (1943).

(*33*) Gold, O., Dissertation, Vienna.

(*33a*) Goldberg A. I., Hohenstein, W. P., and Mark, H., "Intrinsic Viscosity–Molecular Weight Relationship for Polystyrene," *J. Polymer Sci.*, **2**, 503–510 (1947).

(*34*) Guth, E., "Untersuchungen über die Viskosität von Suspensionen und Lösungen. I. Über die Viskosität von Suspensionen," *Kolloid-Z.*, **74**, 147–172 (1936); "Untersuchungen über die Viskosität von Suspensionen und Lösungen. V. Über den Einfluss der Brownschen Bewegung auf die Viskosität von Ellipsoidsuspensionen," *ibid.*, **75**, 15–20 (1936).

(*35*) Guth, E., and Mark, H., Viscosity of Solutions, in Particular of Solutions of Substances of High Molecular Weight, *Ergeb. exakt. Naturw.*, **12**, 146 (1933).

(*36*) Guth, E., and Simha, R., "Untersuchungen über die Viskosität von Suspensionen und Lösungen. III. Über die Viskosität von Kugelsuspensionen," *Kolloid-Z.*, **74**, 266–275 (1936).

(*37*) Huggins, M. L., "The Viscosity of Dilute Solutions of Long-Chain Molecules," *J. Phys. Chem.*, **42**, 911–920 (1938); *ibid.*, **43**, 439–456 (1939); *J. Applied Phys.*, **10**, 700–710 (1939).

(*38*) Huggins, M. L., "Thermodynamic Properties of Solutions of Long-Chain Compounds," *Ann. N. Y. Acad. Sci.*, **43**, 1–32 (1942).

(*39*) Jeffery, G. B., "The Motion of Ellipsoidal Particles Immersed in a Viscous Fluid," *Proc. Roy. Soc. London*, **A102**, 161–179 (1923).

(*40*) Kirkpatrick, A., "Some Relations between Molecular Structure and Plasticizing Effect," *J. Applied Phys.*, **11**, 255–261 (1940).

(*41*) Kirkwood, J. G., and Fuoss, R. M., "Anomalous Dispersion of Dielectric Loss in Polar Polymers," *J. Chem. Phys.*, **9**, 329–340 (1941).

(*42*) Kraemer, E. O., "Molecular Weights of Celluloses and Cellulose Derivatives," *Ind. Eng. Chem.*, **30**, 1200–1203 (1938).

(*43*) Kuhn, W., "Über quantitative Deutung der Viskosität und Strömungsdoppelbrechung von Suspensionen," *Kolloid-Z.*, **62**, 269–285 (1933).

(*44*) Mead, D. J., and Fuoss, R. M. See reference (*28*).

(*45*) Mead, D. J., and Fuoss, R. M., "Viscosities of Solutions of Polyvinyl Chloride," *J. Am. Chem. Soc.*, **64**, 277–282 (1942).

(*46*) Mead, D. J., Tichenor, R. L., and Fuoss, R. M. See reference (*28*).

(*47*) Philippoff, W., and Hess, K., "Über der Konzentrationabhängigkeit der Zähigkeit bei organischen Hochpolymeren," *Ber.*, **B70**, 639–665 (1937).

(*48*) Philippoff, W., and Hess, K., "Zum Viskositätsproblem bei organischen Kolloiden," *Z. physik. Chem.*, **B31**, 237–255 (1936).

(*49*) Reed, M. C., "Behavior of Plasticizers in Vinyl Chloride-Acetate Resins," *Ind. Eng. Chem.*, **35**, 896–904 (1943).

(*50*) Sack, H. S., "Elastic Losses of Natural and Synthetic Rubber as a Function of Frequency and Temperature," American Physical Society, New York, Jan. 1947.

(*51*) Simha, R., "The Influence of Brownian Movement on the Viscosity of Solutions," *J. Phys. Chem.*, **44**, 25–34 (1940).

F. ULTIMATE STRENGTH AND RELATED PROPERTIES

I. INTRODUCTION

Up to this point, little mention has been made of ultimate strength, although this is one of the most important properties of a material, from the practical standpoint. The early part of the stress–strain curve was discussed, but the later part, where actual rupture occurs, was not explained.

As a matter of fact, it is impossible to discuss questions of ultimate strength in as fundamental a fashion as it is possible to discuss elasticity or flow. There are three main difficulties to such a discussion—mathematical, structural, and experimental.

1. A Mathematical Difficulty

In the case of elasticity, flow, or combined plastoelastic response, it is possible to follow continuously the changes which take place. One starts with an initial state described by a set of parameters and ends with a final state described by different values of the same parameters. Furthermore, any *intermediate* state involved in the process can also be defined in terms of these same parameters. This is not true if a rupture of the sample takes place. The actual breaking represents a discontinuity which cannot be avoided. Before the break we have one piece of material; after it we have two or more. The transition cannot be followed by any continuous set of variables. Thus from a phenomenological point of view, it is never possible even to describe mathematically a breaking process, in the sense that it is possible to describe an elastic deformation or a viscous flow. This is a serious barrier to any fundamental treatment.

2. A Structural Difficulty

If one attempts to correlate ultimate strength with molecular and intermolecular structure, a second difficulty arises. The thermodynamic properties of a material (including the elastic constants) depend almost entirely on the dominant local structure. Thus in a crystalline material, the lattice structure is the principal determining factor. Such nonlocal structural factors as crystal size or even mosaic structure contribute only second-order effects to the thermodynamic properties. Further, minor imperfections and defects, deviations from the dominant structure, have little effect as long as they are not too numerous or extreme. In fact, if the arrangement of matter and the interatomic or intermolecular forces within a single unit cell are known in complete detail, it should be possible in principle to calculate the *thermodynamic* properties of the material without serious error.

The ultimate strength of a material, on the other hand, is intimately connected with the nondominant, nonlocal structure, which is much more elusive. The ultimate strength of a crystalline material, for example, depends largely upon crystal size, mosaic structure, and the presence of flaws and imperfections.

As a corollary, "theoretical" ultimate strengths calculated on the basis of dominant local structures are invariably several orders of magnitude too high. This also is a serious handicap, since it is the dominant local structure which can most easily be determined, as for example by x-ray diffraction.

3. An Experimental Difficulty

Even if one makes no attempt to understand the mechanism of breaking, or even to describe phenomenologically the process of breaking, but merely observes breaking strengths in a completely empirical fashion, a difficulty arises which is not present in the study of elasticity or flow. This is the scattering of experimental data.

If one prepares 100 samples of spring brass under as nearly identical conditions as possible, the elastic moduli of all the samples will be extremely close together. The viscosities of 100 samples of highly purified benzene will be practically identical. In contrast to this, 100 samples of rayon filament, all cut from the same continuous piece, will exhibit a decided spread in the values of the stress at which breaking occurs, and still greater spreads are observed in the time to break under a constant dead load.

This may well be considered as a necessary corollary of difficulty 2, above. The dominant local structure of a material is rather sharply determined by powerful thermodynamic potentials. Slight variations in conditions during the establishment of a structure do not have enormous effects on the local structure. Thus it is easy enough to control the conditions of crystallization, for example, so that a solid of reproducible elastic constants is formed. On the other hand, the long range structure of a material—crystal size, mosaic structure, etc., and the defects and irregularities within the structure—are largely determined by the competition between different rate processes. Very minor variations in experimental conditions can cause large differences in these aspects of structure. Thus the structural features which determine *breaking strength* are strongly affected by fortuitous and uncontrollable small differences in conditions of preparation.

For these reasons, little attempt is made to discuss ultimate strength in other than empirical terms. Some of the concepts developed in earlier chapters reappear here in the specification of the polymer structure, but the actual breaking process is handled empirically.

The above difficulties probably apply most strongly to failure by *rupture* ("brittle fracture"). When a sample undergoes plastic failure, it may be possible to describe mathematically the more or less continuous process leading up to the actual breaking. The continuous loss of fatigue resistance during cyclic stressing, for example, would seem to be amenable to mathematical treatment. Even plastic failure, however, must be discussed in a much more empirical fashion than flow and elasticity.

II. GEOMETRIC CONSIDERATIONS

It will be shown that time effects are of fundamental importance in the *breaking* of high polymers, as well as in the plastoelastic response to small stresses. However, to begin with, the purely geometric aspect of the problem of ultimate strength deserves some consideration. Following the procedure of earlier chapters, let us isolate this geometric aspect by considering a material with no time effects. This means that a stress in excess of a certain critical value causes instant rupture, while a stress below this ultimate strength value can be supported by the material indefinitely. (We will, however, depart from this simple time behavior even within this section, in order to include plastic failure.)

Since the stress at a point is made up of six components, the maximum allowable stress cannot be a simple scalar quantity. Any one of the stress components can by itself cause failure, if it is too great in magnitude. Hence there will be a maximum allowable value of s_1, of s_2, of s_3, of s_4, of s_5, and of s_6. Each of these represents the ultimate value of the particular stress component when it is acting alone. Each component in fact, has *two* limiting values, one positive and one negative. For a completely anisotropic material, these twelve "ultimate strengths" should all have different values. Furthermore, if several stress components were simultaneously unequal to zero, failure could be expected to occur before any one component attained its individual ultimate value. Conversely, it is conceivable that a moderate value of one stress component would *increase* the allowable value of some other component. Thus the general specification of allowable stress in an anisotropic material would necessarily be a relation among all six stress components. (If a stress is considered to be defined by a point in six-dimensional space, the continuous set of breaking stresses would lie on a five-dimensional manifold in that space.)

The limiting stress in an *isotropic* material can be specified more simply in terms of the three principal stresses S_1, S_2, and S_3. The various limiting stresses will fall on a surface in $S_1S_2S_3$ space. The form of this surface depends upon the properties of the (isotropic) material, just as the form of the five-dimensional manifold, above, depends upon the properties of the (anisotropic) material under consideration. For no materials, and certainly not for high polymers, are the characteristic limiting stress functions known in complete detail and with absolute certainty. However, a few general remarks may be hazarded.

In the first place, the nature of the failure depends upon the *position* of the stress in the "limiting stress surface" (or manifold). A dilatational stress tends to cause a "brittle" fracture, whereas a compressive stress tends to cause plastic failure. To oversimplify, we might imagine a sharp dividing line between these two types of failure. This would be a closed curve on the "limiting stress surface"—a closed four-dimensional manifold within the five-dimensional "limiting stress manifold," for anisotropic materials. The position of this curve, as well as the form of the surface, will depend upon the material under consideration. Thus pure metals ordinarily fail plastically under the action of a single tensile stress. This would indicate that seven of the eight octants in $S_1S_2S_3$ space correspond to plastic failure. In order to get a brittle fracture, a limiting stress well within the dilatative octant would have to be applied. On the other hand, impure cast zinc undergoes "brittle" fracture in pure tension (as well as throughout the dilatative octant), and even well into the other regions of the critical stress surface. Finally, a typically "brittle" material, such as glass at low temperatures, cast iron, etc., does not show plastic failure unless subjected to a stress well within the "compressive octant." High polymers in general would be expected to act more like pure metals in this regard at high temperatures, more like impure metals at low temperatures. See figure 231 (page 517) in which the stress–strain curve for polystyrene in tension is compared with that in compression.

Even within the "region of plastic failure," it is possible to cause brittle fracture, by applying a very large stress so quickly that no time is allowed for plastic flow to take place. Nadai (7) suggests the use of *two* limiting stress surfaces—a limiting surface of plastic yield, and a limiting surface of rupture. However, if the "timescale of stressing" is held fixed, a single limiting stress surface, containing a region of fracture and a region of plastic failure, would seem to be satisfactory.

Second, the limiting stress surface for any nonporous isotropic material has a sort of pole at the ray $S_1 = S_2 = S_3 < 0$. That is, a nonporous material is extremely resistant to an isotropic compressive stress.

These geometric aspects of ultimate strength are undoubtedly of great importance in the behavior of objects in normal use. However, in the case of high polymers, very little has been done in the direction of determining the "surface of limiting stresses."

A rough step in this direction, however, is made whenever *notched* specimens are used in strength tests. The most significant effect of a notch in a test bar—whether used in a tensile or a bending test, and whether loaded slowly or under impact conditions—is the fact that around the notch the stress is of a different geometric type than elsewhere in the bar. The obvious *concentration* of the stress is of secondary importance. When a (long) unnotched bar is subjected to a bending moment, the stress varies from zero at the neutral axis to a maximum tensile stress at one side and a maximum compressive stress at the other. If a small notch is present in the side which is normally under simple tension, the stress is highly concentrated at the point of the notch. This concentrated stress is not a simple tensile stress, but a three-dimensional "combined" stress. No longer are two of the principal stresses equal to zero. Instead, S_1, S_2, and S_3 all have positive values. Hence the stress in this region is in the *dilative octant* of $S_1S_2S_3$ space.

This type of stress strongly favors a brittle fracture, as contrasted to a ductile failure. A material which, in the form of an unnotched bar, fails in a ductile fashion, may well fracture in the form of a *notched* bar. The use of notched and unnotched test pieces thus serves to establish a crude scale of brittleness. Some materials will undergo "plastic" or "ductile" failure in both a notched and an unnotched bar. Other materials, somewhat more brittle, will give brittle fracture in a notched form, but not in an unnotched form. Still others will fracture in either the notched or the unnotched form. This crude scale can be made more detailed, although no less empirical, by providing a series of standard notch depths and radii, since the position of the concentrated stress in the dilatative octant obviously depends upon the design of the notch. Indeed, it is possible to design a test piece in which the three principal stresses at the point of concentration are nearly identical in magnitude. Such a piece must give a brittle fracture even when composed of very soft materials. A somewhat more detailed analysis of this point appears in the paragraphs on impact strength, since the use of a notched specimen is often a standard procedure in such tests.

Beyond the use of notched specimens, little has been done in the field of high polymers to evaluate the nature of the failure caused by various combinations of stresses. Even the use of notched specimens was introduced largely for empirical reasons, rather than with the deliberate aim of studying combined stresses, and indeed can be considered only as a very inefficient and indirect method of obtaining such information.

Much of this chapter therefore deals with *tensile strength*, and its dependence upon time factors, molecular weight, molecular weight distribution curve, chemical structure of polymer, crystallinity, orientation, and other factors.

III. TIME EFFECTS

1. Breaking Time as a Function of Stress

The "ultimate strength" of a high polymer for any given geometric type of stressing is not a simple numerical quantity, but includes time effects. This is shown, for example, in figure 211. When a sample of cellulose acetate was subjected to a tensile stress of 37.5 kg. per cm.^{2}, it extended and broke after nearly fifty minutes. When a sample of cellulose acetate was subjected to a tensile stress of 43 kg. per cm.^{2}, it extended and broke after about 25 minutes, and with a stress of 53.9 kg. per cm.^{2} the breaking time was little more than 10 minutes. The question of how much tensile load a sample will sustain without breaking, then, depends upon the *length of time* the load is applied. Rather than a sharp value of ultimate tensile stress, there is a *varying breaking time* which is a function of tensile stress, $t_b(S)$. At any given stress, of course, the breaking times for a series of samples will be distributed about a mean value. The spread in experimental values is often quite large. In

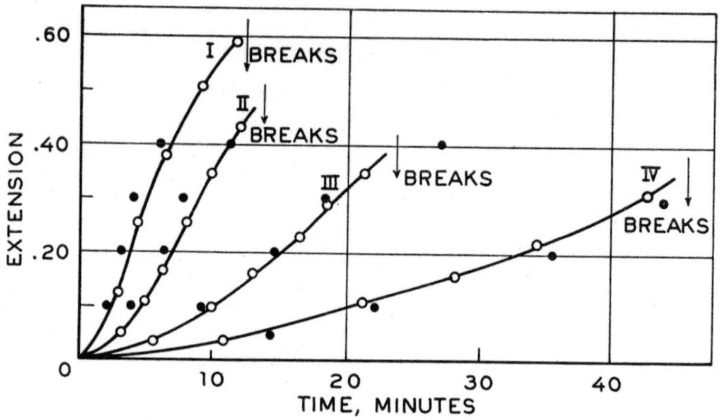

Fig. 211. Behavior of cellulose acetate under constant load (after Haward).

figure 212 is presented the breaking time *vs.* stress relationship found by Busse and co-workers (*24*).

Haward found that if a sample of acetate were released before breaking, allowed to recover (by heating to 65°C.), and stressed again, it was more easily extensible, and broke after a short time. Even though the first deformation had been almost completely recovered, the internal

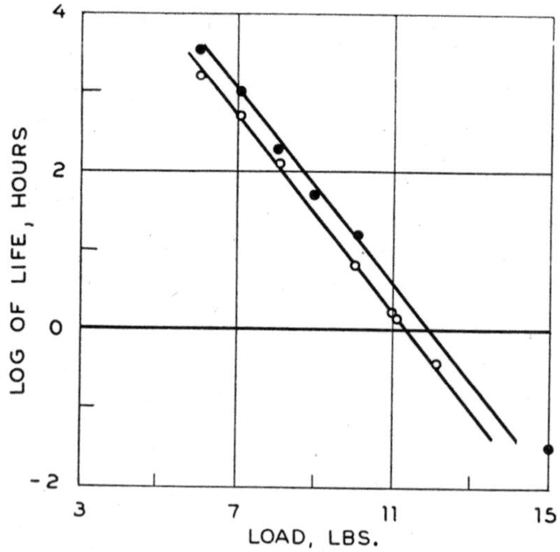

Fig. 212. Life under dead load as a function of load for cotton tire cord (after Busse *et al.*).

structure of the polymer had been irreversibly altered by the mechanical treatment.

Haward then made experiments on the same material in which the sample was extended for a time t_1, the stress removed, and the test piece heated to 65° C. for 10 minutes to allow recovery of the extension. After cooling, the stress was once more applied, and maintained until the sample broke (t_2). The sum of t_1 and t_2 (*i.e.*, the *total time* of application of the stress) was found to be fairly constant, and about equal to the ordinary breaking time for that stress—7 minutes:

t_1	t_2	$t_1 + t_2$	t_1	t_2	$t_1 + t_2$
6.5	1.1	7.6	4.0	2.5	6.5
6.5	0.5	7.0	2.0	4.4	6.4
4.0	1.4	5.4	2.0	4.2	6.2

These results indicate that the weakening of the cellulose acetate caused by extension is not repaired when the deformation is removed at moderate temperature.

Midgley and Pierce (*104*) did pioneering work on this subject, using various textile yarns, as well as single cotton fibers. They found that the ultimate tensile stress supported by a yarn increased about 10% for every tenfold increase in the rate of loading, over the range of loading times from 0.02 sec. to about 18 days. However, the ultimate elongation was reported to be relatively independent of rate of loading. Busse, Lessig, Loughborough, and Larrick (*24*) found a very good linear relationship between the log of breaking time and the dead load on cotton cords.

Busse and co-workers have made a thorough study of the breaking of rayon, cotton, and nylon cords under the action of a constant load with a superimposed cyclic forced strain. They determined the way in which breaking time depended upon load, amplitude of the cyclic strain, frequency, temperature, and past loading history. Among other significant results they found that fatigue entailed irreversible changes. Cords were vibrated under conditions which would lead to breaking after about fifteen hours. After five or ten hours they were removed and allowed to rest for several days, and then put back and vibrated till failure occurred. The total test life was found to be roughly constant, regardless of the manner in which the vibration period is divided up. Other tests showed that cords which have been vibrated could be stored for as long as a month without recovering their original vibration resistance. Treatments such as flexing, or wetting with water, or extracting with solvents, did not restore the fatigue life which had been lost. This corresponds with the similar observation of Haward (*61*) concerning the irreversibility of the breakdown process during static loading.

These authors also found that, other conditons being equal, the breaking time varies with temperature in the exponential fashion which we associate with molecular processes involving activation energies (*i.e.*, $\log t = A + \mathbf{E}/RT$). Values of **E** ranged from about 8200 for rayon, and 12,500 for cotton, to about 20,000 cal. for nylon. (Mark has pointed out that these reported values should be multiplied by 2.303.) As Busse and co-workers point out, such "activation energies" must be interpreted with caution.

A. Combination of Geometric and Time Complexity

The complete specification of the breaking behavior of a material, with the simultaneous recognition of the geometric complexities of Chapter A and the time complexities of Chapter B is obviously an extremely complicated problem. Such a complete specification could be formulated in either of two equivalent fashions:

(1) The breaking time *vs.* stress relation for every (geometric) type of stress could be given, *i.e.*, for every ray from the origin in S_1, S_2, S_3 space (or s_1, s_2, s_3, s_4, s_5, s_6 space) the breaking time must be known as a function of the position along the ray. In this formulation, $t_b(S)$ of the preceding discussion would be replaced by $t_b(S_1, S_2, S_3)$ or $t_b(s_1, s_2, s_3, s_4, s_5, s_6)$.

(2) The limiting stress surface of Chapter A which represented a single fixed timescale, could be replaced by a family of such surfaces, each member of the family representing a different breaking time.

Presumably formulation (1) would be most helpful if the time behavior were the primary question under consideration, and formulation (2) would be most helpful in drawing attention to the geometric aspects of the problem.

At the present time, such a phenomenological framework is of little value, since existing data are insufficient to allow the construction of such a set of curves for even one high polymer.

B. Response to Different Stress Sequences (Hypothetical)

We have seen that a cellulose acetate sample will support a given stress for a total length of time which within experimental error is independent of the manner in which the stressing period is broken up by "rest" periods. This significant fact leads to the possibility of predicting the average breaking time for any arbitrary sequence of stresses from the function $t_b(S)$. (For example, if we know the length of time a sample can be expected to support any constant stress, is it possible to predict its mean breaking time when subjected to a stress which increases linearly with time?) If the same continuous process of internal breakdown takes place at a high stress as at a low, the only difference being in the *rate* of breakdown, then the state of the sample at any time can be represented by a single parameter. (As a matter of fact, it is not actually necessary for the breakdown process at different stresses to be identical in detailed mechanism, so long as they are phenomenologically equivalent and additive. This means that if a sample is subjected to the stress S_1 for the time t_1, the weakened condition which results can be duplicated in a second sample by applying the stress S_2 for the proper period t_2, or in a third sample by applying the stress S_3 for the time t_3 and then applying the stress S_4 for the proper interval t_4, etc.)

Let us introduce the symbol B, which is to represent in some way the amount of internal breakdown of the sample. Several possibilities now present themselves:

(1) At any stress S, the breakdown, represented by B, increases at a rate dB/dt which is a function of S. [$dB/dt = B'(S)$.] When B reaches a critical value, B_c, the sample snaps. If strength loss and failure follows this simple pattern, then a sequence of different stresses will be supported for a time which is simply related to the normal breaking times corresponding to the various stresses. Thus if a sample is subjected to the stress S_1 for one-third of the normal breaking time for that stress, $t(S_1)$, and then subjected to the stress S_2, it will on the average support this second stress for two-thirds of the normal breaking time for the new stress. Failure will occur whenever the sum of all fractional breaking times equals one. If the stress varies with time, $S = S(t)$, then the expected breaking time will be the value of the limit of the integral in equation (1):

$$1 = \int_0^y \frac{S(t)}{t_b(S)}\,dt \tag{1}$$

where y = expected breaking time. This simple hypothesis is quite consistent with the constancy of breaking times at interrupted constant stress, and, equation (1), if correct, could be established by obvious tests. It is, however, a physically improbable hypothesis, for reasons explained in connection with the other possible hypotheses below.

(2) At any stress, the breakdown increases at a rate $B'(S)$, which as in hypothesis (1) is a function only of S. The critical value of B at which failure occurs is also a function of S. That is to say, at a low stress, the breaking time is long not only because of the slow *rate* of breakdown, but also because breakdown must proceed to a great degree before the sample will fail under the action of a small stress. Hence failure is governed by *two* quantities, each a function of stress:

$$\frac{dB}{dt} = B'(S) \qquad \text{and} \qquad B_c = B_c(S) \tag{2}$$

The breaking time at the constant stress S is given by the ratio of these two functions:

$$t_b(S) = \frac{B_c(S)}{B'(S)} \tag{3}$$

Since the observable quantity in a constant stress experiment is $t_b(S)$, it is clear that the two functions $B_c(S)$ and $B'(S)$ cannot be individually evaluated from breaking experiments at constant stress (assuming our second hypothesis to hold). These two functions could be evaluated by a series of tests involving various stress sequences. Thus if the stress S_1 is applied for a time t_1, and then the stress S_2 is applied until failure, the time for which the second stress will be supported is given by t_2 in equation (4):

$$t_1 B'(S_1) + t_2 \cdot B'(S_2) = B_c(S_2) \tag{4}$$

If $t_b(S_1)$ and $t_b(S_2)$ are known from constant stress experiments it is clear that two experiments, in one of which the stress S_1 is applied first and breaking occurs under the action of S_2, and in one of which the reverse procedure is followed, will suffice to determine $B'(S_1)$, $B_c(S_1)$, $B'(S_2)$, and $B_c(S_2)$ on an arbitrary scale.

To check hypothesis (2) it would be necessary to use three stresses, S_1, S_2, and S_3, and proceed as above with *each pair* of stress values.

Hypothesis (2) becomes identical with (1) if the function $B'(S)$ is much more sensitive to changes in stress than the function $B_c(S)$.

(3) It is quite possible that the rate of increase of breakdown, dB/dt, depends not only upon the stress, but also upon the degree of breakdown already present. $dB/dt = B'(BS)$.

Haward interpreted his results with cellulose acetate in terms of a hypothesis which corresponded to hypothesis (2), with a specific form assumed for both the function $B'(S)$ and $B_c(S)$. Haward considers that the original sample has the strength P_0, and loses this strength at a rate which is given by the formula $dP/dt = -(1/K)S_m$. The sample is assumed to break when the strength is reduced to the value of the imposed stress. These assumptions seem reasonable, but it should be pointed out that no hypothesis which resolves the observed breaking times into the factors $B'(S)$ and $B_c(S)$ can be definitely established by a set of experiments each involving a single stress. Haward's special form of hypothesis (2), like the general form, can be definitely established only by means of sequences of different stresses.

(1), (2), (3) The general weakness of the above hypotheses lies in the fact that the governing parameter B is by its very nature an *unobservable* quantity. Only the fact of failure after various stress–time sequences is observable. If hypothesis (2) should happen to be correct, then the equations derived above could be established, but only by means of a rather extensive set of experiments. (The very smallest set of experiments which could be interpreted as even being in positive harmony with the hypothesis, let alone definitely establishing it, would be the breaking time at each of three stresses, plus six experiments in which the six possible two-stress sequences were employed. Each of these nine experiments would have to be repeated many times, to determine the *mean* values of the times involved. And all these determinations would have to be made with samples as nearly identical as possible.)

If the process of breakdown could be followed directly by means of the continuous change in some observable property of the material, the quantity B would take on a more definite meaning. This is not entirely outside the range of possibility. Haward observed that before breaking, acetate samples gradually became white and opaque, indicating a heterogeneity of the weakened material. The breakdown process could presumably be followed by optical means—at least in the later stages. The *thermodynamic* properties of the weakened polymer would differ only very slightly from those of the original, but it is possible that differences in the vapor pressure–concentration curve for swelling agents could be detected. Finally, the mechanical properties of a weakened polymer, as measured by some standard test, might serve to indicate the degree of breakdown. In Haward's form of hypothesis (2), the role of B is played by the quantity (original strength − weakened strength). This would indicate the use of a rapid strength test, perhaps an impact test, to measure B.

C. Ultimate Strength from the Stress–Strain Curve

Investigations such as those of Haward, Midgley, Pierce, Busse, etc., yield a fairly detailed picture of the process of weakening or fatigue which precedes failure. The overwhelming majority of ultimate strength data, however, are obtained in a very different manner, namely, from the stress–strain curve of the material, usually measured at constant rate of deforma-

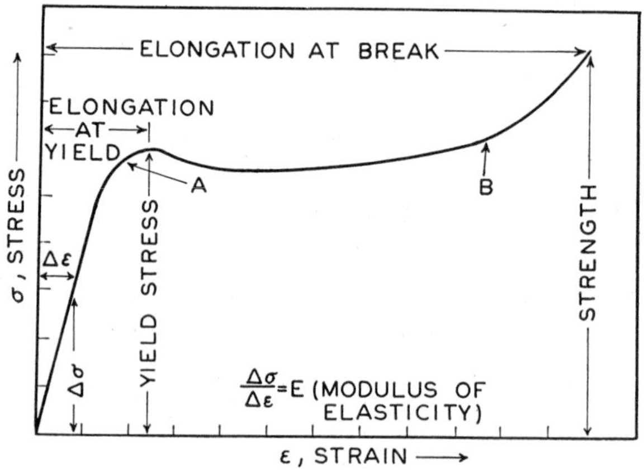

Fig. 213. General form of stress–strain curve for a plastic material (after Carswell and Nason).

tion. If a sample is forcibly deformed (*e.g.*, elongated) at constant rate, there is little breakdown, or loss of strength, at the beginning, because the stress is small. As the extension proceeds, and the stress increases, breakdown becomes more and more rapid. Finally, the sample breaks. Often before breaking takes place the stress, computed on the basis of the original cross section, passes through a maximum and then decreases. The maximum stress supported by the sample is taken as a measure of the ultimate strength. The extension at break is an important associated property. It is clear that both the tensile strength and the elongation at break are more or less dependent upon the *rate* of elongation (cross-head speed). For a material with a $t_b(S)$ function like that of cellulose acetate (Fig. 212), one would expect to observe the largest tensile strengths at the highest cross-head rates and *vice versa*. In order to make any appreciable change in the observed ultimate strength, however, it would be necessary to change the cross-head speed by a sizable factor. For this reason the ultimate strength as determined from a stress–strain curve can probably be safely considered as a good indication of the strength of the material in a given range of experimental timescale. In general, the material will be able to support decidedly larger stresses for very short intervals of time, and on the other hand, much smaller stresses can cause failure if given a sufficiently long time. Two materials with the same tensile strength as measured at one cross-head speed will not necessarily be equal in strength at a different rate of testing.

The stress–strain curves of a wide variety of organic plastics follow the general pattern of figure 213. Carswell and Nason (*27*) point out the utility of such curves in evaluating the ultimate strength properties of a (plastic) as follows:

> The stress–strain curve, whether in tension, compression, bending, or shear, provides a wealth of information concerning the mechanical properties of a material, and a careful examination of stress–strain data at several conditions of temperature (or of other ambient variables) will usually furnish a reasonably accurate picture of the material's behavior.
>
> The stress–strain curve of nearly any plastic material, at equilibrium with any environment, can be represented by a portion of Fig. 213 provided that: (*a*) the curve is obtained by a constant-rate-of-straining type of test, and, (*b*) the point of rupture of the test specimen may occur at any point on the curve. Thus, the behavior of a typical ductile material, such as cellulose acetate at room conditions, may be represented by the entire curve, with the break occurring at point *B*. The behavior of a relatively non-ductile material, such as polystyrene, may be represented by the early portion of the curve only, with rupture occurring at point *A*.
>
> The slope of the initial, straight-line portion of the curve, where stress and strain are more or less proportional, is a measure of the stiffness or rigidity of the material. The ratio of stress to strain in this region is known as the "modulus of elasticity" or "Young's modulus," and is commonly used as a measure of stiffness. The stress at the first knee in the curve, sometimes known as "yield point," is a measure of the strength of the material and of its resistance to permanent deformation. The stress at the breaking point, commonly known as "ultimate strength" or "breaking strength," is a measure of the force required to fracture the material. In those portions of the curve before the "yield point" is reached, elongations are, in large part at least, recoverable, and are a measure of elastic deformation. The elongation from the yield point to the point of rupture, however, is not immediately recoverable, and is a measure of plastic deformation. The area under the stress–strain curve, which represents the work required to fracture the test specimen, is a rough measure of toughness.
>
> In general:
>
> *Soft, weak* materials show low modulus, low yield point, low elongation at rupture.

Hard, brittle materials show high modulus, no well-defined yield point, and low elongation at break.

Soft, tough materials show low modulus, low yield point, and high elongation and high stress at break.

Hard, strong materials show high modulus, high yield point, and moderate elongation.

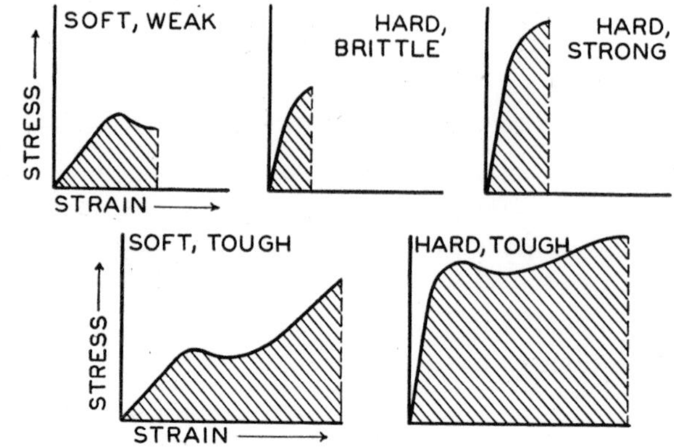

Fig. 214. Stress–strain curves for different types of material.

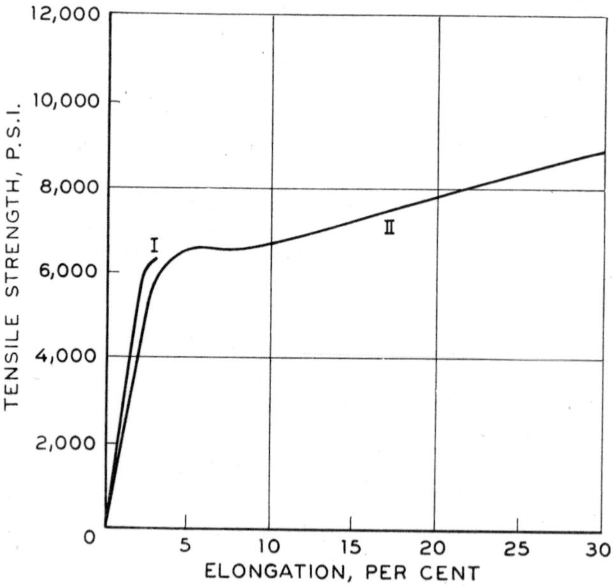

Fig. 215. Stress–strain curves for "brittle" and "tough" thermoplastics: (I) polystyrene; (II) ethyl cellulose.

Hard, tough materials show high modulus, high yield point, high elongation, and high breaking stress.

Stress–strain curves representative of these types of materials are shown in Fig. 214. Figure 215 illustrates these ideas for the "brittle" and "tough" thermoplastics, polystyrene and ethyl cellulose; and Fig. 216 provides similar illustrations for the "brittle" and "tough" thermosetting plastics, wood flour-filled and cotton cord-filled phenolics.

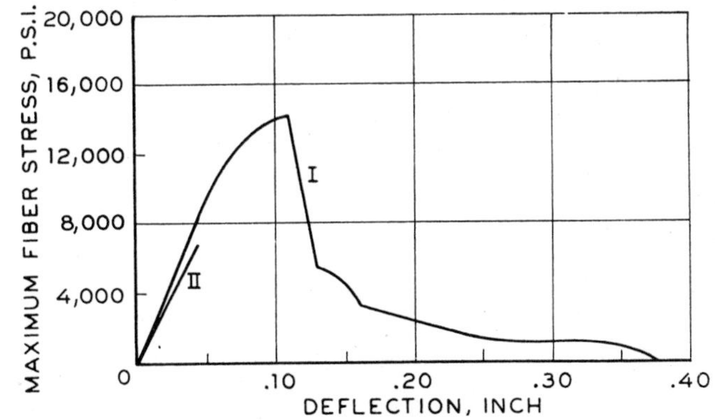

Fig. 216. Stress–strain curves for "brittle" and "tough" thermosetting plastics: (I) cotton cord-filled phenolic; (II) wood flour-filled phenolic.

The important thing to recognize is that not merely the point of actual rupture, but the entire plastic region A–B, should be considered as *failure* phenomena. In this region of the stress–strain curve, irreversible structural changes are occurring which cannot be adequately analyzed in terms only of viscoelastic deformation. These processes are thus analogous to those occurring in a specimen subjected to a large static load. If the straining were stopped before rupture occurred, presumably most of the strain could be removed by proper heat or solvent treatment, but the sample would nevertheless be permanently *weakened* by the previous overstraining. In the case of a polymer which can be crystallized by stretching, or which already contains crystallites that can be oriented by stretching, the structural changes may *strengthen*, rather than *weaken*, the material.

2. Impact Strength

To quote in part, from Gilkey, Murphy, and Bergman (*3*):

Impact loads are loads which are applied suddenly or with shock. The essential difference between static and impact loads is that an impact load always produces a peak stress higher than that produced by a load of the same magnitude if it is applied slowly.

For example, if a weight is applied slowly to the end of a horizontal cantilever beam, the beam deflects slowly to a maximum. During the interval of application of the load, the stresses and strains gradually attain their maximum static values without overrun. If the same load is applied suddenly, without being dropped, the beam deflects twice * as much as it does under the slowly applied load, then springs back almost to the unloaded position, again deflects, and continues to vibrate until it comes to equilibrium in the same position as it does under the slowly applied load. The stresses and strains follow the same cycle of vibrations, attaining temporarily twice the value which they would have if the same load were applied slowly. Thus the rapidly applied load not only produces a range of stress higher than that attained at any stage under a static load of numerically equal magnitude, but it also introduces elements of repeated or fatigue loading because of the induced vibrations. In design for suddenly applied loading (no shock beyond that of 'instantaneous' application), the possible added adverse effect of the induced vibration is disregarded and the load is considered to stress the member twice as severely as it would if the same load were applied statically. If the load is dropped on the member, the general effect will be the same as that of the suddenly applied load, but the deflections, stresses, and strains will be more than twice as much as they would be if the load were applied slowly. Any load which causes vibration is in effect an impact load. . . .

Impact tests are sometimes made on materials, particularly metals, because it is recognized that the resistance of a material to shock is dependent upon factors other than those which control its resistance to a steady or slowly applied load. Resistance to a slowly applied load may be measured in terms of stress, but resistance to impact involves, in addition to the capacity for developing stress, the capacity of the material for being deformed without damage. . . The resistance of a material to impact loading, if all the material develops the same stress, is measured approximately by the area under the stress–strain diagram.† If the same stress is not developed throughout the entire specimen, the distribution of energy is likewise nonuniform, with the result that any determination of the shock-resisting capacity of a given material, or even of a given specimen, becomes largely empirical.

Standardized impact tests on standardized specimens have been developed to provide a basis for comparing the resistance of materials to shock. The results of such tests are valuable in a qualitative but not a quantitative sense. In general, numerical values obtained from the present standard impact tests are not valid for predicting the impact resistance of dissimilar specimen of the same material.

The essential ultimate property measured in an impact test is thus not the maximum *stress* supported by the sample, but rather the amount of *energy* necessary to cause failure. This is connected with the area under the load–deformation curve, and is therefore dependent upon both the ultimate stress value and the *slope* of the load–deformation curve.

* Provided the proportional limit is not exceeded. If it is exceeded, the deflection will be more than twice as much and the final deflection will also be increased.

† This is based on the usual assumption that a material resists an energy load in the same manner as it does a static load. For very rapid applications of load the validity of this assumption is doubtful.

We have already seen the way in which the slope of the load–deformation curve depends upon the rate of testing. For a high polymer, a high *rate* of loading means in general a steep load–deformation curve. Let us assume a straight-line curve, and represent the slope by an apparent modulus E, and the ultimate stress by S_m, then the energy of deformation up to the breaking point is given by:

$$W = \frac{1}{2\,E} S_m^2 \tag{5}$$

A rubberlike material, with low E, will thus have a high impact resistance. A hard material (large E) with the same ultimate strength, S_m, will have a lower impact "strength." From this fact arises the general impression that a hard material is likely to be brittle, and a flexible material to be tough, in an impact test. This is not always true, however, because of the aforementioned dependence of the load–deformation curve upon *rate* of loading. Retarded elasticity, with a retardation time a little below the timescale of ordinary tests, but well above the timescale of an impact test, may result in "anomalous" impact failure. Such a material will be flexible in a slow test, but exhibit a *steep* load–deformation curve under impact conditions, and hence a brittle fracture.

Presumably the effect of different variables, such as temperature, molecular weight, plasticizers, etc., upon impact strength, could be roughly resolved into the effects of these variables upon high speed modulus and upon ultimate strength, S_m.

IV. CORRELATION BETWEEN STRUCTURE AND TENSILE STRENGTH

1. Dependence on Molecular Weight

The dependence of the tensile strength of a high polymer upon chain length (average molecular weight) is qualitatively the same for all polymers. A polymer of very low molecular weight is extremely weak. As molecular weight goes up, tensile strength also increases. For a while, strength is roughly proportional to molecular weight. Later, the curve relating the two quantities levels off; after a certain molecular weight is reached, further increases in molecular weight do not result in appreciable improvements in strength. Figure 217 shows some typical strength *vs.* molecular weight curves for various types of polymers. It is seen that the leveling off of the curve comes at a lower polymerization degree

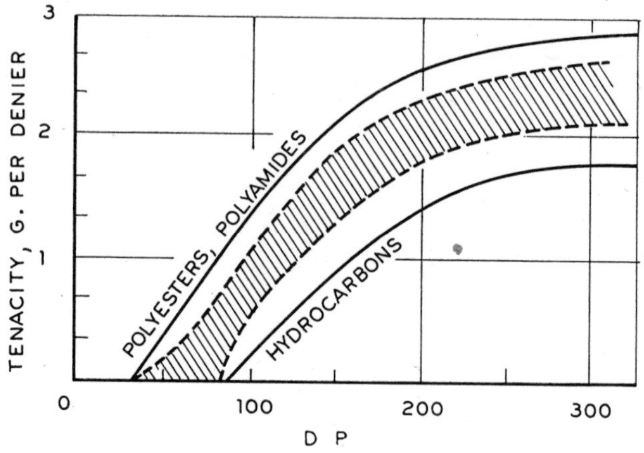

Fig. 217. Tensile strength as a function of DP (after Mark).

for polymers whose molecules strongly attract each other than for polymers with weak intermolecular forces.

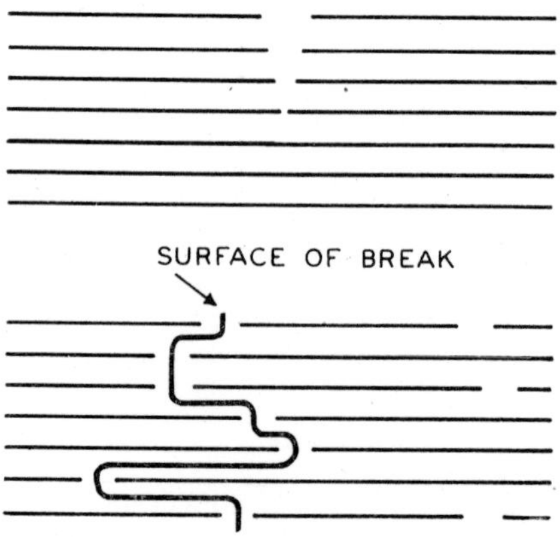

Fig. 218. Weak intermolecular forces allow molecules to slip past one another (top). Accumulation of many weak intermolecular forces holds chains firmly together; individual chains will *break* before slippage occurs (bottom).

One might deduce from these curves that a low molecular weight polymer breaks mainly by pulling apart two intertangled groups of tangled chain ends, whereas a high molecular weight sample breaks largely by the rupture of primary valence chains.

Meyer and Mark (in their book) discuss these two mechanisms of failure in the case of fibrous polymers. They point out that, in a polymer of relatively low molecular weight, neighboring chains can slip past one another, so that the sample breaks without the rupture of primary valence chains (see Fig. 218). With a very high molecular weight sample, this sort of failure would require that long sections of molecular chains would have to slide past one another. Now while the intermolecular forces between any two monomeric segments in neighboring molecules are much weaker than the primary valence forces within a chain, a large number of these intermolecular forces will add up to an enormous amount, so that it will be easier to break the primary valence bonds of the individual molecules than to make the molecules slip past each other (see Fig. 218).

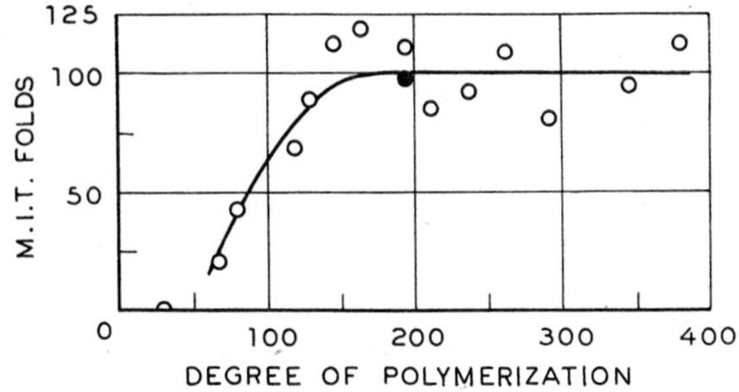

Fig. 219. Fold resistance of cellulose acetate as a function of polymerization degree (after Sookne and Harris).

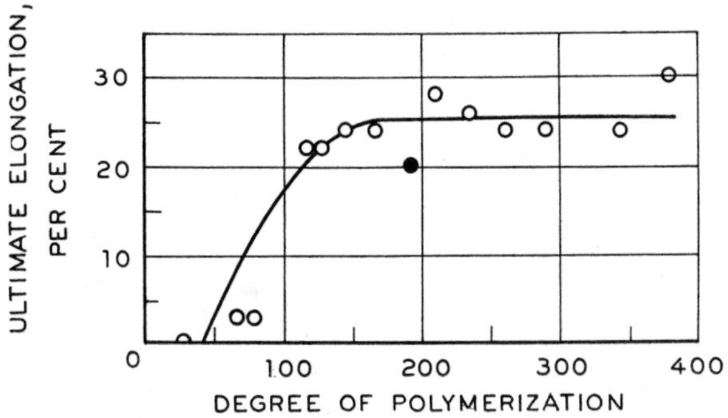

Fig. 220. Ultimate elongation of cellulose acetate as a function of polymerization degree (after Sookne and Harris).

Other mechanical properties, closely related with ultimate tensile strength, show the same general sort of dependence upon molecular weight. Figures 219 and 220 show how fold resistance, and ultimate elongation, vary with chain length for cellulose acetate.

2. Influence of Molecular Weight Distribution

Having seen how ultimate mechanical properties—strength, elongation, etc.—depend upon average molecular weight, the next question is the dependence upon the detailed shape of the molecular weight distribution curve. What effect does the *broadness*, or the *smoothness* of the molecular weight distribution curve, or the amount of very high and very low molecular weight material, have upon the ultimate strength and upon related mechanical properties? These questions cannot be answered

TABLE XXVII

SUMMARY OF REPORTED OBSERVATIONS ON CONNECTION BETWEEN MOLECULAR WEIGHT DISTRIBUTION AND STRENGTH PROPERTIES

Material	Mechanical properties investigated	Conclusions	Investigator
Cellulose acetate films	Tensile strength	Blends superior to fractions of corresponding DP	Rocha
Cellulose acetate filaments	Tensile strength	Blends superior to fractions of corresponding DP	Ohl
Cellulose acetate filaments	Tensile strength	Materials of low DP exert a harmful effect, and those of intermediate DP a beneficial effect on tensile strengths of blends of same average DP	Mark
Cellulose nitrate films	Load–elongation curve	In region of plastic flow of load–extension curve, blends required a higher load to produce a given elongation than do fractions of corresponding DP	Medvedev
Cellulose nitrate films	Tensile strength and ultimate elongation	Little difference between fractions and blends	Rogovin and Glazman
Cellulose nitrate films	Tensile strength, ultimate elongation, and folding endurance	Folding endurance of blends inferior to those of fractions of corresponding DP tensile strengths and ultimate elongation relatively insensitive to changes in heterogeneity	Spurlin
Viscose filaments	Numerous measures of strength and flexibility	Material of low DP exerts a disproportionate harmful influence on mechanical properties of blends	Schieber
Vinyl chloride acetate copolymer plastic	Numerous measures of strength and flexibility	Blend inferior in fatigue resistance and approximately equal in strength to a fraction of corresponding DP	Douglas and Stoops

categorically at the present time. Some investigators have reported that sharp molecular weight fractions give films or filaments with strengths superior to those prepared from blends of these fractions. Others have reported that the blends are superior, or have found little difference between blends and fractions. Sookne and Harris (*144*, *145*) have summarized the literature on this subject (see Table XXVII).

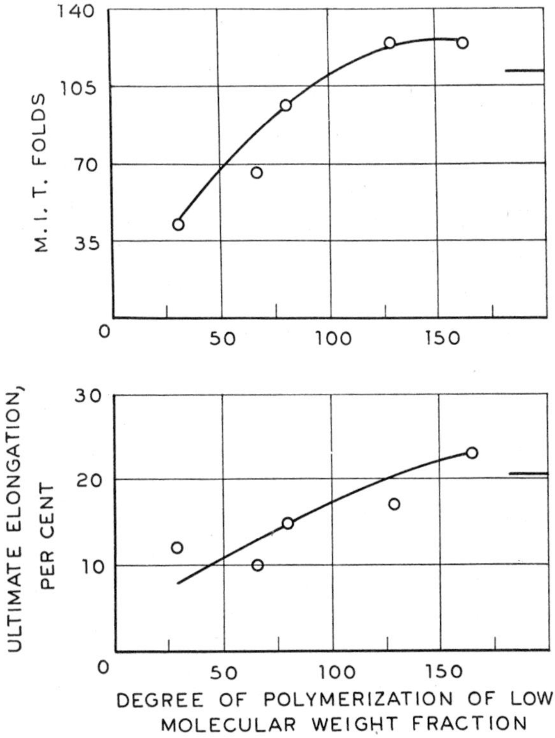

Fig. 221. Mechanical properties of cellulose acetate blends having a weight average DP of 200, and composed of mixtures of a high molecular (DP 380) and a low molecular fraction.

Sookne and Harris, using cellulose acetate, have made what seems to be the most thorough experimental investigation of this question in the case of films. Their results can be summarized as follows:

Fold resistance is more sensitive to molecular heterogeneity than ultimate elongation, and the latter in turn is more sensitive than tensile strength. Low molecular weight material has a disproportionately large harmful effect on all these properties. Figure 221 represents the mechanical properties of a series of blends, all of weight average DP 200. The blends are composed of fractions of DP values 380 and X. The mechanical properties are plotted as functions of X, the viscometric polymerization degree of the low molecular weight component fraction. The deleterious effect of low molecular weight material is clear.

Sookne and Harris found that if they calculated the *number average* polymerization degree of their acetate blends, and compared samples upon this basis, there was little variation in properties among different blends having the same number average DP. That is, the deleterious effect of any low molecular weight components is disproportionate to its concentration on a weight basis, but not to its concentration on a number basis. (Calculation on a number basis automatically gives a preferential weighting to the effects of low molecular weight material, since even a moderate weight fraction of such material represents a large number of molecules.) Spurlin has pointed out, in a private communication to Sookne and Harris, that this result is qualitatively consistent with the concept that a sample will rupture more readily when a sufficient number of chain ends exists close together in the test specimen. The number of chain ends, of course, depends only upon the total number of molecules, regardless of the distribution among molecular weights.

Spurlin (*146*) found that at a given DP nitrocellulose fractions gave films which were superior in folding endurance to those prepared from straight-run commercial nitrocellulose, and that the latter were in turn superior to blends of the straight-run materials. From this it was concluded that a reasonably *smooth* distribution curve is desirable in order to obtain good fold endurance. Sookne and Harris point out that these data might possibly indicate the deleterious effect of low molecular weight components, rather than of lack of *smoothness* in the distribution curve. Since Spurlin's blends were not prepared from fractions, it was impossible to calculate number average molecular weights. His data, however, are qualitatively consistent with those of Sookne and Harris.

To summarize, the effect of the detailed form of the molecular weight distribution curve upon strength properties of films composed of high polymeric materials is not yet known to a completely satisfactory degree. The following conclusions seem warranted, however:

(1) By far the most important characteristic of a molecular weight distribution is the *average* molecular weight of the sample. Probably the

number average molecular weight specifies the strength properties more definitely than does the weight average value.

(2) Short molecular chains have a deleterious effect far out of proportion to their weight fraction in the sample. The effects of such low molecular weight constituents in some cases at least may be simply determined by the *number* of such molecules.

(3) It has never been proved, for any high polymer, that small details of the molecular weight distribution curve have any appreciable affect on the strength characteristics of cast films. By "small details" are meant such features as *smoothness*, general contour, etc.

The finding of Sookne and Harris, that the strength characteristics of their fractions and blends were defined by the single variable M_N, did not extend over a very wide range of molecular weight, and cannot be considered to be a completely established principle. However, it is supported by a reasonable quasi theoretical explanation. Furthermore, no experimental investigation of comparable thoroughness and precision has produced data in essential contradiction to this finding.

At the moment, therefore, it seems likely that the strength properties of a cast film, during the formation of which the molecules had no chance of arranging themselves in an advantageous way, are almost entirely controlled by the *gross features* of the molecular weight distribution curve, rather than by fine details.

Mark has pointed out, however, that the situation seems to be somewhat more involved in the case of spun filaments. During the spinning of a filament, a certain amount of enforced molecular orientation takes place. As a result of this orientation, the tensile strength of a spun filament (along the direction of the fiber axis) is much higher than the tensile strength of the same polymer in the form of an unoriented cast film. If it seems reasonable, as Harris and Sookne suggest, that the effect of molecular weight distribution curve in a cast film arises only from the number of chain ends, it seems equally probable that this is *not* true in the case of a spun filament. Polymers with different distribution curves will differ in the way they respond to the spinning process. The strength of the resulting filaments will depend not only upon the total number of chain ends, but also upon the relative spatial arrangements of these chain ends, which in turn depends upon the response to the spinning process. It may be expected, therefore, that the strength of a spun filament will be much more sensitive to the detailed form of the molecular weight distribution curve than will the strength of a cast film.

3. Influence of Crystallization and Orientation on Tensile Strength

The influence of crystallization and orientation of high polymers on the ultimate tenacity of the material is an intriguing scientific problem and a matter of considerable practical importance.

R. O. Herzog (*cf. 5*) was the first to note and publish that the tensile strength of viscose and cuprammonium rayon appears to increase as the x-ray pattern of the filaments indicate improved alignment of the crystallized domains of the cellulose parallel to the fiber axis. Industrial research of Thiele, Lilienfeld, Weissenberg, and many other workers established the importance of stretch spinning and the spectacular phenomenon of drawing of polyamides, discovered by Carothers, made it obvious that orientation either of individual chain molecules or of groups of them was of decisive influence on the ultimate tenacity of the sample and, in fact, on the whole shape of its stress–strain curve. Whenever, in the course of a stretching, drawing, or rolling operation flexible long chain molecules are parallelized and aligned, there becomes noticeable a certain tendency of them to improve the geometric order along the axes of the chains and, by mutual van der Waals' interaction, the formation of micelles or elongated crystallites takes place. Orientation of linear polymers is therefore frequently, though not always, accompanied by crystallization and the first question which arises is about the relative importance of the two phenomena "orientation" and "crystallization" on the tensile strength of the material.

The only material for which at least a limited amount of direct experimental evidence, bearing on this question, exists, is native Hevea crepe rubber. Experiments by Mark and Valko (*100, 101*), Hauk and Neumann (*58*), and others were carried out between 1930 and 1938 to contribute some facts about the influence of orientation and crystallization separated from each other. Some of the results were published in the articles referred to in the bibliography, the others remained unpublished because of the circumstances. We shall give here a brief review of the more important results of this investigation.

In the case of rubber, it is possible to separate the influence of orientation and crystallization with a fair degree of accuracy. Hevea pale crepe rubber was dissolved in toluene and films of 5 to 15 mils were cast on glass plates. These films were cut in strips and, in the unstretched state, showed no signs of either planar or axial orientation. If stretched to 600%, a very distinct x-ray crystal pattern appeared in a short-time diagram, but started to fade out, after a few minutes, because of the rapid relaxation of the stress in the uncured sample. However, if cooled down to −80°C., the tension was maintained for many hours and experiments could be carried out with the stretched rubber band without difficulties.

The first test was to cut two identical strips from one of the films, orient one of them by stretching up to 600% of its original length, cool both strips down to −80°C. and measure their tensile strength. The stress–strain curve of the samples at the low temperature was taken with an instrument as described by Polanyi and Schmid (*124*) and by Valko (*100*). Figure 222 shows the stress–strain curves of the two samples. It can be seen that the tenacity of the *oriented* and *crystallized* sample (b) is about six times larger than that of the *unoriented, amorphous* material. The elongation to break is, in both cases, very small, because the loading took place at a temperature below the brittle point of the material and, at any rate, so fast (about 1 in. per min.) that no appreciable amount of long range delayed elasticity or plastic flow could develop. The two curves of figure 222 and the corresponding figures in the table represent

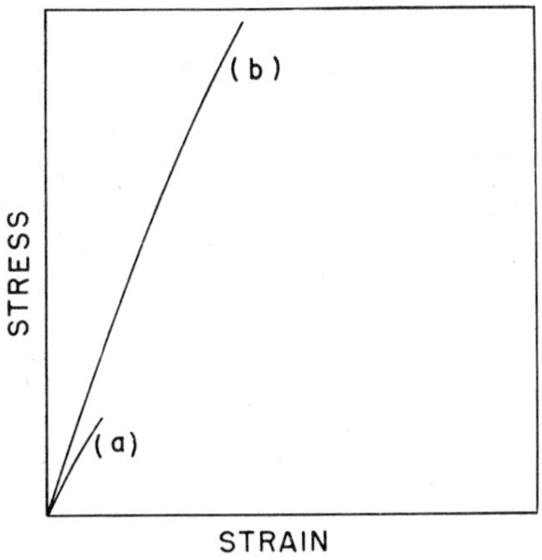

Fig. 222. Stress–strain curves of two samples of Hevea pale crepe rubber.

Prestretching at room temperature, %	Tenacity at −195°C., kg./sq. cm.	
	Latex rubber film	Soft gum stock
0	360	500
200	725	960
400	1390	2330
600	2050	3350

the *combined* influence of orientation and crystallization. In order to separate the two effects the following procedure was adopted. Another pair of strips were taken; one of them was cooled down rapidly from room temperature to −80°C. and kept there; the other was brought to about

0°C., stretched and relaxed several times, kept at that temperature for several weeks, and then cooled down to −80°C. It is known that, under such conditions, native rubber undergoes spontaneous crystallization without stretching and the crystals are entirely at random as is proved by the unoriented powder diagram which such a sample exhibits. The two samples were tested at −80°C. and the unoriented crystallized material found to be almost twice as strong as the unoriented amorphous sample. One may conclude that the amount of crystallization that had taken place during the slow cooling procedure has about doubled the ultimate strength of the material. There were no quantitative intensity measurements or accurate specific gravity measurements carried out with this crystallized sample and, therefore, unfortunately nothing quantitative can be said about how much of the rubber had undergone crystallization. However, qualitatively, it was a highly crystallized sample and one may conclude that crystallization of native rubber of this kind without orientation increases the ultimate strength by a factor of approximately two.

The next experiment was to compare an oriented, but not crystallized sample with an unoriented uncrystallized test piece. After a number of unsuccessful experiments, it was recognized that this cannot be done with native (unvulcanized) rubber, because, whenever one attempts to melt the crystallized domains in an oriented and crystallized test piece, stress relaxation sets in and one loses the orientation together with the crystallinity. It turned out, however, that the experiment can be carried out with slightly vulcanized samples. The rubber films as described above were therefore exposed to an atmosphere of sulfuryl chloride vapor for a few minutes in a desiccator and a low degree of cross linking was produced throughout the samples, which showed sulfur contents between 0.2 and 0.8%. If one stretches such slightly vulcanized rubber bands to about 800 or 900% of their original length, they maintain the tension and the crystallized x-ray pattern for a long time, showing that the individual chains cannot glide along each other and coil up into a relaxed state. However, if one heats such a band under tension to about 70° or 80°C., the crystalline x-ray pattern disappears and is replaced by a diagram indicating that the chains are still parallel to each other, but have lost the strict lateral arrangement which is characteristic for the crystalline phase. Figure 223 shows an example of a diagram of an amorphous, but oriented, rubber. If such a stretched sample is rapidly cooled down to a temperature below freezing point, it retains its peculiar structure because the parallelized chain molecules do not have sufficient time to assume in all details the regular positions needed to produce a three-dimensional crystal lattice: The sample remains oriented, but does not crystallize. Stress–strain curves taken with such samples at low temperatures reveal that their tenacity is higher than that of an unoriented uncrystallized and also higher than that of an unoriented, crystallized specimen under comparable experimental conditions. Data obtained show that the axial orientation of the long chain molecules has the predominant influence on the ultimate strength of the material. Complete lateral orientation of the chains, which is equivalent with crystallization, contributes another increment to tenacity.

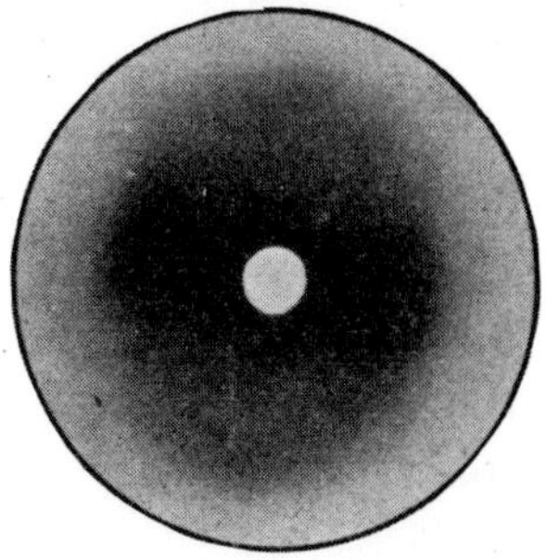

Fig. 223. X-ray diagram of amorphous, oriented rubber.

The experiments described above are restricted to soft rubber, but there is ample evidence that this phenomenon is of rather general character. A few further facts are the following: polystyrene rods or filaments become extensible above 80°C. and can be stretched in this condition up to and above 100% of their original length. Upon rapid cooling below their brittle point (around 80°C.) such samples remain oriented, as shown by strong birefringence and anisotropic mechanical behavior. However, the material does not crystallize. It may be that the phenyl groups are not sufficiently regularly distributed along the chains to permit so well defined lateral distances between the parallelized linear molecules to have x-rays scattered in sharply defined directions. Such oriented polystyrene rods and fibers have been compared with unoriented samples of the same material and it was found that the tenacity of the oriented samples along the axis is between three and four times that of the unoriented material. In connection with this investigation it was observed that polymers of different average degree of polymerization differ in the ease with which they can be oriented by a stretching operation above their brittle point. The longer the chain molecules, the easier it is, in general, to produce a certain degree of orientation. It was also found that polymers, prepared under different experimental conditions, such as temperature, nature and concentration of the catalyst, extent of conversion, etc., show a different degree of orientability.

Another experiment which indicates the influence of orientation alone is to cast a thin film of the polymer under consideration, stretch it to a certain degree (between 100 and 200% of its original length), cut strips out of the stretched film at various angles to the direction of stretch and determine the tenacity of these strips. Such experiments were carried out with films of cellulose, cellulose nitrate, and cellulose acetate. The data show a few values indicating the ultimate strength of such strips (cut from an oriented cellulose acetate film) as depending upon the angle between the direction of the stretch of the original film and the axis of the strip, the tenacity of which was tested. It can be seen that the transversal tenacity is only about one-sixth of the longitudinal tensile strength. Compared with the results on rubber and polystyrene, this seems to be very low, but it must be kept in mind that this lateral tenacity does not refer to the unoriented material (as it does in the case of rubber and polystyrene), but to a material oriented in the wrong way, namely, perpendicular to the direction in which the tensile strength is measured.

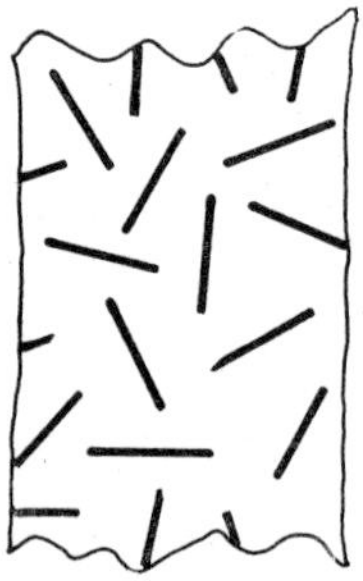

Fig. 224. Suspension of rigid rodlike particles.

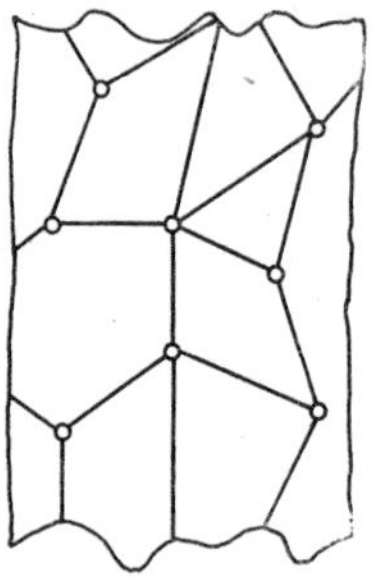

Fig. 225. Network of crystallites connected by flexible joints.

Recently Berkley (*19*) and Kerr (*79*), in a series of very interesting investigations, showed that in cotton there exists a rather close connection between orientation and tenacity at the same (or very approximately the same) degree of crystallinity and they have even used the orientation of a sample to predict its tenacity successfully. Considering, therefore, the influence of orientation alone, there are obviously *two* questions which have to be answered in order to get at an understanding of the influence of stretching on the ultimate strength of polymers:

(1) How does the orientation of a given sample depend upon the degree of stretching which the material has undergone?

(2) How does the tensile strength depend upon orientation?

Numerous contributions have been made by Hermans (*65–68*), Kratky (*82, 83*), Platzek (*68*), Oka (*116*), and others to the first of these two problems. Working with cellulose, cellulose xanthate, and cellulose acetate at different degrees of swelling, it has been shown that each individual sample behaves as if it were a mixture of *two extreme cases*, the behavior of which one can at least approximately describe with the aid of a mathematical analysis.

The first extreme case is represented by a suspension of rigid, rodlike particles of a certain axis ratio in a viscous liquid (Figs. 224, 225). If such a system is subjected to a shear action, the liquid will flow, and a certain parallelization of the elongated particles will result. Assuming this

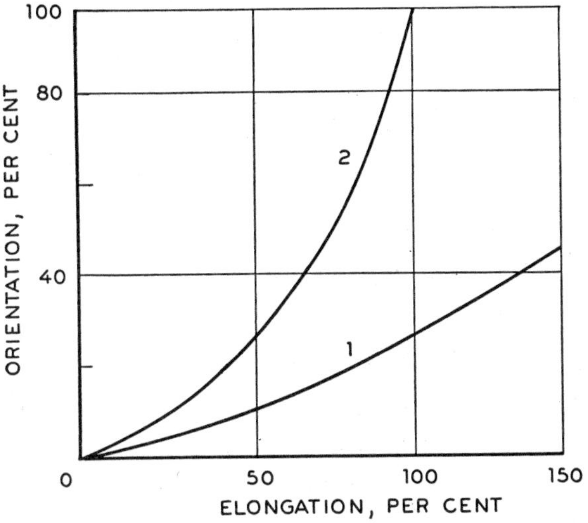

Fig. 226. Orientation as a function of elongation for two types of structure: (1) structure of figure 224; (2) structure of figure 225.

model, one can express the number of particles, the axes of which fall into a differential cone which includes an angle between α and $\alpha + d\alpha$ with the direction of the stress, as a function of the elongation by the following equation:

$$N(\alpha)\, d\alpha = N_0 \frac{v^3\, d\alpha}{[1 + (v^3 - 1)\sin^2 \alpha]^{3/2}} \qquad (6)$$

where $N(\alpha)$ = number of crystallites whose long axis makes an angle between α and $\alpha + d\alpha$ with the fiber axis, N_0 = total number of crystallites, and v = relative elongation of the sample.

Figure 226 represents graphically the relationship expressed in equation (6). One sees that systems of this (extreme) type need comparatively high elongations in order to achieve a noticeable degree of orientation. It does not lend itself easily to orientation, which is not implausable if one considers that the particles do not exert any direct influence upon each other, but are merely oriented and aligned by the flow of the viscous medium in which they are embedded.

The other extreme case is represented by a network of elongated particles such as crystallites or bundles of chain molecules which are connected by flexible joints. Figure 225 tries to give a schematic picture of such a system. If one extends a film or filament having this structure, one produces, very efficiently, parallelization of the rodlike particles because they can swing into the direction of the stress by rotation at the junction points.

Hermans and Kratky (*66*) have derived a mathematical expression between elongation and orientation in a system of this kind:

$$N(\alpha)\, d\alpha = N_0 e^{2r}\, d\alpha[1 + \tan^2(\alpha/2)]^2[1 + e^{2r}\tan^2(\alpha/2)]^{-1/2} \quad (7)$$

where $N(\alpha)$ = number of crystallites whose long axis has an angle between α and $\alpha + d\alpha$ with the fiber axis, N_0 = total number of crystallites, and r is connected with v by the following equation:

$$v = [\sinh 2r - 2v + 2v \ln \cosh r][\sinh r]^2 \quad (8)$$

where v = relative elongation of the sample.

Curve 2 in figure 226 is a graphical expression of equation (8). It can be seen that, in this extreme case, the sample is much more susceptible to orientation than before. The curve rises steeply, and reaches complete orientation already at an elongation of 100%.

Equations (6) and (7) hold for the extreme cases of very weak and very strong interaction between the suspended particles and are fictitious cases; each actual sample of a given polymer, however, can be considered approximately as being a certain mixture of these two limiting cases; its orientation–elongation curve will fall between the two curves of figure 226. If a solution is very dilute, a gel thoroughly swollen or a polymer highly plasticized, curve 1 of figure 226 will be approached. On the other hand, concentrated solutions, stiff gels, and unplasticized samples will behave more like curve 2.

In order to check experimentally equations (6) and (7), it is necessary to measure the orientation of a polymer caused by a certain elongation. There are several methods to determine the degree of orientation in a stretched sample:

(1) Most polymers exhibit, in the unstretched state, an x-ray pattern, which either consists of a number of sharp rings or of a few diffuse halos. The first case indicates the presence of a large number of very small crystallites (bundles of chains, micelles) which are arranged entirely at random; the second points to the existence of a liquidlike structure in which only a short (4 to 8 Å.) range order but no long (50 Å. or more) range organization exists. The intensity of the rings and halos extends over their whole circumference 2π. If the sample is oriented by stretch or shear the rings or halos degenerate into two segments, which are arranged symmetrically on both sides of the incident beam. Let the angle at which the intensity of each segment reaches half of the maximum intensity be β. Then the total angular half intensity width is 2β and the degree of orientation can be expressed by:

$$O = \frac{180 - \beta}{180} \tag{9}$$

If $\beta = 180$, O is zero and the sample is unoriented; if $\beta = 0$, O is unity and the sample is completely oriented; O ranges from zero to one. This method is particularly applicable to crystallized samples. It requires good x-ray patterns, careful consideration of absorption of the radiation in the sample and photometric or ionometric intensity measurements; if properly handled it gives rather reproducible and reliable determinations of the orientation of polymers.

(2) Solutions, highly swollen gels, or plasticized polymers frequently do not give appealing x-ray diagrams at all but only produce on the film a very diffuse and indefinite halo, the intensity of which cannot be measured satisfactorily. In such cases one has to resort to other experimental methods to determine the (complete or partial) orientation of the long chain molecules, which causes the sample to become *anisotropic.* One well known and well developed method is the optical birefringence of oriented fibers or films, which permits at least a relative determination of the degree of orientation. It has been found that, in general, the polarizability of a linear molecule is larger parallel to its axis than perpendicular to it. This rule, which is in agreement with the consequences of Silberstein's theory, is only violated (again in conformity with the theory) if the chain possesses substituents of high polarizability, such as the nitro groups in cellulose nitrate. In general, however, the double refraction of oriented chain polymers is positive; the larger refractive index is found to exist parallel to the direction along which the chains have been oriented. When comparative observations have been carried out (cellulose acetate,

cellulose xanthate, and rubber) it appears that x-ray diagram and double refraction lead to compatible results as to the degree of orientation in stretched filaments or films. When the x-ray method is not applicable (polystyrene, vinyl type copolymers, vinyl–diene copolymers) one observes a considerable degree of birefringence in stretched samples, which—in the absence of a vigorous quantitative theory—permits at least an empirical determination of orientation.

(3) A third method for measuring the orientation of amorphous or disordered samples is the anisotropy of swelling. If objects with randomly arranged macromolecules are brought into a swelling agent they undergo an isotropic volume increase. As soon, however, as the chain molecules become aligned and parallelized in a certain direction, the sample shows increased swelling perpendicular to this direction. This is because the cohesion of the material perpendicular to the linear molecules is established by comparatively weak, van der Waals' forces, which allow the swelling agent to penetrate and to displace the main valence chains perpendicular to their own axis. Along the axes of the chains, strong covalent bonds are active, which give the sample a high degree of rigidity in this direction and prevent the molecules of the swelling agent from forming any layers perpendicular to the direction of stretch. A highly oriented sample shows, therefore, *more* swelling *perpendicular* to the direction of orientation than parallel to it. This is just opposite to the normal behavior of double refraction, where the *larger* refractive index is usually *parallel* to the direction of orientation.

(4) There exist a few other methods for the determination of the anisotropy of oriented chain polymers, such as the coefficient of thermal expansion, the elastic modulus in tension and compression, and the dielectric constant. The coefficient of thermal expansion of a stretched monofilament of polystyrene was found to be twice as large perpendicular to the direction of the stretch than parallel to it; for stretched rubber a very considerable anisotropy of all mechanical properties was observed. The elastic moduli in tension and compression are larger parallel to the direction of the stretch, which is obviously caused by the stronger forces which provide for the cohesion of the sample in this direction.

(5) Finally, it may be mentioned that the adsorption of anisotropic dyestuff molecules has proved in some cases to be a very valuable help in the detection of small degrees of orientation. Such molecules are very susceptible to orientation of their own through adsorption on an oriented substrate and can be used to show up very small amount of orientation of

a long chain polymer. Adsorbed or dispersed dyestuff layers of this kind do not only exhibit strong birefringence but, in some instances, also a considerable degree of dichroism.

Using one or more of the methods enumerated above, Hermans and Kratky have shown that, for certain materials, such as cellulose xanthate or cellulose acetate, the orientation of stretched samples can be fairly satisfactorily represented by equations (6) and (7). The higher the degree of swelling of the sample, the more one approaches the behavior as predicted by relation (6), while slightly swollen films and filaments perform more according to equation (7). Intermediate degrees of swelling (from about 100 to 500%) require a superposition of (6) and (7) in order to correlate orientation with stretch.

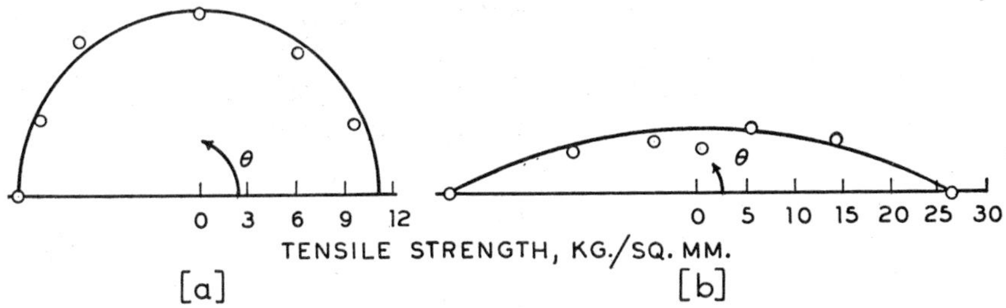

Fig. 227. Tensile strength as a function of direction in unoriented [a] and oriented [b]. θ measures the angle between the direction of orientation and the direction of the applied tensile stress.

As a result of this brief review of work on the orientability of high polymers we may summarize that the expressions as derived by Hermans, Kratky, and others (*66*) can be considered as preliminary but very useful steps to establish a quantitative relation between elongation and orientation in linear high polymers.

The next question is: How does the ultimate tensile strength of a polymer depend upon its orientation?

A few experiments have already been mentioned (compare page 500) which show that orientation as such, without crystallization, causes a rather marked increase of the tensile strength. The only existing attempt at a theoretical interpretation of this fact is a rather crude consideration as to how the parallelization of elongated particles having a certain (large) axis ratio would result in an increase of the area of mutual contact of these particles and, therefore, contribute to a more effective cohesion and, finally, to an increased tenacity of the bulk material. The orientation of the sample can be conveniently measured by comparing the opening, ω, within which 50% of all particles are situated with 180° and defining the orientation, O, as:

$$O = \frac{180 - \omega}{180} \tag{10}$$

If the sample is entirely random, $\omega = 180°$ and O equals zero; if, on the other hand, all particles are exactly parallel, $\omega = 0$ and O becomes unity.

It has in general been observed that, as long as O is small, the gain in tenacity on orientation, dT/dO, is also small. This may not be unexpected, because in a material with a large number of weak spots, it will not matter very much if one removes a few of them. Many others remain and prevent the sample from exhibiting a high tenacity. Later, as the packing of the system becomes more and more perfect, a small amount of additional orientation dO is apt to cause a larger increment of dT and the specific gain of tenacity dT/dO increases as O goes from zero to unity. A preliminary and obviously oversimplified way to describe this situation would be:

$$dT/d\theta = \alpha O \tag{11}$$

which leads to:

$$T = T_u + \frac{\alpha}{2} O^2 \tag{12}$$

where T_u could be called the *cohesion* of the material, and the coefficient α could be called the *orientation efficiency*. Both T_u and α are characteristic for the polymer under investigation and depend upon such quantities as average DP, molecular weight distribution curve, specific molar cohesion, etc.

There is, unfortunately, only little experimental material available to check the usefulness of equation (12). Schieber and Doerr have published tenacity measurements of cellulose fibers (staple fiber produced by the viscose process) having different degrees of orientation. Using their values of tensile strength and orientation and figuring them over into quantities as used in this presentation, one obtains the points of figure 228. The drawn-out curve corresponds to equation (12). It can be seen that in first approximation the tenacity of viscose rayon fibers depends upon orientation in the way predicted by equation (12). There is one sample of Schieber's data, however, which is off the curve and has a noticeably higher tensile strength than corresponds to its orientation. It may be significant that the aged alkali cellulose used for preparing this yarn had a higher average DP (*ca.* 450) than the material used to make the other yarns (DP *ca.* 280). This seems to indicate that a polymer of higher DP permits establishing a certain ultimate tensile strength at a lower degree of orientation and hence at a lower degree of anisotropy. Whenever one wants to combine favorable transversal properties of yarns or films with high ultimate tenacity it appears advisable to keep the average DP of the polymer as high as possible and, eventually, to avoid the presence of low molecular weight fractions in the molecular weight distribution curve. In the sense of equation (12) one would suspect that the point which represents the behavior of the material with the higher DP belongs to another curve, with two other parameters T_u and α. This curve, having a higher unoriented tenacity (a higher "cohesion") and a better orientation efficiency, is introduced in figure 228 as a dotted line. Finally it must be emphasized that this evaluation of the measurements of Schieber (*137*) presumably represents an exaggeration of the actual significance of those experiments because many important factors (such as fiber cross section, crystallinity, etc.) have not been controlled sufficiently during these measurements (or at least this is not evident from the study of the papers) in order to make a comparison with equation (12) permissible. It would be very desirable for our understanding of the importance of orientation, if more elaborate measurements of the ultimate tenacity of polymers of different degree of orientation were available.

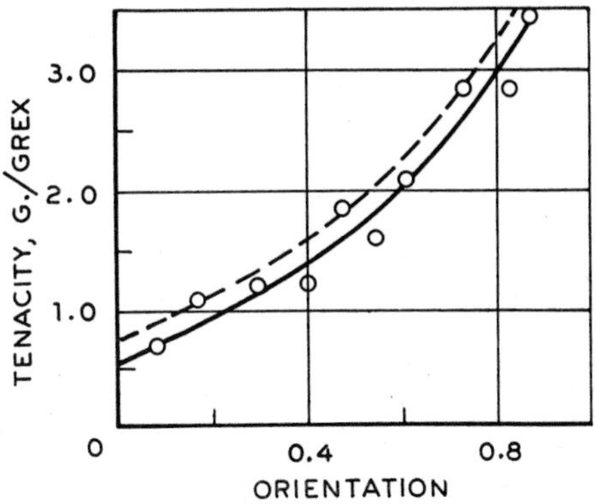

Fig. 228. Tenacity as a function of orientation.

The next step in this presentation will be (compare Chapter D) to discuss the influence of *crystallization* on ultimate strength and the first question to be answered is: What experimental methods are available at present to measure the degree of crystallinity of a polymer?

It seems that in certain cases the measurement of the specific volume (or density) of the polymer under consideration can be a very accurate and reliable way to determine the proportion of crystallized and disordered (amorphous) material in a given sample. This method is particularly successful if one can obtain the polymer completely in the amorphous state, because then it is possible to determine the specific volume of the pure amorphous phase with considerable accuracy. X-ray diagrams, on the other hand, permit the computation of the specific volume of the pure crystalline phase, if one succeeds in interpreting the patterns so far that one can work out a reliable elementary cell. This value for the density of the crystalline phase is correct, even if only part of the sample is crystallized, because the interference spots on the x-ray diagram are only caused by the ordered constituents and not (or only very slightly) affected by the presence of the disordered material. If one knows accurately the specific volumes both of the ordered and disordered state, it is obviously possible to arrive at an accurate determination of the ratio of both states in any given sample, by measuring its specific volume and interpolating between the two (extreme) values of the pure states. This method has been used with great success by Bekkedahl and Wood (*16*), Holt and McPherson (*72*); it works best with the rubbery polymers, which—in the unstretched state—exhibit no noticeable crystallinity at all, but develop a distinct x-ray diagram upon stretching. Typical examples for the application of this method are native rubber, polyisobutylene, polychloroprene, polyvinylisobutyl ether and polyphosphonitrile chloride.

In such cases Gehman and Field (*53*) have also used very successfully the intensity of the diffuse halo, which is produced by the scattering of x-rays in the disordered regions, to obtain qualitative information about the proportion of the disordered phase in a given sample.

Both methods indicate that the above-mentioned rubbery polymers are all disordered in the unstretched state at room temperature and above, but can all be brought into a state of very high crystallinity (up to and above 90%) by a sequence of appropriate stretching and cooling steps. A high degree of crystallinity can also be obtained by cooling alone, in which case no noticeable orientation of the sample takes place. It has already been mentioned that this gives an opportunity to compare the ultimate tenacity of an amorphous and crystalline sample of the same polymer in the absence of any orientation.

Unfortunately, there are many polymers, such as cellulose and its derivatives, polyvinyl chloride, polyethylene, etc., which have never yet been obtained in the completely disordered state and, therefore, cannot be investigated by either of the two methods mentioned above. In such cases, there exists as yet no reliable way to arrive at a quantitative proportion between crystalline and amorphous constituents. However, several methods at least permit one to obtain an approximate idea as to the relative frequency of ordered and disordered domains.

One of them is again the specific volume of the sample under consideration. In these cases one only knows accurately the specific volume of the pure crystalline phase (from the elementary cell as determined by the x-ray method), while one does not know the density of the completely amorphous state. It is therefore necessary to make a reasonable assumption about this density and then interpolate the observed value between the two extreme values for crystalline and amorphous, respectively. Because of the uncertainty of the latter, this method can only lead to an approximate value for the crystallinity of the sample.

Another way to obtain a semiquantitative indication for the degree of crystallinity is to measure on a carefully prepared x-ray diagram of the sample under consideration the intensities of one or more selected diffraction spots and compare them with the intensities measured on the same diagram *between* the crystal interference spots. The ratio of the intensity *in the direction* of a Bragg reflection and *outside of such a direction* obviously represents a measure for the ratio between crystalline and amorphous constituents. Such determinations of crystallinity have been carried out by Gehman and Field (*53*), Hengstenberg (*63*), Kratky (*84*), and others, but are not of an entirely quantitative character. First of all, one has to take considerable care in taking the diagrams for such measurements. Any kind of diffuse scattering except that caused by the amorphous areas has to be strictly avoided. One has, therefore, to use monochromatized or, at least, carefully filtered radiation, has to avoid diffuse scattering by the air and the wrapping of the film, and has to develop the film in such a way as to cause as little haze as possible. But even upon fulfillment of all these precautions, there is still some diffuse (incoherent) scattering because of the heat content of the crystalline domains, their zero point energy, and the Compton radiation. Nevertheless, it must be emphasized that this method is of great value in getting qualitative information about the relative frequency of ordered and disordered areas in such polymers, which cannot be investigated by one of the quantitative approaches.

It may be added here that recently a third method has been introduced to measure the degree of order in samples of cellulose and its derivatives by investigating the rate with which they undergo certain mild chemical reactions. Nickerson (*110*), Goldfinger (*55*), Scroggie and Conrad (*33*), and Assaf *et al.* (*10*) have observed that the hydrolysis of cellulose in a mixture of hydrochloric acid and ferric chloride, the oxidation of cellulose with periodic acid and other chemical processes in which the reactive groups of the material are involved, start out at a rather high rate, but slow down after a certain conversion to a slow zero order reaction. This behavior is, at present, interpreted by assuming that there exists an *easily accessible* or *loosely packed* fraction of the sample which reacts rapidly and accounts for the steep initial slope of the take-up or conversion curve. As soon as these highly reactive domains are saturated the reaction slows down because it now takes place in the *densely packed* and hence *difficultly accessible* areas. From the little numerical information available to date, it seems that, in general, the amount of easily accessible areas is proportional to the amount of the amorphous or disordered phase. Recently, Frilette (*47a*) has shown that the exchange of the hydrogen in the hydroxyl groups of cellulose by deuterium offers another simple way to measure the proportion of easily accessible domains in a cellulose sample, without actually affecting the material at all chemically. The various accessibility methods, as enumerated here, do not agree with each other quantitatively, if applied to the same samples, but their results are compatible with each other qualitatively. Equally one does not obtain numerically the same values for the crystallinity of a cellulose fiber by means of x-rays and the kinetic analysis, but those examples which show a higher degree of accessibility as indicated by the chemical methods, also produce x-ray diagrams of a more diffuse character, the evaluation of which leads to the presence of a larger proportion of the disordered phase.

It seems, therefore, that, even in the case of polymers which cannot be obtained in the completely disordered state, at least a qualitative estimate of the ratio of crystalline and amorphous state is possible.

Using these ratios and comparing them with the ultimate tensile strength of the corresponding samples, it becomes evident that increased crystallization very distinctly raises the modulus of elasticity and the ultimate strength of a polymer. There seems not to be enough numerical material available in order to establish a firm relationship between the degree of crystallinity and tensile strength, but there can be little doubt that the removal of disordered areas consolidates the structure and increases its resistance to ultimate failure. Attempts have been made by Pierce (*121*) to develop a theory of ultimate strength of fibers on the basis of the existence of weak spots and it has been shown that the ultimate failure of a fiber in the tensile test has to be considered to be a failure in tear, which starts at the weakest spots and propagates transversally through the sample because of stress accumulation at the edge of the crack. It has been suggested that the chain ends or groups of them represent weak spots as long as they are surrounded by disordered or amorphous material, because they have a tendency to slip along each other even at small external tensions and thereby produce a tiny hole inside of the amorphous material, which may increase to a crack and be responsible for the tear of the sample at this place. If, however, chain ends are embedded in a crystalline region, their presence is bound to show up much less drastically, because the strong van der Waals' bonds between individual molecules prevent gliding of the chains along each other, even in the neighborhood of chain ends. It may therefore be that the influence of crystallization on ultimate tenacity is essentially a reinforcement of the polymer in the immediate neighborhood of chain ends.

4. Effect of Environmental Conditions

The ultimate strength of any high polymer depends not only upon its own structure but also, of course, upon the temperature, humidity, etc. The effects of such environmental conditions upon the ultimate strength of plastics has been well summarized by Carswell and Nason (*27*):

Temperature Effects:

Temperatures ranging from -40 F. to $+120$ F. are commonly encountered in the continental United States. Since the development of high-altitude flying, temperatures as low as -70 F. may be reached in less than an hour over nearly any spot on the globe, and even lower readings have been reported. Metal equipment standing in the sun can easily reach temperatures of 160 F. in the southern parts of the United States, and temperatures exceeding 200 F. have been measured inside the wing structures of metal aircraft on the North African desert. Designers of military materiel now consider that temperatures from -60 F. to $+160$ F. are routine limits which may be encountered by any piece of equipment. Hence, a knowledge of material properties over this range is necessary.

With all true thermoplastics, and with the less highly cross-linked thermosetting materials, the stress–strain curve changes in the following ways as the ambient temperature is varied:

1. The slope of the initial "hookean" or "elastic" portion changes, decreasing as temperature is increased or increasing as temperature is decreased.

2. The magnitude of the maximum stress at the "yield" point changes, decreasing as temperature is increased or increasing as temperature is decreased (except that at very low temperatures ductility may be so low that rupture will occur well down on the linear portion of the curve and before the maximum potential stress can be attained).

3. The point of rupture tends to move along the curve toward higher values of strain as temperature is increased, or toward lower values of strain as the temperature is decreased.

Thermosetting materials follow the first two of these principles, although to a lesser degree than thermoplastics, and tend to follow the third; only primary chemical linkages,

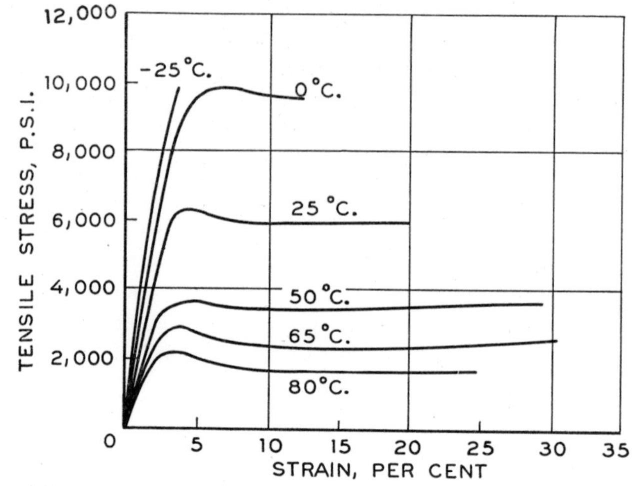

Fig. 229. Effect of temperature on tensile stress–strain curve of cellulose acetate.

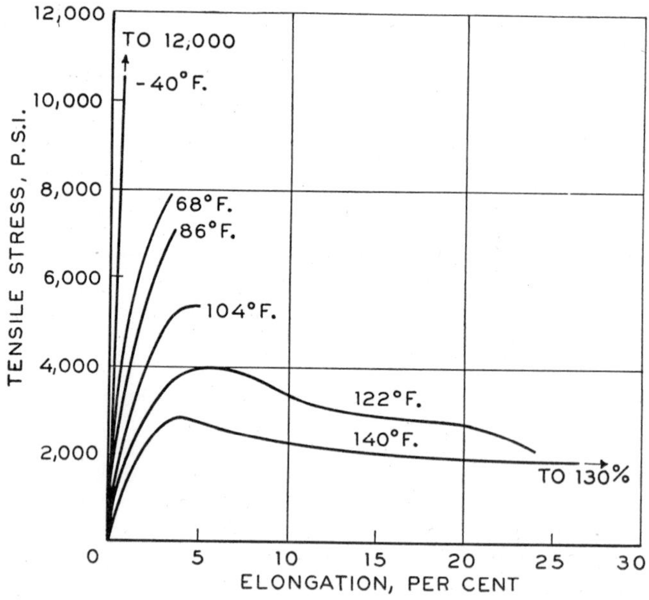

Fig. 230. Effect of temperature on tensile stress–strain curve of polymethylmethacrylate.

which cannot be strained beyond a certain limit without initiating rupture, restrict ductility of such materials at high temperatures.

A plastic which is "tough" and ductile at room temperature, for example, cellulose acetate . . ., may become "brittle" and hard at low temperatures. Stress–strain curves illustrating this type of behavior are shown in Fig. 229. Similarly, plastics which are "brittle" and hard at room temperature, for example, polymethyl methacrylate, may become "tough" and ductile at elevated temperatures. Stress–strain curves illustrating this are shown in Fig. 230. This kind of behavior is not limited to organic plastics by any means; many metals behave similarly, although usually over a wider range of temperatures.

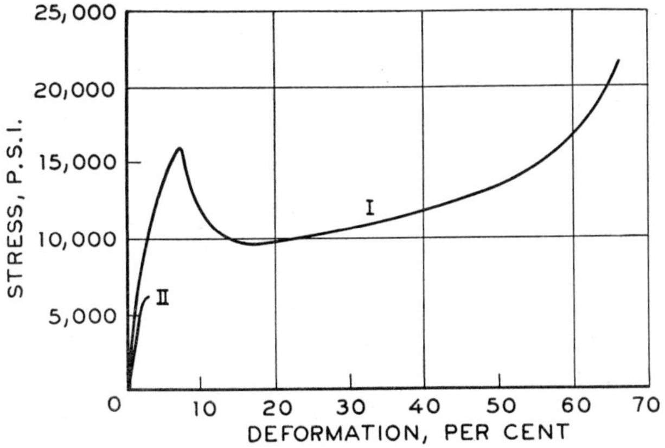

Fig. 231. Stress–strain curves for polystyrene at 77°F. in compression (I) and in tension (II).

Due to variations in stress distribution and in magnitude of combined stresses (tension, compression, and shear) acting simultaneously, it is possible for a material held at constant temperature to be "tough" and ductile under one set of test conditions but "brittle" and hard under another. The stress–strain curves shown in Fig. 231 illustrate this type of behavior for polystyrene which appears "tough" in the compression test but "brittle" in the tension test.

A fair conception of the mechanical characteristics of a plastic can be obtained by determining stress–strain curves over the desired range of temperatures and evaluating these for elastic modulus (slope of linear portion), stress at "yield" point, stress at rupture, and elongation at rupture. The last two of these are the most familiar test values.

The effect of ambient temperature on the strength properties of a number of plastics has been studied intensively during the last few years. Data have been published for cast and molded phenoplasts, molded aminoplasts, laminated phenoplasts, polystyrene, polymethyl methacrylate, cellulose nitrate, cellulose acetate, cellulose acetobutyrate, ethyl cellulose, benzyl cellulose, polyvinyl formal, polyvinyl butyral, Nylon, polyvinyl chloride, casein plastics, and rubber.

Data showing the effect of temperature on tensile properties are summarized in Figs. 232 to 236, inclusive. Figures 232 and 233 show data for tensile strength of several

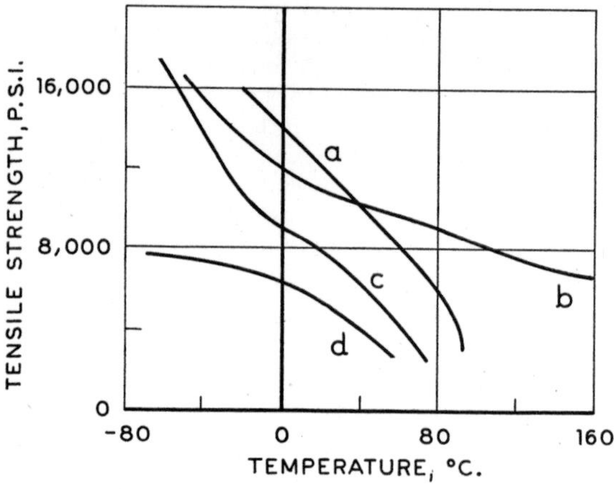

Fig. 232. Effect of temperature on tensile strength of several thermoplastics: (a) Formvar; (b) nylon; (c) cellulose nitrate sheet; (d) cellulose acetate sheet.

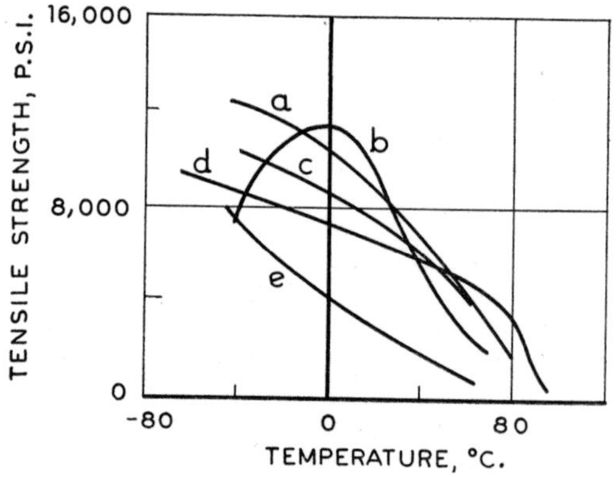

Fig. 233. Effect of temperature on tensile strength of several thermoplastics: (a) polymethylmethacrylate; (b) polyvinyl chloride; (c) ethyl cellulose; (d) polystyrene; (e) cellulose acetate and acetobutyrate (soft).

common thermoplastics, and Fig. 234 shows comparable data for several thermosetting plastics. . . . Figure 235 shows the effect of temperature on the ultimate elongation for several common thermoplastics. Very little data is available concerning the effect of temperature on the elongation of thermosetting plastics, largely because of the difficulty of measuring the very small extensions exhibited by these materials. . .

At very low temperatures, rubber and other elastomeric plastics become both stiff and brittle. While stiffness increases gradually, brittleness, under fixed test conditions, seems to occur at a rather sharply defined temperature, and this "brittle point" is widely used as a characteristic property of rubbery materials. It probably represents the temperature at which both elastic modulus and plastic viscosity become so high that sufficient deformation cannot take place rapidly enough to prevent the stresses imposed in a short-time test from exceeding the strength of the material. Considerable data on brittle points have been published recently.

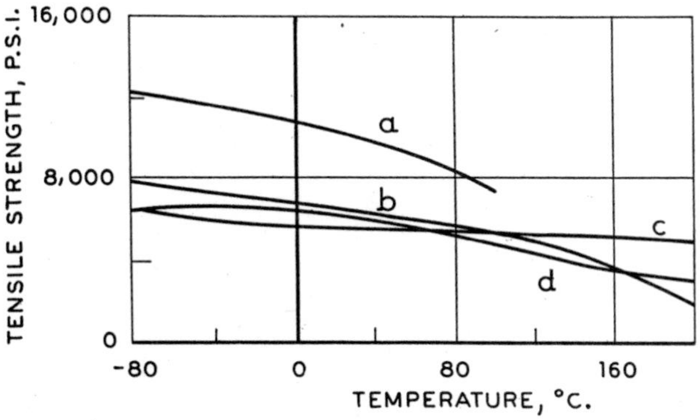

Fig. 234. Effect of temperature on tensile strength of several thermosetting plastics: (a) fabric laminate (coarse weave); (b) fabric-filled melamine; (c) asbestos-filled phenolic; (d) wood flour-filled phenolic.

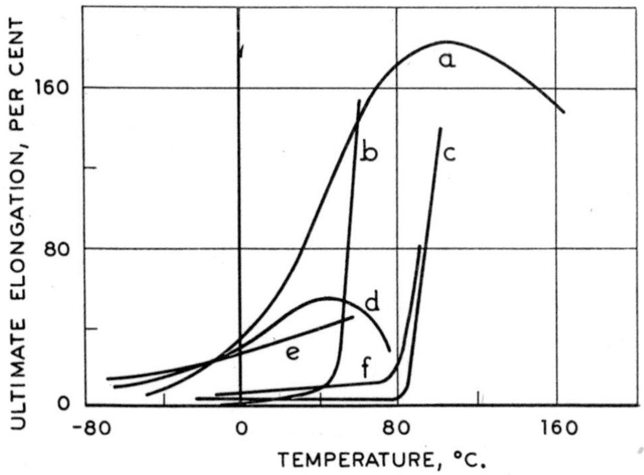

Fig. 235. Effect of temperature on the ultimate elongation of several thermoplastics: (a) nylon; (b) polymethylmethacrylate; (c) polystyrene; (d) cellulose nitrate sheet; (e) cellulose acetate sheet; (f) Formvar.

The compressive properties of plastics show about the same response to ambient temperature as do tensile properties. Data showing the effect of temperature on the compressive strength of several materials are given in Fig. 236. It is worth noting that compressive yield stress is much more satisfactory as an indication of compressive strength of soft, highly ductile plastics than is the stress at the point of rupture. Be-

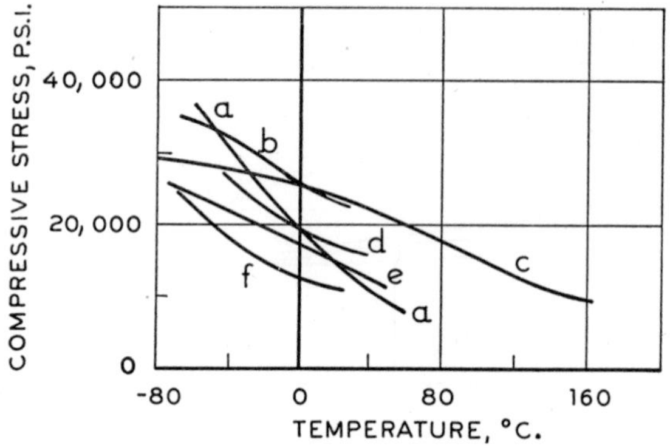

Fig. 236. Effect of temperature on compressive strength of several plastics: (a) polymethylmethacrylate (breaking stress); (b) wood flour-filled phenolic (yield stress); (c) paper-base phenolic laminate (breaking stress); (d) cast phenolic (yield stress); (e) polystyrene (yield stress); (f) polyvinyl chloride (yield stress).

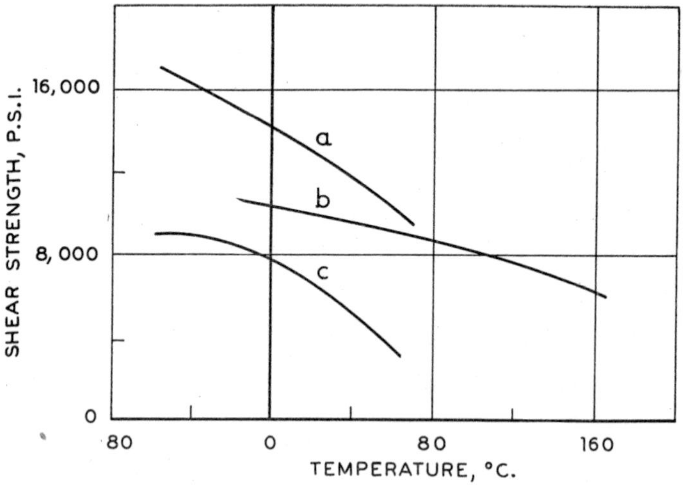

Fig. 237. Effect of ambient temperature on shear strength of several plastics: (a) paper-base phenolic laminate; (b) wood flour-filled molded phenolic; (c) polymethylmethacrylate.

tween these two points, the plastic is radically deformed with a large change in shape and dimensions. . .

Relatively little information concerning the effect of temperature on shear strength has been published. Figure 237 shows data for polymethyl methacrylate, a wood flour-filled phenolic, and a paper-base laminated phenolic. It can be seen that shear strength varies with ambient temperature in about the same way as do tensile strength and flexural strength.

The impact test is commonly accepted as a measure of the toughness of a material. Although the quantitative significance of impact data is still disputed, the results of the Charpy and Izod tests do provide a comparative basis for estimating the relative shock

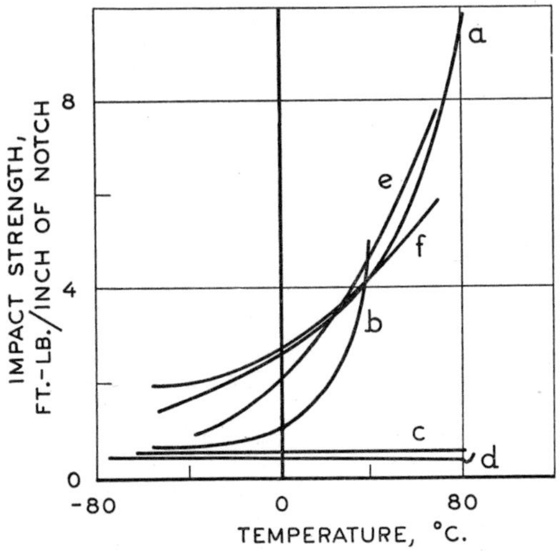

Fig. 238. Effect of temperature on Izod impact strength of several plastics: (a) nylon; (b) polyvinyl butyral; (c) polymethylmethacrylate; (d) polystyrene; (e) ethyl cellulose; (f) cellulose nitrate sheet.

resistance of plastic materials. The results usually correlate fairly well with tensile and flexural data. The effect of ambient temperature on Izod impact strengths of several plastics is summarized in Figs. 238 and 239.

The above data indicate the strength properties of plastics in thermal equilibrium with their environment; relatively short periods of exposure at each temperature are involved. Continuous exposure for long periods of time may produce degradative changes and the effect on mechanical properties of such long-time exposure at elevated or reduced temperatures is an important matter which must be studied carefully. Considerable data of this type have been made available recently.

Thermoplastics, in general, soften and lose their mechanical usefulness at temperatures below those which cause serious thermal decomposition or degradation. Plastics based on nitrocellulose are an exception; these may lose in strength and ductility and become brittle upon prolonged exposure to temperatures as low as 122 F., due to thermal degradation of the nitrocellulose molecule. Continuous exposure to temperatures slightly below the softening point will cause appreciable loss of plasticizer from many types, however, with resultant increase in stiffness and strength, and decrease in ductility and toughness.

Thermosetting materials, on the other hand, ordinarily exhibit no well-defined softening point, and many of these plastics retain good mechanical properties up to fairly high temperatures. With such materials, prolonged exposure may lead to decomposition with a resultant decrease in strength. In general, the thermosetting resins themselves do not show appreciable thermal degradation below about 390 F., and mineral-filled compositions remain usable under continuous exposure to temperatures

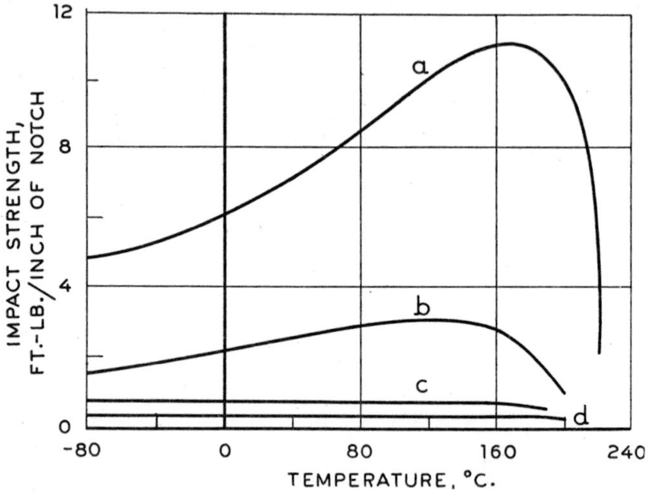

Fig. 239. Effect of temperature on Izod impact strength of several plastics: (a) cord-filled phenolic; (b) fabric-filled phenolic; (c) fabric-filled melamine; (d) wood flour-filled phenolic.

at least this high. Cellulose-filled compositions, however, are seldom satisfactory for continuous use above about 265 to 300 F., since cellulose itself suffers considerable breakdown and loss of strength at temperatures above 250 F. . .

Prolonged exposure to sub-zero temperatures has relatively little permanent effect on the strength properties of most plastics unless cracking or checking occur, or unless a slowly-reversible crystallization takes place. Cracking or checking will occur where ductility at low temperature is too small to equalize strains set up by shrinkage or by differential dimensional changes around inserts. Crystallization is rarely encountered but may sometimes take place in materials of well-ordered molecular structure.

Moisture Effects:

The moisture content of the atmosphere, like the temperature, is subject to wide variation. Saturated air at −40 F. contains only 0.0079 per cent, by weight, of water vapor, and such air if warmed to room temperature (70 F.) would have a relative humidity of only 0.6 per cent. Such dry conditions are common in the northern parts of the

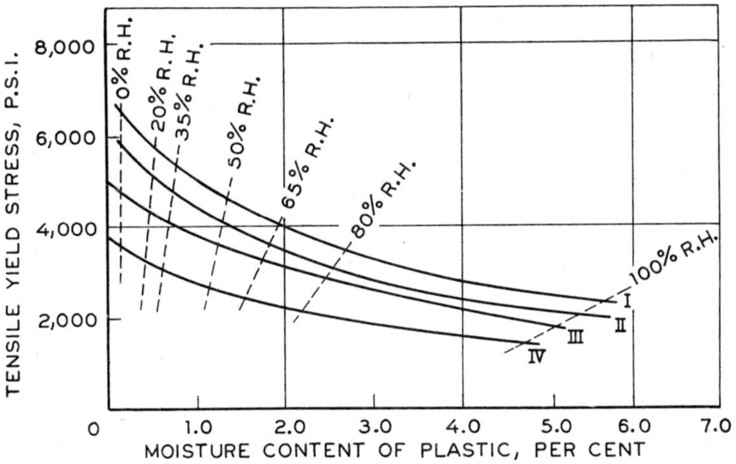

Fig. 240. Effect of moisture on tensile yield stress of cellulose acetate at 77°F.: (I) "H" flow, 29.6% plasticizer; (II) "MH" flow, 31.5% plasticizer; (III) "MS" flow, 33.3% plasticizer; (IV) "ES" flow, 37.5% plasticizer.

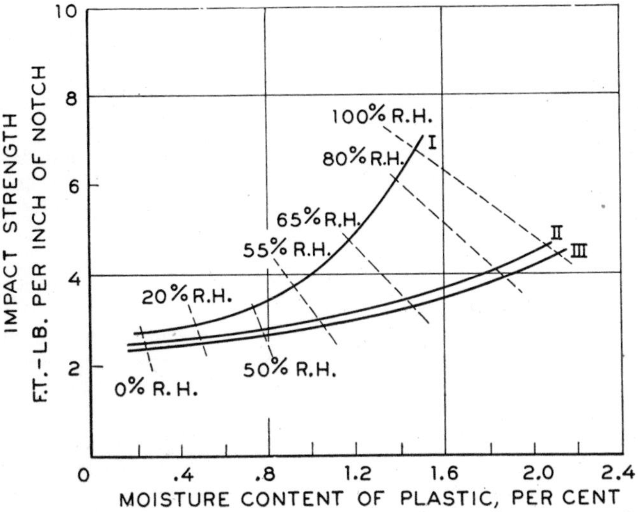

Fig. 241. Effect of moisture on Izod impact strength of cellulose acetate at 77°F.: (I) "ES" flow, 37.5% plasticizer; (II) "MS" flow, 33.3% plasticizer; (III) "H" flow, 29.6% plasticizer.

United States during the winter months. On a 90 F. day with 70 per cent relative humidity, a common summer condition, the air contains 4.1 per cent, by weight, of moisture, and contents from 7.5 to 10 per cent are common under jungle conditions. Normal seasonal variations in the moisture content of the atmosphere are large and will produce similarly large variations in the moisture content of hygroscopic materials exposed thereto. Many organic plastics are hygroscopic to a greater or lesser degree.

Water acts as a powerful plasticizer for many plastics, and tends to reduce strength and modulus, but to increase ductility and toughness. The extent of these effects is roughly proportional to the amount of water absorbed by the material, and plastics which are capable of absorbing a large amount of moisture are more affected than those which absorb little. In general, cellulose compounds, protein derivatives, and polyamides (that is, those compounds with hydrophilic OH, COOH, or NH groups) are

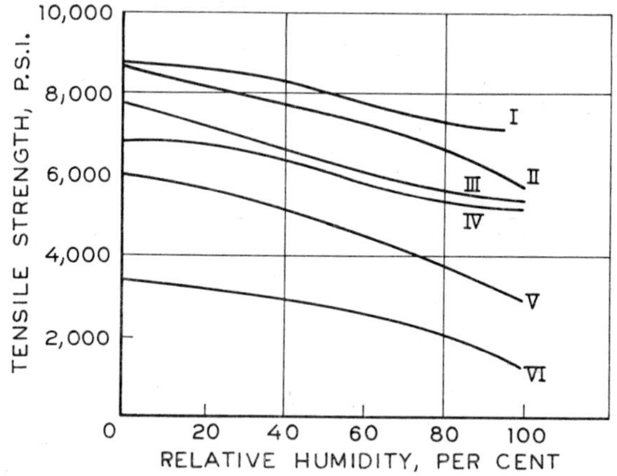

Fig. 242. Effect of relative humidity on tensile strength of several thermoplastics at 77°F.: (I) hard ethyl cellulose; (II) polymethylmethacrylate; (III) cellulose nitrate; (IV) medium-hard ethyl cellulose; (V) medium-hard cellulose acetate (yield point); (VI) soft cellulose acetate (yield point).

sensitive to moisture, while compounds poor in oxygen and nitrogen but rich in carbon, hydrogen, or halogen are moisture-resistant.

Quantitative data showing the effect of moisture content on mechanical properties have been scarce until lately, but considerable recent information along these lines is now available. Figures 240 . . . 241 . . . show the effect of moisture on tensile . . . and impact properties of four cellulose acetate formulations, differing only in plasticizer content, at 77 F. Cellulose acetate is a fairly hygroscopic plastic and its behavior is typical of such materials. . . It will be noted that plasticizer content affects not only the strength but also the sensitivity to moisture. . . and figure 242 shows the relationship between relative humidity and tensile strength for several thermoplastics.

Data for thermosetting plastics is still scarce and very little complete information is available for these materials. One investigator has recently shown that the compressive strength of fabric-filled phenolic moldings is changed as much as 25 per cent by comparatively small changes in moisture content.

All of the data presented above are for variations in moisture content at room temperature. Where both temperature and relative humidity are changed, the effect on strength properties may be more pronounced. Combination of high temperature and high humidity is especially severe on most materials and may produce permanent damage in some materials by inducing chemical degradation, loss of plasticizer, etc. Similarly, prolonged exposure to moisture or to the leaching action of liquid water may produce considerable permanent damage.

BIBLIOGRAPHY

BOOKS

(*1*) *ASTM Standards for Plastics*, American Society for Testing Materials, Philadelphia, 1945.

(*2*) Carothers, W. H., *Collected Papers on High Polymeric Substances* (High Polymers, Vol. I). Interscience, New York, 1940.

(*3*) Gilkey, H. J., Murphy, G., and Bergman, E. O., *Materials Testing*. McGraw-Hill, New York, 1941. Quotation on pages 491 and 492 courtesy McGraw-Hill Book Co., Inc.

(*4*) Houwink, R., *Elasticity, Plasticity, and the Structure of Matter*. Cambridge Univ. Press, London, 1937.

(*5*) Mark, H., *Physik und Chemie der Cellulose*, Springer, Berlin, 1932. (*a*) Figs. 39A and B. (*b*) Pages 61 *et seq.*

(*6*) Meyer, K. H., *Natural and Synthetic High Polymers* (High Polymers, Vol. IV). Interscience, New York, 1942.

(*7*) Nadai, A., *Plasticity*. McGraw-Hill, New York, 1931.

(*8*) Ott, E., *Cellulose and Cellulose Derivatives* (High Polymers, Vol. V). Interscience, New York, 1943, page 1006.

ARTICLES

(*9*) Alfrey, T., "Equilibria and Rates in Crystallization of High Polymers," *Polymer Bull.*, **1**, 40–46 (1945).

(*10*) Assaf, A. G., Haas, R. H., and Purves, C. B., "A Study of the Amorphous Portion of Dry, Swollen Cellulose by an Improved Thallous Ethylate Method," *J. Am. Chem. Soc.*, **66**, 59–65 (1944).

(*11*) Badgley, W., Frilette, V. J., and Mark, H., "Recent Progress in Cellulose Chemistry," *Ind. Eng. Chem.*, **37**, 227–232 (1945).

(*12*) Bartol, W. F., "Service-Temperature Flow Characteristics of Thermoplastics," *Mech. Eng.*, **61**, 892–894 (December, 1939).

(*13*) Bartol, W. F., "Strength and Properties of Plexiglas," *Aviation*, **42**, No. 1, 128–131, 135 (1943); **42**, No. 3, 140, 143, 145, 147, 359 (1943).

(*14*) Beaupre, P. J., Mohrman, H. W., and Dunlop, R. D., *unpublished data, Monsanto Chemical Co.*, Springfield, Mass.

(*15*) Beeuwkes, R., "Effect of Strain and Rate of Strain on Tensile Tests at Normal and Elevated Temperatures," *Physics*, **5**, 135–139 (1934).

(*16*) Bekkedahl, N., and Wood, L. A., "Influence of the Temperature of Crystallization on the Melting of Crystalline Rubber," *J. Chem. Phys.*, **9**, 193 (1941); "Crystallization of Vulcanized Rubber," *Ind. Eng. Chem.*, **33**, 381–384 (1941).

(*17*) Bellinson, H. R., "Effect of Rate of Load on the Stress–Strain Properties of Viscose," *Textile Research*, **10**, 316–322 (1940).

(*18*) Bellinson, H. R., "Viscose Rayon: Stress–Strain Properties. III. Effect of Relative Humidity," *Textile Research*, **10**, 372-379 (1940).

(*19*) Berkley, E. E., "Cellulose Orientation, Strength and Cell Wall Development of Cotton Fibers," *Textile Research*, **9**, 355–373 (1939).

(*20*) Boyer, R. F., and Spencer, R. S., "Thermal Expansion and Second-Order Transition Effects in High Polymers. II. Theory," *J. Applied Phys.*, **16**, 594–607 (1945).

(*21*) Brown, K. C., Mann, J. C., and Pierce, F. T., "Influence of Humidity on the Elastic Properties of Cotton. V. The Tensile Behavior," *J. Textile Inst. Trans.*, **21**, T186–T204 (1930).

(*22*) de Bruyne, N. A., "Improving the Creep Stress of Plastics," *Modern Plastics*, **14**, No. 7, 44–45, 77–78 (March, 1937).

(*23*) Buchmann, W., "Festigkeit und zulässige Beanspruchung von Polyvinylchlorid-Kunststoff," *Z. Ver. deut. Ing.*, **84**, 425–431 (1940).

(*24*) Busse, W. F., Lessig, E. T., Loughborough, D. L., and Larrick, L., "Fatigue of Fabrics," *J. Applied Phys.*, **13**, 715–724 (1942).

(*25*) Carothers, W. H., and Hill, J. W., "Studies of Polymerization and Ring Formation. XV. Artificial Fibers from Synthetic Linear Condensation Superpolymers," *J. Am. Chem. Soc.*, **54**, 1579–1587 (1932).

(*26*) Carswell, T. S., and Hayes, R. F., "Styramic for High Frequency Insulation," *Modern Plastics*, **19**, No. 6, 68–70, 108 (February, 1942). Carswell, T. S., Hayes, R. F., and Nason, H. K., "Physical Properties of Polystyrene as Influenced by Temperature," *Ind. Eng. Chem.*, **34**, 454–457 (1942).

(*27*) Carswell, T. S., and Nason, H. K., "Effect of Environmental Conditions on the Mechanical Properties of Organic Plastics," in *Symposium on Plastics.* American Society for Testing Materials, Philadelphia, 1944.

(*28*) Carswell, T. S., Telfair, D., Haslanger, R. U., "Effects of Continuous Heat on Phenolics," *Modern Plastics*, **20**, No. 6, 79–82, 126 (February, 1943).

(*29*) Castricum, M., and Benson, A. N., "The Effect of Rate of Loading on Tensile Strength of Cord and Yarn," *Proc. Am. Soc. Testing Materials*, **41**, 1214–1216 (1941).

(*30*) Chasman, B., "Creep and Time—Fracture Strength of Plastics under Tensile Stresses," *Modern Plastics*, **21**, No. 6, 145–148, 176 (February, 1944).

(*31*) Clark, F. M., "Factors Affecting the Mechanical Deterioration of Cellulose Insulation," *Electrical Eng.*, **61**, 742–749T (1942).

(*32*) Clayton, F. H., and Pierce, F. T., "The Influence of Humidity on the Elastic Properties of Cotton. IV—The Rigidity of Soda-Boiled Cotton, and Effects Thereon of History and Temperature," *J. Textile Inst.*, **20**, T315–332 (1929).

(*33*) Conrad, C. C., and Scroggie, A. G., "Chemical Characterization of Rayon Yarns and Cellulosic Raw Materials," *Ind. Eng. Chem.*, **37**, 592–598 (1945).

(*34*) Couzens, E. G., and Wearmouth, W. G., "Mechanical Testing and Flow Properties of Industrial Plastics," *J. Soc. Chem. Ind.*, **61**, No. 5, 69–74 (1942).

(*35*) Davis, W. C., and Nason, H. K., *unpublished data, Monsanto Chemical Co.*, Springfield, Mass.

(*36*) Delmonte, J., "Permanence of the Physical Properties of Plastics," *Trans. Am. Soc. Mech. Engrs.*, **62**, 513–524 (1940); *Modern Plastics*, **17**, No. 10, 65–68, 84, 86 (June, 1940).

(*37*) Delmonte, J., "Shear Strength of Molded Plastic Materials," *ASTM Bull.*, No. 114, 25 (January, 1942).

(*38*) Delmonte, J., "Effect of Solvents upon Solid Organic Plastics," *Ind. Eng. Chem.*, **34**, 764–770 (1942).

(*39*) Douglas, S. D., and Stoops, W. N., "Polymer Distribution in Vinyl Ester Resins," *Ind. Eng. Chem.*, **28**, 1152–1155 (1936).

(*40*) Duggan, F. W., and Filgor, K. K., "Fatigue Resistance of Flexible Plastic Sheetings," *Ind. Eng. Chem.*, **35**, 172–176 (1943).

(*41*) Dunkel, M., "Zur Berechnung der zwischenmolekularen Kräfte organischer Verbindungen," *Z. physik. Chem.*, **A138**, 42–54 (1928).

(*42*) Durez Plastics and Chemicals, Inc., Aberg, T. P., Schwartz, R. T., and Shinn, D. A., "Mechanical Properties of Plastics at Normal and Subnormal Temperatures," *Modern Plastics*, **20**, No. 8, 2 (April, 1943).

(*43*) Eckling, K., and Kratky, O., "Zum Deformationsmechanismus der Faserstoffe," *Naturwissenschaften*, **18**, 461–464 (1930).

(*44*) Field, P. M., "Basic Physical Properties of Laminates," *Modern Plastics*, **20**, No. 12, 91–102, 126, 128, 130 (August, 1943).

(*45*) Findley, W. N., "Mechanical Tests of Cellulose Acetate," *Proc. Am. Soc. Testing Materials*, **41**, 1231–1243 (1941).

(*46*) Findley, W. N., "Mechanical Tests of Cellulose Acetate," *Modern Plastics*, **20**, No. 7, 99–105, 138 (March, 1943); *Trans. Am. Soc. Mech. Engrs.*, **65**, 479–487 (1943).

(*47*) Findley, W. N., and Hintz, O. E., Jr., "The Relation Between Repeated Blow Impact Tests and Fatigue Tests," *Proc. Am. Soc. Testing Materials*, **43**, 1226–1235 (1943).

(*47a*) Frilette, V. J., *Doctoral Thesis*, Polytechnic Institute of Brooklyn.

(*48*) Frölich, K., "Dynamische Bestimmung des Elastizitätsmoduls von Kunststoffen," *Kunststoffe*, **30**, 10–12 (January, 1940).

(*49*) Fry, L. H., "Speed in Tension Testing and Its Influence on Yield Point Values," *Proc. Am. Soc. Testing Materials*, **40**, 625–636 (1940).

(*50*) Fuller, F. B., "Engineering Properties of Plastics," *Modern Plastics*, **20**, No. 10, 95–98, 130 (June, 1943).

(*51*) Fuller, F. B., and Oberg, T. T., "Fatigue Characteristics of Natural and Resin-Impregnated, Compressed, Laminated Woods," *J. Aeronaut. Sci.*, **10**, 81–85 (1943).

(*52*) Gardner, T. S., and Purves, C. B., "The Distribution of Acetyl Groups in a Technical Acetone-Soluble Cellulose Acetate," *J. Am. Chem. Soc.*, **64**, 1539–1542 (1942).

(*53*) Gehman, S. D., and Field, J. E., "An X-Ray Investigation of Crystallinity in Rubber," *J. Applied Phys.*, **10**, 564–572 (1939).

(*54*) Goldberg, A. I., Hohenstein, W. P., and Mark, H., "Intrinsic Viscosity–Molecular Weight Relationship for Polystyrene," *J. Polymer Sci.*, **2**, 503–510 (1947).

(*55*) Goldfinger, G., Mark, H., and Siggia, S., "Kinetics of Oxidation of Cellulose with Periodic Acid," *Ind. Eng. Chem.*, **35**, 1083–1086 (1934).

(*56*) Grard, J., "Propriétés mécaniques de l'acétate de cellulose," *Bull. soc. chim.*, **53**, 1308–1312 (1933).

(*57*) Graves, F. L., and Davis, A. R., "Evaluating Low-Temperature Stiffness and Brittle Point in Elastomers," *India Rubber World*, **109**, 41–44 (1943).

(58) Hauk, V., and Neumann, W., "Die Temperaturabhängigkeit der Spannung im Kautschuk bei konstanter Dehnung," *Z. physik. Chem.*, **A182**, 285–294 (1938).

(59) Hauser, E. A., "A New Hypothesis of Rubber Structure Based on Most Recent X-Ray Researches," *Ind. Eng. Chem.*, **19**, 169–170 (1927).

(60) Hauser, E. A., and Mark, H., "Zur Kenntnis der Struktur gedehnter Kautschukproben," *Kolloid-Beihefte*, **22**, 63–94 (1926).

(61) Haward, R. N., "The Extension and Rupture of Cellulose Acetate and Celluloid," *Trans. Faraday Soc.*, **38**, 394–403 (1942).

(62) Haward, R. N., "The Fast and Slow Extension of Some Plastic Materials," *Trans. Faraday Soc.*, **39**, 267–280 (1943).

(63) Hengstenberg, J., and Mark, H., "Über Form und Grösse der Mizelle von Zellulose und Kautschuk," *Z. Krist.*, **69**, 271–284 (1928).

(64) Hercules Powder Co., Wilmington, Del., "Effect of Heat and Light on Nitrocellulose Films."

(65) Hermans, P. H., "Die Festigkeits-Dehnungs-Diagramme isotroper Zellulosefäden im Lichte der theoretischen Beziehung zwischen Quellungsanisotropie, Orientierung und Festigkeit," *Kolloid-Z.*, **89**, 345–348 (1939).

(66) Hermans, P. H., Kratky, O., and Platzek, P., "Die Netzstruktur von gequollener Hydratzellulose," *Kolloid-Z.*, **86**, 245–254 (1939).

(67) Hermans, P. H. (Breda-Ginneken), and Platzek, P., "Neue Ergebnisse über die Beziehung zwischen Quellungsanisotropie und Deformationsmechanismus bei Hydratzellulosegelen," *Kolloid-Z.*, **87**, 296–308 (1939).

(68) Hermans, P. H., and Platzek, P., "Beiträge zur Kenntnis des Deformationsmechanismus und der Feinstruktur der Hydratzellulose. IX. Über die theoretische Beziehung zwischen Quellungsanisotropie und Eigendoppelbrechung orientierter Fäden," *Kolloid-Z.*, **88**, 68–72 (1939).

(69) Herzog, R. O., "Zur Erkenntnis der Cellulose-Faser," *Ber.*, **B58**, 1254–1262 (1925); "Über den Zusammenhang zwischen der Struktur der organischen Fasern mit den elastischen Eigenschaften," *Naturwissenschaften*, **16**, 420–421 (1928).

(70) Herzog, R. O., and Hoffman, H., "Rayon, Bands, etc., from Viscose," U. S. Pat. 2,036,752 (April 7, 1936).

(71) Hoften, J., "Effect of Conditioning on Some Physical Properties of Urea-Formaldehyde Moldings," *Brit. Plastics*, **14**, 377–380 (1942).

(72) Holt, W. L., and McPherson, A. T., "Change of Volume on Stretching Effects of Time, Elongation, and Temperature," *J. Research Natl. Bur. Standards*, **17**, 657–678 (1936).

(73) Hunt, R. H., Jr., *unpublished data, Monsanto Chemical Co.*, Springfield, Massachusetts.

(74) Iguchi, M., and Schossberger, F., "Roentgenographische Untersuchungen an gedehntem vulkanisiertem Kautschuk," *Kautschuk*, **12**, 193–195 (1936).

(75) Jones, P. G., and Moore, H. F., "Effect of Rate of Strain on Yield Strength, Tensile Strength, Elongation, and Reduction of Area in Tension Tests," *Proc. Am. Soc. Testing Materials*, **41**, 488–491 (1941).

(76) Katz, J. R., "Röntgenspektrographische Untersuchungen am gedehnten Kautschuk und ihre mögliche Bedeutung für das Problem der Dehnungseigenschaften dieser Substanz," *Naturwissenschaften*, **13**, 410–416 (1925).

(77) Katz, J. R., and Bing, K., "Ist Rohkautschuk teilweise kristallisiert?," *Z. angew. Chem.*, **38**, 439–441 (1925).

(78) Kemp, A. R., Malm, F. S., and Winspear, G. G., "Brittle Temperature of Rubber under Variable Stress," *Ind. Eng. Chem.*, **35**, 488–492 (1942).

(79) Kerr, T., and Bailey, I. W., *J. Arnold Arboretum*, **15**, 327 (1938); **16**, 273 (1939).

(80) King, G. E., "Bend-Brittle and Shatter Points of Rubberlike Materials," *Ind. Eng. Chem.*, **35**, 949–951 (1943).

(81) Koch, E. A., "Einführung der Biegefestigkeitsprüfung für Weichgummi, als Mittel zur Bestimmung des Erstarrungspunktes und der Veränderung der elastischen Eigenschaften bei hohen und tiefen Temperaturen," *Kautschuk*, **16**, 151–156 (1940); *Chem. Abstracts*, **35**, 4631 (1941).

(82) Kratky, O., "Zum Deformationsmechanismus der Faserstoffe, I," *Kolloid-Z.*, **64**, 213–222 (1933).

(83) Kratky, O., "Über den mizellaren Aufbau und die Deformationsvorgänge bei Faserstoffen, V," *Kolloid-Z.*, **84**, 149–168 (1938).

(84) Kratky, O., and Mark, H., "Zur Frage der individuellen Cellulosemicellen," *Z. physik. Chem.*, **B36**, 192–139 (1937).

(85) Kroker, G., and Becker, K., "Das Verhalten von Zellulosetriazetat," *Elektrotech. Z.*, **62**, 825–829 (1941).

(86) Küch, W., "New Research on the Use of Hardening Plastics for Aircraft Construction," *J. Roy. Aeronaut. Soc.*, **44**, 44–73 (1940); "Neuere Untersuchungen über die Verwendung härtbarer plastischer Massen im Flugzeugbau," *Jahrbuch deutscher Luftfahrtforschung*, **1**, 561–573 (1938).

(87) Küch, W., "Die Mechanischen Eigenschaften durchsichtiger Kunststoffe bei 20°," *Luftfahrtforschung*, **19**, 111–120 (1942).

(88) Kuntze, W., and Nitsche, R., "Untersuchung von Kunststoffen auf Schlagbiegefestigkeit," *Kunststoffe*, **29**, No. 2, 33–41 (1939).

(89) Kuntze, W., and Pfeiffer, F., "Zur Messung des Elastizitätsmoduls von Kunststoffen," *Kunststoffe*, **30**, 293–296 (1940).

(90) Lawton, T. S., Jr., *unpublished data, Monsanto Chemical Co.*, Springfield, Massachusetts.

(91) Lazan, B. J., "Behavior of Plastics under Vibrations," *Modern Plastics*, **20**, No. 3, 83–88, 136, 138, 140, 142, 144 (November, 1942); "Some Mechanical Properties of Plastics and Metals under Sustained Vibrations," *Trans. Am. Soc. Mech. Engrs.*, **65**, No. 2, 87–104 (1943).

(92) Leaderman, H., "Plastics and the Time Factor," *Am. Dyestuff Reptr.*, **31**, 227–230, 246–248 (1942).

(93) Leaderman, H., "Impact Testing of Textiles," *Textile Research*, **13**, No. 8, 21–29 (1943).

(94) Lilienfeld, L., "Cellulose Solution," U. S. Pat. 1,658,606 (February 7, 1928).

(95) Lutts, C. G., and Himmelfarb, D., "The Creep Phenomenon in Ropes and Cords," *Proc. Am. Soc. Testing Materials*, **40**, 1251–1255 (1940).

(96) Mahoney, J. F., and Purves, C. B., "New Methods for Investigating the Distribution of Ethoxyl Groups in a Technical Ethylcellulose," *J. Am. Chem. Soc.*, **64**, 9–15 (1942).

(97) Mann, J. C., "High-Velocity Tension-Impact Tests," *Proc. Am. Soc. Testing Materials*, **36**, Part II, 85–97 (1936).

(*98*) Mann, J. C., and Pierce, F. T., "Time Factor in (Cotton) Hair Testing," *Shirley Inst. Mem.*, **5**, 7–18 (1926).

(*99*) Mark, H., "Relation between Chain Length Distribution Curve and Tenacity," *Paper Trade J.*, **113**, No. 3, 34–40 (1941).

(*100*) Mark, H., and Valko, E., "Vorgänge bei der mechanischen Verformung von Kautschuk," *Kautschuk*, **6**, 210–215 (1930).

(*101*) Mark, H., and Valko, E., "Les phénomènes dans la déformation mécanique du caoutchouc," *Rev. gén. caoutchouc*, **7**, No. 64, 11–16 (1930).

(*102*) Medwedew, A. J., "Zur Frage der Beeinflussung der mechanischen Eigenschaften von Nitrozellulose Filmen durch Zusätze," *Kunststoffe*, **23**, 249–253 (1933).

(*103*) Melville, H. W., "Plastics in Industrial Physics," *Reports on Progress in Physics*, **5**, 64–81 (1938).

(*104*) Midgley, E., and Peirce, F. T., "VIII, Tensile Tests for Cotton Yarns. iii, The Rate of Loading," *Shirley Inst. Mem.*, **5**, 102 (1926).

(*105*) Morris, R. E., James, R. R., and Werkenthin, T. A., "Brittle Points of Natural and Synthetic Rubber Stocks," *Ind. Eng. Chem.*, **35**, 864–867 (1943).

(*106*) Moyer, H. R., "Strength of Plastics, Structural Data for Thermosetting Compounds," *Product Eng.*, **13**, 379–381 (July, 1942).

(*107*) Murphy, G., "Stress–Strain–Time Characteristics of Materials," *ASTM Bull.*, No. 101, 19 (December, 1939).

(*108*) Myers, C. S., "Impact Strength of Plastic Sheet," *Modern Plastics*, **20**, No. 2, 81–87, 116, 118 (1942).

(*109*) Nason, H. K., *unpublished data, Monsanto Chemical Co.*, Springfield, Massachusetts.

(*110*) Nickerson, R. F., "Cotton Fibers, Constitution, Structure, and Mechanical Properties," *Ind. Eng. Chem.*, **32**, 1454–1462 (1940); "Hydrolysis and Catalytic Oxidation of Cellulosic Materials; Hydrolysis of Natural, Regenerated, and Substituted Celluloses," *ibid.*, **33**, 1022–1027 (1941); "Structure, Properties, and Utilization of Cotton. Influence of Common Agencies on Behavior," *ibid.*, **34**, 1149–1154 (1942).

(*111*) Nitsche, R., and Salewski, E., "Einfluss der Temperatur auf die Festigkeit von Kunststoffen. I. Bericht. Vorversuche-Biegefestigkeit und Durchbiegung bei hohen und tiefen Temperaturen," *Kunststoffe*, **29**, No. 8, 209–220 (1939).

(*112*) Nitsche, R., and Salewski, E., "Einfluss der Temperatur auf die Festigkeit von Kunststoffen. 2. Bericht. Schlagbiegefestigkeit bie hohen und tiefen Temperaturen" *Kunststoffe*, **31**, 381–388 (1941).

(*113*) Nuckolls, A. H., "Methods for Conducting Physical Tests on Rubber Products," *Trans. Am. Soc. Testing Materials*, **22**, Part II, 541–547 (1922).

(*114*) Oberg, T. P., Schwartz, K. T., and Shinn, D. A., "Mechanical Properties of Plastics at Normal and Subnormal Temperatures," *Modern Plastics*, **20**, No. 8, 87–100, 122, 124, 126, 128 (April, 1943); *Air Corps Tech. Rept.*, No. 4648, Material Lab., U. S. Army Air Forces, Wright Field, Dayton, Ohio.

(*115*) Ohl, F., "Versuchsergebnisse aus fraktionierten Fällungen von Zelluloseacetat unter besonderer Berücksichtigung der Kunstseidenherstellung," *Kunstseide*, **12**, 468–472 (1930).

(*116*) Oka, S., "Über den mizellaren Aufbau der Faserstoffe. I. Mizellen-Orientierung als Funktion des Dehnungsgrades," *Kolloid-Z.*, **86**, 242–245 (1939).

(*117*) Parker, E. R., and Ferguson, C., "The Effect of Strain Rate on the Tensile Impact Strength of Some Materials," *Trans. Am. Soc. Metals*," **30**, 68–79 (1942).

(*118*) Parsons, G. B., "Strength of Plastic-Bonded Plywood," *Modern Plastics*, **19**, No. 12, 74–79, 110, 112, 114 (August, 1942).

(*119*) Penning, C. H., and Meyer, L. W. A., "Cold Flow of Thermoplastic Materials," *Modern Plastics*, **17**, No. 3, 91–93, 124, 126, 128 (November, 1939).

(*120*) Perkuhn, H., "Kriechverhalten geschichteter Kunstharzpressstoffe," Ber. deut. Versuchsanstalt Luftfahrt, *Luftfahrtforschung*, **18**, No. 1, 32–37 (February 28, 1941); Technical Memorandum No. 995, National Advisory Committee for Aeronautics.

(*121*) Peirce, F. T., X, Tensile Tests for Cotton Yarns. v, 'The Weakest Link.' Theorems on the Strength of Long and of Composite Specimens," *J. Textile Inst.*, **17**, T355–368 (1926).

(*122*) Place, S. W., "Effect of Heat on Phenolic Laminates," *Modern Plastics*, **18**, 59–62 (September, 1941).

(*123*) "Technical Data on Plastic Materials," Plastic Materials Manufacturers' Assn., Washington, D. C., May, 1943.

(*124*) Polanyi, M., Schmid, E., *et al.*, "Dehnungsversuche an Rohkautschuk," *Z. tech. Physik.*, **9**, 98 (1928).

(*125*) Prettyman, I. B., "Tread Cracking of Natural Stocks," *Ind. Eng. Chem.*, **36**, 29–33 (1944).

(*126*) Reed, M. C., "Stress–Strain Characteristics of Vinyl Elastomers," *Ind. Eng. Chem.*, **35**, 429–431 (1943).

(*127*) Reed, M. C., "Behavior of Plasticizers in Vinyl Chloride-Acetate Resins," *Ind. Eng. Chem.*, **35**, 896–904 (1943).

(*128*) Riechers, K., "Versuche an Kunststoffen für den Flugzeugbau," *Z. Ver. deut. Ing.*, **82**, No. 22, 665–671 (May 28, 1938).

(*129*) Rinehart, J. S., "Temperature Dependence of Young's Modulus and Internal Friction of Lucite and Karolith," *J. Applied Phys.*, **12**, 811–816 (1941).

(*130*) Rocha, H. J., "Fraktionierte Fällung von azetonlöslicher Azetylzellulose," *Kolloid-Beihefte*, **30**, 230–248 (1930).

(*131*) Rogovin, Z., and Glazman, S., Physical Heterogeneity of Cellulose Nitrates and the Properties of Fractions Prepared from Them, *J. Applied Chem., U.S.S.R.*, **8**, 1237–1246 (1935).

(*132*) Rogovin, Z., and Ivanova, Z., The Structure and Properties of Cellulose and Its Esters. XIX. Methods for Raising the Stability of Acetylcellulose Films at Low Temperatures, *J. Applied Chem. U.S.S.R.*, **14**, 834–842 (1941).

(*133*) Röhrs, W., and Hauck, K. H., Investigations on the Mechanical Properties of Plastics in the Low Temperature Region and Their Dependence on Preparation and Pretreatment, *Kunststoff-Tech. u. Kunststoff-Anwend.*, **11**, No. 8, 213–228 (1941).

(*134*) Roth, Frank L., and Holt, W. L., "Tensile Properties of Rubber Compounds at High Rates of Stretch," *J. Research Natl. Bur. Standards*, **23**, 603–616 (November, 1939).

(*135*) Rundle, G. W., and Norris, W. C., "The Study of Nitrocellulose Lacquers by the Stress–Strain Method," *Proc. Am. Soc. Testing Materials*, **26**, Part II, 546–555 (1926).

(*136*) Russell, J. J., "Behavior of Polyvinyl Chloride Plastics under Stress," *Ind. Eng. Chem.*, **32**, 509–512 (April, 1940).

(*137*) Schieber, W., "Die Verteilung der Kettenlängen in der Cellulose," *Papier-Fabr., Tech.-wiss. Tl.*, **37**, 245–250 (1939); *Angew. Chem.*, **52**, 487–488 (1939); "Physikalische und chemische Prüfverfahren zur Zellwolle," *ibid.*, **52**, 561–568 (1939).

(*138*) Schmitz, J., "Über Dehnungsmessungen an Kunstharzpressstoffen," *Kunststoff-Tech. u. Kunststoff-Anwend.*, **10**, No. 2, 25–28 (1940).

(*139*) Schröder, W., "Verhalten von Zellulosetriazetat bei höheren Temperaturen," *Kunststoffe*, **32**, 82 (1942).

(*140*) Selker, M. L., Winspear, G. G., and Kemp, A. R., "Brittle Point of Rubber on Freezing," *Ind. Eng. Chem.*, **34**, 157–160 (1942).

(*141*) Silberstein, L., "Transparencies of Turbid Materials," *Phil. Mag.*, **33**, 92, 215, 521 (1927).

(*142*) Smith, H. D. W., "Apparatus for the Measurement of Flow and Relaxation of Textile Filaments," *J. Textile Inst.*, **22**, T158–169 (1931).

(*143*) Smith, H. D. W., and Eisenschitz, R., "The Flow and Relation of Rayon Filaments," *J. Textile Inst.*, **22**, T170–196 (1931).

(*144*) Sookne, A. M., and Harris, M., "Controlled Molecular Length," *Textile Research*, **13**, No. 3, 17–31 (1943).

(*145*) Sookne, A. M., and Harris, M., "Polymolecularity and Mechanical Properties of Cellulose Acetate," *Ind. Eng. Chem.*, **37**, 478–482 (1945).

(*146*) Spurlin, H. M., "Homogeneity and Properties of Nitrocellulose," *Ind. Eng. Chem.*, **30**, 538–542 (1938).

(*147*) Spurlin, H. M., in Ott, E., *Cellulose and Cellulose Derivatives* (High Polymers, Vol. V). Interscience, New York, 1943, p. 936.

(*148*) Stambaugh, R. M., "Vibration Properties of Rubberlike Materials," *Ind. Eng. Chem.*, **34**, 1358–1365 (1942).

(*149*) Straka, C. J., "Chemical Resistance of Laminates," *Modern Plastics*, **20**, No. 11, 80–84, 136, 138 (July, 1943); No. 12, 124 (August, 1943).

(*150*) Street, J. N., and Dillon, J. H., "Physical Characteristics of Synthetic Rubbers," *J. Applied Phys.*, **12**, 45–54 (1941).

(*151*) Susich, G. v., "Die 'Schmelzkurve' von Naturkautschuk," *Naturwissenschaften*, **18**, 915–916 (1930).

(*152*) Telfair, D., Carswell, T. S., and Nason, H. K., "Creep Properties of Molded Phenolic Plastics," *Modern Plastics*, **21**, No. 6, 137–144, 174, 176 (February, 1944).

(*153*) Telfair, D., and Davis, W. C., "Creep and Recovery Data for Vinyl Sheet Plastics, *unpublished report*, *Monsanto Chemical Co.*, Springfield, Mass., February 10, 1942.

(*154*) Telfair, D., and Nason, H. K., "Impact Testing of Plastics—I: Energy Considerations," *Proc. Am. Soc. Testing Materials*, **43**, 1211–1219 (1943).

(*155*) Telfair, D., and Watt, J. H., *unpublished data*, *Monsanto Chemical Co.*, Springfield, Mass.

(*156*) Thorndike, R., "Tensile Testing of Rubber Compound at High Temperatures," *Rubber Age*, **50**, No. 5, 345–352 (1942).

(*157*) Thum, A., Creth, A., and Jacobi, H. R., Fatigue Tests on Molded Resins, *Kunststoffe u. Pressstoffe*, **2**, 16–24 (1937).

(*158*) Thum, A., and Jacobi, H. R., "Die Dauerfestigkeit von Kunstharzpressstoffen," *Maschinenschaden*, **15**, 85–91, 101–105 (1938).

(*159*) Thum, A., and Jacobi, H. R., "Mechanische Festigkeit von Phenol-Formaldehyd-Kunststoffen," *V.D.I.—Forschungsheft* 396, Supplement to "Forschung auf dem Gebiete des Ingenieurwesens," Part B, **10**, 156–157 (1939).

(*160*) Thum, A., and Jacobi, H. R., "Festigkeitseigenschaften von hochfesten Kunstharz-Pressstoffen," *Z. Ver. deut. Ing.*, **83**, 1044–1048 (1939).

(*161*) Turner, L. W., "Structure and Physical Properties of Plastics," *Chemistry & Industry*, **62**, 492–495 (1943).

(*162*) Wakeman, R. L., "Dimensional Changes of Plastics in Boiling Water," *Modern Plastics*, **18**, No. 11, 65–68, 86 (July, 1941).

(*163*) Weissenberg, K., "La mécanique des corps déformables. I, Introduction. II, La cinématique de l'élément de volume," *Arch. sci. phys. nat.*, **17**, 44–106 (1935).

(*164*) Weissenberg, K., "La mécanique des corps déformables. III, La dynamique de l'élément de volume et les principes de la mécanique. IV, La mécanique de l'élément de volume," *Arch. sci. phys. nat.* **17**, 130–171 (1935).

(*165*) Welch, W. E., and Hayes, R. F., *unpublished data, Monsanto Chemical Co.*, Springfield, Mass.

(*166*) Welter, G., and Morski, S., "Dynamic Tensile Properties and Stress–Strain Diagrams of Some Constructional Materials," *J. Inst. Metals*, **66**, 97–107 (1940).

(*167*) Werring, W. W., "Impact Testing of Insulating Materials," *Proc. Am. Soc. Testing Materials*, **26**, Part II, 634–650 (1926).

(*168*) Whitby, G. S., and Barnes, W. H., in C. C. Davis and J. Blake, *Chemistry and Technology of Rubber*. Reinhold, New York, 1937, Fig. 10A, page 80.

(*169*) Whitlock, C. H., and Haslanger, R. U., "High Impact Molding Compounds," *Modern Plastics*, **19**, No. 10, 70–71 (June, 1942).

(*170*) Wood, L. A., in *Advances in Colloid Science*, Vol. II. Interscience, New York, 1946, pp. 57–93.

(*171*) Wood, L. A., Bekkedahl, N., and Roth, F. L., "Density Measurements on Synthetic Rubbers," *Ind. Eng. Chem.*, **34**, 1291–1293 (1942).

(*172*) Yerzley, F. L., and Fraser, D. F., "Effects of Low Temperatures on Neoprene Vulcanizates," *Ind. Eng. Chem.*, **34**, 332–336 (1942).

APPENDIX I

TENSOR REPRESENTATION OF STRESS AND STRAIN

A most useful definition of stress and strain, and the most concise statements of stress–strain relationships, are formulated in terms of tensors.

The stress tensor, σ_{ij}, has 9 elements, of which only 6 are independent, because $\sigma_{ij} = \sigma_{ji}$. Numerically, each of these elements is equal to one of the six "stress components" of chapter A.

$$\begin{aligned} \sigma_{11} &\equiv S_{xx} & \sigma_{12} &= \sigma_{21} \equiv S_{xy} \\ \sigma_{22} &\equiv S_{yy} & \sigma_{23} &= \sigma_{32} \equiv S_{yz} \\ \sigma_{33} &\equiv S_{zz} & \sigma_{31} &= \sigma_{13} \equiv S_{zx} \end{aligned} \tag{1}$$

(In the tensor notation the 3 coordinate directions x, y, and z are represented by the symbols x_1, x_2, and x_3.)

The strain tensor, ϵ_{ij}, which is also a symmetric tensor of the second order, has elements defined as follows:

$$\epsilon_{ij} = \frac{1}{2}\left(\frac{\partial u_i}{\partial x_j} + \frac{\partial u_j}{\partial x_i}\right) \tag{2}$$

where u is the displacement vector. In terms of tensor notation, this can be written as:

$$\epsilon_{ij} = \tfrac{1}{2}(u_{i,j} + u_{j,i}) \tag{3}$$

Here the comma indicates differentiation with respect to the coordinate corresponding to the subscript which follows the comma. It is clear that the nine elements of the strain tensor are simply related in numerical magnitude to the six strain components of chapter A.

$$\begin{aligned} \epsilon_{11} &\equiv \gamma_{xx} & \epsilon_{12} &= \epsilon_{21} \equiv \tfrac{1}{2}\gamma_{xy} \\ \epsilon_{22} &\equiv \gamma_{yy} & \epsilon_{23} &= \epsilon_{32} \equiv \tfrac{1}{2}\gamma_{yz} \\ \epsilon_{33} &\equiv \gamma_{zz} & \epsilon_{31} &= \epsilon_{13} \equiv \tfrac{1}{2}\gamma_{zx} \end{aligned} \tag{4}$$

In view of the close numerical connection between the elements of the stress and strain tensors and the components of stress and strain as used in chapter A, it may appear that only trivial differences exist between the two definitions. Actually, use of tensor transformation laws and of the condensed notation developed in tensor calculus makes it possible to write all stress–strain equations in an extremely concise form. Furthermore, certain auxiliary tensors—the *deviatoric* stress and strain tensors—provide a very straightforward means of isolating volumetric changes from shape deformations.

The mean normal stress, σ, is defined as $\frac{1}{3}(\sigma_{11} + \sigma_{22} + \sigma_{33})$. The deviatoric stress tensor, s_{ij}, is then defined as follows:

$$s_{ij} = \sigma_{ij} - \sigma\delta_{ij} \tag{5}$$

where δ_{ij}, the Kroneker Delta, is defined as:

$$\begin{aligned} \delta_{ij} &= 0 \qquad (i \neq j) \\ \delta_{ii} &= 1 \end{aligned} \tag{6}$$

In a similar fashion, the strain tensor, ϵ_{ij}, can be resolved into the mean normal strain, ϵ, plus the deviatoric strain tensor, e_{ij}:

$$\epsilon = \tfrac{1}{3}(\epsilon_{11} + \epsilon_{22} + \epsilon_{33}) \tag{7}$$

$$e_{ij} = \epsilon_{ij} - \epsilon\delta_{ij} \tag{8}$$

The mean normal stress is a measure of the pressure, and the mean normal strain of the volumetric deformation. The deviatoric tensors, on the other hand, isolate the shear stresses and strains. In the case of an isotropic elastic material, this leads to particularly simple stress–strain relationships:

$$\sigma = B\epsilon \tag{9}$$

$$s_{ij} = 2\,Ge_{ij} \tag{10}$$

where B is the bulk modulus and G the shear modulus.

In the case of an isotropic material where $B \gg G$, it is often justifiable to neglect volume changes and to assume that $\epsilon = 0$. In this case (the incompressible case) the stress–strain relationships can be condensed to the single equation:

$$s_{ij} = 2\,Ge_{ij} \tag{11}$$

The following appendices are written in terms of tensor notation. In the text, a different and less condensed notation has been used. The author feels that the tensor notation, while concise and elegant, might involve difficulty for a reader unfamiliar with it, particularly when the subject matter under discussion is also new. For the reader with mathematical inclinations, the equations and discussions throughout the book can be easily translated into tensor nomenclature. Most of such equations involve a simple shear stress and strain, labeled s and γ, with no subscripts. In all such cases we can replace the shear stress s by the entire deviatoric stress tensor s_{ij}, and the shear strain γ by twice the deviatoric strain tensor e_{ij}. For example, equation (12):

$$\dot{\gamma} = \frac{1}{G}\dot{s} + \frac{1}{\eta}s \qquad (12)$$

becomes

$$2\,\dot{e}_{ij} = \frac{1}{G}\dot{s}_{ij} + \frac{1}{\eta}s_{ij} \qquad (13)$$

APPENDIX II*

VARIOUS MATHEMATICAL METHODS OF SPECIFYING VISCOELASTIC PROPERTIES

I. INTRODUCTION

. . . No less than seven distinct methods have been employed to define the properties (in shear) of viscoelastic materials. It is the purpose of this paper to examine these methods and show that they are all mathematically equivalent and that they are all interconnected by definite relationships.

We are only concerned with *incompressible, isotropic, viscoelastic* materials. The term incompressible indicates that the material is much more easily deformed in shear than in compression; thus, the viscoelastic deformation is essentially a constant-volume process. The term isotropic requires that in the unstrained state the properties of the material are the same in all directions. The term viscoelastic is here restricted to designate those materials whose reponse to stress obeys the superposition principle; that is, materials which can be represented by a model constructed from elements which obey Hooke's elastic law and elements which obey Newton's viscosity law.

The seven distinct methods of specifying the properties of viscoelastic materials may be divided into two classes. In Class I may be listed the four that are more general and fundamental in nature:

A. The Voigt model, consisting of a set of Voigt elements (retarded elastic elements) coupled in series.
B. The Maxwell model, consisting of a set of Maxwell elements coupled in parallel.
C. The operator equation, $\mathbf{P}s = 2\,\mathbf{Q}\epsilon$, where **P** and **Q** are linear differential operators.
D. The mechanical impedance function, $\mathbf{Z}(\omega)$.

* Reproduction, in part, courtesy Dr. Paul M. Doty and *Journal of Applied Physics* (Volume 16, November, 1945, pages 700–713).

In Class II may be listed the obvious experimental curves which serve to "map out" the viscoelastic character of the material:

E. The creep curve, consisting of the strain as a function of time at constant stress.
F. The relaxation curve, consisting of the stress as a function of time at constant strain.
G. The dynamic modulus curve, consisting of the elastic modulus as a function of frequency.

The Class I methods are more satisfactory as specifications of properties since they are of the nature of differential equations which can be solved for a wide variety of transient conditions. Class II methods on the other hand represent special solutions of the fundamental differential equations for very particular cases. Consequently, these latter functions are not so well adapted to the treatment of a wide range of transient conditions.

It is obviously important to be able to transform readily from one fundamental mode of description to another, to be able to derive the basic properties of a material (Class I) from experimental data (Class II), to be able to predict behavior in special conditions (Class II) from the properties (Class I), and to be able to predict behavior in one special set of conditions from the known behavior under other conditions. If Class II methods are accepted as specifying the properties of a viscoelastic material, then all of these problems are concerned with the transformation from one of the seven modes of description to another.

Some of these transformations have been worked out and are of a form simple enough to be of practical value. In figure 244 these transformations are indicated and labeled as $a, b, \cdots, m$. Several other transformations have been formally developed but are perhaps too cumbersome to serve as practical working schemes. These are indicated in figure 245 and labeled $n, o, \cdots, t$. Finally, several transformations can be made by simple approximation methods. These are also summarized in figure 245 and labeled u, v, w, and x.

II. METHODS OF SPECIFYING VISCOELASTIC PROPERTIES

A. The Voigt Model

A Voigt element consists of a spring (representing Hooke's law behavior) and a dashpot (representing Newton's viscosity law behavior) in parallel. This element expresses the simplest form of retarded elastic behavior. [This method has been used extensively in the text of this book; particularly in chapter B.] . . .

The strain, 2ϵ, associated with the element follows the differential equation:

$$s = 2\,G\epsilon + 2\eta\dot{\epsilon} \tag{1}$$

where s is the stress. The factor 2 in this and following equations arises from the fact that our ϵ represents a shear component of the strain tensor, and is thus equal to 1/2 of the corresponding "classical" shear strain. It follows that s represents the corresponding component of the deviatoric stress tensor. In the case of simple shear, s is the shear stress and 2ϵ is the shear strain. . . .

Figure 68 (page 167) shows a Voigt model consisting of ··· Voigt elements, one of which is degenerated into a spring with no dashpot and one into a dashpot with no spring. The material is thus defined by the values of six parameters, J_1, J_2, η_2, J_3, η_3, and η_4. The total strain, ϵ, is made up of the contributions from the ··· elements: $\epsilon = \epsilon_1 + \epsilon_2 + \epsilon_3 + \epsilon_4$. The retarded elastic elements obey the differential equations:

$$s = 2\,G_2\epsilon_2 + 2\,\eta_2\epsilon_2 \tag{2a}$$

$$s = 2\,G_3\epsilon_3 + 2\,\eta_3\dot{\epsilon}_3 \tag{2b}$$

For the degenerate elements these reduce to:

$$s = 2\,G_1\epsilon_1 \tag{3a}$$

$$s = 2\,\eta_4\dot{\epsilon}_4 \tag{3b}$$

More generally, the behavior of a material which is represented by n retarded elastic elements is governed by a set of n-differential equations of the form:

$$s = 2\,G_i\epsilon_i + 2\,\eta_i\epsilon_i \tag{4}$$

(of which one or two may be degenerate) plus the relation $\epsilon = \sum^{n} \epsilon_i$. In the limit, the set of discrete Voigt elements may be replaced by a continuous distribution of elastic compliance as a function of retardation time. That is, the finite set of physical constants—J_1, η_1, J_2, η_2, ···, J_n, η_n—is now replaced by a continuous function $J(\tau)d\tau$ which tells how much elastic compliance has the retardation time, τ, in the range of $d\tau$. The total retarded strain is given by the integral:

$$\epsilon(t) = \int_0^\infty \epsilon^*(t,\tau)d\tau \tag{5}$$

where ϵ^* is governed by the differential equation:

$$s(t) = \frac{2\,\epsilon^*(t,\tau)}{J(\tau)} + \frac{2\,\tau}{J(\tau)}\frac{\partial \epsilon^*(t,\tau)}{\partial t} \tag{6}$$

B. The Maxwell Model

Figure 63 (page 133) shows a Maxwell model consisting of ··· Maxwell elements, one of which is degenerated to a spring and one to a dashpot. In this model the strains associated with all elements are equal, but the total stress is divided among the elements. The stress on the ith element is related to the strain by the differential equation:

$$2\,\epsilon = \frac{1}{G_i}\,\dot{s} + \frac{1}{\eta_i}\,s_i \tag{7}$$

which takes on simpler form for the two degenerated elements. As in the previous method, the behavior of the material is governed by a set of first order differential equations.

In the limit, this behavior goes over into a continuous distribution of elastic moduli as a function of relaxation time. The finite set of physical constants G_1, τ_1 ··· G_n, τ_n is replaced by a function $G(\tau)d\tau$, telling the amount of elastic modulus with the relaxation time τ in the range $d\tau$. The total stress is given by the integral:

$$s(t) = \int_0^\infty s^*(t,\tau)d\tau \tag{8}$$

where $s^*(t,\tau)$ follows the differential equation:

$$2\,\dot{\epsilon}(t) = \frac{1}{G(\tau)}\frac{\partial s^*(t,\tau)}{\partial t} + \frac{s^*(t,\tau)}{\tau G(\tau)} \tag{9}$$

C. The Operator Equation $\mathbf{P}s = 2\,\mathbf{Q}\epsilon$

Method A involved a set of n differential equations of the first order, each relating a particular strain contribution with the total stress. Method B involved a set of n differential equations of the first order, each relating a fraction of the stress with the total strain. Method C involves a single differential equation of the nth order, relating the total stress with the total strain:

$$\mathbf{P}s = 2\,\mathbf{Q}\epsilon \tag{10}$$

where:

$$\mathbf{P} = \frac{\partial^m}{\partial t^m} + p_{m-1}\frac{\partial^{m-1}}{\partial t^{m-1}} + \cdots + p_0$$

$$\mathbf{Q} = q_n\frac{\partial^n}{\partial t^n} + q_{n-1}\frac{\partial^{n-1}}{\partial t^{n-1}} + \cdots + q_0$$

The parameters p_i, q_i, fix the properties of the viscoelastic material. It will be demonstrated in Part III that the same number of independent parameters are required to characterize a material, regardless of which method (A, B, or C) is used. . . .

D. The Mechanical Impedance Function

The analogy between electrical networks and the mechanical models designed to describe viscoelastic behavior have been discussed in detail [in chapter B]. Voltage corresponds to stress, resistance to viscosity, current to the time derivative of strain and the reactance to $-G/\omega$. Consequently, the steady-state response of a viscoelastic material to a sinusoidal stress $s = s_0 \cos \omega t$ can be related to a (complex) mechanical impedance **Z**. $\mathbf{Z} = a + ib$, where a is the "viscous resistance," η, and b the "elastic reactance," $-G/\omega$. Both a and b depend in magnitude upon the frequency. The complex mechanical impedance function $\mathbf{Z}(\omega)$ fixes the properties of a viscoelastic material in a manner completely equivalent to those of methods A, B, and C. Although the most obvious use of the impedance function is in connection with steady-state response to sinusoidal stress, the Fourier and Laplace transformations make it as general as methods A, B, and C in its definition of viscoelastic properties.

E. The Creep Function

If a relaxed specimen of a viscoelastic material is suddenly subjected (at the time $t = 0$) to a stress s which thereafter is held constant, the strain will increase with time according to some function $2\,\epsilon(t)$. Since the strain at any time is proportional to the stress s, dividing through by s gives a creep function $\phi(t)$ which is independent of the stress, that is:

$$\phi(t) = 2\,\epsilon(t)/s \qquad (11)$$

A given creep function is consistent with only one model of either type and with only one operator specification. Although the creep function can be said to define the viscoelastic properties of a material, as has been pointed out, it is less satisfactory than methods A, B, C, and D for such a specification.

F. The Relaxation Function

If a sample is quickly forced to take on the strain ϵ, and is then held fixed in such a fashion that the strain must remain constant, the stress will decay with time according to some function $s(t)$. Since the stress at any time is proportional to the strain, dividing through by the strain gives a relaxation function $\psi(t)$ which is independent of the strain, that is:

$$\psi(t) = s(t)/2\,\epsilon \qquad (12)$$

The relaxation function of a material defines its viscoelastic properties in precisely the same sense as does the creep function.

G. The Dynamic Modulus

When subjected to a stress which varies sinusoidally with time ($s = s_0 \cos \omega t$), a viscoelastic material will respond with a strain $2\,\epsilon(t)$ which (in the steady state) will also vary sinusoidally with time: $2\,\epsilon = 2\,\epsilon_0 \cos(\omega t - \alpha)$. The ratio $s_0/2\,\epsilon_0$, can be called the dynamic modulus, $G(\nu)$, and will in general be a function of the frequency. A given dynamic modulus function will be consistent with only one model of either type, and with only one operator specification. Hence, $G(\nu)$ can be said to specify the viscoelastic properties of a material.

III. EXACT RELATIONSHIPS AMONG THE METHODS

While any one of the above methods is in principle sufficient to define the properties of a given viscoelastic material, it is desirable to understand how the various methods are related to one another. . . .

In this section, a number of exact relationships will be discussed. These may be divided into two classes—those which are simple enough to be used as working methods, and those which are chiefly formal in nature. The diagram in figure 243 shows the translations which can be made exactly and yet fairly simply; in figure 244 the formal relationships, more difficult to utilize, are indicated together with approximate relationships. The lettering in these figures corresponds to that in this section.

A. Voigt Model to Creep Function

If the viscoelastic properties of a material have been specified by a Voigt model, it is always easy to compute the response of the material, $2\,\epsilon(t)$, to any simple stress sequence $s(t)$, since the response of each Voigt element can be calculated separately, and then the individual contributions to the strain can be added together. The creep curve is a

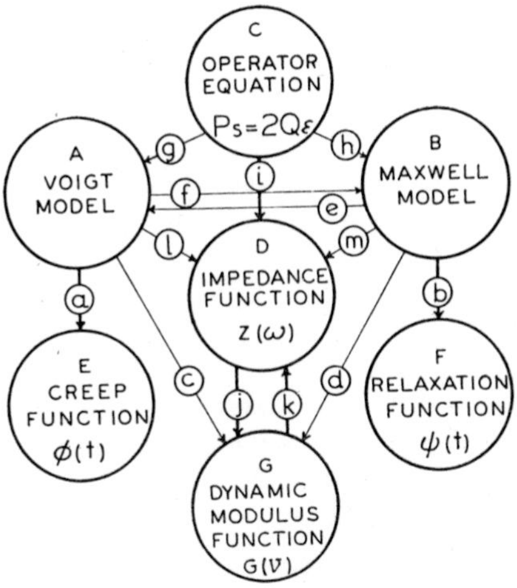

Fig. 243. Diagram of practical relationships.

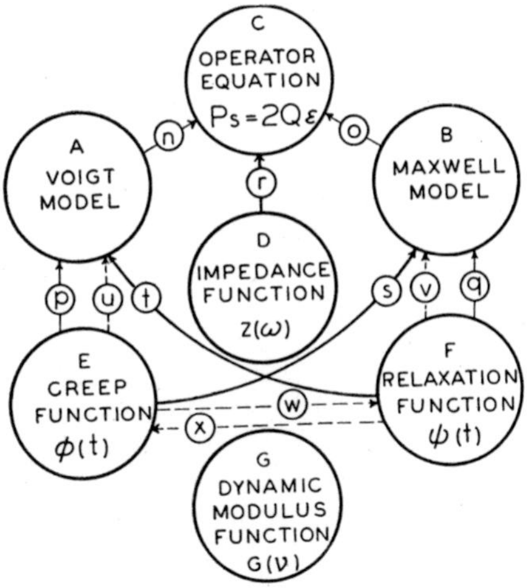

Fig. 244. Diagram of formal (—) and approximate (- - -) relationships.

particularly simple case. A constant stress s, imposed upon a single relaxed Voigt element at time zero, causes a strain response, $2\,\epsilon(t)$, which must obey the differential equation:

$$2\,G\epsilon + 2\,\eta\dot{\epsilon} = s \tag{13}$$

where s = constant. The general solution of this equation is:

$$2\,\epsilon(t) = Ae^{-t/\tau} + (s/G) \tag{14}$$

Inserting the initial condition that $\epsilon = 0$ at time $t = 0$ for a sample containing no residual strains we can evaluate the arbitrary constant, A, and obtain the particular solution:

$$2\,\epsilon(t) = \frac{s}{G}[1 - e^{-t/\tau}] = sJ[1 - e^{-t/\tau}] \tag{15}$$

If the model consists of n retarded elastic elements, each with its own compliance and retardation time, the total response of the model is given by:

$$2\,\epsilon(t) = s\sum^{n} J_i[1 - e^{-t/\tau_i}] \tag{16}$$

If in addition to n complete Voigt elements the model includes an unretarded compliance J_1 and a true viscous flow governed by the viscosity

η, the response becomes:

$$2\,\epsilon(t) = s\left[J_1 + \sum_{i=2}^{n} J_i(1 - e^{-t/\tau_i}) + \frac{1}{\eta}t\right] \tag{17}$$

Finally, if the series n Voigt elements is replaced by a continuous distribution of elastic compliance, $J(\tau)$, over a range of τ, equation (17) becomes:

$$2\,\epsilon(t) = s\left[J_1 + \int_0^\infty J(\tau)(1 - e^{-t/\tau})d\tau + \frac{1}{\eta}t\right] \tag{18}$$

Each of these functions can be changed to the standard creep function $\phi(t)$ simply by cancelling out the constant s from the right-hand side.

B. Maxwell Model to Relaxation Function

While the Voigt specification allows a simple prediction of the strain as a function of time for a known $s(t)$, the Maxwell model is designed to allow an equally simple prediction of the stress as a function of time when a known strain sequence, $2\,\epsilon(t)$, is forced upon the material. $s(t)$ for the known $2\,\epsilon(t)$ can be computed for each Maxwell element separately and the results added together. The relaxation of stress at constant strain is a particularly simple case. (It is here assumed that the strain $2\,\epsilon$ is suddenly imposed upon a relaxed sample at $t = 0$.) The stress in a given Maxwell element must follow the differential equation:

$$2\,\dot{\epsilon} = (1/G)\dot{s} + (1/\eta)s \tag{19}$$

This leads to the explicit relation:

$$s(t) = s_0 e^{-(G/\eta)t} = 2\,G\epsilon e^{-t/\tau} \tag{20}$$

For a set of n Maxwell elements in parallel and a spring of modulus G, with no dashpot for relaxation, equation (20) becomes:

$$s(t) = 2\,\epsilon\left[G_1 + \sum_{i=2}^{n} G_i e^{-t/\tau_i}\right] \tag{21}$$

We need not consider here the case where an isolated dashpot is present. Finally, if the set of n Maxwell elements is replaced by a continuous distribution of relaxation times, $G(\tau)$, the stress relaxation at constant strain follows the relation:

$$s(t) = 2\,\epsilon \int_0^\infty G(\tau)e^{-t/\tau}d\tau \tag{22}$$

C AND D. VOIGT AND MAXWELL MODELS TO DYNAMIC MODULUS FUNCTION

These transformations are discussed in chapter B.

E AND F. MAXWELL MODEL TO AND FROM VOIGT MODEL

The translations from a Voigt model to a Maxwell model, and *vice versa*, have been indicated in figure 244 as being relatively simple. This is only partly true. If we are given a Voigt model, and must construct the equivalent Maxwell model, the first step is to find the correct structural *form* of the unknown model, and the second is to compute the numerical values of the unknown parameters. The first, or topological, step is controlled by rules which can be formulated simply, but the second step can be easily made only in very simple cases.

The following rules govern the topological relationships between the two kinds of model:

1. The Maxwell model will contain the same number of springs and the same number of dashpots as the equivalent Voigt model.
2. A standard Voigt model (no incomplete elements) corresponds to a "doubly degenerate" Maxwell model (one isolated spring and one isolated dashpot).
3. A standard Maxwell model corresponds to a "doubly degenerate" Voigt model.
4. A singly degenerate Voigt model with one isolated (unretarded) spring corresponds to a singly degenerate Maxwell model with one isolated (nonrelaxing) spring.
5. A singly degenerate Voigt model with one isolated dashpot corresponds to a singly degenerate Maxwell model with one isolated dashpot.
6. The rather involved general rule which embraces 2, 3, 4, and 5 is the following: The *presence* of an isolated element of *one* kind in a model corresponds to the *absence* of an isolated element of the *opposite* kind in the conjugate model (*e.g.*, the presence of an isolated *spring* in a Voigt model implies the *absence* of an isolated *dashpot* in the equivalent Maxwell model).

The numerical computation of the parameters of one model from those of its equivalent is much more involved. It is, indeed, out of the question to write down general functional relationships for one set in terms of the other. The complexity which arises can be estimated from the . . . explicit equations for the relatively simple case of two Maxwell elements in parallel, corresponding to one unretarded spring, one Voigt element, and one dashpot in the other language. [See equations (16) to (25), chapter B.] Because of this complexity, it is suggested that numerical computations of this sort be made in two steps, via the operator formulation, rather than directly.

G. OPERATOR EQUATION TO VOIGT MODEL

The first step in translating an operator equation $\mathbf{P}s = 2\,\mathbf{Q}\epsilon$ into the equivalent Voigt model is to establish the correct structural form (topology) of the model. The following rules govern the form of the model:

1. The total number of ultimate elements of the model is equal to the total number of parameters involved in the operators **P** and **Q**.
2. If the Voigt model contains no isolated springs or dashpots, the order of **P** is one less than that of **Q**. ($n = m + 1$.) The "standard" operator equation which is equivalent to a set of n complete Voigt elements can therefore be written:

$$\frac{\partial^{n-1}s}{\partial t^{n-1}} + p_{n-2}\frac{\partial^{n-2}s}{\partial t^{n-1}} + \cdots + p_0 s = 2\,q_n\frac{\partial^n \epsilon}{\partial t^n} + \cdots + 2\,q_0\epsilon \qquad (23)$$

3. If the coefficient q_n vanishes, then one Voigt element of the equivalent model degenerates to a spring with no dashpot.
4. If the coefficient q_0 vanishes, one Voigt element of the equivalent model degenerates to a dashpot with no spring.
5. If q_0 and q_n both vanish, the corresponding Voigt model is *doubly* degenerate.

The second step of the problem is the determination of numerical values for the parameters of the model. This step is discussed in detail in another paper.[1] The standard, or nondegenerate, case will be briefly outlined here.

It is clear that in order for the operator equation and the Voigt model to be mathematically equivalent, they must give the same prediction for the strain, $\epsilon(t)$, when any given stress sequence $s(t)$ is imposed. It is sufficiently general to equate the two responses to a stress sequence $s(t) = t^{n-1}$. The general solution of the equation $\mathbf{P}s = 2\,\mathbf{Q}\epsilon$ is the sum of the general solution of the associated homogeneous equation $s(t) = 0$ and the particular polynomial solution of the complete equation. In the same way, the response of the model to the stress $s(t)$ is the sum of the general response to a zero stress plus a particular polynomial response to the stress t^{n-1}. In order for the response of the model to be identical with that predicted by the operator equation, the parameters of the model must fit the following rules. First, the n retardation times of the n Voigt elements are the negative reciprocals of the n roots of the characteristic equation of the operator **Q**; that is $\tau_i = -1/x_i$, where x_i are the roots of the equation $q_n x^n + \cdots + q_0 = 0$. Thus, the n retardation times of the model are determined by the general solution of the homogeneous differential equation.

In order to complete the specification of the model the particular polynomial solution must now be used. The particular polynomial solution of the equation $\mathbf{P}(t^{n-1}) = 2\,\mathbf{Q}\epsilon$ will be of the form:

$$2\,\epsilon(t) = a_0 + a_1 t + a_2 t^2 + \cdots + a_{n-1}t^{n-1} \qquad (24)$$

[1] T. Alfrey, *Quart. Applied Math.*, **3**, July, 1945.

The coefficients $a_0, a_1, \cdots a_{n-1}$ can be determined by ordinary methods. The particular polynomial solution derived from the model will be of the form:

$$2\,\epsilon(t) = (n-1)!\sum^{n}\frac{J_i}{x_i^{\,n-1}} + \left(\frac{(n-1)!}{2!}\sum^{n}\frac{J_i}{x_i^{\,n-2}}\right)t + \cdots + \left(\frac{(n-1)!}{(n-2)!}\sum^{n}\frac{J_i}{x_i}\right)t^{n-2} + \sum^{n} J_i t^{n-1} \quad (25)$$

It follows that the n compliances $J_1, J_2, \cdots J_n$ must be the roots of the following set of linear algebraic equations:

$$\begin{aligned} a_{n-1} &= \sum^{n} J_i \\ \frac{1}{n-1}\,a_{n-2} &= \sum \frac{J_i}{x_i} \\ \frac{1}{(n-1)(n-2)}\,a_{n-3} &= \sum \frac{J_i}{x_i^2} \\ &\cdots\cdots \\ \frac{1}{(n-1)!}\,a_0 &= \sum \frac{J_i}{x_i^{\,n-1}} \end{aligned} \quad (26)$$

The Voigt model is completely specified when the compliance and retardation time of each Voigt element are determined.

The degenerate cases where q_n or q_0 vanish can also be simply handled.[1]

H. Operator Equation to Maxwell Model

A Maxwell model with no degenerate elements corresponds to an operator equation in which both q_n and q_0 vanish. The m relaxation times of the m Maxwell elements are equal to the negative reciprocals of the m roots of the characteristic equation of the operator **P**. The specification of the model can then be completed by the solution of a set of m linear equations in m unknowns:

$$\begin{aligned} \frac{1}{m}\,a_{m-1} &= \sum^{m} \eta_i \\ \frac{1}{m(m-1)}\,a_{m-2} &= \sum^{m} \frac{\eta_i}{x_i} \\ \frac{1}{m(m-1)(m-2)}\,a_{m-3} &= \sum^{m} \frac{\eta_i}{x_i^2} \\ &\cdots\cdots \\ \frac{1}{m!}\,a_0 &= \sum^{m} \frac{\eta_i}{x_i^{\,m-1}} \end{aligned} \quad (27)$$

I. Operator Equation to Impedance Function

In electrical network theory it is shown that the complex impedance, $\mathbf{Z}(\omega)$, is equal to the ratio of the Fourier transform of the potential to the transform of the current. Since the current corresponds to the time derivative of the strain it is necessary to note the equivalent expression for the Fourier transform of $\dot{\epsilon}$, that is:

$$\int_{-\infty}^{\infty} \dot{\epsilon}(t)e^{-i\omega t}dt = (i\omega)\int_{-\infty}^{\infty} \epsilon(t)e^{-i\omega t}dt \tag{28}$$

$\mathbf{Z}(\omega)$ can now be calculated from the operators $\mathbf{P}$ and $\mathbf{Q}$ as follows:

$$\mathbf{P}s = 2\,\mathbf{Q}\epsilon \tag{29a}$$

$$\ddot{s}_2 + p\dot{s}_1 + p_0 s = 2[q_3\dddot{\epsilon} + q_2\ddot{\epsilon} + q_1\dot{\epsilon} + q_0\epsilon] \tag{29b}$$

The Fourier transforms of each term are found by integrating over t after multiplying by $e^{i\omega t}$. Using (28), this procedure yields after collecting terms:

$$[(i\omega)^2 + p_1(i\omega) + p_0]\int_{-\infty}^{\infty} se^{-i\omega t}dt$$

$$= 2[q_3(i\omega)^3 + q_2(i\omega)^2 + q_1(i\omega) + q_0]\int_{-\infty}^{\infty} \epsilon e^{-i\omega t}dt \tag{30}$$

Thus the form of the impedance function is found to be:

$$\begin{aligned}\mathbf{Z}(\omega) &= \frac{\int s(t)e^{-i\omega t}dt}{(i\omega)2\int \epsilon(t)e^{-i\omega t}dt}\\ &= \frac{q_3(i\omega)^3 + q_2(i\omega)^2 + q_1(i\omega) + q_0}{(i\omega)[(i\omega)^2 + p_1(i\omega) + p_0]}\\ &= \frac{\mathbf{Q}(i\omega)}{(i\omega)\mathbf{P}(i\omega)}\end{aligned} \tag{31}$$

J. Impedance Function to Dynamic Modulus

The relation between the impedance function and the response to sinusoidal stresses is, of course, particularly simple. At a given frequency, $\omega/2\pi$, where the mechanical admittance, $1/\mathbf{Z}(\omega)$, has the value $A + iB$, the steady-state response to the stress, $s = s_0 \cos \omega t$, will be:

$$2\,\dot{\epsilon}(t) = s_0 A \cos \omega t - s_0 B \sin \omega t \tag{32a}$$

$$2\,\epsilon(t) = \frac{s_0}{\omega} A \sin \omega t + \frac{s_0}{\omega} B \cos \omega t \tag{32b}$$

In this connection, the relationship between sinusoidal stress and strain (in the presence of a lumped mass) is sometimes written as:

$$M\ddot{\epsilon} + A\dot{\epsilon} + B\epsilon = s_0 \cos \omega t \tag{33}$$

or as some obvious variant of this equation. It is quite true that such an equation will hold for a particular frequency. In order for it to hold at *any* frequency, A and B must become functions of frequency, rather than numerical constants This has, of course, been recognized by those using equation (33). It is, however, possible to write a differential equation relating stress and strain in which all coefficients are true constants. This is the operator equation, $\mathbf{P}s = 2\,\mathbf{Q}\epsilon$, which for this problem (after the introduction of a lumped mass) becomes:

$$M\ddot{\epsilon} + 2\,\mathbf{Q}\epsilon = \mathbf{P}(s_0 \cos \omega t) \tag{34}$$

K. Dynamic Modulus to Impedance Function

The reverse transformation, by which the impedance function is derived from experimental data on the steady-state relation between sinusoidal stress and strain, is also simple. If the amplitude and phase of the strain relative to the stress, $s = s_0 \cos \omega t$, is known, the strain can always be written as:

$$2\,\epsilon(t) = Cs_0 \cos \omega t + Ds_0 \sin \omega t \tag{35}$$

where C and D are known functions of ω. A, the real part of the admittance function, is equal to $D\omega$; and B, the imaginary part, is given by $C\omega$. Thus the impedance function is:

$$\mathbf{Z}(\omega) = 1/[\omega(D + iC)] \tag{36}$$

L and M. Voigt and Maxwell Models to Impedance Function

These transformations have been discussed in chapter B.

N and O. Voigt or Maxwell Model to Operator Equation

To go from a Voigt model or a Maxwell model to the corresponding operator equation is a little more involved than the reverse transformations (G) and (H). A general method for these conversations has been developed, however, and is described elsewhere.[1] There exists in addition an obvious method which can easily be carried out for models which contain only a small number of elements. To illustrate this simple method, let us consider a Voigt model consisting of two Voigt elements—

G_1, η_1, G_2, η_2. The material under consideration is governed by the two differential equations:

$$s = 2\,G_1\epsilon_1 + 2\,\eta_1\dot{\epsilon}_1 \tag{37a}$$

$$s = 2\,G_2\epsilon_2 + 2\,\eta_2\dot{\epsilon}_2 \tag{37b}$$

The second of these can be rewritten in terms of the total strain, $\epsilon = \epsilon_1 + \epsilon_2$ as follows:

$$s = 2\,G_1\epsilon_1 + 2\,\eta_1\dot{\epsilon}_1 \tag{38a}$$

$$s = 2\,G_2\epsilon - 2\,G_2\epsilon_1 + 2\,\eta_2\dot{\epsilon} - 2\,\eta_2\dot{\epsilon}_1 \tag{38b}$$

Let us now differentiate equations (38a) and (38b), obtaining:

$$\dot{s} = 2\,G_1\epsilon_1 + 2\,\eta_1\ddot{\epsilon}_1 \tag{39a}$$

$$\dot{s} = 2\,G_2\epsilon - 2\,G_2\epsilon_1 + 2\,\eta_2\ddot{\epsilon} - 2\,\eta_2\ddot{\epsilon}_1 \tag{39b}$$

Equations (37)–(39) can now be combined in such a way as to remove the strain contribution ϵ_1, and its derivatives, by multiplying each equation by the proper factor and adding. The resulting differential equation of the third order involves only the *total* strain and stress and is the desired equivalent equation.

P. Creep Function to Voigt Model

Since the creep curve of a viscoelastic material is a known function of the parameters of the specifying Voigt model, it is obviously possible to derive the values of these Voigt parameters from the shape of the creep curve *in those cases where the model consists of a discrete set of Voigt elements with markedly different τ values.* In general, however, this will not be the case. It is still possible to *assume a topological form* for the model, and then compute a reasonable set of parameters for the model. The result is an approximation which may be quite good if enough adjustable parameters are used, but the choice is rather arbitrary. Two different investigators may well obtain entirely different numerical values for the individual elements of their approximating models—even though the over-all behavior of both models is quite similar. This is an obvious disadvantage. A specification, to be most useful, should be unique as well as accurate. It is for this reason that method (U) will be advanced.

Q. Relaxation Function to Maxwell Model

The construction of a Maxwell model from a known relaxation curve is precisely equivalent to the construction of a Voigt model from a known creep curve. Method (V) will be advanced to handle this problem in an accurate, unique fashion.

R. Impedance Function to Operator Equation

Since the impedance function is related to the parameters of the operator equation by equation (31), it is possible in principle to derive the operator equation by factoring the known impedance function into a ratio of two polynomials in $(i\omega)$. In practice, using an empirical $\mathbf{Z}(\omega)$, this will usually be impracticable. The authors see no simple means for this conversion.

S. Creep Function to Maxwell Model

Simha [2] has shown that the distribution function $G(\tau)$, which defines a continuous Maxwell model, can be derived from the creep curve of the material. The method, which is based upon the use of Fourier transforms, is rather involved and is not described here. Instead, a much simpler, although approximate, method is developed in section IV.

T. Relaxation Function to Voigt Model

Because of the symmetry of the relationships among the methods of representation, the problem of deriving an equivalent Voigt model from a relaxation function is mathematically very similar to that of deriving a Maxwell model from a creep function. The method of Simha, with slight alterations, could be used for an exact transformation; an approximate method will be developed in the next section.

IV. SOME NEW APPROXIMATION METHODS

The conversions described in the previous section are exact. This advantage, however, is offset by the fact that they involve complicated computations for materials whose viscoelastic models contain a large number of elements. For this reason a set of *approximation* methods will be developed in this section.

U. Creep Curve to Voigt Model

A creep curve shows how strain varies with time at constant stress.[3] The strain at any time will be made up of two parts—elastic deformation and flow. If plotted as $2\ \epsilon$ *vs.* log t, the (*retarded*) *elastic part* of the strain will yield a sigmoidal curve. The total strain can easily be resolved into

[2] R. Simha, *J. Applied Phys.*, **13**, 201 (1942).
[3] H. Leaderman, *Ind. Eng. Chem.*, **35**, 374 (1943).

the two parts, if the creep data cover a wide range of time scale. The viscosity η can be immediately calculated from the flow component. The computation of the viscoelastic spectrum $J(\tau)$ from the sigmoidal elastic creep curve, however, is not so simple. The following method gives an approximation to $J(\tau)$. We will actually derive an approximation to the function L (log τ), where $L(\log \tau) d \log \tau = J(\tau) d\tau$.

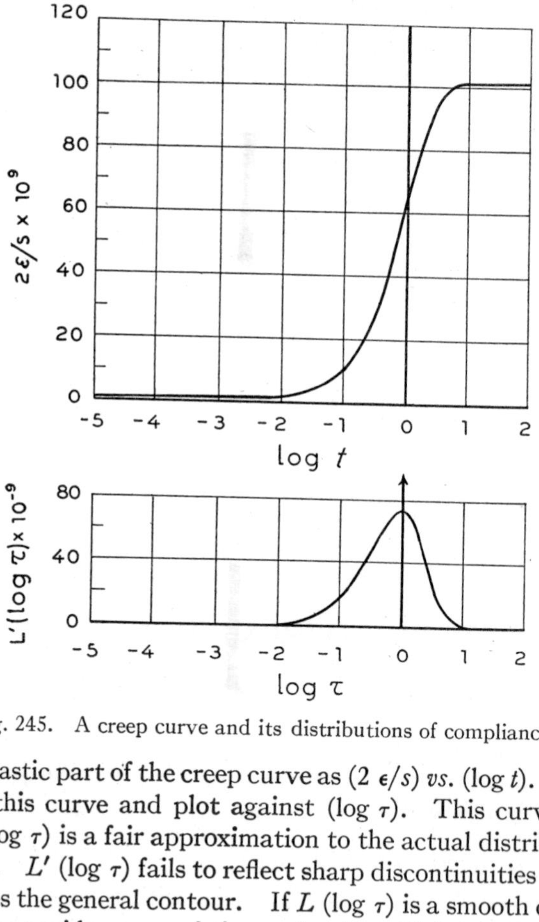

Fig. 245. A creep curve and its distributions of compliance.

Plot the elastic part of the creep curve as ($2\,\epsilon/s$) *vs.* (log t). Determine the slope of this curve and plot against (log τ). This curve which we may call L' (log τ) is a fair approximation to the actual distribution function L (log τ). L' (log τ) fails to reflect sharp discontinuities in L (log τ), but reproduces the general contour. If L (log τ) is a smooth distribution, extending over a wide range of timescale, then L' (log τ) is a very good approximation. If L (log τ) contains discontinuities, then L' (log τ) is not so good an approximation.

Let us investigate the closeness of the approximation in the most unfavorable case—that of an extremely sharp distribution function. Consider a material whose Voigt model consists of an instantaneous compliance of 10^{-9} cm^2 per dyne and a retarded elastic compliance of 10^{-7} cm^2 per dyne whose retardation time is 1 second. (The viscosity of the retarding dashpot is thus 10^7 poise.)

The upper part of figure 245 shows the exact creep curve for such a material. The lower part of figure 245 shows the derived distribution of compliance L' (log τ). This can be compared with the true distribution L (log τ), which is the discontinuous function. The area under the hump in L' (log τ) is exactly equal to the correct value of J_2, and the maximum of L' (log τ) comes at 1 second. Furthermore, the correct value for the instantaneous compliance is obtained. The approximation, however, blurs the sharpness of the distribution. Actually many viscoelastic materials possess distributions which spread over as many as twelve decades of log t.

V. Relaxation Curve to Maxwell Model

In the same way, the distribution of Maxwellian relaxation times can be approximated from the relaxation curve. Plot the relaxation curve as $s/2\,\epsilon$ *vs.* log t. Determine the slope at each point and plot the negative of the slope *vs.* log τ. The resulting function, which may be called K' (log τ), is a good approximation to the true distribution function K (log τ)—where:

$$K\ (\log \tau) d \log \tau = G(\tau) d\tau \tag{40}$$

W and X. Creep Function to and from Relaxation Function

The creep function, $\phi(t)$, and the relaxation function, $\psi(t)$, are approximately the reciprocals of one another at any time. (*This is not an exact relationship, in spite of the superficial appearance of these two functions.*) The approximate reciprocal relation leads us to a very simple graphical method for going from one function to the other.

Plot the creep function as log (ϕ) *vs.* log t. The mirror image of this curve can be obtained by reflecting through the horizontal zero-line, thus replacing every ordinate by its negative. The reflected curve will be an approximation to the relaxation function plotted as log (ψ) *vs.* log t. This method obviously works equally well in both directions.

Let us now investigate the closeness of this approximation for a very concentrated distribution of compliance. We already have the creep curve for a Voigt model with $J_1 = 10^{-9}$, $J_2 = 10^{-7}$, $\eta_2 = 10^7$. We can also compute, exactly, the relaxation function for this model. This is shown in the upper part of figure 246 (solid curve). Using the known creep curve and the approximation method here advanced, we obtain the approximate relaxation function shown in the upper part of figure 246 (broken line).

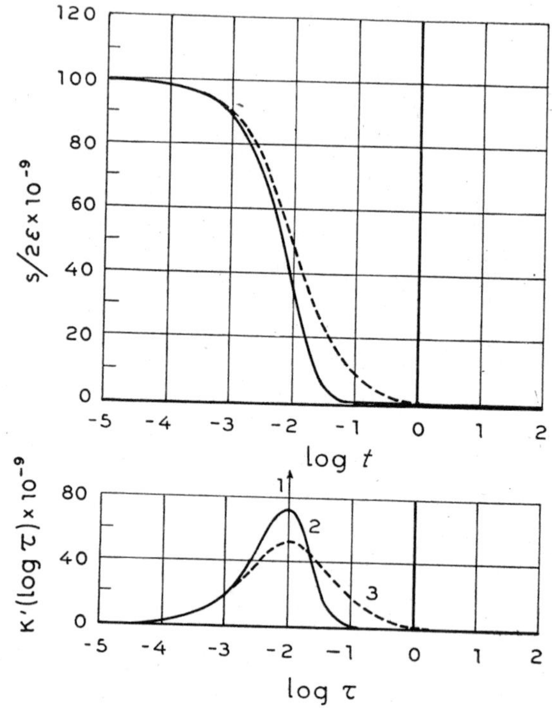

Fig. 246. A relaxation curve and its distribution of Maxwellian relaxation times.

It may also be of interest to see how closely this method allows an estimation of the distribution of Maxwellian relaxation times, $K(\log \tau)$, from a creep curve. Using the same model as before, we can obtain three different distribution functions:

1. The exact form of the Maxwell model. This is indicated by the infinitely sharp distribution curve (1) in figure 246 (lower part).

2. $K'(\log \tau)$ can be approximated from the exact relaxation function by means of (V).

3. The approximate relaxation function can be approximated from the creep curve by (W), and then (V) can be applied as a second approximate step. The result is shown in figure 246 (lower part).

V. CRITICAL COMPARISON OF THE SEVEN METHODS OF REPRESENTATION

Having discussed, in previous sections, seven methods of representing the mechanical properties of viscoelastic materials, and the important mathematical relationships among these methods, we now proceed to a critical evaluation of the methods.

First of all—as indicated in the discussion—Class I methods would seem to be preferable to the direct experimental functions of Class II from the standpoint of describing the properties of a material. This is because Class I methods are in the nature of *differential* equations which hold for any and all stress and strain sequences, whereas Class II methods are special solutions applying to only one type of experiment. . . We will limit the rest of this section to a relative evaluation of Class I methods as *specifications* of properties, followed by a relative evaluation of Class II methods as *experimental* tools.

A sharp distinction can now be made between methods A and B on the one hand, and C and D on the other. From the standpoint of a phenomenological study of the mechanics of continua, methods C and D are superior to A and B. This is because in any phenomenological study of mechanical behavior the only observable quantities are the components of the (total) stress and strain tensors; the "strain contributions" of A and the "stress contributions" of B are, strictly speaking, unobservable quantities. This very fact, however, makes A and B more suitable than C and D for the formulation of molecular theories of deformation. In a molecular study, each contribution to the strain may often be identified with some specific molecular process; and hence the strain contributions as well as the total strain can be said to possess a physical significance. Likewise, some authors have identified the various stress contributions of a Maxwell model with individual "molecular mechanisms of supporting stress."

Our conclusion is that methods A and B are more suitable than C and D for a study of the molecular mechanisms of viscoelastic deformation, but that within the discipline of the mechanics of continua C and D are to be preferred.

From the standpoint of the mechanics of continua, there is a practical as well as an absolute criterion which must be considered. This is the ease with which a method can be used to predict behavior in special cases; *i.e.*, the ease with which the fundamental differential equations can be solved subject to definite constraints. We may compare Class I methods on the basis of this practical criterion.

Method A, the Voigt specification, is extremely well adapted to the solution of all problems in which the stress is specified as a function of time, and the resulting strain is desired. The reverse type of problem, in which a known strain is enforced upon the material and the stress is to be calculated, is very difficult to handle by method A.

The Maxwell specification is the exact inverse. Problems in which the strain is specified can be solved very easily; those in which $s(t)$ is specified are very difficult.

The operator equation C is intermediate in character. Problems involving a known $s(t)$ or $\epsilon(t)$ can both be solved readily, although perhaps not quite so simply as with the more applicable of methods A and B.

If the impedance function is known, problems of both types can be solved by the use of Fourier or Laplace transforms. . . .

The experimental evaluation of the viscoelastic properties of a material can be conveniently divided into two parts—the relatively fast response (say faster than one second) and the relatively slow response (say slower than one second). In principle, either method E, F, or G can be used to evaluate both aspects of the viscoelastic behavior. In practice, this is not true.

For the rapid part, determination of the steady-state response to sinusoidal stresses (*as a function of frequency*) is the most convenient method. Creep and relaxation studies of the response which occurs in a timescale of 0.01 or 0.001 second are rather impracticable.

On the other hand, creep and relaxation tests are much better suited to the evaluation of the *slow* response than are vibration tests. The dividing line of one second, above, is purely arbitrary, and there is no reason why the range of applicability of the "slow" and "fast" methods cannot be made to overlap.

The most promising experimental approach would seem to be the following: Map out the fast response of the material by means of sinusoidal stresses. Then map out the slow response by a creep curve or a relaxation curve. Finally, synthesize the two sets of data and express in terms of one of the fundamental methods of representation, *e.g.*, a Voigt model. The resulting specification of the viscoelastic properties will cover the entire range of timescale—from the fastest frequency of the sinusoidal tests to the total duration of the creep curve.

APPENDIX III*

TENSOR TREATMENT OF NONHOMOGENEOUS STRESSES IN VISCOELASTIC MEDIA

I. INTRODUCTION

The purpose of this paper is the extension of the theory of elasticity to include viscoelastic media. The materials considered in this paper are *isotropic* and *incompressible*, and are characterized by *linear* relations between the components of stress, strain, and their derivatives with respect to time. As in the classical theory of elasticity, only *small* strains will be considered. Body forces, in particular inertia forces, will be neglected.

In the following, σ_{ik} $(i, k = 1, 2, 3)$ and ϵ_{ik} denote the components of the tensors of stress and strain with respect to a system of rectangular axes x_i. $\sigma_{11}, \sigma_{22}, \sigma_{33}$ are the normal stresses, $\sigma_{12} = \sigma_{21}, \sigma_{23} = \sigma_{32}, \sigma_{31} = \sigma_{13}$ the shear stresses. Similarly, $\epsilon_{11}, \epsilon_{22}, \epsilon_{33}$ are the normal strains, $\epsilon_{12} = \epsilon_{21}$, $\epsilon_{23} = \epsilon_{32}$, $\epsilon_{31} = \epsilon_{13}$ the shear strains. If u_i are the components of the displacement vector:

$$\epsilon_{ik} = \tfrac{1}{2}(u_{i,k} + u_{k,i}) \tag{1}$$

where the index after a comma denotes differentiation with respect to the corresponding coordinate x, *i.e.*, $u_{i,k} = \partial u_i/\partial x_k$; $u_{k,i} = \partial u_k/\partial x_i$.

Irrespective of the mechanical properties of the material, the stresses must satisfy the equilibrium conditions:

$$\sigma_{ik,k} = 0 \tag{2}$$

where the summation convention of tensor calculus has been used.[1]

* Reproduction, in part, courtesy *Quarterly of Applied Mathematics* (Volume 2, July, 1944, pages 113–119).

[1] According to this convention $\sigma_{ik,k}$ stands for the sum of all the terms obtained by giving k the values 1, 2, 3. In general, whenever a subscript appears twice in the same monomial, this subscript is to be given the values 1, 2, 3 and the resulting terms are to be added. Such a repeated subscript is called a *dummy subscript.*

Similarly, the strain components must satisfy the conditions of compatibility:

$$\epsilon_{ik,lm} + \epsilon_{lm,ik} = \epsilon_{il,km} + \epsilon_{km,il} \tag{3}$$

where $\epsilon_{ik,lm} = \partial^2\epsilon_{ik}/\partial x_l \partial x_m$, etc. While there are obviously three equations of equilibrium (corresponding to the three values which the subscript i in equation (2) can assume), it may at first glance appear that there are 3^4 equations of compatibility. On account of the high degree of symmetry in equation (3), the number of equations of compatibility reduces, however, to six—three equations of the type obtained from (3) when *e.g.*, $i = k = 1$ and $l = m = 2$, and three equations of the type obtained from (3) when *e.g.*, $i = k = 1, l = 2, m = 3$.

By themselves, equations (2) and (3) are not sufficient to determine the states of stress and strain in a body subject to given surface stresses. A further necessary set of equations are those relating the stress components to the strain components in the general case of combined stresses. It is through these *stress–strain* relations that the properties of the material enter the problem.

In the case of an incompressible material, $\epsilon_{ii} = \epsilon_{11} + \epsilon_{22} + \epsilon_{33} = 0$. The stress–strain relations are most easily discussed when the following decomposition of the stress tensor is introduced. Define the *mean normal stress* as:

$$\sigma = \tfrac{1}{3}\sigma_{ii} = \tfrac{1}{3}(\sigma_{11} + \sigma_{22} + \sigma_{33}) \tag{4}$$

and the *deviatoric part* of the stress tensor as:

$$s_{ik} = \sigma_{ik} - \sigma\delta_{ik} \tag{5}$$

where:

$$\delta_{ik} = \begin{cases} 0 & \text{if} \quad i \neq k \\ 1 & \text{if} \quad i = k \end{cases}$$

The stress–strain relations of an isotropic, incompressible elastic material can then be written in the form:

$$s_{ik} = 2\,G\epsilon_{ik} \tag{6}$$

where G denotes the modulus of rigidity.

In view of equation (5), the equilibrium condition (2) yields:

$$s_{ik,k} + \sigma_{,k}\delta_{ik} = s_{ik,k} + \sigma_{,i} = 0 \tag{7}$$

But, according to equations (6) and (1):

$$s_{ik,k} = 2\,G\epsilon_{ik,k} = G(u_{i,kk} + u_{k,ik}) = Gu_{i,kk} \tag{8}$$

since for an incompressible material $u_{k,k} = 0$ and, consequently, $u_{k,ik} = u_{k,ki} = 0$. Comparing equations (7) and (8), we find:

$$\sigma_{,i} = -Gu_{i,kk} \tag{9}$$

Hence:

$$\sigma_{,ii} = -Gu_{i,kki} = 0 \tag{10}$$

on account of the incompressibility of the material.

According to equation (5):

$$\sigma_{ik,ll} = s_{ik,ll} + \sigma_{,ll}\delta_{ik} = s_{ik,ll}$$

on account of equation (10). Making use of (6), (1) and (9), we transform this in the following manner:

$$\sigma_{ik,ll} = 2G\epsilon_{ik,ll} = G(u_{i,kll} + u_{k,ill}) = -2\sigma_{,ik}$$

Thus:

$$\sigma_{ik,ll} + 2\sigma_{,ik} = 0 \tag{11}$$

In the case of an incompressible elastic body in equilibrium the boundary conditions may be given in the form of three functions $f_i(x)$ which define the components of the forces (per unit area) applied to the surface of the body. The forces f_i must, of course, be in equilibrium, *i.e.*, the surface integral of $f_i(x)$ must vanish for $i = 1, 2, 3$. If n_k denotes the unit vector directed along the exterior normal of the surface of the body, the stress components at the surface must then satisfy the conditions:

$$\sigma_{ik}n_k = f_i \tag{12}$$

The values of the surface stresses, in conjunction with equations (2) and (11), define the stress distribution in the body and, consequently, also the strain distribution and, to within a rigid body displacement of the entire body, the displacement components.

On the other hand, the displacement components may be given on the surface of the body. These given surface displacements must, of course, be compatible with the assumed incompressibility of the material, *i.e.*, the surface integral of the normal displacement component u_in_i must vanish. Elimination of σ from equation (9) furnishes $u_{i,kkl} - u_{l,kki} = 0$, or, after a change of subscripts:

$$u_{i,kll} - u_{k,ill} = 0 \tag{12a}$$

Equations (12) in conjunction with the condition of incompressibility, $u_{l,l} = 0$, and the given surface values determine the displacement components.

II. STRESS-STRAIN RELATIONS OF VISCOELASTIC MATERIALS

Equations similar to (11) and (12a) may be derived for viscoelastic materials characterized by linear relations between the components of stress, strain, and their derivatives with respect to time.

In the case of an incompressible material of the type considered by Voigt [2] we have the stress–strain relations:

$$s_{ik} = 2\,G\epsilon_{ik} + 2\,\eta\dot{\epsilon}_{ik} \tag{13}$$

where η is the *coefficient of viscosity.*

In the case of an incompressible material of the Maxwell type, we have:

$$\epsilon_{ik} = \frac{1}{2\,G}\,\dot{s}_{ik} + \frac{1}{2\,G\tau}\,s_{ik} \tag{14}$$

where dots denote differentiation with respect to time, and τ is the *relaxation time.*

Generalizing, we may consider incompressible materials characterized by stress–strain relations of the form:

$$\left(\frac{\partial^m}{\partial t^m} + a_{m-1}\frac{\partial^{m-1}}{\partial t^{m-1}} + \cdots + a_0\right) s_{ik} = \left(b_n\frac{\partial^n}{\partial t^n} + b_{n-1}\frac{\partial^{n-1}}{\partial t^{n-1}} + \cdots + b_0\right)\epsilon_{ik} \tag{15}$$

where $a_{m-1}, \cdots, a_0, b_n, b_{n-1} \cdots, b_0$ are constants characteristic of the material.

For such materials two types of boundary value problems may be considered. In the first case the surface forces $f_i(x,t)$ are given as functions of the position x and the time t; for $t = 0$ these surface forces and their $m - 1$ first derivatives are supposed to vanish as well as all stress components and their derivatives up to the order $m - 1$. Moreover, at any given time the forces f_i must be in equilibrium. If, for $t \geqq 0$, the forces are analytic functions of time, this implies that the surface integral of any derivative $\partial^p f_i/\partial t^p$ must vanish for, say, $t = 0$. The *first boundary value problem* calls for the determination of the stress distribution $\sigma_{ik}(x,t)$ fulfilling these boundary conditions and initial conditions.

In the second case the surface displacements $u_i(x,t)$ are given as functions of the position x and the time t; for $t = 0$ these surface displacements and their $n - 1$ first derivatives are supposed to vanish, as well as the displacements in the interior of the body and their derivatives up to the

[2] W. Voigt, *Abhandl. Göttingen Ges. Wiss.*, **36**, 47 pp. (1899).

order $n - 1$. Moreover, on account of the assumed incompressibility of the material, the surface integral of the normal displacement component $u_i n_i$ must vanish for any time. If, for $t \geqq 0$, the displacements are analytic functions of time, this means that the surface integral of all expressions of the form $(\partial^p u_i/\partial t^p)n_i$ must vanish for, say, $t = 0$. The *second boundary value problem* calls for the determination of the displacements $u_i(x, t)$ in the interior of the body, fulfilling these boundary conditions and initial conditions.

Let us rewrite the stress–strain relation (15) in the form:

$$\mathbf{P}s_{ik} = 2\,\mathbf{Q}\epsilon_{ik} \tag{16}$$

where **P** and **Q** denote the linear differential operators:

$$\begin{aligned} \mathbf{P} &= \frac{\partial^m}{\partial t^m} + a_{m-1}\frac{\partial^{m-1}}{\partial t^{m-1}} + \cdots + a_1\frac{\partial}{\partial t} + a_0 \\ \mathbf{Q} &= b_n\frac{\partial^n}{\partial t^n} + b_{n-1}\frac{\partial^{n-1}}{\partial t^{n-1}} + \cdots + b_1\frac{\partial}{\partial t} + b_0 \end{aligned} \tag{16a}$$

Starting from the stress–strain relations (16) and repeating the various steps which led to the equations (11) and (12a), we obtain:

$$\mathbf{P}(\sigma_{ik,ll} + 2\sigma_{,ik}) = 0 \tag{17}$$

and:

$$\mathbf{Q}(u_{i,kll} - u_{k,ill}) = 0 \tag{18}$$

as the equations governing the solution of the first and second boundary value problem, respectively.

For example, consider the first boundary value problem for an incompressible material of the Voigt type. Comparing equations (13), (16) and (16a), we see that for this material:

$$\mathbf{P} = 1, \qquad \mathbf{Q} = \eta\frac{\partial}{\partial t} + G$$

Equation (17) consequently takes the same form as for an incompressible elastic material (see Eq. 11). This means that, *in the case of the first boundary value problem, the stress distribution in an incompressible material of the Voigt type is identical with that in an incompressible elastic material under the same instantaneous surface forces.* This stress distribution does not depend on the past stressing history, although, of course, the displacements do.

This result is readily extended to the case of an incompressible viscoelastic material characterized by a stress–strain relation (16). Consider, for instance, the first boundary value problem for a given set of surface forces $f_i(x,t)$ which, in addition to fulfilling the conditions stipulated above, are supposed to be analytic functions of time for $t \geqq 0$. If $\bar{\sigma}_{ik}(x,t)$ denotes the *static*[3] stress distribution in an incompressible elastic body of the same shape which is subjected to the surface forces $f_i(x,t)$, the required stress distribution in the viscoelastic body is given by:

$$\sigma_{ik}(x,t) = \bar{\sigma}_{ik}(x,t)$$

Indeed, by definition, the stresses $\bar{\sigma}_{ik}$ satisfy the conditions (2), (11), and (12) for any value of t. Since, like the surface forces, these stresses are analytic functions of time, this means that they also satisfy the condition (17). *The result formulated above for the first boundary value problem of an incompressible material of the Voigt type applies, therefore, to any viscoelastic material characterized by stress–strain relations of the form* (16).

A similar result is obtained in the case of the second boundary value problem for an incompressible viscoelastic material obeying stress–strain relations of the form (16), if the prescribed surface displacements $u_i(x,t)$ fulfill the conditions formulated above and, in addition, are analytic functions of time for $t \geqq 0$. The displacements $u_i(x,t)$ then equal the *static* displacements $\bar{u}_i(x,t)$ of an incompressible elastic body of the same shape, subjected to the given surface displacements $u_i(x,t)$.

III. DETERMINATION OF DISPLACEMENTS IN THE FIRST BOUNDARY VALUE PROBLEM OF VISCOELASTICITY

Let us first consider the particularly simple case, where the given surface forces can be factored into the form:

$$f_i = f_i(x)g(t) \tag{19}$$

According to what has been said above, the stress distribution which these surface forces produce in the viscoelastic body has then the form:

$$\sigma_{ik}(x,t) = \bar{\sigma}_{ik}(x)g(t) \tag{20}$$

where $\bar{\sigma}_{ik}(x)$ denotes the stresses which the surface forces $f_i(x)$ produce in an incompressible elastic body of the same shape. Introducing the stresses (20) into the stress–strain relation (16), we see that the strains in the viscoelastic body can be written in the form:

$$\epsilon_{ik}(x,t) = \bar{\epsilon}_{ik}(x)h(t) \tag{21}$$

[3] The term "static" is used here to indicate that, though the stresses $\bar{\sigma}_{ik}$ depend on t as do the forces f_i, no inertia effects should be taken into account in computing these stresses. In fact, as far as this elastic body is concerned, t plays the role of a parameter which need by no means be identified with the time.

where $h(t)$ satisfies the differential equation:

$$\mathbf{Q}h = \mathbf{P}g \tag{22}$$

while h and its derivatives up to the order $n - 1$ vanish for $t = 0$. As regards the quantities $\bar{\epsilon}_{ik}(x)$, they are related to the stresses $\bar{\sigma}_{ik}(x)$ by:

$$\bar{s}_{ik} = 2\,\bar{\epsilon}_{ik} \tag{23}$$

where $\bar{s}_{ik}$ denotes the deviatoric part of the stress tensor $\bar{\sigma}_{ik}$. In other terms, the quantities $\bar{\epsilon}_{ik}$ are the strains in an incompressible elastic body of the same shape and of unit modulus of rigidity, which is subjected to the surface forces $f_i(x)$. We shall call these strains the *equivalent elastic strains*. In order to obtain the function $h(t)$, all we have to do is to consider the *response* of the viscoelastic material under consideration to a simple shear stress s varying according to $s = 2\,g(t)$. The shear strain produced by this stress equals $h(t)$. The strains produced in the viscoelastic body by the surface forces $f_i(x)\,g(t)$ are then obtained by multiplying the equivalent elastic strains by the response function $h(t)$.

Since the differential equations for stresses and strains are linear, solutions of this type may be superimposed on each other. Let us, now, assume that our result holds good even if, contrary to the assumption made above, the surface forces are not analytical functions of time for $t \geqq 0$. In particular consider the case when $f_i = f_i(x)\,g(\xi,t)$, where $g(\xi,t)$ is Heaviside's unit step function defined by:

$$g(\xi,t) = \begin{cases} 0, & \text{if} \quad t < \xi \\ 1, & \text{if} \quad t \geqq \xi \end{cases}$$

Let $h(\xi,t)$ denote the response of the viscoelastic material under consideration to a simple shear stress $s = 2\,g(\xi,t)$. Since the surface forces $f_i(x,t)$ can be represented in the form:

$$f_i(x,t) = \int_0^\infty \dot{f}_i(x,\xi)\,g(\xi,t)\,d\xi \tag{24}$$

the following formal integral representation of the strains produced by these surface forces in the viscoelastic body suggests itself:

$$\epsilon_{ik}(x,t) = \int_0^\infty \bar{\epsilon}_{ik}(x,\xi)\,h(\xi,t)\,d\xi \tag{25}$$

where $\bar{\epsilon}_{ik}(x,\xi)\,d\xi$ are the equivalent elastic strains corresponding to the surface forces $\dot{f}_i(x,\xi)\,d\xi$. It can be shown that equation (25) indeed furnishes the strains of the viscoelastic body whenever the surface forces can be represented in the form (24). Moreover, to within a rigid body displacement the displacements of the viscoelastic body are given by:

$$u_i(x,t) = \int_0^\infty \bar{u}_i(x,\xi)\, h(\xi,t)\, d\xi \tag{26}$$

where $\bar{u}_i(x,\xi)\, d\xi$ are *equivalent elastic displacements* produced in an incompressible elastic body of the same shape and of unit modulus of rigidity, by the surface forces $f_i(x,\xi)\, d\xi$.

IV. DETERMINATION OF THE STRESSES IN THE SECOND BOUNDARY VALUE PROBLEM OF VISCOELASTICITY

A similar procedure leads to the determination of the stresses in the second boundary value problem of viscoelasticity. Consider first the case when the given surface displacements can be factored into the form $u_i = u_i(x)\, g(t)$, and denote by $\bar{\sigma}_{ik}(x)$ the *equivalent elastic stresses, i.e.*, the static stresses set up in an incompressible elastic body by the surface displacements $u_i(x)$. Furthermore, determine the *response function* $h(t)$, *i.e.*, half the shear stress produced in the viscoelastic material under consideration by a simple shear strain $g(t)$. The required stress distribution in the viscoelastic body is then given by $\sigma_{ik}(x,t) = \bar{\sigma}_i(x)\, h(t)$.

In the general case, the stresses in the second boundary value problem may be represented in the form:

$$\sigma_{ik}(x,t) = \int_0^\infty \bar{\sigma}_{ik}(x,\xi)\, h(\xi,t)\, d\xi \tag{27}$$

where $\bar{\sigma}_{ki}(x,\xi)\, d\xi$ are the equivalent elastic stresses corresponding to the surface displacements $\dot{u}_i(x,\xi)\, d\xi$, and $2\, h(\xi,t)$ is the response of the viscoelastic material to a simple shear strain:

$$g(\xi,t) = \begin{cases} 0, & \text{if} \quad t < \xi \\ 1, & \text{if} \quad t \geqq \xi \end{cases}$$

APPENDIX IV

EXPERIMENTAL METHODS IN THE SCIENTIFIC MECHANICAL TESTING OF HIGH POLYMERS

The general problem of mechanical testing of high polymers has been excellently set forth in a discussion by Mooney,[1] from which we quote at length:

Methods of testing materials may be classified as being either purely "practical," purely "scientific," or hybrid.

The ideal "practical" test is a service test, or test by trial in the use for which the material is intended. Service tests are usually expensive, slow, and so inaccurate that many are required to give a reliable average result. Laboratory tests must therefore often be used. The best laboratory "practical" test is the one which imitates most faithfully some actual service condition while giving, at the same time, quick and accurate results.

A "scientific" test is one which measures some specific physical property of the material. In order for the test to do this, it is essential that the measurement shall be unaffected by extraneous physical properties and shall be expressible in absolute units, independent of the design and dimensions of the testing equipment.

A "hybrid" test is one that stands somewhere between the "practical" and the "scientific." It does not represent faithfully any particular service condition; and it is not designed so as to permit the calculation of any basic physical property. Most such tests in common use have been designed with half an eye on service conditions, and an eye and a half on speed and accuracy of the laboratory test. If the measurements have any scientific value, it is largely a result of chance, or oversight.

Concerning the relative merits of these different types of testing, it is obvious that the scientific type gives the most complete and accurate information concerning the tested property of the material. For general purposes, therefore, this type of test is to be preferred.

On the other hand, there are many service conditions which are very complex in geometrical form or other aspects. Hence, it often is impossible to analyze these service conditions theoretically, or to predict just how and to what extent the various physical properties affect the results of a service test. Complicated problems may sometimes be solved by a combination of incomplete theory, dimensional analysis, and physical

[1] Courtesy M. Mooney, *Symposium on Consistency*, pages 9–12 (June 29, 1937), and American Society for Testing Materials, Philadelphia.

testing. However, until such a program has been carried out, in difficult problems the engineer or technologist can rely only upon practical tests for a final decision or rating. He should make his practical laboratory test resemble as closely as feasible the service condition he is interested in; and he owes no apology to the scientific world for doing so.

However, it is not to be inferred from the preceding paragraph that scientific measurements are of no value in practical problems. There are many service conditions which can be analyzed, at least approximately. In such cases the material's behavior can be expressed in terms of the relevant physical properties; and it is then most advantageous to have these physical properties separately measured in separate scientific tests. Even when the service conditions cannot be completely analyzed, knowledge of the physical properties of the materials is of inestimable value in research and development work, if not in control work.

Concerning the hybrid type of test, there is little, in the author's opinion, that can be said to justify it. If the test neither resembles closely any service condition nor yields data concerning the basic physical properties, the results will neither predict with certainty the behavior of the material in complex service conditions, nor permit reliable calculations in simple conditions that can be analyzed.

Without any detailed discussion of the tests [see page 10 of Mooney], it will be obvious that most of them belong to the hybrid type. According to the above arguments, therefore, it would be desirable to modify radically most of these tests so as to make them either truly scientific or truly "practical." How easy it would be to make the tests practical, that is, to make them resemble particular service conditions, the author is not in a position to say. Concerning the possibilities of making them scientific, it is the author's belief and working faith that a test can be developed to measure in absolute units any clearly defined physical property possessed by the test material under normal conditions. The apparatus required may or may not be more complicated than that already in use; but if it must be more complicated, it will then give more complete and more reliable information than was obtainable with the old.

No attempt is made here to describe the currently used service tests and "hybrid" tests which are so important as means of practical evaluation and empirical comparison, respectively, of plastics, elastomers, and textile fibers. Both established and tentative procedures in regard to these tests are to be found in the A.S.T.M. Standards, which are published every three years, and in the annual supplements to these standards. The aim of this chapter is rather to discuss the "scientific" testing of high polymers—the evaluation of specific physical properties.

The more complex the mechanical properties of a material, the more rigid are the requirements of physical simplicity in the testing instrument, if any fundamental insight into those properties is to be obtainable. By physical simplicity is meant a simple geometry, and a simple sequence in time of the controlled variables. This might be spoken of as "simplicity from the point of view of the material being tested," and does not necessarily coincide with simplicity from the point of view of the technician who carries out the measurements. The very demand for physical simplicity may necessitate the use of much more elaborate equipment than is necessary if this demand is somewhat relaxed. Thus the Ostwald pipette, which is very simple and easy to use, is physically an extremely complicated instrument. Although its purpose is to give information about the relation between shear stress and rate of flow (velocity gradient), the shear stress changes from point to point across the capillary cross section, and changes through time as drainage reduces the driving pressure head. In spite of these variations, the Ostwald pipette is very satisfactory in the determination of the flow curve of a Newtonian liquid, because of the extreme simplicity of this flow curve. The efflux time of a non-Newtonian liquid in an Ostwald pipette, however, does not define its flow curve. In a Bingham capillary plastometer, where the driving pressure head can be held constant throughout each determination, and varied from one determination to the next, the flow curve of a non-Newtonian material can be determined, but only by the use of fairly complicated mathematical transformations. In the case of a thixotropic material, any capillary tube instrument is out of the question as a means of satisfactorily determining the rheological properties. Geometric simplicity is unnecessary in the case of tthe simple Newtonian liquid, is desirable in the case of the more complicated non-Newtonian liquid, and is absolutely imperative in the case of the still more complicated thixotropic fluid.

It has been pointed out that any one of several distinctly different types of complication can appear in the mechanical behavior of a high polymer. Each type of complication in the properties of a material makes its own demands for simplicity of a specific type in the testing methods to be used. In the following paragraphs an attempt is made to state explicitly the requirements for physical simplicity in the testing method which arise from various types of departure from simplicity in the material under consideration.

(I) Complex time behavior in the material gives rise to the demand for simple time sequences in the mechanical test. High polymers in general possess a series of retarded elastic mechanisms of response to stress, as well as instantaneous elasticity and flow. As a result, the mechanical tests most easily interpreted are those in which either stress or strain is held constant. When rate of strain is held constant, the interpretation of data becomes mathematically more difficult.

A material exhibiting only instantaneous elasticity makes no such demands. A stress–strain curve for such a simple material is independent of the rate of strain, and represents the equilibrium stress–strain relationship of the material. Finally, it is apparent that while a test involving a complex time sequence of the controlled variable (stress or strain) is not best suited to the investigation of materials possessing complex time effects, nevertheless such a method can serve *to indicate the presence* of such time effects. Thus if the ordinary stress–strain curve of a material is changed by a change in the rate of cross-head motion, then the material is not an ideal elastic substance.

(II) Nonlinearity of elastic or flow elements gives rise to the demand for spatial homogeneity of stress and strain in the sample under test. This point has been discussed in detail in connection with non-Newtonian liquids. It applies also to non-Hookian elastic solids, and to plastoelastic materials whose analogous mechanical networks contain nonlinear elements. A mechanical test in which the sample is subjected to a nonhomogeneous stress may of course serve to *detect* the presence of nonlinear mechanisms of response, even though it is not best suited for the quantitative evaluation of the extent of nonlinearity.

As a corollary to I and II, above, a material which exhibits both complex time effects and nonlinearity (*e.g.*, a material represented by a plastoelastic network some of whose elements are nonlinear) demands *both* types of physical simplicity in a testing method which is to yield fundamental physical data.

(III) A material exhibiting thermomechanical effects demands a testing method in which temperature is held constant. Even instantaneous elastic deformation is in general an endothermic or an exothermic process. If the heat generated during an exothermic deformation is not dissipated, the temperature of the sample rises. The greater the heat effect during deformation, the greater is the possible temperature change. Furthermore, the greater the heat effect, the more marked is the dependence of the elastic constants upon temperature. A material for which $(\partial T/\partial \gamma)_H$ is large, also exhibits a large $(\partial s_{i,j}/\partial T)_\gamma$. Thus the stress–strain relation of even an instantaneous elastic material, which shows a large heat effect during deformation, depends very strongly upon whether the temperature is held constant or whether the temperature is allowed to build up. In a plastoelastic material, the necessity for constant temperature is even more pronounced. All viscosity terms, and hence all retardation times and relaxation times, decrease rapidly with increasing temperature. Hence, if work done against flow elements produces any considerable amount of heat, this heat must be dissipated so as to hold the test sample at constant temperature. (In the case of instantaneous elasticity, perfectly adiabatic tests may in some cases be acceptable, as well as perfectly isothermal tests.)

(IV) If phase change accompanies deformation, it is advisable to augment the purely mechanical test with some independent means of following the phase change. X-ray measurements, specific volume determinations, and other experimental methods have been used for this purpose.

(V) It has been pointed out that the classical definition of strain, upon which all of the discussions of this book have been based, is not applicable for large deformations. Since no analysis of complex time behavior has yet been couched in terms of definitions of the strain components which are applicable for large as well as small deformations, there exists no phenomenological framework into which can be fitted data involving both large strains and complex time effects. This mathematical combination may be realizable, but until it is made, there can be no unequivocable reduction to fundamental quantities of experimental data involving plastoelastic materials at large deformation.

It would be foolish to conclude from this fact that a fundamental mechanical test should not involve large deformations. It is true that a test which is limited to small deformations can be more readily interpreted than a test which covers the range of large deformations. Such a limited test, however, cannot yield complete information of the mechanical properties of a typical high polymer. The mechanical behavior at large deformation is just as fundamental as the behavior at small deformation. Thus the mathematical complications connected with large deformations are unavoidable, in contrast to the complications arising from nonhomogeneity of stress and strain, complex time sequences of controlled variables, temperature variation, etc.

On the other hand, it is reasonable to conclude that a scientific mechanical test should be sensitive enough to yield useful information concerning the region of small deformation, as well as that of large deformation. In many testing appliances, mechanical play makes it impossible to measure small deformations accurately, and frictional forces make it impossible to measure small stresses accurately. In such cases, information concerning the region of small stress and small deformation can be obtained only by extrapolation from larger values. This is unfortunate. The region of large deformations should not be neglected merely because of mathematical difficulties, but testing methods should at least be designed to study small stresses and deformations as well as large. The unambiguous interpretation which can be made of small-deformation data must necessarily be a help in the tentative interpretation of large-deformation data. (By "interpretation" is meant herein simply reduction to a standard set of phenomenological mechanical properties, in the sense that flow data for a Newtonian fluid can be reduced to a viscosity coefficient, and elasticity data for a Hookian solid can be reduced to a set of twenty-one elastic constants, etc. It cannot be said that interpretation of data in the more ambitious sense of explanation on the basis of molecular theory can be made completely rigorous and unambiguous, even in the region of small strains.)

SUBJECT INDEX

R

S